ONTARIO EDITION

ADDISON-WESLEY

Mathematics 9

**Addison-Wesley
Secondary
Mathematics
Authors**

Robert Alexander
Paul Atkinson
Maurice Barry
Barbara J. Canton
Ron Coleborn
Fred Crouse
Garry Davis
Jane Forbes
George Gadanidis
Liliane Gauthier
Florence Glanfield
Katie Pallos-Haden
Peter J. Harrison
Brendan Kelly
Stephen Khan
Ron Lancaster
Rob McLeish
Jim Nakamoto
Nick Nielsen
Linda Rajotte
Margaret Sinclair
David Sufrin
Paul Williams
Elizabeth Wood
Rick Wunderlich
Leanne Zorn

Robert Alexander

Mathematics Teacher and Consultant, Richmond Hill

Barbara J. Canton

Head of Mathematics,
Loyalist Collegiate and Vocational Institute, Kingston
Limestone District School Board

Peter J. Harrison

Curriculum Coordinator: Mathematics,
Toronto District School Board

Rob McLeish

Head of Mathematics and Computer Science,
Sir Robert Borden High School, Nepean
Ottawa Carleton District School Board

Nick Nielsen

Mathematics Teacher,
Alternative Scarborough Education 2 (ASE 2),
Toronto District School Board

Margaret Sinclair

Head of Mathematics,
Francis Libermann Catholic High School, Scarborough
Toronto Catholic District School Board

Addison-Wesley

An imprint of Addison Wesley Longman Ltd.

Don Mills, Ontario • Reading, Massachusetts
Harlow, England • Glenview, Illinois
Melbourne, Australia

Managing Editor, Mathematics
Claire Burnett

Senior Consulting Editor
Lesley Haynes

Developmental Editor
Charlotte Urbanc

Coordinating Editor
Mei Lin Cheung

Editorial Contributors
Rosina Daillie
Annette Darby
Frank Heijmans

Design/Production
Pronk&Associates

REVIEWERS

Dr. Lynda Colgan
Assistant Professor, MSTE Group,
Queen's University, Kingston

Keith McLean
Northern Secondary School,
Toronto

Wendy Solheim
Thornhill Secondary School,
Thornhill

Kevin Spry
Centre Dufferin District High School,
Shelburne

Frank Stranges
John Paul II Catholic Secondary School,
London

Barb Vukets
Waterloo County District School Board

Mike Wierzba
Toronto District School Board

Contents

Contents

$$\pi = 3.14159...$$

Contents

Contents

Welcome to Addison-Wesley Mathematics 9

We hope this book helps you see that mathematics is useful, interesting, and enjoyable.

You can use this book if you are taking the Applied or Academic grade 9 mathematics course. Almost all the lessons cover essential content for both courses. The book signals any activities that are better suited for Applied or Academic students.

This book is about ...

... Relationships

Real-life situations often involve two quantities that relate to each other in a systematic way. In this book, you will investigate relationships many times, to develop an understanding of special relationships, and how to analyze them.

... Technology

Calculators and computers are common tools in the world around you, and they will be important tools in your study of mathematics. Graphing calculators or graphing software enable you to examine relationships in different ways: by listing values in a table, by making a graph, by using an equation. This book also provides opportunities for using spreadsheet and database software, as well as dynamic geometry software.

... Problem Solving

One of the most important reasons for studying mathematics is to develop new ways to solve problems. In this book, you will find a wide variety of problems, and develop different strategies for solving them. Some of these problems have many possible layers of insight and understanding; these rich problems are emphasized in the Mathematical Modelling sections.

The following pages explain how a chapter is organized.

Each chapter starts with a short **Mathematical Modelling** section that presents a rich problem. At the start of the chapter, you may not have the mathematics skills you need to solve the problem. You will return to the problem after developing some of those skills.

FYI Visit refers you to our web site, where you can connect to other sites with information related to the chapter problem.

The first section in each chapter gives you a chance to review certain topics and skills before you start the chapter.

This list tells you what skills or knowledge you need for the chapter.

This Reviewing Your Skills presents a graph of postal rates in Canada through the 1900s. The exercises help you recall what you know about graphing and interpreting graphs.

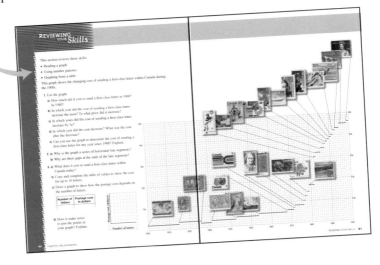

Concept Development

Each student has different strengths and interests, so it is helpful to examine new concepts in different ways. The teaching sections in each chapter offer several approaches to new concepts.

Investigations lead you to discover new concepts and the thinking behind them.

In some Investigations, you will use concrete materials. In others, you might use graphing technology or geometry software. Some Investigations are structured exercises that reveal patterns and their significance.

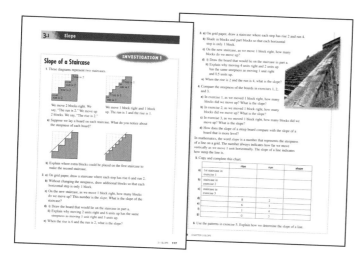

Examples with full solutions provide you with a model of new methods.

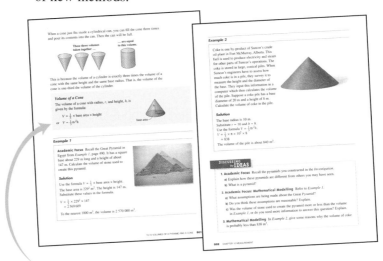

Colour boxes highlight important results.

Discussing the Ideas gives you a chance to talk about the Investigations and Examples with your teacher and other students. This discussion can help to clarify your understanding.

Exercises help reinforce your understanding. There are three levels of exercises.

A exercises involve the simplest skills of the lesson.

B exercises usually require several steps, and they may involve applications or problem solving.

Logos tell you when an exercise requires the use of technology.

C exercises are more thought-provoking. They may call on previous knowledge or foreshadow upcoming work.

Communicating the Ideas helps you confirm that you understand important concepts. It may involve writing, speaking, or constructing a diagram.

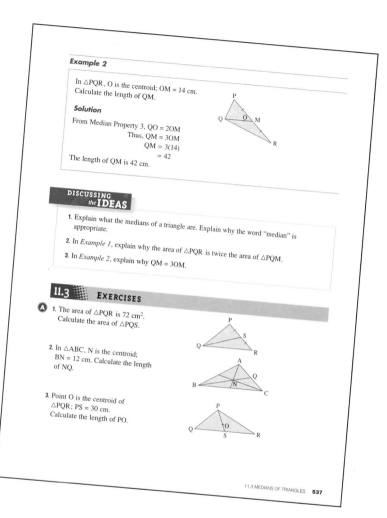

Example 2

In △PQR, O is the centroid; OM = 14 cm. Calculate the length of QM.

Solution

From Median Property 3, QO = 2OM

Thus, QM = 3OM

QM = 3(14)

= 42

The length of QM is 42 cm.

DISCUSSING the IDEAS

1. Explain what the medians of a triangle are. Explain why the word "median" is appropriate.

2. In *Example 1*, explain why the area of △PQR is twice the area of △PQM.

3. In *Example 2*, explain why QM = 3OM.

11.3 EXERCISES

A 1. The area of △PQR is 72 cm². Calculate the area of △PQS.

2. In △ABC, N is the centroid; BN = 12 cm. Calculate the length of NQ.

3. Point O is the centroid of △PQR; PS = 30 cm. Calculate the length of PO.

11.3 MEDIANS OF TRIANGLES **537**

Mathematical Modelling

Some numbered sections take you back to the Mathematical Modelling problem at the beginning of the chapter.

In Chapter 2, the Mathematical Modelling is about relating the lifetimes of humans and cats or dogs. In this section, you look at relationships represented:

- As a written rule
- Using a table of values
- Using a graph

Each representation is a **mathematical model** of the problem situation: it's a mathematical way to solve an applied problem.

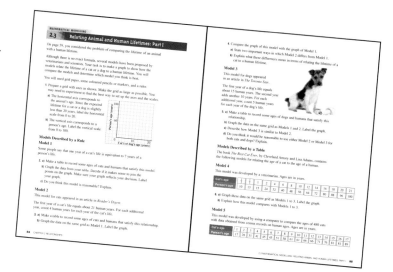

By looking at many possible models, you learn to identify your assumptions, recognize how accurate a model might be, and revise a model if you think it's necessary.

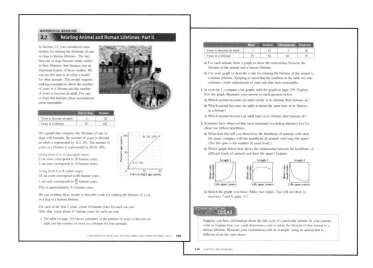

In Chapter 2, a third look at the Mathematical Modelling situation develops new models for relating human lifetimes to those of other animals. You obtain more information, relating lifetimes to heartbeats or numbers of breaths. You work with this information to select and refine a new mathematical model.

Applied and Academic Sections

Some numbered sections establish content that is required for only one of the grade 9 courses. Look for the **Academic Focus** or **Applied Focus** sections.

The Academic course requires more work with algebraic manipulation. This section (Factoring Polynomials) is required for Academic students only.

If you're taking grade 9 Applied but are interested in taking grade 10 Academic, your teacher may require you to complete this section.

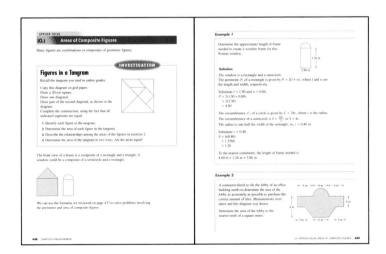

This measurement section is required for Applied students only.

The Applied course involves more extensive work with applications and technology tools. The Applied course requires work with measurements of plane figures.

Applied Focus Subsections

Most numbered sections present content for both Applied and Academic students. Some of these sections have individual exercises, activities, or subsections that are best suited for one course only.

This **Applied Focus** presents an interesting problem, and a hands-on approach to its solution. It's more appropriate for Applied students.

The colour lines around the exercises tell you that they belong together. Complete all these exercises for best understanding.

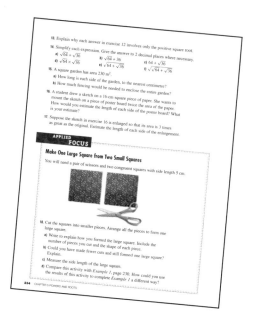

Academic Focus Subsections

This **Academic Focus** presents an interesting context, and several related exercises.

Sometimes an individual exercise is best suited for Academic students. The book indicates an **Academic Focus** right in the exercise.

Other Focus Subsections

Focus subsections can also highlight connections to other subject areas, or to specific applications. This Consumer Focus is about the value of Canadian money compared to American money.

Complete all the exercises within the colour border for an in-depth look at this situation.

Other Focus subsections include:

- Problem Solving Focus
- Sports Focus
- Art Focus
- Science Focus
- Design Focus
- Technology Focus

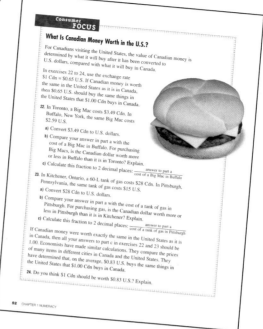

Boggle Your Mind

Some numbered sections include Boggle Your Mind.

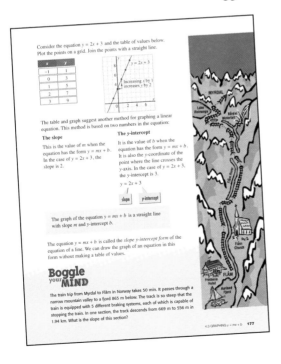

These short problems present interesting facts, and give you more opportunities to practise your problem-solving skills. Often the answers you reach will "boggle your mind."

Technology provides tools for learning and doing mathematics in ways that weren't possible a few years ago.

Graphing Technology

The graphing calculator helps you explore relationships graphically, numerically, and symbolically. It does not replace the need to develop good graphing skills, but it can enhance your mathematical understanding.

In some Investigations, you will learn specific steps for the TI-83 graphing calculator. Any comparable calculator would also be appropriate for completing the work. In Examples and Exercises, you will see more opportunities for using the graphing calculator.

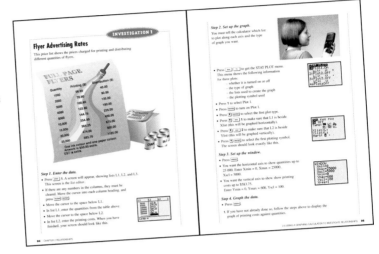

Graphing technology is supported by specialized data-gathering equipment. One piece of equipment is the Calculator-Based Ranger (CBR) from TEXAS Instruments. Chapter 2 includes a section that provides instruction in the use of the CBR.

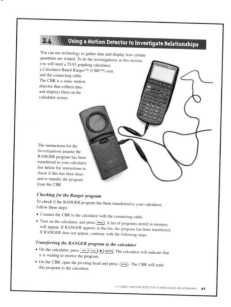

Graphing technology, and the use of technological data-gathering devices, are both requirements of the Ontario curriculum guidelines for grade 9 mathematics. This book will show you how these technologies relate to the mathematical content in grade 9.

Dynamic Geometry Software

Dynamic geometry software is another powerful technology tool.
This software was designed to support learning in mathematics.

One popular type of geometry software is *The Geometer's Sketchpad*.
In this book, there are Investigations in Chapter 11 that feature
The Geometer's Sketchpad.

Using this software, you can create geometric figures. When you stretch, skew,
or move the figures you can observe the effects and derive general conclusions.

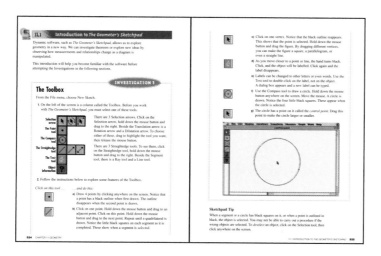

This book provides explicit instruction in the use of *The Geometer's Sketchpad*.
An introductory lesson in Chapter 11 focuses on the software use.

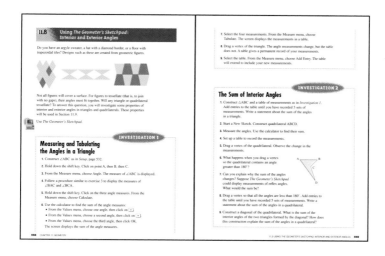

Subsequent lessons lead you through specific steps on the computer,
to help you develop general geometric principles.

Spreadsheets and Databases

Spreadsheets and databases are other technologies that can provide some exciting mathematical insights.

This computer logo tells you that the exercise involves a spreadsheet. Your teacher may provide a template for the spreadsheet, from the *Addison-Wesley Mathematics 9 Technology Kit*.

Other exercises require the use of a computer database. The CD logo tells you that the data are available from *Addison-Wesley Mathematics 9 Technology Kit*. These databases provide authentic data for you to analyze.

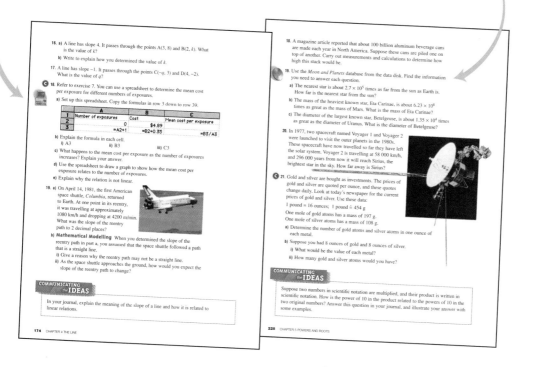

The Technology Kit also provides your teacher with programs for the TI-83 graphing calculator. It contains applets from *The Geometer's Sketchpad* that give you a head start on some of the geometry investigations.

As you progressed through the chapter, you used a variety of approaches to learning new content. This review section reflects the different ways in which you have learned.

Investigative approaches: An Investigation presents a hands-on opportunity for review.

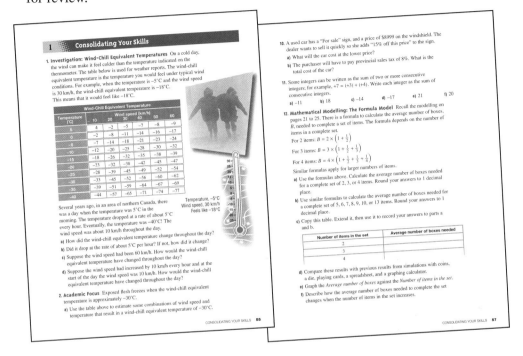

Practice and problems: Exercises provide practice with key mathematical concepts and problem-solving skills.

Mathematical Modelling: The chapter presented a rich problem with many strategies for you to try out in developing a mathematical model. The Mathematical Modelling in Consolidating Your Skills gives you a chance to solve an open-ended problem, and to develop new strategies on your own.

Cumulative Review

Selected chapters will also provide a Cumulative Review. Review the concepts and skills for all chapters that come before the Cumulative Review.

CHAPTER 1

Numeracy

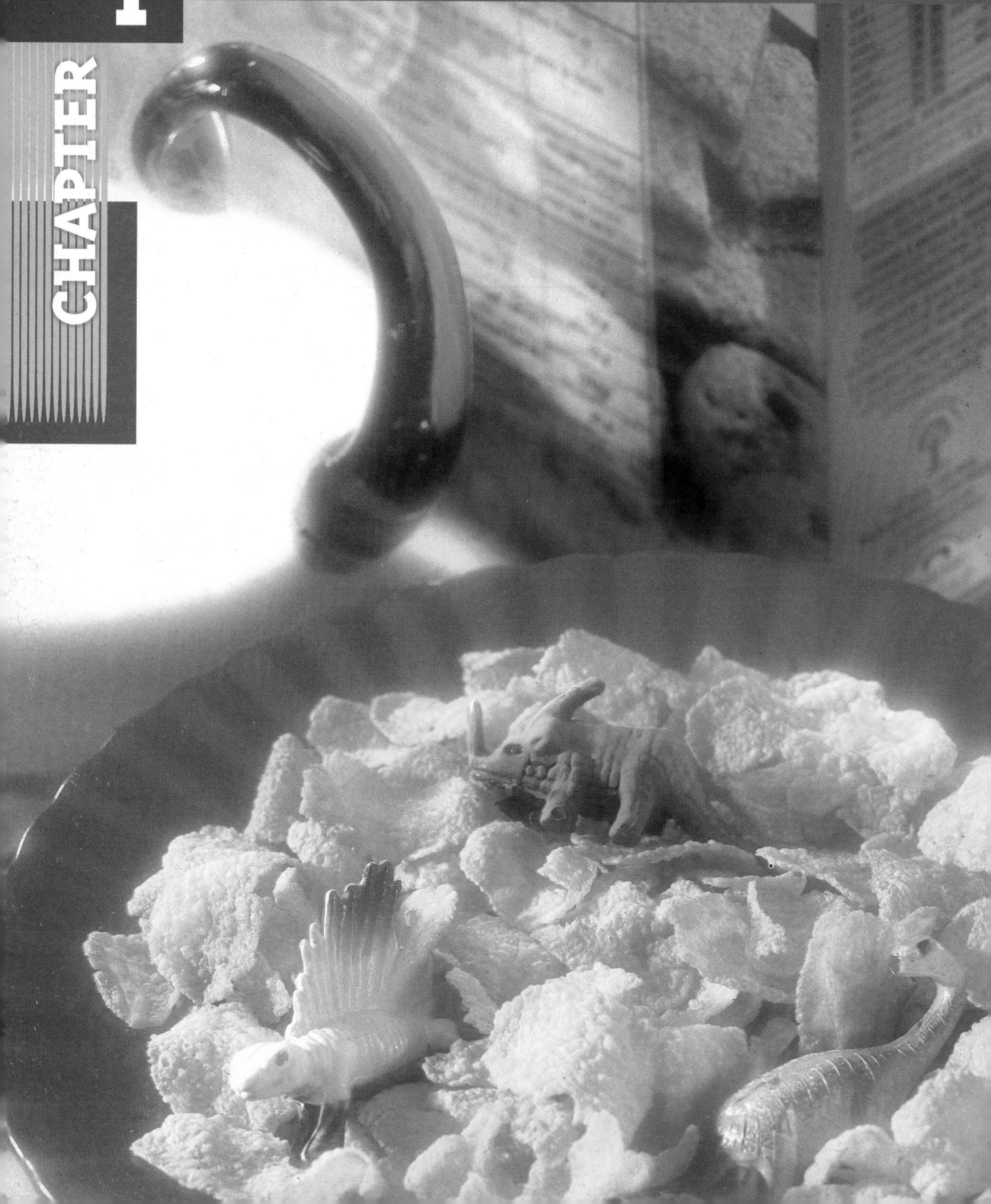

How Many Cereal Boxes?

Many cereal companies package their products to appeal to young children. In each box, there is an item that is part of a set of similar items. To obtain a complete set of items, the consumer has to purchase several boxes.

How many boxes must be purchased to obtain a complete set of items?

You will solve this problem in different ways later in this chapter. Each way to solve the problem is called a mathematical model.

A *mathematical model* is a way to solve an applied problem.

Until you develop the models to solve the problem, here are some things to consider.

Suppose there are only 2 different items in a complete set.

1. Is it possible to get a complete set of items by purchasing only 2 boxes? Do you think this is likely to happen? Explain.

2. Is it possible to purchase many boxes and still not get a complete set? Do you think this is likely to happen? Explain.

You will return to this problem in Section 1.3.

 **FYI Visit** www.awl.com/canada/school/connections

For information related to the above problem, click on <u>MATHLINKS</u>, followed by <u>AWMath</u>. Then select a topic under How Many Cereal Boxes?

This section reviews these skills and concepts:

- Problem solving
- Using a calculator
- Basic multiplication and division facts
- Rounding
- Reducing fractions to lowest terms
- Estimation

Vancouver

St. Joh

Thunder Bay

Ottawa

On April 12, 1980, Terry Fox left St. John's Newfoundland on a cross-country run to raise money for cancer research. In September, 1980, Terry was forced to end the run near Nipigon, Ontario, when cancer was discovered in his lungs. Terry's courageous run was called the "Marathon of Hope."

1. Terry ran 5373 km in 143 days. What was the mean distance he ran each day?

2. a) When Terry ended the Marathon of Hope, he had raised $1.7 million. Calculate the mean amount of money raised per kilometre.

   b) When Canadians learned that Terry had to abandon the run, they contributed another $23 million in 1980. Calculate the mean amount of money raised per kilometre when these donations are included.

   c) During his many speaking engagements on his route, Terry said that he hoped that each Canadian would be able to contribute $1 to cancer research. In 1980, the population of Canada was approximately 25 million. Was Terry's hope realized that year? Explain.

3. Between 1980 and 1998, a total of $166 million has been raised by Terry Fox runs.

   a) Calculate the mean amount raised per kilometre that Terry ran.

   b) Calculate the mean amount raised per year.

   c) Calculate the mean amount raised per Canadian.

There are 100 multiplication facts from $1 \times 1 = 1$ to $10 \times 10 = 100$. Exercises 4 to 6 refer to these 100 multiplication facts.

4. a) In some facts, such as $2 \times 8 = 16$, the product is a perfect square. How many multiplication facts have a product that is a perfect square? Explain.

   b) How many multiplication facts, such as $4 \times 6 = 24$, have a product that is 1 less than a perfect square?

   c) How many multiplication facts have a product that is 1 more than a perfect square?

5. a) Some multiplication facts involve consecutive digits. For example, $3 \times 4 = 12$ involves the digits 1, 2, 3, and 4. How many multiplication facts involve consecutive digits? Explain.

b) How many multiplication facts have three of the digits the same, as in $6 \times 6 = 36$?

c) How many multiplication facts have two of the digits the same, as in $3 \times 3 = 9$ and $3 \times 5 = 15$?

d) How many multiplication facts have all the digits different, as in $7 \times 4 = 28$?

6. a) How many multiplication facts have the first factor equal to the second factor, as in $5 \times 5 = 25$?

b) How many multiplication facts have the first factor 1 less than the second factor, as in $4 \times 5 = 20$?

c) Repeat part b, replacing the words "1 less than" with:
   i) 2 less than   **ii)** 3 less than   **iii)** 4 less than   **iv)** 5 less than
   v) 6 less than   **vi)** 7 less than   **vii)** 8 less than   **viii)** 9 less than

7. a) You know many multiplication facts such as $7 \times 6 = 42$. Use these three numbers to:
   i) write another multiplication fact   **ii)** write two division facts

b) The two multiplication facts and the two division facts in part a form a "family of facts." Write two multiplication facts and two division facts that form another family of facts.

8. Since $4 \times 14 = 56$, what does $56 \div 14$ equal? Explain.

9. Use a calculator to simplify each expression. Round your answers to 2 decimal places.
   a) $4.50 \div 1.72$ **b)** $\dfrac{18.25}{0.28}$ **c)** $7 \times \dfrac{229}{3.87}$

10. Reduce to lowest terms.
   a) $\dfrac{4}{12}$ **b)** $\dfrac{18}{27}$ **c)** $\dfrac{21}{98}$

11. Estimation Only three of the expressions below have a value less than 50. Use estimation to decide which expressions they are.
   a) 6.3×8.9 **b)** 9.7×4.9 **c)** $425 \div 6.4$
   d) $72.6 \div 2.9$ **e)** $102.5 \times \dfrac{2.3}{8.4}$ **f)** $33.7 \times \dfrac{2.9}{1.3}$

Each year, Statistics Canada estimates the number of Canadians who move from one province to another. The results (rounded to the nearest thousand) for recent years are shown in the population table. Some numbers in the table are positive and others are negative. All the numbers in the table are integers.

Where Canadians Move Within Canada
(thousands of persons)

Years	YT	NWT	BC	Alta	Sask	Man	Ont	Que	NB	NS	PEI	Nfld
1976-81	−1	−4	123	186	−10	−42	−58	−156	−10	−7	−1	−19
1981-86	−3	0	7	−32	−3	−3	122	−81	0	7	1	−15
1986-91	1	−2	126	−26	−60	−35	47	−26	−6	−5	−1	−14
1991-96	1	0	150	4	−20	−19	−47	−37	−2	−6	1	−23

A positive number shows that more Canadians moved into that province than out of that province. For example, from 1976 to 1981, about 186 000 more Canadians moved into Alberta than out of Alberta. The *net gain* in population was 186 000.

A negative number shows that more Canadians moved out of that province than into that province. For example, from 1976 to 1981, about 58 000 more Canadians moved out of Ontario than into Ontario. The *net loss* in population was 58 000.

We say that the *net change* in population from 1976 to 1981 was +186 000 for Alberta and −58 000 for Ontario.

Adding Integers

To determine the net change in Ontario's population from 1976 to 1996, add the integers in the Ontario column.

Think: $(-58) + (+122) + (+47) + (-47)$
Write: $-58 + 122 + 47 - 47$

Add the integers in any order.
$$-58 + 122 + 47 - 47 = 122 - 58$$
$$= 64$$

From 1976 to 1996, about 64 000 more Canadians moved into Ontario than out of Ontario.

Subtracting Integers

From 1981 to 1986, the net change in British Columbia's population was +7000.
From 1986 to 1991, the net change was +126 000.
The net change increased by 119 000.

Write this as a subtraction statement:
$(+126) - (+7) = +119$
Compare with this addition statement:
$(+126) + (-7) = +119$

From 1981 to 1986, the net change in Manitoba's population was −3000.
From 1986 to 1991, the net change was −35 000.
The net change decreased by 32 000.

Write this as a subtraction statement:
$(-35) - (-3) = -32$
Compare with this addition statement:
$(-35) + (+3) = -32$

These examples suggest that adding the opposite of an integer gives the same result as subtracting the integer.

To subtract an integer, add its opposite.

Multiplying Integers

From 1981 to 1986, the net change in population in each of Manitoba, Saskatchewan, and Yukon was −3000.

To calculate the total net change, multiply −3000 by 3.

To multiply integers, we must define these products:

(+3)(+3)   (+3)(−3)   (−3)(+3)   (−3)(−3)

Since +3 can be written as 3, we know that
(+3)(+3) = 9.

Recall that multiplication means repeated addition.
For example, 3 × (−3) means (−3) + (−3) + (−3).
Therefore, (+3) × (−3) = −9

What does (−3)(+3) mean?

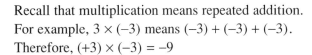

It does not make sense to say that it means to add negative three 3s.

Since we multiply whole numbers in any order, we shall also multiply integers in any order.
Then, (−3) × (+3) = (+3) × (−3);
that is, (−3) × (+3) = −9

What does (−3)(−3) mean?

We shall extend the number patterns we found for positive integers to negative integers.

Recall the number patterns you studied in an earlier grade.
We should define (−3)(−3) to be equal to +9.

Definitions for Multiplication

(+3)(+3) = 9   The product of two integers with the same signs is positive.
(−3)(−3) = 9
(+3)(−3) = −9   The product of two integers with different signs is negative.
(−3)(+3) = −9

The total net change is (−3000)(3) = −9000.
From 1981 to 1986, 9000 more Canadians moved out of Manitoba, Saskatchewan, and Yukon than moved in.

Dividing Integers

From 1991 to 1996, the net change in Saskatchewan's population was $-20\ 000$.
To calculate the mean net change each year, divide $-20\ 000$ by 5.

To divide integers, we must define these quotients:

$$\frac{+20}{+5} \qquad \frac{+20}{-5} \qquad \frac{-20}{+5} \qquad \frac{-20}{-5}$$

Division is the inverse of multiplication. This means that we can obtain division facts from multiplication facts.

For example, since $5 \times 4 = 20$, then $\frac{20}{5} = 4$

Similarly, since $(+5)(-4) = -20$, then $\frac{-20}{+5} = -4$

Since $(-5)(+4) = -20$, then $\frac{-20}{-5} = +4$

Since $(-5)(-4) = +20$, then $\frac{+20}{-5} = -4$

The definitions for division are similar to those for multiplication.

Definitions for Division

The quotient of two integers with the same signs is positive.

$$\frac{+20}{+5} = 4 \qquad \frac{-20}{-5} = 4$$

The quotient of two integers with different signs is negative.

$$\frac{-20}{+5} = -4 \qquad \frac{+20}{-5} = -4$$

The mean net change in Saskatchewan's population each year was $\frac{-20\ 000}{+5} = -4000$.
On average, from 1991 to 1996, 4000 more Canadians moved out of Saskatchewan each year than moved in.

DISCUSSING the IDEAS

1. All the numbers in the population table on page 6 are integers. None of these numbers is an integer: $\frac{2}{3}, 6.5, -3\frac{1}{2}, -4.07, -\frac{5}{4}$.
Explain how you can tell whether a given number is an integer.

2. To calculate the numbers in the table, Statistics Canada used this formula:

Net change in population	$=$	Number of Canadians moving in	$-$	Number of Canadians moving out

Use this formula to explain why some numbers in the table are negative and others are positive.

A **1.** Order the numbers from least to greatest.

a) $-2, 0, 1, -3, -1, 3, 2$ b) $-7, 0, -3, -13, 5, -10, 7$

2. Add.

a) $(+4) + (-2)$ b) $(+3) + (-5)$ c) $(+2) + (-6)$ d) $(-3) + (+7)$

e) $(-3) + (-2)$ f) $(-4) + (+2)$ g) $(-7) + (-8)$ h) $(+5) + (-7)$

i) $0 + (-9)$ j) $(+10) + 0$ k) $(+7) + (+8)$ l) $(-10) + (-1)$

m) $(-2) + (-5) + (+6)$ n) $(+9) + (-3) + (-7)$ o) $(-1) + (+5) + (-8)$

3. Subtract.

a) $(+6) - (+12)$ b) $(+2) - (+6)$ c) $(+5) - (-2)$ d) $(+3) - (+7)$

e) $(-5) - (+3)$ f) $(-2) - (+5)$ g) $(+4) - (-8)$ h) $(-3) - (-7)$

i) $0 - (-6)$ j) $(-8) - (-2)$ k) $(-7) - 0$ l) $0 - (+4)$

m) $(+6) - (-1)$ n) $(-3) - (-2)$ o) $0 - (+3)$ p) $(+3) - (-9)$

4. Multiply.

a) $(+3)(+4)$ b) $(+2)(-3)$ c) $(+4)(-5)$ d) $(-3)(-1)$

e) $(-2)(+4)$ f) $(-5)(+2)$ g) $(+7)(+2)$ h) $(0)(-7)$

i) $(+6)(0)$ j) $(-6)(+5)$ k) $(-5)(+6)$ l) $(+7)(-3)$

m) $(-5)(-4)$ n) $(-2)(+3)(-4)$ o) $(+3)(+4)(-5)$ p) $(-1)(-2)(-3)(-4)$

5. Compare the products in exercise 4. What appears to be true for:

a) the product of an even number of negative integers?

b) the product of an odd number of negative integers?

6. Rewrite as a product.

a) $\frac{-25}{+5} = -5$ b) $\frac{-5}{-1} = +5$ c) $\frac{-10}{-5} = +2$

d) $\frac{-6}{+3} = -2$ e) $(+6) \div (-2) = -3$ f) $(+24) \div (-8) = -3$

7. Divide.

a) $\frac{+16}{+4}$ b) $\frac{-16}{-4}$ c) $\frac{-10}{+2}$ d) $\frac{-18}{+3}$

e) $(+12) \div (-3)$ f) $(-15) \div (-3)$ g) $(0) \div (-1)$ h) $(+72) \div (-9)$

i) $(-56) \div (+8)$ j) $0 \div (+6)$ k) $\frac{-24}{4}$ l) $\frac{-35}{-7}$

ACADEMIC FOCUS

Why Is the Product of Two Negative Numbers Positive?

If you have been wondering why the product of two negative numbers is positive, you are not alone. When mathematicians began working with negative numbers hundreds of years ago, they also had difficulties accepting this. Some situations are described below. Answer the questions to help you understand why the product of −3 and −2 should be +6.

8. *Using gains and losses*

A person spends $3 per week on lotteries, but never wins.

a) Two weeks ago, how did the amount of money he had compare with the amount he has now?

b) What does $(-3)(-2)$ represent in this context?

9. *Travelling on a number line*

Suppose the integers on a number line are 1 cm apart. A toy car is travelling to the left along the number line at 3 cm/s.

a) Two seconds ago, how did the position of the car compare with its present position?

b) What does $(-3)(-2)$ represent in this context?

10. *Eliminating possibilities*

During the 18th century, the great Swiss mathematician Leonhard Euler argued that $(-1)(-1)$ had to be equal to either +1 or −1. Since $(+1)(-1) = -1$, he said that $(-1)(-1)$ could not also equal −1, and so it must be equal to +1. Using this reasoning, why does $(-3)(-2) = +6$?

11. Read each expression as a sum of integers. Then simplify the expression.

a) $5 + 9 - 7$ b) $-3 + 8 - 1$ c) $2 - 6 - 3 + 1$

d) $-1 - 2 + 9$ e) $5 - 3 - 7 + 12$ f) $-8 + 4 - 10 - 2$

12. Copy and complete the chart. Add 3 when moving to the right. Subtract 2 when moving up. What patterns do you notice on the diagonals? Explain why the patterns occur.

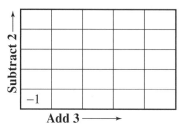

Subtract 2 ↑

-1

Add 3 →

13. For each statement, write an expression involving integers.

a) a gain of $3 followed by a loss of $2

b) a gain of $3 followed by a loss of $9

c) a loss of $8 followed by a loss of $4

d) a loss of $3 followed by a gain of $2

e) a drop of 4°C followed by a rise of 9°C

f) a drop of 9°C followed by a drop of 5°C

g) a rise of 20°C followed by a rise of 15°C

h) 7 steps backward, then 9 steps forward

i) ascending 3 floors, then descending 9 floors

j) descending 4 floors, then ascending 2 floors, then descending 3 floors

k) moving 4 km east, then moving 9 km west

l) gaining 3 kg, then losing 4 kg, then gaining 2 kg

14. Write a quotient or a product for each statement.

a) A company twice suffers a loss of 3 trucks.

b) On 3 occasions, an angler loses 4 spinners.

c) A carpet store gets 5 orders for 4 m² each.

d) The mean daily loss when $3000 is lost over 5 days

e) The velocity of a car when it reverses 10 m in 2 s

15. Kerri's father kept a weekly log during his dieting. His mass at the beginning of his dieting was 96 kg. The results are shown on page 13. Write an expression to show the gains and losses. Use your expression to find his final mass.

WEEK	RESULT
1	gained 2 kg
2	lost 4 kg
3	gained 2 kg
4	lost 1 kg
5	lost 3 kg

For each of exercises 16 to 22, write an expression, then use it to complete the exercise.

16. The temperature is −3°C. As the day progresses, the temperature increases by 8°C, then drops by 6°C. Find the final temperature.

17. The temperature is +5°C. As a storm approaches, it drops by 7°C. As evening comes on, it drops another 3°C. Find the final temperature.

18. An elevator is on the 14th floor. The elevator descends 9 floors, then ascends 6 floors. On which floor is the elevator now?

19. A submarine is at a depth of 30 m. It descends another 20 m, then rises 40 m. What is its final depth?

20. The items on a company balance sheet show these entries for income and expenses: income, $25 000; wages expense, $22 000; taxes, $4000; proceeds from sales, $5000. The profit is the difference between the income and the expenses. What is the profit?

21. An overall loss of $12 000 occurred over a 5-day period. Find the mean loss per day.

22. A player was fined $2 for each of the 4 penalties she received during a game. Find her total fine.

23. a) From 1981 to 1986, which provinces had more Canadians moving in than moving out? What was the net change in population for each province?

b) From 1981 to 1986, which provinces had more Canadians moving out than moving in? What was the net change in population for each province?

24. a) Compare the net change in Nova Scotia's population from 1976 to 1981 and from 1981 to 1986. What do you know about the number of people moving into and out of Nova Scotia during those years?

b) Integers such as –7 and 7, which differ only in sign, are called *opposites*. Find other examples of opposites in a column in the table. What do they tell you about the people moving into and out of that province?

c) What is the sum of an integer and its opposite?

25. Determine the net change in population for each province from 1976 to 1996.

26. Only one province has all positive net changes in population from 1976 to 1996.

   a) Which province is this?

   b) Why do you think more Canadians are moving into this province than leaving it?

27. a) Which provinces have all negative net changes in population from 1976 to 1996?

   b) Why do you think more Canadians are leaving these provinces than moving into them?

28. Why do you think so many Canadians moved into Alberta from 1976 to 1981 and then out of Alberta after 1981?

C **29.** On January 1, 2000, many people around the world celebrated the beginning of the 21st century. However, other people say that the 21st century does not begin until January 1, 2001.

   a) To determine which is correct, you need to know that there was no year zero. Our dating system went directly from 1 B.C. to A.D. 1. Use this information. Decide whether the 21st century begins on January 1, 2000 or on January 1, 2001. Explain.

   b) Similarly, there was no zero century. The first century began on January 1, in the year A.D. 1. Explain why the century that begins on January 1, 2001 is called the 21st century and not the 20th century.

30. List all the ways the integer 12 can be expressed as:

   a) a product of 3 positive integers   **b)** a product of 3 integers

COMMUNICATING *the* IDEAS

A student was overheard saying "two negatives make a positive."
  a) What did the student mean by this?
  b) Are there any examples where "two negatives make a negative"?
  c) Are there any examples where "two negatives sometimes make a positive and sometimes make a negative"?

Record your ideas in your journal.

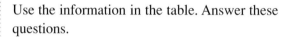

INVESTIGATION

Sharing the Cost of a Business Jet

A 1998 newspaper article described the advantages for a
business to buy part of a jet airplane. A purchaser owns a
fractional share of the airplane. The article contained this table.
It shows the cost and flying time available for a popular jet with
10 seats. There are also usage and monthly management fees.

Use the information in the table. Answer these
questions.

1. a) How many hours does the airplane fly per
year?

   b) Explain some different ways to answer the
question in part a.

2. a) What is the purchase price of the airplane?

   b) Explain some different ways to answer the
question in part a.

3. Find three rows in the table with this property:

Two fractions add up to the third fraction.

   a) Do the purchase prices in the first two rows
add up to the purchase price in the third row?
Explain.

   b) Do the number of hours per year in the first
two rows add up to the number of hours per
year in the third row? Explain.

4. Write the fractions in the table in decimal form.

5. Repeat exercise 3 in as many different ways as you can.
How many different ways can you find?

6. Is the pricing structure in the table fair to all purchasers,
regardless of the size of their share? Explain.

Pricing for a Flexjet Challenger 604

Ownership share	Purchase price ($)	Hours per year
$\frac{1}{8}$	2 738 000	100
$\frac{3}{16}$	4 107 000	150
$\frac{1}{4}$	5 476 000	200
$\frac{5}{16}$	6 845 000	250
$\frac{3}{8}$	8 214 000	300
$\frac{7}{16}$	9 583 000	350
$\frac{1}{2}$	10 952 000	400

Calculations with fractions can be done mentally, using paper and pencil, or with a calculator. Changing fractions to decimals often simplifies calculations.

Example 1

Calculate. Explain the solution method used.

a) $\frac{3}{4} - 0.5$ b) $40.5 - 3.9$ c) $\frac{42.5}{9.3 + 2.5}$

Solution

a) We know that $\frac{3}{4} = 0.75$, so we can write $0.75 - 0.5 = 0.25$.

b) $40.5 - 3.9$ is about $40.5 - 4$, or 36.5. Since 4 is $3.9 + 0.1$, add 0.1 to obtain 36.6.

c) Use a calculator. Here is a typical keying sequence.
   Press: 42.5 [÷] [( ] 9.3 [+] 2.5 [ )] [=] to display: 3.601694915
   Round the quotient to 1 decimal place: 3.6

Example 2

Simplify. a) $\frac{5}{6} + \frac{3}{4}$ b) $\frac{5}{6} \div \frac{3}{4}$

Solution

a) $\frac{5}{6} + \frac{3}{4} = \frac{5}{6} \times \frac{2}{2} + \frac{3}{4} \times \frac{3}{3}$

$= \frac{10}{12} + \frac{9}{12}$

$= \frac{19}{12}$, or $1\frac{7}{12}$

b) $\frac{5}{6} \div \frac{3}{4} = \frac{5}{6} \times \frac{4}{3}$

$= \frac{20}{18}$

$= \frac{10}{9}$, or $1\frac{1}{9}$

DISCUSSING the IDEAS

1. Explain another way to simplify the expression in *Example 1a*.

2. a) In *Example 1c*, which operation must be performed first? Explain.

   b) Explain another way to simplify the expression in *Example 1c*. Which way do you prefer? Why?

3. a) In *Example 2a*, why were the two fractions multiplied by $\frac{2}{2}$ and $\frac{3}{3}$, respectively?

   b) What other ways are there to add the fractions in *Example 2a*?

1. Each diagram represents 1 unit. Write the fraction represented by the shaded part.

a)   b)    c)   d)

2. Reduce to lowest terms.

a) $\dfrac{3}{15}$ b) $\dfrac{6}{15}$ c) $\dfrac{9}{15}$ d) $\dfrac{12}{15}$

e) $\dfrac{8}{10}$ f) $\dfrac{8}{20}$ g) $\dfrac{8}{30}$ h) $\dfrac{8}{40}$

3. Write in decimal form, to 2 decimal places where necessary.

a) $\dfrac{3}{10}$ b) $\dfrac{24}{100}$ c) $\dfrac{12}{50}$ d) $\dfrac{2}{5}$

e) $\dfrac{9}{15}$ f) $\dfrac{25}{15}$ g) $\dfrac{3}{4}$ h) $\dfrac{5}{5}$

i) $\dfrac{7}{8}$ j) $\dfrac{10}{4}$ k) $\dfrac{8}{9}$ l) $\dfrac{7}{3}$

4. Write as a fraction, or a mixed number.

a) 0.6   b) 0.03   c) 0.221   d) 1.2

e) 1.25   f) 3.125   g) 4.85   h) 3.63

i) 6.94   j) 10.08   k) 2.71   l) 1.3

5. On this 100-square, what fraction would be represented if the indicated numbers were shaded?

a) all the even numbers

b) all the odd numbers

c) all the multiples of 5

d) all the multiples of 4

e) all the multiples of 3

f) all the perfect squares

g) all 1-digit numbers

h) all 2-digit numbers

i) all 3-digit numbers

j) all numbers divisible by both 3 and 4

k) all 2-digit numbers whose digits are equal

1	2	3	4	5	6	7	8	9	10
11	12	13	14	15	16	17	18	19	20
21	22	23	24	25	26	27	28	29	30
31	32	33	34	35	36	37	38	39	40
41	42	43	44	45	46	47	48	49	50
51	52	53	54	55	56	57	58	59	60
61	62	63	64	65	66	67	68	69	70
71	72	73	74	75	76	77	78	79	80
81	82	83	84	85	86	87	88	89	90
91	92	93	94	95	96	97	98	99	100

l) all 2-digit numbers whose tens digit is greater than the units digit

m) all numbers containing the digit 7

6. In these diagrams, the 100 flat represents 1 unit. Write the number represented by each diagram as a fraction and as a decimal.

a)

b)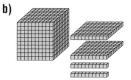

7. In these diagrams, the large cube represents 1 unit. Write the number represented by each diagram as a fraction and as a decimal.

a) **b)** **c)** **d)**

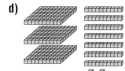

Symmetry in Portraits

A 1998 newspaper article contained the statement, below right.

8. In the library or resource centre of your school, or elsewhere, find some examples of portraits made by artists.

a) Complete this exercise for each portrait. Show the results in a table.

i) Measure the width of the portrait.

ii) Measure the distance from the left edge of the portrait to the eye that comes closest to the middle of the portrait.

iii) Divide the measurement in part b by the measurement in part a.

b) Do your results agree with the statement in the article? Explain.

9. Carry out a similar investigation with portraits by photographers. Are the results the same? Explain.

A scientist who studies vision and the brain has made a curious discovery about portrait painting. Artists almost always place one eye of their subject at the horizontal centre – a point halfway between the left and right edges of the picture frame.

B **10.** Add or subtract.

a) $\frac{1}{5} + \frac{1}{2}$ b) $\frac{2}{5} + \frac{1}{2}$ c) $\frac{3}{5} + \frac{1}{2}$ d) $\frac{4}{5} + \frac{1}{2}$

e) $\frac{1}{5} - \frac{1}{10}$ f) $\frac{2}{5} - \frac{1}{10}$ g) $\frac{3}{5} - \frac{1}{10}$ h) $\frac{4}{5} - \frac{1}{10}$

11. Multiply or divide.

a) $\frac{1}{2} \times \frac{3}{4}$ b) $\frac{2}{3} \times \frac{1}{5}$ c) $\frac{5}{6} \times \frac{2}{3}$ d) $\frac{4}{5} \times \frac{4}{3}$

e) $\frac{2}{3} \div 2$ f) $\frac{4}{5} \div 2$ g) $\frac{1}{9} \div \frac{1}{3}$ h) $\frac{5}{11} \div \frac{2}{3}$

12. a) Add $\frac{2}{3} + \frac{5}{6}$, then write the sum in decimal form.

b) Write $\frac{2}{3}$ and $\frac{5}{6}$ in decimal form, then find their sum. How does this sum compare with the sum for part a?

c) Repeat the procedure of parts a and b for these expressions.

i) $\frac{3}{4} + \frac{2}{5}$ ii) $\frac{5}{8} - \frac{1}{4}$ iii) $\frac{1}{6} - \frac{5}{9}$ iv) $\frac{2}{9} - \frac{5}{11}$ v) $\frac{7}{16} + \frac{5}{12}$

13. Nahal coaches a baseball team. She calculates the batting averages of the team players. Nahal divides the number of hits by the number of times at bat, and rounds the quotient to 3 decimal places.

Batter	Times at bat	Number of hits
Maral	106	33
Ari	119	34
Kim	104	30
Ange	116	31
Nicki	91	28

a) Calculate the batting averages of Nahal's 5 top batters.

b) List the players in order of their batting averages from greatest to least.

c) Who do you think is Nahal's most reliable batter? Explain.

d) Mathematical Modelling In parts a to c, you modelled the performance of the players by calculating their batting averages. Do you think that a player's batting average can be used to predict future performance? Explain.

14. Refer to the table on page 15 that shows the cost of fractional shares of a jet. Make a similar table to show the cost of these fractional shares.

a) $\frac{9}{16}, \frac{5}{8}, \frac{11}{16}, \frac{3}{4}, \frac{13}{16}, \frac{7}{8}$ b) $\frac{1}{12}, \frac{1}{6}, \frac{1}{4}, \frac{1}{3}, \frac{5}{12}, \frac{1}{2}$

15. A Learjet 31A has 6 seats. It costs $6.18 million. Make a table similar to the one on page 15 to show the cost of fractional shares of a Learjet 31A.

16. a) El-ran fences a section of his yard using these lengths of fencing material: 5.9 m, 1.5 m, and 6.3 m. The fencing material costs $12.79/m. How much will the fencing cost?

b) Mathematical Modelling A mathematical model often gives results that are slightly different from actual results. In part a, you modelled the cost of fencing a section of a yard. Give some reasons why the cost of fencing the yard would be greater than the cost you calculated.

17. Use a calculator. Do each calculation using as few key strokes as possible. Record the keying sequences as well as the answers. Discuss your method with a partner. Is there a more efficient calculator key sequence?

a) $37.4 \times (64.1 - 37.8)$

b) $(56.2 + 12.7) \times (42.7 - 29.4)$

c) $(13.7 - 8.9) \times (59.7 - 41.3)$

d) $(45.2 - 27.8) \times (97.8 - 36.4)$

e) $\dfrac{26.3 \times 14.7}{19.5}$

f) $\dfrac{109.4}{9.2 \times 4.1}$

g) $\dfrac{32.5 - 16.9}{12.8 \times 3.5}$

h) $\dfrac{(16.2 - 9.3) \times (65.3 - 42.7)}{23.8 \times (73.6 - 47.2)}$

i) $(36.5 - 13) \div (22.3 - 14.7)$

j) $\dfrac{259.3}{7.5 \times 25.4} - 1$

k) $\dfrac{0.015 \times 20\ 000}{12} + 20\ 000$

18. a) Add 1 to the numerator of the fraction $\frac{1}{3}$. How does the size of the fraction change?

b) Add 1 to the denominator of $\frac{1}{3}$. How does the size of the fraction change?

c) How does the size of the fraction $\frac{1}{3}$ change when both the numerator and the denominator are increased by 1?

19. Repeat exercise 18 for the fraction $\frac{7}{3}$.

20. Compare your answers to exercises 18 and 19. What do you notice?

C **21.** Refer to the table on page 15. The table shows only the purchase prices. According to the article in which this table appeared, if a business purchased a $\frac{1}{8}$ share, there would be additional costs of $15 660 per month plus $2330 for each hour of flying. Suppose a business purchased a $\frac{1}{8}$ share and flew the plane for 100 hours each year for 5 years.

a) Determine the total cost to purchase and operate the plane for 5 years.

b) Determine the mean cost per hour to fly during the 5 years.

22. Use the information in exercise 21. Make a table similar to the one on page 15. Show the following information for all seven fractional shares: the purchase price; the number of hours per year of flying; the monthly cost; the cost per hour of flying; the total cost to purchase and operate the plane for 5 years; and the mean cost per hour to fly during the 5 years.

COMMUNICATING the IDEAS

Look up the word "fraction" in a dictionary. In your journal, describe the various ways this word is used. Ask several people to say a sentence that contains the word "fraction." Compare these uses to those you found in the dictionary. Which use is the most common?

1.3 How Many Cereal Boxes?

On page 2, you considered the situation in which each box of a certain kind of cereal contains an item that is part of a set of similar items. In this situation, the following problem arises:

How many boxes must be purchased to obtain a complete set of items?

Since you may get duplicates of items before you get the last item you need to complete the set, an exact answer to this question is not possible. However, it is possible to estimate the number of boxes you would need. We can do this in different ways. In all of these ways, we will make these assumptions:

- All the items are distributed randomly in the boxes.
- The total number of each item is the same.
- Each box contains only one item.

These assumptions mean that every time you open a box there is an equal chance of getting any one of the items.

Experimental Models

Instead of buying the boxes of cereal, we can simulate the problem using a coin, a die, or a set of playing cards.

Simulations using a coin

Suppose there are only 2 different items in a complete set. To simulate picking items from the boxes, we conduct this experiment:

Let heads represent item #1 and tails item #2. Toss a coin several times until we get at least one H and at least one T.

Suppose we get these results: T T T H.

This corresponds to getting item #2 in the first three boxes we open, and item #1 in the fourth box. In this case, it takes 4 boxes to complete the set.

If we repeat the experiment, we may get a different result. However, we can repeat the experiment many times and calculate the mean of the results. This should give a reasonable estimate of the number of boxes needed to complete the set.

1. a) Repeat the above experiment several times and record the results.

 b) Find the mean of the results to determine an estimate of the number of boxes needed to complete the set. Record this number for later use.

Suppose there are 4 different items in a complete set. We can toss 2 different coins, such as a nickel and a quarter. Let the results correspond to the four items in the boxes:

Nickel	Quarter	
H	H	Item #1
H	T	Item #2
T	H	Item #3
T	T	Item #4

2. Conduct this experiment.

 a) Toss 2 coins. Use the table above to determine the number of the corresponding item. Record this number.

 b) Repeat part a until you have at least one of each item. Record the number of times you tossed the 2 coins.

3. a) Repeat the experiment in exercise 2 several times. Record the results.

 b) Find the mean of the results to determine an estimate of the number of boxes needed to complete the set. Record this number for later use.

Simulations using a die

4. Design and conduct experiments using a die to estimate the number of boxes needed to obtain a complete set. Assume a complete set contains the following numbers of items. Repeat each experiment several times and determine the mean of the results. Record the estimates for later use.

 a) 6 items **b)** 3 items **c)** 2 items

Simulations using playing cards

5. Design and conduct experiments using a deck of playing cards to estimate the number of boxes needed to obtain a complete set. Assume a complete set contains the following numbers of items. Repeat each experiment several times and determine the mean of the results. Record the estimates for later use.

 a) 4 items **b)** 2 items **c)** 13 items **d)** 10 items

Summary

6. Copy this table. Use it to summarize your results.

Number of items in a complete set	Estimated number of boxes needed, using		
	Coins	Dice	Playing cards
2			
3			
4			
6			
10			
13			

7. Draw a graph to show the estimated number of boxes for different numbers of items in a complete set. Plot the *Number of items* horizontally and the *Estimated number of boxes* vertically. If the estimates for 2 items are different, use the mean of the estimates. Do the same for 4 items.

8. In exercises 1 to 7, you modelled the situation involving items in cereal boxes using coins, a die, and playing cards. Which model most closely represents the situation about the items in the boxes? Explain.

Technology Models

You can use the random number feature of a computer or a graphing calculator to simulate the problem.

Using a spreadsheet

9. Use a spreadsheet program. Set up a table similar to this, entering the information in the first four rows.

	A	B	C	D
1	Cereal Box Prize Simulation			
2	Number in a complete set:		4	
3	Box #	Prize #		
4	1			
5	=A4+1			

In cell A5, enter the formula shown.

Copy this formula down to cell A15 or farther.

In cell B4, enter a formula:

If you are using ClarisWorks®, use =RAND(D2)

If you are using Microsoft Works™, use =INT(RAND()*D2)

Copy the formula in cell B4 down to cell B15 or farther.

10. a) Look at the numbers in column B until you see at least one of each possible item. Record the corresponding number of boxes from the first column. In the example at the right, you would record 9 because 9 boxes are needed to get all 4 different items. This corresponds to one experiment.

Box #	Prize #
1	2
2	4
3	4
4	4
5	2
6	1
7	2
8	1
9	3
10	1

b) A spreadsheet has a Calculate Now feature on one of its menus. Use this feature to recalculate the spreadsheet. When you recalculate the spreadsheet, the values in column B change, because they are determined randomly. This corresponds to repeating the experiment. Select Calculate Now, and repeat part a. Continue doing this until you have 10 values.

c) Determine the mean of the 10 values you recorded in part b. The result is an estimate of the average number of boxes needed for a complete set of 4 items.

11. Repeat exercise 10 using these numbers in cell D2. You may need to extend the formulas in columns A and B farther down the spreadsheet to get the values you need.

a) 2   **b)** 3   **c)** 5   **d)** 6

12. a) Copy this table. Record your results from exercises 10 and 11.

Number of items in a complete set	Average number of boxes needed
2	
3	
4	
5	
6	

b) Compare these results with your results from simulations with coins, a die, and playing cards.

13. Graph the *Average number of boxes* against the *Number of items in a complete set*.

Using a graphing calculator

14. Use a TI-83 graphing calculator. Follow the steps below to produce
   numbers at random. Each number is 1, 2, 3, or 4.

   a) Press [MATH] [▶] [▶] [▶] 5 1 [,] 4 [)] [ENTER]. A display similar to
   the one below left will appear. In this case, the calculator
   produced the number 3. This corresponds to getting item #3 in the
   first box of cereal. To produce more numbers, press [ENTER] a few
   more times. Count the number of times you do this. Stop when
   you have at least one 1, one 2, one 3, and one 4, corresponding
   to a complete set of items. The screen below right shows that
   this happened when 6 numbers were produced. Record the
   number of boxes needed, 6. This completes one experiment.

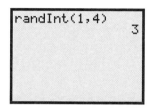
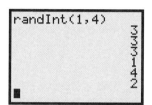

   b) To repeat the experiment, press [CLEAR]. Start pressing [ENTER]
   again. As before, look for at least one 1, one 2, one 3, and one
   4, then record the corresponding number of boxes needed.

   c) Determine the mean of the 10 values you recorded in part b.
   The result is an estimate of the average number of boxes
   needed for a complete set of 4 items.

15. Repeat exercise 14. Estimate the average number of boxes needed if a
   complete set contains:

   a) 2 items   **b)** 3 items   **c)** 5 items   **d)** 6 items

16. a) Copy the table in exercise 12a. Record your results from exercises 14 and 15.

   b) Compare these results with your results from simulations with coins, a
   die, playing cards, and a spreadsheet.

17. Graph the *Average number of boxes* against the *Number of items in a
   complete set*.

COMMUNICATING
   ***the*IDEAS**

In your journal, write a set of instructions to estimate the number of boxes of cereal needed
to obtain a complete set of 2 items.

Where Would You Live?

In a 1998 nation-wide poll, a large sample of Canadians were asked: "If you could live in any of the following Canadian cities—and enjoy the same standard of living as you do now—which one would you choose to live in?"

Here are the results. An example of how to read the table is shown by the shaded cells. This shows that 6% of the people in Winnipeg would prefer to live in Ottawa.

Where They Live Now

Preferred Residence	Van.	Cgy.	Edm.	Wpg.	Tor.	Ott.	Mtl.	Que.
Vancouver	82%	10%	24%	15%	23%	14%	17%	14%
Calgary	7%	73%	9%	24%	8%	1%	4%	4%
Edmonton	2%	0%	56%	3%	1%	0%	1%	2%
Winnipeg	1%	1%	1%	38%	0%	0%	0%	1%
Toronto	3%	0%	0%	3%	53%	4%	5%	6%
Ottawa	1%	3%	1%	6%	4%	68%	4%	4%
Montreal	1%	3%	2%	5%	3%	7%	53%	6%
Quebec City	0%	1%	0%	0%	1%	1%	13%	62%

Population in 1998	
Vancouver	1 927 998
Calgary	885 130
Edmonton	899 466
Winnipeg	677 291
Toronto	4 511 966
Ottawa	1 045 249
Montreal	3 384 233
Quebec City	700 197

1. What percent of the people in Toronto would prefer to live in each location?

   a) Vancouver   **b)** Calgary

   c) Montreal   **d)** Toronto

   e) any city except Toronto

2. Use your answers to exercise 1 and the table on page 26. Determine the number of people in Toronto who would prefer to live in each location in exercise 1.

3. Determine the number of people in Ottawa who would prefer to live in each location.

   a) Vancouver   **b)** Calgary

   c) Montreal   **d)** Ottawa

   e) any city except Ottawa

4. **a)** In which city would most people prefer to stay where they are?

   b) In which city would most people prefer to move to a different city? To which city would they prefer to move?

   c) In which cities would more than 60% of the people prefer to stay where they are?

5. **a)** To which city would most people prefer to move?

   b) To which city would most people prefer not to move?

Recall that "percent" means the number of parts per hundred. For example, from the table on page 26, 9% of the people in Edmonton would prefer to live in Calgary. Since 9% means $\frac{9}{100}$, or 0.09, the number of people in Edmonton who would prefer to live in Calgary is $0.09 \times 899\,466$, or 80 952.

Example

In the poll on page 26, 3016 people were surveyed. The number of these people who said that they would prefer to live in Vancouver was 724.

a) What percent of people surveyed would prefer to live in Vancouver?

b) In 1998, the population of Canada was 30 300 400. Use the survey result. Estimate the number of Canadians who would prefer to live in Vancouver.

Solution

a) Think: 724 out of 3016 is $\frac{724}{3016}$.

To express this fraction as a percent, multiply by 100%.

$$\frac{724}{3016} \times 100\% \doteq 0.24 \times 100\%$$
$$\doteq 24\%$$

About 24% of the people surveyed would prefer to live in Vancouver.

b) Think: 24% is approximately 25%, or $\frac{1}{4}$.

$\frac{1}{4}$ of 30 300 400 is approximately 7 500 000.

About 7 500 000 Canadians would prefer to live in Vancouver.

DISCUSSING the IDEAS

1. Discuss some things that influence where people want to live.

2. In the poll results on page 26, more people want to live in Vancouver than in any other city. Suggest some reasons for this.

3. **a)** In the *Example* part b, what assumptions are made?

   b) Do you think these assumptions are reasonable? Explain.

1.4 EXERCISES

1. Express each fraction as a percent.

   a) $\frac{1}{5}$ **b)** $\frac{2}{5}$ **c)** $\frac{3}{5}$ **d)** $\frac{4}{5}$

2. Express each fraction or decimal as a percent.

   a) 0.8   **b)** 0.25   **c)** $\frac{1}{8}$ **d)** $\frac{1}{3}$ **e)** $\frac{5}{6}$ **f)** $\frac{5}{9}$

   g) 2.5   **h)** $\frac{8}{3}$ **i)** 1.6   **j)** 2.4   **k)** $\frac{17}{25}$ **l)** $\frac{23}{40}$

3. Express each percent as a decimal.

   a) 24%   **b)** 39%   **c)** 57.4%   **d)** 3%   **e)** 5.8%

   f) 11.5%   **g)** 1.6%   **h)** 0.9%   **i)** 137%   **j)** 264%

   k) 375%   **l)** 375.8%   **m)** 0.1%   **n)** 2.03%   **o)** 0.25%

4. Express each percent as a fraction in lowest terms.

   a) 15%   **b)** 30%   **c)** 45%   **d)** 60%

5. Express each percent as a fraction in lowest terms.

a) 27%   b) 36%   c) 60%   d) 28%   e) 75%   f) 45%

g) 48%   h) 16%   i) 85%   j) 19%   k) 125%   l) 215%

6. Find:

a) 20% of 20   b) 20% of 40   c) 20% of 60   d) 20% of 80

e) 20% of 50   f) 40% of 50   g) 60% of 50   h) 80% of 50

7. Find:

a) 25% of 40   b) 15% of 40   c) 0.6% of 150   d) 5% of 35

e) 109% of 75   f) 4% of 150   g) 0.7% of 95   h) 65% of 18

i) 112% of 92   j) 0.25% of 500   k) 115% of 752   l) 0.5% of 25 000

8. Determine the number in each statement.

a) 20% of a number is 20.   b) 40% of a number is 20.

c) 60% of a number is 20.   d) 80% of a number is 20.

9. Determine the number in each statement.

a) 50% of a number is 10.   b) 20% of a number is 3.

c) 40% of a number is 10.   d) 75% of a number is 30.

e) 60% of a number is 42.   f) 15% of a number is 15.

g) $66\frac{2}{3}$% of a number is 18.   h) 10% of a number is 8.

i) 104% of a number is 26.   j) 130% of a number is 91.

10. The regular price of a bicycle is $227.50. It is on sale for 15% off. What is the price change? What is the sale price?

11. Skis are on sale for 45% off. A pair of skis regularly sells for $180. What is the price after the discount?

12. Economists predict that food costs will change over the coming year. They estimate an increase of 11.7%. Last year, one family spent $8400 on food. How much might the family expect to spend in the coming year?

13. Estimation A calculator is on sale for $9.98. This price reflects a 25% discount. What is its regular price?

14. The managers of a recording company expect sales income to change this year. They hope for a 60% increase over last year's sales of $2 500 000. What is the company's projected income for this year?

15. In April, 800 000 people were unemployed. In May this figure decreased by 0.16%. How many fewer people were unemployed in May?

16. **Estimation** Each year, more people are using the Internet. In 1998, it was estimated that 41% of Canadians were on line, compared with 23% in 1996. The population of Canada was approximately 30 million at the time.

a) Estimate the number of people in Canada who started using the Internet between 1996 and 1998.

b) In 1998, approximately 35% of Canadians used e-mail, but only 24% checked it daily. Estimate how many Canadians used e-mail, and how many checked it daily.

c) In 1998, approximately 32% of the Canadians who used the Internet bought something on line. Estimate how many Canadians bought something on line in 1998.

17. At some point in your high school career, you will have to write examinations. In a course where there is an examination, a teacher may use this equation to calculate the students' final marks.

$$\frac{\text{Final}}{\text{Mark}} = \frac{80\% \text{ of}}{\text{Term Mark}} + \frac{20\% \text{ of}}{\text{Exam Mark}}$$

The term mark is usually based on tests, assignments, projects, and portfolios.

a) Suppose your term mark is 84%. How will your mark change when the examination mark has been taken into account? Copy and complete the table.

b) Write to explain how your final mark changes as your examination mark goes from great to not so good.

Term mark	Examination mark	Final mark
84%	100%	
84%	90%	
84%	80%	
84%	70%	
84%	60%	
84%	50%	
84%	40%	
84%	30%	
84%	20%	
84%	10%	
84%	0%	

18. Open the *Provinces of Canada* database. Choose a province and a 5-year time period after 1971.

a) i) For each year, express the number of births as a percent of the population.
   ii) What is the mean percent over the 5 years?

b) i) For each year, express the number of deaths as a percent of the population.
   ii) What is the mean percent over the 5 years?

c) Subtract the mean percent of deaths from the mean percent of births. This is the net percent growth due to natural causes.

d) Use the total population in the first year and this net percent growth. Determine what the population should be at the end of the 5 years. Is this number close to the actual population? What other factors affect population change?

19. The table shows the percent of households that had certain products in 1988, and the estimated percents for the year 2000.

Estimated Percents of Households Using Selected Products	% in Canada		% in USA	
	1988	2000	1988	2000
Colour televisions	92	96	93	96
Projection televisions	1	7	3	12
Stereo televisions	10	40	20	50
Video cassette recorders	52	75	56	80
Laptop and personal computers	15	35	17	40
Microwave ovens	54	85	70	90
Compact disc/digital tape equipment	8	75	4	85
Electronic home security systems	5	12	8	15
Three or more telephones	22	45	25	50

a) Which product is expected to have the largest percent change in use from 1988 to 2000 in Canada? In the United States?

b) Which product is expected to have the smallest percent change in use from 1988 to 2000 in Canada? In the United States?

ACADEMIC FOCUS

How the Other 0.00001 Percent Lives

In 1998, a newspaper article with the above headline stated that "Mustique is Caribbean cottage country for British royalty, Swiss bankers, North and South American tycoons, the international jet set, and the just plain rich". According to the article, a villa on the island can be rented for between $3000 and $22 000 (U.S.) per week.

20. Express each percent in fraction form.

a) 10%   **b)** 1%   **c)** 0.1%   **d)** 0.01%

e) 0.001%   **f)** 0.0001%   **g)** 0.000 01%

21. What does the headline mean?

22. The population of Canada is about 30 million. What is 0.000 01% of the population of Canada?

23. The population of the world is about 6 billion. What is 0.000 01% of the population of the world?

24. Estimation This graph shows how the enrolment of men and women in Canadian universities and colleges has changed since 1971–72.

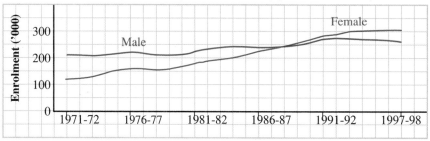

University and College Enrolment in Canada
(Total postsecondary full-time students by gender, 1971 to 1998)

Source: Statistics Canada

a) i) Estimate the enrolment of men and women in 1971–72.

   ii) Estimate the percent of female university and college students in 1971–72.

b) i) Estimate the enrolment of men and women in 1997–98.

   ii) Estimate the percent of female university and college students in 1997–98.

c) i) Estimate the percent increase in male enrolment from 1971–72 to 1997–98.

   ii) Estimate the percent increase in female enrolment from 1971–72 to 1997–98.

d) Why do you think the percent of female university and college students has increased so dramatically since 1971–72?

25. Estimation A 1998 newspaper article reported about the world population approaching 6 billion. The article contained this graph. Use the information on the graph.

a) Estimate the number of people in 1998 who were:

   i) 14 years old or younger

   ii) from 15 to 24 years old

   iii) from 25 to 64 years old

   iv) 65 years old or older

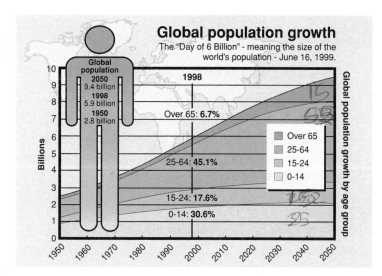

Global population growth
The "Day of 6 Billion" - meaning the size of the world's population - June 16, 1999.

Global population
2050 9.4 billion
1998 5.9 billion
1950 2.8 billion

1998
Over 65: **6.7%**
25-64: **45.1%**
15-24: **17.6%**
0-14: **30.6%**

Over 65
25-64
15-24
0-14

Global population growth by age group

b) Estimate the predicted number of people in 2050 who will be:

   i) 14 years old or younger   **ii)** from 15 to 24 years old

   iii) from 25 to 64 years old   **iv)** 65 years old or older

c) Estimate the corresponding percents in part b.

26. In 1998, a newspaper article claimed that the average family's tax bill had soared by almost 1200% since 1961. The article stated that in 1961 the average family earned $5000 and paid $1675 in taxes. Also, in 1998 the average family earned $46 488 but paid $21 288 in taxes.

a) Calculate to confirm the percent tax increase from 1961 to 1998.

b) By what percent did the earnings increase?

27. Read this article. It was printed in the *You Asked Us* column of a newspaper in 1993.

From this article, we may think that there were fewer Canadians playing hockey in the NHL in 1992–93 than there were in 1991–92.

a) Is this a correct assumption? Explain.

b) Is it possible that there were actually more Canadian players in the NHL in 1992–93 than ever before? Explain.

c) What information do you need to answer part b?

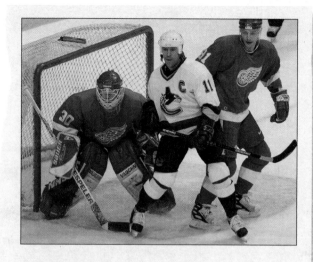

Canadian Content in NHL

Q What percent of Canadian-born players make up the National Hockey League?

A Of the 609 players on the 24 NHL rosters at the outset of the 1992-93 season, 403 (66%) were Canadians. That's a sharp drop from the 71% Canadian content of the previous season.

In the 1967-68 season, when the league expanded to 12 teams from the original six, almost 97% of the players were Canadian. Just under 2% of the players were born in the U.S. and slightly over 1% came from outside North America.

Look in a newspaper or a magazine for an article that gives information about how something has changed over a period of time. Use the information to explain to a friend the two ways to express how something changes. Be sure that your friend clearly understands the difference between the amount by which something has changed and the percent by which it has changed.

Stock Market Report

A person who owns stocks in a company is a part owner of that company. The stock market report in a newspaper shows how the value of the stocks changes.

This Week on the Toronto Stock Exchange

Stock	Vol. (100s)	High	Low	Close	Chge	Last 52 wks High	Low
Chin Op	14	10.10	10.10	10.10	0	12.75	8.50
CHUM	1	40.00	40.00	40.00	−5.00	56.50	36.00
Cinar rv	87	31.00	29.05	29.40	−2.50	38.25	22.70
Cinram	1086	19.85	18.75	18.75	+0.05	26.85	14.30
Cintech Tel	107	3.39	3.10	3.28	−0.11	3.89	0.60
Club Mona	1776	8.25	7.85	8.25	+0.55	14.50	3.10
Daimler	2	158.60	156.75	156.75	−0.75	164.00	128.75
Danier Leath	5	8.80	8.80	8.80	−0.20	11.95	7.00

The change in the value of a stock is listed in the **Chge** column. These numbers are repeated below.

0   −5.00   −2.50   +0.05   −0.11   +0.55   −0.75   −0.20

All these numbers are examples of rational numbers. Although they are written in decimal form in the stock report, they can all be written as fractions with numerators and denominators as integers. For example:

$$-5.00 = -\frac{500}{100}, \text{ or } -\frac{5}{1} \qquad\qquad +0.05 = +\frac{5}{100}, \text{ or } +\frac{1}{20}$$

1. Write each number in the **Chge** column as a fraction with numerator and denominator as integers.

2. Make a number line showing numbers from −5 to +5. Locate some of the numbers in the stock report on your number line. If you drew a number line showing numbers beyond 5 and beyond −5, do you think that it would be possible to locate every number in the stock report on it? Explain.

Any number that can be written in the form $\frac{m}{n}$, where m and n are integers and $n \neq 0$, is called a *rational number*.

You can represent any rational number on a number line.
You can write any rational number as a decimal by dividing the numerator by the denominator.

Example 1

Show how to represent the number 0.42 on a 100-square.

Solution

0.42 means $4 \times \frac{1}{10} + 2 \times \frac{1}{100}$.

There are 10 columns on a 100-square.
One column represents $\frac{1}{10}$ of the square.
To represent $4 \times \frac{1}{10}$, shade 4 columns.
To represent $2 \times \frac{1}{100}$, shade two more squares.

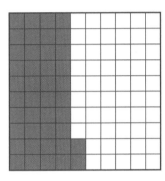

In *Example 1*, there are many different ways to represent the number 0.42 on a 100-square. Here are two other possibilities.

Use rows instead of columns.
It does not matter which other
2 squares are shaded.

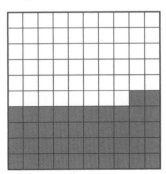

0.42 also means $42 \times \frac{1}{100}$, or $\frac{42}{100}$.
Shade any 42 squares, such as those enclosed by a 7 by 6 rectangle.

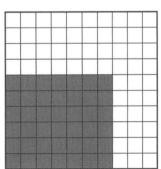

Example 2

Show how to represent the number −0.42 on a number line.

Solution

−0.42 means $-4 \times \frac{1}{10} - 2 \times \frac{1}{100}$.

Draw a line segment 10 cm long to represent 1 unit from −1 to 0. Since each centimetre represents $\frac{1}{10}$ of the segment, $-4 \times \frac{1}{10}$ is represented by a point 4 cm to the left of 0. One millimetre represents $\frac{1}{100}$ of the line segment. Mark point A 2 mm to the left of −0.4. On this number line, point A represents −0.42.

| −1 | | −0.8 | | −0.6 | | A | | −0.2 | | 0 |

1. In *Example 1*, the rational number was positive. Could a negative rational number be illustrated on a 100-square? Explain.

2. On page 35, there are three ways to represent the number 0.42. What other ways can you think of?

3. In *Example 2*, the rational number was negative. Could a positive rational number be illustrated on a number line? Explain.

Boggle your MIND

According to *The Guinness Book of Records*, Mrs. Shakuntala Devi is the fastest calculating prodigy in the world. In 1980, in a supervised test at the Computer Department of Imperial College, in London, England, she correctly multiplied 7 686 369 774 870 by 2 465 099 745 779 in 28 seconds without mechanical aid. How many digits are there in the product?

A **1.** State the rational number represented by the shaded part of each 100-square.

a)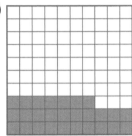

b)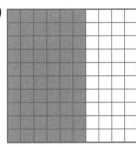

c)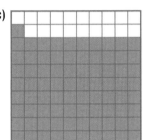

d)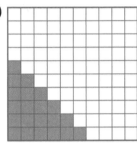

2. How would you represent each rational number using a 100-square?

a) 1.42   b) 2.42   c) 42.42   d) 0.7

e) 0.70   f) 0.73   g) 0.730   h) 0.073

3. State the rational number for each letter on the number line.

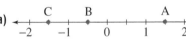

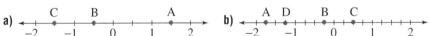

4. Mental Math Which rational number is greater? Explain how you know.

a) $\frac{1}{4}, -\frac{3}{4}$ b) $-\frac{1}{4}, -\frac{3}{4}$ c) $\frac{3}{2}, -\frac{5}{2}$

d) $\frac{1}{2}, \frac{2}{3}$ e) $\frac{1}{2}, -\frac{2}{3}$ f) $-\frac{1}{2}, -1\frac{1}{4}$

5. Mental Math and Estimation Which rational number is greater? Explain how you know.

a) $\frac{2}{5}, \frac{4}{5}$ b) 0.8, 0.9   c) $\frac{-2}{3}, \frac{5}{6}$ d) 0.9, −0.9   e) $\frac{1}{3}, \frac{5}{18}$ f) 9.8, −8.9

g) $\frac{-2}{3}, \frac{3}{4}$ h) 0.3, −0.33   i) $\frac{-7}{12}, \frac{-8}{18}$ j) 6.77, −7.66   k) $\frac{6}{15}, \frac{4}{9}$ l) 5.9, 5.99

6. Round each rational number to the nearest integer.

a) −3.7   b) −5.2   c) −6.7   d) −0.4   e) 0.2   f) −0.6

g) −0.97   h) −0.35   i) −7.52   j) $-\frac{22}{5}$ k) $-\frac{67}{4}$ l) $-\frac{37}{5}$

7. Write to explain whether each statement is true or false, and why.

   a) −8 is both a rational number and an integer.

   b) −4 is both an integer and a whole number.

   c) −9 is a rational number, but not a whole number.

   d) 3.5 is a rational number and an integer.

   e) −18 is a rational number but not an integer.

   f) $-5\frac{2}{3}$ is a rational number and an integer.

8. Which statements are true? Which are false? Explain your answers.

   a) Every natural number is an integer.   b) Every integer is a natural number.

   c) All integers are rational numbers.   d) Some rational numbers are integers.

9. List in order from least to greatest.

   a) $-\frac{1}{5}, -\frac{3}{5}, -\frac{2}{5}$ b) $\frac{5}{8}, -\frac{1}{2}, \frac{1}{4}$ c) $1\frac{2}{5}, \frac{3}{7}, -\frac{2}{9}$

   d) $-\frac{1}{4}, \frac{1}{4}, -\frac{1}{2}$ e) $-\frac{5}{6}, \frac{2}{3}, -\frac{1}{2}$ f) $-\frac{3}{2}, -\frac{5}{4}, \frac{1}{3}$

B 10. **Mental Math and Estimation** Which of these rational numbers can be written as integers?

   a) $\frac{-8}{-2}$ b) $\frac{-7}{+3}$ c) $\frac{+51}{-3}$

   d) $\frac{630}{-7}$ e) $-\frac{240}{81}$ f) $\frac{-480}{16}$

   g) $-\frac{3248}{-4}$ h) $-\frac{-84}{-29}$ i) $\frac{1000}{-33}$

11. State the rational number represented by each letter on the number line.

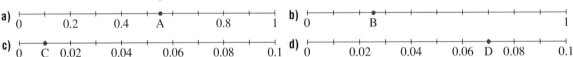

12. Copy this number line. Mark a dot on the line to represent each rational number.

   a) $\frac{3}{8}$ b) $-\frac{3}{16}$ c) $-\frac{3}{4}$ d) $\frac{1}{4}$

   e) $-\frac{7}{16}$ f) $-\frac{7}{8}$ g) 0.125   h) −0.625

13. **Estimation** For this number line, estimate the rational number represented by each letter.

14. Construct a number line. Mark a dot on the line to represent each rational number.

a) $\frac{2}{3}$ b) 0.5   c) $-\frac{4}{5}$ d) −1.1   e) $1\frac{1}{4}$ f) 2.4

g) $-3\frac{1}{2}$ h) −0.1   i) $-2\frac{7}{10}$ j) 1.7   k) $2\frac{1}{6}$ l) −1.9

15. List in order from greatest to least.

a) $0.6, \frac{1}{9}, -\frac{6}{5}, 1.0, -\frac{1}{2}, 0$ b) $\frac{1}{8}, \frac{7}{5}, 0.5, \frac{1}{3}, -3.25, -\frac{5}{6}$

c) $-1.375, \frac{3}{8}, \frac{1}{2}, 0.9, -\frac{1}{10}, -0.7, 0, 5$ d) $-1.1, \frac{9}{8}, -\frac{10}{5}, 2.75, -\frac{5}{12}, -3.6, \frac{7}{6}$

16. List in order from least to greatest.

a) $-\frac{2}{3}, 0.5, -\frac{1}{2}, -1.3, \frac{1}{4}, 1.8$ b) $\frac{9}{15}, -0.6, \frac{1}{5}, 1.2, -\frac{2}{5}, -1.3$

c) $-\frac{5}{12}, -0.75, \frac{1}{4}, -1.4, -\frac{1}{6}, 0.8$ d) $\frac{2}{3}, 0.67, \frac{3}{4}, -0.7, \frac{1}{7}, 0.11, -\frac{1}{3}$

17. Represent each rational number on a number line.

a) 0.48   b) 0.76   c) 0.19   d) 0.69

18. Represent each rational number on a 100-square in two different ways.

a) 0.25   b) 0.56   c) 0.37   d) 0.71

19. Write in decimal form, to 3 decimal places where necessary.

a) $\frac{3}{5}$ b) $\frac{2}{-3}$ c) $\frac{4}{9}$ d) $-\frac{3}{8}$

e) $\frac{7}{21}$ f) $\frac{-3}{22}$ g) $\frac{15}{7}$ h) $-\frac{1}{6}$

i) $\frac{5}{16}$ j) $\frac{-17}{27}$ k) $\frac{11}{12}$ l) $\frac{13}{11}$

20. Express each rational number in decimal form.

a) $\frac{-3}{-10}$ b) $\frac{+5}{-6}$ c) $\frac{-12}{+5}$

d) $\frac{+3}{-8}$ e) $\frac{4}{-9}$ f) $\frac{-8}{-15}$

21. Reduce to lowest terms.

a) $\frac{5}{-10}$ b) $\frac{10}{-15}$ c) $\frac{-12}{-30}$ d) $-\frac{6}{15}$

e) $-\frac{-6}{11}$ f) $-\frac{-6}{18}$ g) $-\frac{4}{-14}$ h) $-\frac{-14}{-25}$

i) $-\frac{-15}{-35}$ j) $-\frac{-24}{-72}$ k) $-\frac{-42}{-28}$ l) $-\frac{54}{-81}$

22. **Mental Math and Estimation** Compare each pair of rational numbers. Replace the comma with < or >.

a) $6.4, -\frac{25}{4}$ b) $-\frac{23}{7}, -3.5$ c) $\frac{3}{8}, -\frac{5}{11}$ d) $\frac{-57}{100}, -0.5$

e) $-8.6, -\frac{75}{9}$ f) $-15.8, -\frac{76}{5}$ g) $\frac{51}{16}, 3.175$ h) $\frac{7}{11}, \frac{16}{25}$

23. **Estimation** Without calculating the answers, state which expressions are positive.

a) $\frac{5}{-3}$ b) $\frac{(5)(-3)}{-7}$ c) $\frac{5}{(-5)(-7)}$ d) $\frac{-3}{(5)(-7)}$ e) $\frac{5}{(-3)+(-7)}$

f) $\frac{5-(-3)}{-7}$ g) $\frac{5-(-3)}{5-(-7)}$ h) $\frac{5}{-3}+\frac{5}{-7}$ i) $\frac{-3}{-7}-\frac{5}{-3}$ j) $\frac{(-7)(-3)(-7)}{(-5)(5)(-3)}$

24. Use a calculator. For each expression:

   a) Record the keystrokes used to get the answer.

   b) Complete the calculation in a different way and record the keystrokes used.

   c) Explain why one method uses fewer keystrokes than the other.

   i) $(18.3 - 4.7) \times (32.5 + 12.6)$ **ii)** $(76.1 - 47.1) \times (5.9 - 17.6)$

   iii) $\dfrac{28.4}{42.5 + 12.3}$ **iv)** $\dfrac{16.3 - 29.7}{9.3 \times (14.3 - 32.7)}$

C **25.** If $x > 0$, $y < 0$, and $z < 0$, which expressions are always positive?

   a) $\dfrac{x}{y}$ **b)** $\dfrac{xy}{z}$ **c)** $\dfrac{x}{yz}$ **d)** $\dfrac{y}{xz}$ **e)** $\dfrac{x}{y+z}$

   f) $\dfrac{x-y}{z}$ **g)** $\dfrac{x}{x-y}$ **h)** $\dfrac{x-y}{x-z}$ **i)** $\dfrac{x}{y} + \dfrac{x}{z}$ **j)** $\dfrac{y}{z} - \dfrac{x}{y}$

ACADEMIC FOCUS

Explaining Repeating Decimals

26. Here is the paper-and-pencil calculation for expressing $\frac{22}{7}$ as a decimal.

   The last three remainders appeared earlier in the calculation. What does this tell you about the rest of the digits in the quotient? Explain your answer.

```
        3.14285714
7)22.00000000
   21
    10
     7
    30
    28
    20
    14
    60
    56
    40
    35
    50
    49
    10
     7
    30
    28
     2
```

27. Suppose you express any rational number in decimal form by paper-and-pencil calculation. Explain why you will eventually get a zero remainder or a remainder that appeared earlier in the calculation.

28. Do you think it is possible to have a number in decimal form that never repeats? Would this be a rational number? Explain your answer.

COMMUNICATING the IDEAS

During the next two days, make a note of the numbers you use in your daily activities outside school. When do you use the numbers? What kinds of numbers do you use? In your journal, illustrate your answers to both questions with specific examples.

1.6　Adding and Subtracting Rational Numbers

You know how to add and subtract integers. Integers are rational numbers. Do you think you could add and subtract rational numbers using the same methods as those for adding and subtracting integers?

INVESTIGATION

Adding and Subtracting Rational Numbers

Sums of Rational Numbers	
Sums of Integers	
(+3) + (−2)	(+3.5) + (−2.1)
(−5) + (+1)	(−5.6) + (+1.3)
(−4) + (−3)	(−4.8) + (−3.5)

Look at the box above.

1. For each sum of integers on the left, there is a sum on the right. In what way is the sum on the right similar to the sum on the left? In what way is it different?

2. Add each pair of integers on the left. Use the result to help you add the rational numbers on the right.

Differences of Rational Numbers	
Differences of Integers	
(+3) − (−2)	(+3.5) − (−2.1)
(−2) − (+7)	(−2.6) − (+7.3)
(−6) − (−1)	(−6.8) − (−1.5)

Look at the box above.

3. For each difference of integers on the left, there is a difference on the right. In what way is the difference on the right similar to the difference on the left? In what way is it different?

4. Subtract each pair of integers on the left. Use the result to help you subtract the rational numbers on the right.

The methods to add and subtract rational numbers are the same as those to add and subtract integers. When the numbers are in fraction form, the methods to add and subtract fractions apply.

Example

Estimate each difference or sum, then calculate it.

a) $(-1.5) - (-0.83)$ **b)** $(+0.75) + (-0.67)$

c) $(+0.125) - (-1.25)$ **d)** $(-0.55) + (-0.75)$

Solution

a) To estimate: $(-1.5) - (-0.83)$ is approximately $(-1.5) - (-1)$
To subtract, add the opposite.
$$-1.5 - (-1) = -1.5 + 1$$
$$= -0.5$$
To calculate:
$$(-1.5) - (-0.83) = (-1.5) + (+0.83)$$
$$= -1.5 + 0.83$$
$$= -0.67$$

b) To estimate: $(+0.75) + (-0.67)$ is approximately
$$(+1) + (-1) = 1 - 1$$
$$= 0$$
To calculate:
$$(+0.75) + (-0.67) = 0.75 - 0.67$$
$$= 0.08$$

c) To estimate: $(+0.125) - (-1.25)$ is approximately
$$(+0.1) - (-1.3) = 0.1 + 1.3$$
$$= 1.4$$
To calculate:
$$(+0.125) - (-1.25) = (+0.125) + (+1.25)$$
$$= 0.125 + 1.25$$
$$= 1.375$$

d) To estimate: $(-0.55) + (-0.75)$ is approximately
$$(-0.6) + (-0.8) = -0.6 - 0.8$$
$$= -1.4$$
To calculate:
$$(-0.55) + (-0.75) = -0.55 - 0.75$$
$$= -1.3$$

DISCUSSING the IDEAS

Observe that + and − signs appear many times in the solution of the *Example*.

1. Some + signs represent addition and some indicate that a number is positive. Explain how you can tell what a + sign represents.

2. Some − signs represent subtraction and some indicate that a number is negative. Explain how you can tell what a − sign represents.

A **1.** Add.

a) $(+3.5) + (-4.2)$ b) $(-1.7) + (-1.3)$ c) $(-2.4) + (+6.1)$

d) $0.75 + (-0.25)$ e) $(-1.25) + (-0.5)$ f) $(-1.5) + 0.4$

2. Subtract.

a) $(+4.5) - (-0.5)$ b) $(-3.1) - (-1.4)$ c) $(+6.2) - (+8.7)$

d) $0.5 - (-0.25)$ e) $0.33 - 0.5$ f) $(-0.75) - (-1.5)$

3. Add or subtract, as indicated.

a) $(+3.5) + (-2.5)$ b) $(+3.5) + (-4.5)$ c) $(+3.5) - (+4.5)$

d) $(+3.5) - (-1.5)$ e) $(+3.5) - (+2.5)$ f) $(+3.5) + (-0.5)$

4. Add or subtract, as indicated.

a) $\left(+\frac{1}{5}\right) + \left(+\frac{3}{5}\right)$ b) $\left(+\frac{1}{6}\right) + \left(+\frac{5}{6}\right)$ c) $\left(+\frac{1}{8}\right) + \left(+\frac{3}{8}\right)$

d) $\left(+\frac{5}{4}\right) - \left(+\frac{3}{4}\right)$ e) $\left(+\frac{4}{10}\right) - \left(+\frac{3}{10}\right)$ f) $\left(+\frac{3}{4}\right) - \left(+\frac{1}{2}\right)$

5. Estimation Estimate the sum or difference.

a) $(+2.4) + (-1.7)$ b) $(-3.5) + (+6.3)$ c) $(-2.2) + (-1.6)$

d) $(+1.7) - (-1.4)$ e) $(-3.2) - (+4.8)$ f) $(-1.1) - (-2.1)$

g) $(+3.4) + (-1.1)$ h) $(-4.2) - (-8.1)$ i) $(-0.2) - (-1.1)$

6. Add or subtract, as indicated.

a) $(+2.3) + (-8.3)$ b) $(-4.1) + (-3.1)$ c) $(-2.8) - (-1.2)$

d) $(-6.3) - (+3.3)$ e) $2.9 - (-3.9)$ f) $(-4.6) + (-2.6)$

7. A student has a chequing account at a local bank. Here are some entries from her statement for one month:

Date	Item	Debit	Credit	Balance
Jan 10 99				55.40
Jan 14 99	CHQ	69.20		13.80 DR
Jan 15 99	DEP		100.00	86.20

a) How much money was in the account on January 10?

b) What happened on January 14? Why do the letters 'DR' appear beside the balance? Check that the balance on this day is correct.

c) What happened the next day? Check that the balance on this day is correct.

8. Two pieces of wood were joined together. One piece was 4.5 cm long. The other piece was 2.2 cm long. What was the combined length of the wood?

9. A piece of pipe is 146.3 cm long. A piece 13.7 cm long is cut off. How long is the remaining piece?

10. A piece of paper is 11.8 cm long. A piece 1.5 cm long is cut off. How long is the remaining piece?

11. On a certain day, the temperature at Canmore, Alberta is −4.5°C. It is 2.5°C colder at Banff. What is the temperature at Banff?

B **12.** Add or subtract, as indicated.

a) $\left(-\frac{7}{5}\right) + \left(+\frac{2}{5}\right)$

b) $\left(+\frac{1}{2}\right) - \left(+\frac{3}{8}\right)$

c) $\left(+\frac{1}{5}\right) + \left(+\frac{7}{10}\right)$

d) $\left(+\frac{2}{3}\right) + \left(+\frac{11}{12}\right)$

e) $\left(+\frac{7}{5}\right) - \left(+\frac{7}{15}\right)$

f) $\left(+\frac{4}{9}\right) - \left(+\frac{5}{18}\right)$

g) $\left(+\frac{4}{3}\right) - \left(+\frac{7}{6}\right)$

h) $\left(+\frac{6}{7}\right) - \left(+\frac{1}{2}\right)$

i) $\left(+\frac{2}{5}\right) + \left(+\frac{3}{10}\right)$

j) $\left(+\frac{7}{6}\right) - \left(+\frac{3}{4}\right)$

k) $\left(+\frac{3}{8}\right) + \left(+\frac{7}{6}\right)$

l) $\left(+\frac{5}{6}\right) - \left(+\frac{5}{9}\right)$

13. Add or subtract as indicated.

a) $-\frac{4}{5} - \frac{3}{5}$

b) $\frac{17}{3} - \frac{15}{3}$

c) $-\frac{5}{12} + \frac{2}{12}$

d) $\frac{13}{17} + \frac{5}{17}$

e) $-\frac{3}{2} + \frac{1}{6}$

f) $\frac{3}{4} - \frac{3}{10}$

14. Add or subtract, as indicated.

a) $0.67 - 0.83$

b) $-1.5 + 1.25$

c) $-0.125 - 0.25$

d) $1.4 - 0.9$

e) $0.83 - 0.22$

f) $-0.583 + 0.625$

15. Use rational numbers to write a number sentence for each question.

a) Juan dives from a 26.7-m ledge on the cliffs in Acapulco, Mexico. The water is 3.6 m deep. What is the change in height from the ledge to the bottom of the sea?

b) The temperature in St. John's is 6.5°C. In Corner Brook it is 8.0°C colder. What is the temperature in Corner Brook?

c) In 1997, the Canadian national debt was $651.24 billion. In 1998, the debt decreased by $2.54 billion. What was the national debt in 1998?

16. Copy each chart. Add the numbers in each row and each column. Find the sum of the numbers in each chart in two different ways.

a)

+5	−6	+2	
−4	+12	−8	
+7	−6	−10	

b)

−5.2	−8.9	+2.6	
−6.0	+3.3	+9.4	
+8.5	−5.7	+15.1	

17. Here is a pattern of integers in three rows. Assume the pattern continues in both directions.

Row 1	...	−8	−5	−2	1	4	7	...
Row 2	...	−7	−4	−1	2	5	8	...
Row 3	...	−6	−3	0	3	6	9	...

a) Describe the pattern.

b) What are the next five integers in row 2?

c) In which row will each of these integers appear?

  i) 36   ii) 62   iii) 100   iv) −24   v) −47   vi) −64

18. This table lists the work schedules for Ann and Bob.

Worker	Mon.	Tues.	Wed.	Thurs.	Fri.
Ann	0.75 h	1.25 h	1.4 h	2.25 h	
Bob	$1\frac{1}{2}$ h	$\frac{3}{4}$ h			$2\frac{1}{3}$ h

a) Find the time each person worked that week.

b) Which worker had the most hours? How much longer did he or she work?

19. Henry estimates that it takes him $\frac{1}{4}$ h to prepare dough, $\frac{1}{10}$ h to grate cheese, $\frac{1}{3}$ h to prepare toppings, and $\frac{2}{5}$ h to bake the pizza. What is the total time from beginning preparation until the pizza is ready?

20. **Estimation** A guardrail needs to be exactly 19.77 m long. A contractor has 3 pieces measuring 2.21 m, 9.14 m, and 3.21 m.

a) Estimate the combined length of the pieces.

b) To complete the guardrail, what length is needed?

21. a) A piece of board is initially 488.5 cm long. From it, the carpenter cuts boards measuring 124.7 cm, 114.9 cm, and 96.4 cm. What is the length of the remaining piece?

b) **Mathematical Modelling** In part a, you modelled the problem of determining the length of the remaining piece of wood after other pieces have been cut from a board.

  i) Explain why the remaining piece of wood will be shorter than the length you calculated.

  ii) Estimate the length of the remaining piece.

22. **Estimation** Three companies are working together to complete a highway. One company will construct 15.2 km, another will construct 7.8 km, and the third company will construct 25.8 km.

a) Estimate the total length of the highway.

b) The completed highway will be 73.9 km long. How much of the construction will have to be completed at a later date?

23. **Estimation** A customer in a supermarket had $20. In his basket, he put items that cost $0.99, $3.78, $9.87, $4.41, and $0.45. None of the items was taxable.

a) Estimate the total cost of the items.

b) Will the customer have enough money to pay for the items?

24. Two friends left work together and had supper at G.T.'s. Shortly after they placed their orders, a third friend joined them. She quickly ordered a meal too. The total bill (without taxes) for these three people was $18.55.

a) What time did each person arrive at the restaurant?

b) How many answers are there to the question in part a? Explain.

4^{30} 7^{00}

THE TIME YOU ARRIVE IS THE PRICE YOU PAY

Valid between 4:30 and 7:00 p.m. every day on the following dinners:

TOP SIRLOIN STEAK   STUFFED SOLE
CHICKEN OSCAR   NEW YORK SIZZLE

Plus Changing Specials

FOR EXAMPLE: IF YOU ARRIVE AT 5:10 P.M. YOU PAY $5.10

G.T.'s RESTAURANT

COMMUNICATING the IDEAS

Find a way to use a calculator to add or subtract rational numbers in fraction form. In your journal, write a description of your method with some examples. Compare your method with a classmate's method.

You know how to multiply and divide integers. Integers are rational numbers. Do you think you could multiply and divide rational numbers using the same methods as those to multiply and divide integers?

INVESTIGATION

Multiplying and Dividing Rational Numbers

Products of Rational Numbers		
Products of Integers		
$(+3)(-2)$	$(+3.5)(-2)$	$(+3)(-2.5)$
$(-4)(+5)$	$(-4.2)(+5)$	$(-4)(+5.1)$
$(-5)(-2)$	$(-5.5)(-2)$	$(-5)(-2.2)$

Look at the box above.

1. For each product of integers on the left, there are two products on the right.

   a) In what ways are these products similar to the one on the left?

   b) In what ways are they different?

2. Multiply each pair of integers on the left. Use the result to help you multiply the rational numbers on the right.

Quotients of Rational Numbers		
Quotients of Integers		
$\dfrac{-10}{+5}$	$\dfrac{-9}{+5}$	$\dfrac{-10.5}{+5}$
$\dfrac{+8}{-2}$	$\dfrac{+7}{-2}$	$\dfrac{+7.6}{-2}$
$\dfrac{-6}{-3}$	$\dfrac{-6.3}{-3}$	$\dfrac{-6}{-4}$

Look at the box above.

3. For each quotient of integers on the left, there are two quotients on the right.

   a) In what ways are these quotients similar to the one on the left?

   b) In what ways are they different?

4. Divide each pair of integers on the left. Use the result to help you divide the rational numbers on the right.

The methods to multiply and divide rational numbers are the same as those to multiply and divide integers.

- The product or quotient of two rational numbers with the same signs is positive.
- The product or quotient of two rational numbers with different signs is negative.

When the rational numbers are in fraction form, the methods to multiply and divide fractions apply.

Example

Estimate the quotient or product, then calculate it.

a) $(+1.95) \div (-1.3)$ **b)** $(-1.8) \times (-3.1)$ **c)** $(-0.8) \times (+0.7)$ **d)** $(-8.99) \div (-3.1)$

Solution

a) To estimate: $(+1.95) \div (-1.3)$ is approximately $(+2) \div (-1) = -2$

To calculate: $(+1.95) \div (-1.3)$, use a calculator.
Key in: 1.95 $\boxed{\div}$ 1.3 $\boxed{+/-}$ $\boxed{=}$ to display -1.5

b) To estimate: $(-1.8) \times (-3.1)$ is approximately $(-2) \times (-3) = +6$

To calculate: $(-1.8) \times (-3.1)$, use a calculator.
Key in: 1.8 $\boxed{+/-}$ $\boxed{\times}$ 3.1 $\boxed{+/-}$ $\boxed{=}$ to display 5.58

c) To estimate: $(-0.8) \times (+0.7)$ is approximately $(-1) \times (+1) = -1$

But each factor is numerically less than 1; so we know the product will be numerically less than 1.

To calculate: $(-0.8) \times (+0.7)$, think $8 \times 7 = 56$

The signs are opposite, so the product is negative.

The product is numerically less than 1. It is -0.56.

d) To estimate: $(-8.99) \div (-3.1)$ is approximately $(-9) \div (-3) = 3$

To calculate: $(-8.99) \div (-3.1)$, use a calculator.
Key in: 8.99 $\boxed{+/-}$ $\boxed{\div}$ 3.1 $\boxed{+/-}$ $\boxed{=}$ to display 2.9

1. A product, such as 3×4, is defined as: 3×4 means $4 + 4 + 4$. Explain how each product is defined.

   a) 3×4.2 b) 3.5×4 c) 3.5×4.2

   d) $3 \times (-4.2)$ e) $3.5 \times (-4.2)$ f) $(-3.5) \times (-4.2)$

2. A quotient, such as $35 \div 5$, is defined as: $35 \div 5 = 7$ because $7 \times 5 = 35$. Explain how each quotient is defined.

   a) $35 \div 6$ b) $36 \div 5$ c) $39.6 \div 7.2$

   d) $35 \div (-6)$ e) $36 \div (-5)$ f) $(-39.6) \div (-7.2)$

1.7 EXERCISES

Estimation Estimate to complete exercises 1 to 4. Then use a calculator to check your answers.

1. Suppose you multiply each rational number below by -2.5. Which will give a product greater than 10?

   a) -5.5 b) $+7.2$ c) -4.1 d) -3.2 e) -8 f) $+200$

2. Which product is closest to -36?

   a) $(-3.5) \times (+9.5)$ b) $(-14.7) \times (-1.9)$ c) $(+5.9) \times (-6.2)$

3. Suppose you divide each rational number below by $\frac{1}{2}$. Which will give a quotient less than 1?

   a) $\frac{2}{3}$ b) -5 c) $\frac{3}{4}$ d) -0.6 e) $+0.45$ f) -0.01

4. Suppose -24 is divided by each rational number below. Which will give a quotient greater than -24?

   a) 6 b) -3.8 c) 0.75 d) -4.8 e) $\frac{1}{2}$ f) 0.01

5. In 4 h, the effect of the tide at a sea port changed the water level by -4.8 m. What was the average hourly change in water level?

6. **Estimation** Estimate the product, then multiply.

   a) $(+3.2) \times (+3)$ **b)** $(-4) \times (+1.2)$ **c)** $(-1.1) \times (-5)$

   d) $(-2.4) \times (-1.6)$ **e)** $(+0.21) \times (-1.3)$ **f)** $(-4.5) \times (+1.7)$

7. Multiply.

   a) $(+4.3) \times (-2)$ **b)** $(-1.5) \times (-3.2)$ **c)** $(-0.25) \times (+8.4)$

   d) $\frac{3}{8} \times \frac{2}{3}$ **e)** $\frac{4}{3} \times \frac{1}{6}$ **f)** $\frac{1}{2} \times \frac{3}{2}$

8. **Mental Math and Estimation** Estimate the quotient, then divide.

   a) $(+6) \div (+1.5)$ **b)** $(+9) \div (+2.25)$ **c)** $(-5.2) \div (-1.3)$

   d) $(-6.2) \div (-3.1)$ **e)** $\frac{1.3}{5.2}$ **f)** $\frac{-13.95}{-4.5}$

9. Divide.

   a) $(-2.4) \div 2$ **b)** $36 \div (-1.5)$ **c)** $(-18.7) \div (-6.8)$

   d) $\frac{2}{3} \div \frac{1}{6}$ **e)** $\frac{1}{2} \div \frac{4}{3}$ **f)** $\frac{1}{3} \div \frac{3}{2}$

B 10. Multiply or divide, as indicated.

   a) $(+4.2) \times (-2)$ **b)** $(-3.1) \times 10$ **c)** $(-12.5) \div (+5)$

   d) $18.6 \div (-10)$ **e)** $(-4.8) \times 9$ **f)** $(-10) \div (-2.5)$

   g) $(+23.5) \div (-0.5)$ **h)** $(-9.6) \times (-1.5)$ **i)** $(-5.2) \div (+0.3)$

11. Multiply or divide, as indicated.

   a) $(-0.8) \times (-1.5)$ **b)** $\frac{1}{3} \times \frac{5}{2}$ **c)** $\frac{2}{3} \div \frac{4}{5}$ **d)** $0.77 \times (-0.6)$

   e) $(-0.375) \div (-1.25)$ **f)** $\frac{2}{5} \div \frac{8}{3}$ **g)** $\frac{3}{10} \times \frac{4}{9}$ **h)** $4.5 \times (-1.3)$

12. Use rational numbers to write a number sentence for each question.

   a) A diver descends at a rate of 12.4 m/min. What is her depth after 2.5 min?

   b) The temperature drops 10.5°C over a 6-h period. What is the mean temperature change per hour, to the nearest tenth of a degree?

   c) The temperature drops about 2.5°C for every 500 m increase in altitude. What is the approximate change in temperature for an altitude increase of 3000 m?

13. A room measures 2.3 m by 3.4 m. What is its area?

14. How many square metres of cloth are required to make 2 curtains, each measuring 1.8 m by 0.7 m?

15. A sheet of paper measures 27.4 cm by 21.3 cm. What is the area of one-third of the sheet?

16. A room measures 5.2 m by 3.9 m.

a) Estimate the area of the room.

b) Calculate the area of the room. How does the calculated area compare with the estimated area?

c) Carpet costs $18.25/m^2, underlay costs $3.25/m^2, and installation costs $3/m^2. Calculate the total cost (excluding tax) to carpet the room.

d) **Mathematical Modelling** In parts a to c, you modelled the problem of calculating the cost to carpet a room. Give at least two reasons why the actual cost in part c will be greater than the calculated answer.

17. A tub contains 2.3 L of ice cream. It is shared equally among 5 people. How much will each person get?

18. A pizza costs $15.81. You pay for $\frac{1}{3}$ of the pizza. How much do you pay?

19. Suppose you find $\frac{1}{3}$ of a pizza in the fridge. You eat one-half of it. What fraction of the whole pizza have you eaten?

20. A jug has a capacity of 1.75 L. It is one-quarter full. How much does it contain?

21. Many people in Ontario who visit the United States drive from Fort Erie, Ontario, to Buffalo, New York. They use the Peace Bridge, which crosses the Niagara River. There is no charge for using the Peace Bridge to enter the United States. However, when a person returns to Canada, she has to pay a toll. The sign below is in front of the tollbooth. In January, 1999, $1 Cdn was worth approximately 65¢ U.S.

a) Would it be cheaper to pay $2.00 U.S. or $2.50 Cdn to cross the bridge? Explain.

b) How much would $1 Cdn have to be worth in U.S. currency to change your answer in part a?

c) Why do you think people are charged a toll driving in only one direction across the bridge?

TOLL FOR CARS
$2.00 U.S. or $2.50 CDN

What Is Canadian Money Worth in the U.S.?

For Canadians visiting the United States, the value of Canadian money is determined by what it will buy after it has been converted to U.S. dollars, compared with what it will buy in Canada.

In exercises 22 to 24, use the exchange rate $1 Cdn = $0.65 U.S. If Canadian money is worth the same in the United States as it is in Canada, then $0.65 U.S. should buy the same things in the United States that $1.00 Cdn buys in Canada.

22. In Toronto, a Big Mac costs $3.49 Cdn. In Buffalo, New York, the same Big Mac costs $2.59 U.S.

    a) Convert $3.49 Cdn to U.S. dollars.

    b) Compare your answer in part a with the cost of a Big Mac in Buffalo. For purchasing Big Macs, is the Canadian dollar worth more or less in Buffalo than it is in Toronto? Explain.

    c) Calculate this fraction to 2 decimal places: $\dfrac{\text{answer to part a}}{\text{cost of a Big Mac in Buffalo}}$

23. In Kitchener, Ontario, a 60-L tank of gas costs $28 Cdn. In Pittsburgh, Pennsylvania, the same tank of gas costs $15 U.S.

    a) Convert $28 Cdn to U.S. dollars.

    b) Compare your answer in part a with the cost of a tank of gas in Pittsburgh. For purchasing gas, is the Canadian dollar worth more or less in Pittsburgh than it is in Kitchener? Explain.

    c) Calculate this fraction to 2 decimal places: $\dfrac{\text{answer to part a}}{\text{cost of a tank of gas in Pittsburgh}}$

If Canadian money were worth exactly the same in the United States as it is in Canada, then your answers to part c in exercises 22 and 23 should be 1.00. Economists have made similar calculations. They compare the prices of many items in different cities in Canada and the United States. They have determined that, on the average, $0.83 U.S. buys the same things in the United States that $1.00 Cdn buys in Canada.

24. Do you think $1 Cdn should be worth $0.83 U.S.? Explain.

25. Estimation Each turn of the handle of a vice moves the jaw by 0.25 cm. Estimate how many turns will be required to move the jaw 2.125 cm. Calculate the number of turns required.

26. Estimation A stack of boards is 40.5 cm tall. Each piece is 2.25 cm thick. Estimate how many boards are in the pile. Calculate the number of boards.

27. A piece of lumber is 3.7 m long. It is to be cut into pieces 0.74 m long. How many pieces can be cut from the original piece?

28. A section of fence requires 18 pieces of cedar. Each piece is 1.6 m long.

a) How many metres of cedar are required?

b) Cedar costs $0.85/m. What will the total cost be (excluding tax)?

29. A person plans to construct a fence. The materials are listed below. Copy and complete the table. Calculate the total cost of materials for the project.

Item	Number required	Length (m)	Cost/m	Cost per item
Posts	12	2.4	$3.35	
Rails	24	2.4	$1.63	
Palings	176	1.8	$1.42	
Nails				$18.35
			Total cost	

30. A gas tank has a capacity of 63.5 L. On a certain trip, one-half of a tank of gas was used.

a) The tank was $\frac{7}{8}$ full at the start. What fraction remains after the trip?

b) Calculate the amount of fuel left in the tank.

c) The car is taken to a gas station for a fill-up. How much gas will be required?

d) The gas costs 59.9¢ L. Calculate the cost for the fill-up.

e) Mathematical Modelling In part d, give some reasons why the actual cost for the fill-up might differ from the calculated answer.

31. The daily high temperatures for one week were recorded. The mean high temperature was 2.6°C. The temperatures for 6 days were +12.8°C, –6.3°C, 0°C, –4.7°C, –2.1°C, and +5.6°C.

a) Estimate the temperature on the seventh day. Explain how you estimated.

b) Calculate the temperature on the seventh day.

c) How do the estimated and calculated temperatures compare?

32. a) What fraction is one-half as great as $\frac{2}{3}$?

b) What fraction is one-third as great as $\frac{3}{5}$?

c) What fraction is one-half as great as $\frac{3}{4}$?

33. You can use positive and negative rational numbers on a spreadsheet to observe some patterns. Set up this spreadsheet:

	A	B	C	D	E
		add 2	add –2	Multiply by 2	Multiply by –2
1					
2		=A2+2	=A2–2	=A2*2	=A2*–2
3	=A2+1	=A3+2	=A3–2	=A3*2	=A3*–2

a) Explain each formula in row 3. Copy Down the formulas in row 3 for 15 rows.

b) Enter any rational number in decimal form in cell A2. Look at columns B and C. Describe the difference between numbers in the same row. Explain the difference.

c) Look at columns D and E. Compare the patterns in these two columns. Describe the effect of multiplying a rational number by a negative number.

C **34.** A student spends one-half her money on a CD. She spends one-third of the money she has left on lunch. She has $12.50 left. How much money did the student have before she bought the CD?

35. Choose a rational number in the form $\frac{m}{n}$, where m and n are positive integers, and $n \neq 1$. Reduce both the numerator and the denominator by 1, to form a different rational number. Is the second rational number equal to, greater than, or less than the first one? Does your answer depend on whether $m = n$, $m < n$, or $m > n$? Explain.

COMMUNICATING the **IDEAS**

A rule for subtracting rational numbers is "add the opposite." A rule for dividing rational numbers is "multiply by the reciprocal." In your journal, describe how these rules are similar. Illustrate your answer with examples.

1. **Investigation: Wind-Chill Equivalent Temperatures** On a cold day, the wind can make it feel colder than the temperature indicated on the thermometer. The table below is used for weather reports. The wind-chill equivalent temperature is the temperature you would feel under typical wind conditions. For example, when the temperature is −5°C and the wind speed is 30 km/h, the wind-chill equivalent temperature is −18°C. This means that it would feel like −18°C.

Wind-Chill Equivalent Temperature						
Temperature (°C)	Wind speed (km/h)					
	10	20	30	40	50	60
5	4	−2	−5	−7	−8	−9
0	−2	−8	−11	−14	−16	−17
−5	−7	−14	−18	−21	−23	−24
−10	−12	−20	−25	−28	−30	−32
−15	−18	−26	−32	−35	−38	−39
−20	−23	−32	−38	−42	−45	−47
−25	−28	−39	−45	−49	−52	−54
−30	−33	−45	−52	−56	−60	−62
−35	−39	−51	−59	−64	−67	−69
−40	−44	−57	−65	−71	−74	−77

Several years ago, in an area of northern Canada, there was a day when the temperature was 5°C in the morning. The temperature dropped at a rate of about 5°C every hour. Eventually, the temperature was −40°C! The wind speed was about 10 km/h throughout the day.

Temperature, −5°C
Wind speed, 30 km/h
Feels like −18°C

a) How did the wind-chill equivalent temperature change throughout the day?

b) Did it drop at the rate of about 5°C per hour? If not, how did it change?

c) Suppose the wind speed had been 60 km/h. How would the wind-chill equivalent temperature have changed throughout the day?

d) Suppose the wind speed had increased by 10 km/h every hour and at the start of the day the wind speed was 10 km/h. How would the wind-chill equivalent temperature have changed throughout the day?

2. **Academic Focus** Exposed flesh freezes when the wind-chill equivalent temperature is approximately −30°C.

a) Use the table above to estimate some combinations of wind speed and temperature that result in a wind-chill equivalent temperature of −30°C.

b) Draw a graph that shows this combinations of temperature and wind speed that cause exposed flesh to freeze.

3. Copy and complete this chart. Subtract 4 when moving to the right. Add 7 when moving up. What patterns do you notice on the diagonals? Explain why the patterns occur.

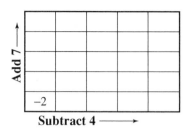

4. The greatest temperature variation in a single day in Alberta's Chinook belt was from 17°C to −28°C. What was the change in temperature?

5. This chart lists the amount of time it would take 4 different animals to travel 100 m at top speed. How many times as fast as each of the other animals is the lion?

Animal	Time to travel 100 m
Lion	4.5 s
Giraffe	5.6 s
Giant tortoise	22 min
Snail	2 h 40 min

6. A car's gas tank can hold 45.2 L of fuel.

a) It is $\frac{1}{2}$ full. How many litres of fuel does it contain?

b) It is $\frac{7}{8}$ full. How many litres of fuel does it contain?

c) Gas costs 57.9¢/L. You buy half a tank. How much will you pay?

7. A clock loses 3.2 min per day.

a) How many days will pass before the clock loses one hour?

b) How many days will pass before the clock loses 24 h?

8. There is $\frac{2}{3}$ of a pizza left. You wish to divide it equally among three people. What fraction of a pizza will each person get?

9. Sacha purchased some ski equipment. Here is the list of prices.

Skis	$275
Boots	$180
Bindings	$145
Clothing	$165

a) Suppose the boots and bindings are on sale at a 20% discount. What was the total cost for all the items?

b) Suppose the clothing was on sale at a 35% discount. What was the total cost for all the items?

c) Suppose Sacha bought the items at the listed prices. She paid 8% provincial sales tax and 7% GST. What was the total cost?

d) Suppose the skis were on sale for $195. What percent reduction is this?

10. A used car has a "For sale" sign, and a price of $8999 on the windshield. The dealer wants to sell it quickly so she adds "15% off this price" to the sign.

a) What will the car cost at the lower price?

b) The purchaser will have to pay provincial sales tax of 8%. What is the total cost of the car?

11. Some integers can be written as the sum of two or more consecutive integers; for example, $+7 = (+3) + (+4)$. Write each integer as the sum of consecutive integers.

a) -11 b) 18 c) -14 d) -17 e) 21 f) 20

12. **Mathematical Modelling: The Formula Model** Recall the modelling on pages 21 to 25. There is a formula to calculate the average number of boxes, B, needed to complete a set of items. The formula depends on the number of items in a complete set.

For 2 items: $B = 2 \times \left(1 + \frac{1}{2}\right)$

For 3 items: $B = 3 \times \left(1 + \frac{1}{2} + \frac{1}{3}\right)$

For 4 items: $B = 4 \times \left(1 + \frac{1}{2} + \frac{1}{3} + \frac{1}{4}\right)$

Similar formulas apply for larger numbers of items.

a) Use the formulas above. Calculate the average number of boxes needed for a complete set of 2, 3, or 4 items. Round your answers to 1 decimal place.

b) Use similar formulas to calculate the average number of boxes needed for a complete set of 5, 6, 7, 8, 9, 10, or 13 items. Round your answers to 1 decimal place.

c) Copy this table. Extend it, then use it to record your answers to parts a and b.

Number of items in the set	Average number of boxes needed
2	
3	
4	

d) Compare these results with previous results from simulations with coins, a die, playing cards, a spreadsheet, and a graphing calculator.

e) Graph the *Average number of boxes* against the *Number of items in the set*.

f) Describe how the average number of boxes needed to complete the set changes when the number of items in the set increases.

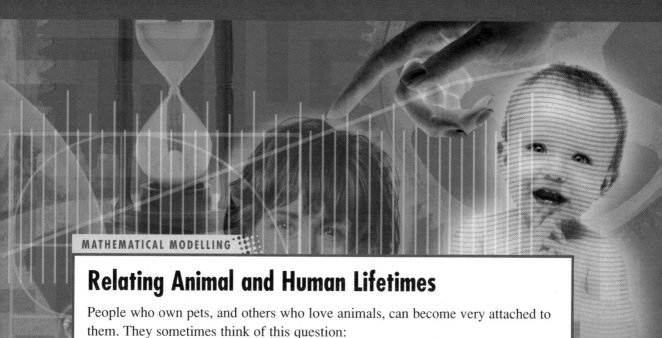

Relating Animal and Human Lifetimes

People who own pets, and others who love animals, can become very attached to them. They sometimes think of this question:

How can the lifetime of an animal be related to a human lifetime?

In this chapter you will develop some models to relate the lifetime of a cat or a dog to a human lifetime. You will also consider whether the models can be applied to other animals.

1. What do you think is a reasonable number of years for a cat or a dog to live? What is a reasonable number of years for a human to live?

2. Do you know a method that can be used to relate the years of a cat's (or a dog's) lifetime to the years of a person's lifetime? If so, describe the method. Do you think this method makes sense? Explain.

3. Do you think the same method would apply to both cats and dogs? Explain.

You will return to the problem of relating animal and human lifetimes in Sections 2.3 and 2.7.

 FYI Visit www.awl.com/canada/school/connections

For information related to the above problem, click on <u>MATHLINKS</u> followed by <u>AWMath</u>. Then select a topic under Relating Animal and Human Lifetimes.

REVIEWING YOUR Skills

This section reviews these skills:

- Reading a graph
- Using number patterns
- Graphing from a table

This graph shows the changing cost of sending a first-class letter within Canada during the 1900s.

1. Use the graph.

   a) How much did it cost to send a first-class letter in 1960? In 1980?

   b) In which year did the cost of sending a first-class letter increase the most? To what price did it increase?

   c) In which years did the cost of sending a first-class letter increase by 1¢?

   d) In which year did the cost decrease? What was the cost after the decrease?

   e) Can you use the graph to determine the cost of sending a first-class letter for any year since 1900? Explain.

2. a) Why is the graph a series of horizontal line segments?

   b) Why are there gaps at the ends of the line segments?

3. a) What does it cost to send a first-class letter within Canada today?

   b) Copy and complete the table of values to show the cost for up to 10 letters.

   c) Draw a graph to show how the postage cost depends on the number of letters.

Number of letters	Postage cost in dollars

   d) Does it make sense to join the points in your graph? Explain.

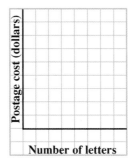

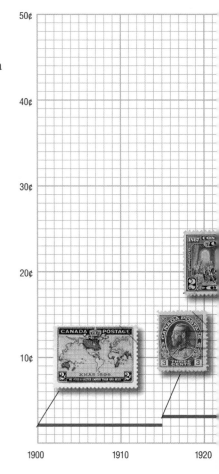

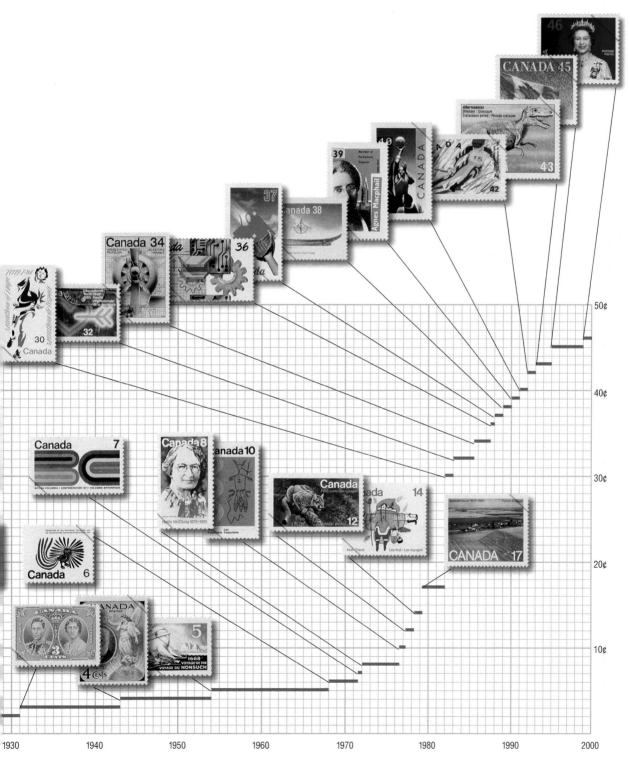

Relating Height and Time at Canada's Wonderland

At Canada's Wonderland, visitors can choose from a wide variety of rides.

Vikings Rage™ is a large ship that swings higher and higher. At its highest position, people on the ride feel as if they will fall out of their seats.

1. Imagine that you are on *Vikings Rage*.

  a) Visualize how high above the ground you are as the ride progresses from the beginning to the end.

  b) Which graph below best represents the relationship between your height above the ground and the elapsed time? Explain your choice.

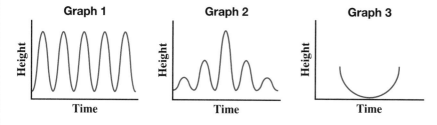

Graph 1

Height

Time

Graph 2

Height

Time

Graph 3

Height

Time

Drop Zone Stunt Tower™ is a 23-storey free-fall ride. People in open cockpit seats are lifted to the top of the ride, where there is a brief stop. Then they are dropped straight down, reaching speeds of 100 km/h before coming to a complete stop.

2. Imagine you are on *Drop Zone Stunt Tower*.

   a) Visualize how high above the ground you are as the ride progresses from the beginning to the end.

   b) Which graph below best represents the relationship between your height above the ground and the elapsed time? Explain your choice.

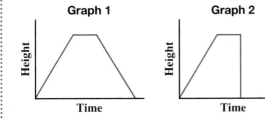

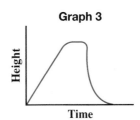

Have you ever heard the saying, "A picture is worth a thousand words"? A graph is a picture of a relationship between 2 quantities. When we draw a graph, we show how 1 quantity changes with respect to the other. One quantity is frequently time.

Example 1

Use this graph to answer each question.

a) What was the world's population each year? Show the populations in a table.

1800   1850   1900   1950   2000

b) When did the population reach 4 billion?

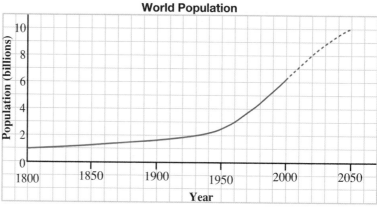

Solution

a) Start with the year on the horizontal axis. Visualize a vertical line from the year to the graph, then visualize a horizontal line to the population on the vertical axis. These are the results.

Year	1800	1850	1900	1950	2000
Population (billions)	1.0	1.3	1.7	2.5	6.2

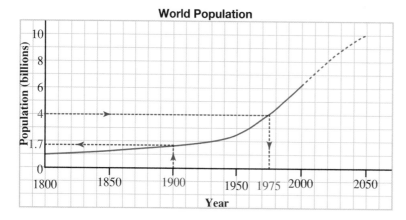

b) From 4 billion on the vertical axis, draw a horizontal line to meet the
graph. From the graph, draw a vertical line to meet the horizontal axis.
The population reached 4 billion around 1975.

Example 2

This graph appeared in *The Globe and Mail* in 1998.
Use the graph to answer each question.

a) What percent of the world's population lived in
industrialized countries each year? Show the
percents in a table.
1800   1850   1900   1950   2000

b) When was the industrialized countries' population
approximately 30% of the world's population?

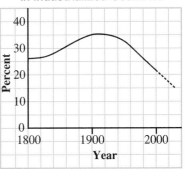

**Percent of World's Population
in Industrialized Countries**

Solution

a) Start with the year on the horizontal axis. Visualize a vertical line from the
year to the graph, then visualize a horizontal line to the population on the
vertical axis. These are the results for the given years.

Year	1800	1850	1900	1950	2000
Percent of world population in industrialized countries	26	30	35	33	21

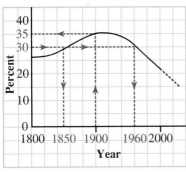

**Percent of World's Population
in Industrialized Countries**

b) From 30 on the vertical axis, draw a horizontal line to meet the graph at
two points. From each point, draw a vertical line to meet the horizontal
axis. The industrialized countries' population was 30% of the world's
population in about 1850 and 1960.

Example 3

Use the information in the graphs in *Example 1* and *Example 2*.

a) Determine the population of the world's industrialized countries for the years 1800, 1850, 1900, 1950, and 2000.

b) Draw a graph to show the population of the world's industrialized countries from 1800 to 2000.

Solution

a) Use the results from *Example 1* and *Example 2*. Make a table to show the world population and the percent of the world's population in industrialized countries for the years 1800, 1850, 1900, 1950, and 2000. To determine the population of the industrialized countries, multiply each population by the corresponding percent (written as a decimal).

Year	World population (from *Example 1*)	Percent in industrialized countries (from *Example 2*)	Population of industrialized countries (billions)
1800	1.0	26	0.26
1850	1.3	30	0.39
1900	1.7	35	0.60
1950	2.5	33	0.83
2000	6.2	21	1.30

b) Use the data in the first and last columns of the table in part a to draw a graph. Join the plotted points with line segments.

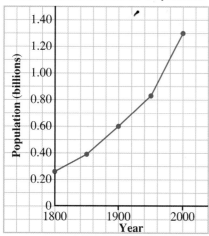

Industrialized Countries' Population

1. Refer to the graph in *Example 2*.

   a) What is meant by "industrialized countries"?

   b) Explain why the percent of the world's population living in industrialized countries increased from 1800 to about 1925, then started decreasing.

2. Countries that are not among the industrialized countries are usually referred to as developing countries. Suppose a graph is drawn similar to the graph in *Example 2* for developing countries. Explain how it would be different from the graph in *Example 2*.

3. Compare the graph in *Example 3* with the graph in *Example 2*. Explain how it is possible that the population in industrialized countries is increasing (*Example 3*), but the percent of the population in industrialized countries is decreasing (*Example 2*).

4. In *Example 3*, the plotted points were joined with line segments. What could have been done instead?

5. In *Example 3*, how would the vertical scale change if the populations were in millions?

6. On all the graphs on pages 63–66, time is plotted along the horizontal axis. Could time have been plotted along the vertical axis? Explain.

2.1 EXERCISES

 1. Which graph below best represents each scenario?

   a) the height of a tree over time

   b) the height of a Ferris wheel seat as the wheel rotates

   c) the number of hours you might sleep each day over your whole lifetime

   d) the number of computers sold, compared to the selling price

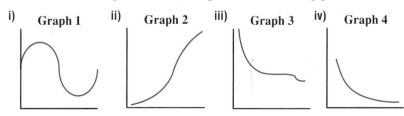

i) **Graph 1** ii) **Graph 2** iii) **Graph 3** iv) **Graph 4**

2. Describe the relationship indicated by each graph.

a)

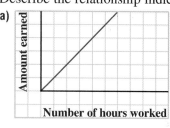

b)

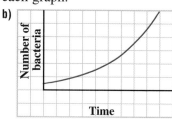

c)

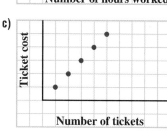

d)

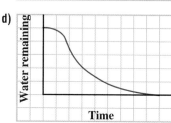

B **3.** This graph shows the height of water in a bathtub over a period of time. Describe what happened to the water in the bathtub. Think about the name on each axis and the points where the graph intersects the axes, as well as possible reasons for changes at the points indicated.

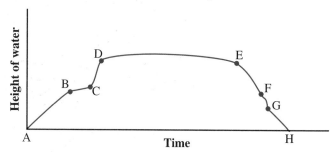

4. Suggest a possible scenario for each graph. Describe the significance of any key points or changes in the graph.

a)

b)

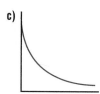

c)

d)

5. Draw a graph to represent each statement. Suggest two quantities that might be described by the statement. Write these quantities on the appropriate axes of your graph.

a) When one quantity increases, the other increases.

b) When one quantity decreases, the other decreases.

c) When one quantity decreases, the other increases.

d) When one quantity increases, the other decreases.

e) Both quantities change independently of each other.

6. People who give speeches sometimes get instant feedback from the audience. Audience members use an electronic device to indicate whether they agree or disagree with what the speaker is saying at that moment. The results are averaged and displayed in graphical form on a monitor visible to the speaker. Two complete graphs are shown.

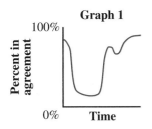

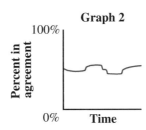

a) Describe the audience reaction to each speech.

b) Which speech do you think the audience found more interesting? Explain.

7. Shakira walks for exercise. This graph shows her distance from home during one of her walks. Describe her walk.

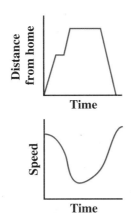

8. This graph shows the speed of Raoul's bike as he rides from home to school. Write a possible description of Raoul's journey.

9. Draw a graph, with clearly labelled axes, to fit each activity. Decide which quantity to plot along the vertical axis and which quantity to plot along the horizontal axis.

a) a person running the 3000-m race around a track

b) a person walking along a level road, climbing a hill, stopping to rest at the top, then walking back down the hill

c) a person diving off a diving board

d) a ski jumper jumping during a competition

e) an alpine skier skiing in a slalom race

10. Select one graph you drew in exercise 9. Write to describe how your graph fits the activity.

11. Use this graph to complete this exercise.

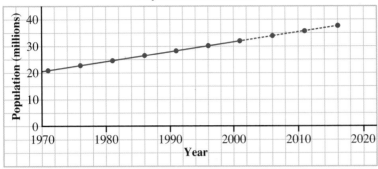

Population of Canada

a) Estimate the year when Canada's population was 30 000 000.

b) Estimate Canada's population in 1980.

c) Estimate Canada's population for the year you were born.

12. This graph was published in *The Globe and Mail* in 1998. Use this graph to complete this exercise.

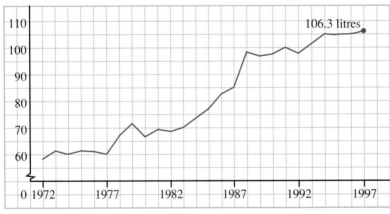

Knocking Them Back
Soft drinks consumed in Canada in litres per person

106.3 litres

a) Estimate the per capita consumption for each year.
   1972   1977   1982   1987   1992   1997

b) Use the graph in exercise 11. Estimate the population of Canada for each year in part a.

c) Use the results of parts a and b. Determine the annual consumption of soft drinks in Canada for each year in part a.

d) Show the results of part c on a graph.

13. In a science experiment, students suspended an object on a spring, then pulled the object down and released it to measure its motion. The graph displays the height of the object above the floor during the first few seconds of the experiment.

Motion of object on a spring

a) Find the height of the object after 1 s; 2 s; 3 s.

b) Find when the object was 6 cm above the floor; 10 cm above the floor.

c) Find how long it takes the object to move up and down once.

d) How does the height change during each of the first three seconds?

e) For each answer in part d, describe how the object is moving relative to the floor.

f) Suppose the students continued to measure the motion of the object for 5 min, then plotted the graph. Describe how you think the graph would look. Explain your thinking.

COMMUNICATING
the IDEAS

In your journal, describe how a graph with no numerical scales on its axes can represent a relationship between two quantities. What is the effect of adding numerical scales to a graph?

By conducting experiments and making measurements, we discover many interesting relationships. Sometimes the relationships are simple and obvious. For example, the more hours you work, the more you are paid. Sometimes the relationships are difficult to determine. For example, scientists are still trying to determine the relation between smoking and lung cancer.

In this investigation, you will use graphing to look into possible relationships in data.

INVESTIGATION

A Pendulum Experiment

Complete this experiment with a partner. You will need about 1 m of string, a small object such as a key or a washer, some tape, a tape measure or metre stick, and a watch that indicates times in tenths of a second.

1. Start a table to record the length of each pendulum you will make, and the time it takes the pendulum to swing back and forth 5 times.

A Pendulum Experiment

Length of pendulum (cm)	Time for 5 swings (s)
70	
60	
50	
40	
30	
20	
10	

2. To make a pendulum, tie the object to the string. Tape the string to the edge of a desk so the object hangs freely. Start with the object close to the floor. Swing the pendulum gently to ensure it has a clear path.

3. a) Measure and record the length of the pendulum.

b) Pull the object to an angle of about 30° from the rest position. Release the weight. Measure and record the time it takes the pendulum to swing back and forth 5 times.

Be sure to pull the object so the string remains taut. One partner should count the swings while the other partner records the time.

4. Repeat exercise 3 for shorter and shorter lengths of the pendulum. To shorten the length, lift the tape at the top and pull the string up. Try to get measurements for at least six different lengths, including very short lengths.

5. Plot the data from the table. Label the axes and use appropriate scales. Discuss with your partner whether you should join the points in the graph, or draw a smooth curve near them, and why.

6. Describe the relationship between the length of the pendulum and the time required for it to swing 5 times.

7. Describe a way to predict how long it would take a 45-cm pendulum to swing back and forth 5 times. Justify your method.

8. Describe how the graph would change if you were to repeat this experiment but measured the time for a number of swings that is:

a) greater than 5　　　　　　　　**b)** less than 5

Graphs and tables of data help to emphasize relationships between quantities. In mathematics, a relationship between a pair of quantities is called a *relation*.

Example 1

Student volunteers reported on the shelf space taken up by books in a storeroom. Examine the table of values for patterns, and relate those patterns to the graph.

French-English Dictionaries

Number of books	Shelf space (cm)
1	3
2	6
3	9
4	12
5	15

Space used by books on a shelf

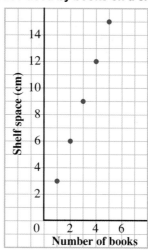

Solution

As the number of books increases by 1, the shelf space increases by 3 cm. To see the effect on the graph, start at any point and trace the horizontal and vertical movements to reach a neighbouring point.

Each point is 1 unit right and 3 units up from the preceding point. This consistent pattern means that the points must lie along a straight line. It is a result of the constant changes in the table of values.

Space used by books on a shelf

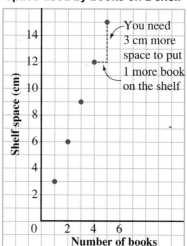

You need 3 cm more space to put 1 more book on the shelf

Example 2

The table of values and graph below show possible heights and bases of triangles with area 9 square units.

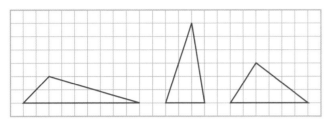

Height	Base
1	18
2	9
3	6
6	3
9	2
18	1

Triangles with area 9 square units

Describe patterns in the table of values. Relate those patterns to the graph.

Solution

The numbers increase and decrease by different amounts. As the numbers in the first column increase, the numbers in the second column decrease. This pattern is reflected by the downward-sloping curve of the graph.

The numbers in the second column are the same as the numbers in the first column, except in reverse order. The product of the numbers is always 18.

A small increase in the height results in a large decrease in the base.
A large increase in the height results in a small decrease in the base.

Triangles with area 9 square units

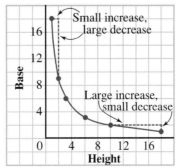

All the points on the graph of a *linear relation* lie on a straight line. *Example 2* illustrates a non-linear relation. All the points on the graph of a *non-linear* relation do not lie on a straight line.

As you progress through this course, you will study linear relations in greater depth. You will also encounter many examples of non-linear relations.

DISCUSSING the IDEAS

1. Look at your results for the *Investigation*. Describe any patterns in the table of values. For each pattern in the table, describe a corresponding pattern on the graph.

2. In *Example 1*, why is it not appropriate to join the points?

3. In *Example 2*, why is it appropriate to join the points?

2.2 EXERCISES

A 1. Describe the relationship between the quantities in each table. Explain how one quantity changes as the other quantity increases or decreases.

a)
Mass suspended from a spring, m grams	1	2	3	4	5
Extension of the spring, e centimetres	2.4	4.8	7.2	9.6	13.1

b)
Distance from the basket, in metres	2	3	4	5	6
Percent of baskets sunk, p	82	68	50	30	25

c)
Time of day, t hours	10:00	11:00	12:00	13:00	14:00
Temperature, T degrees Celsius	22	25	28	27	25

B 2. a) Construct a graph of these data.

Number of coins	4	8	12	16	20
Mass (g)	100	200	300	400	500

b) Describe any patterns in the data, and relate them to the graph.

c) Did you join the points? Explain.

d) What is the mass of one coin?

e) What is the mass of 18 coins?

3. a) Construct a graph of these data.

Length of side (cm)	1	2	3	4	5
Area of square (cm²)	1	4	9	16	25

b) Describe any patterns in the data, and relate them to the graph.

c) Did you join the points? Explain.

d) What is the area of a square that has one side measuring 3.5 cm?

e) What is the side length of a square with area 20 cm²?

f) When the length of the side of a square is doubled, does the area double? Explain.

4. a) Construct a graph of these data.

Numbers of stairs climbed	5	10	15	20	25
Heart rate (beats/min)	70	80	98	119	147

b) Describe any patterns in the data, and relate them to the graph.

c) Did you join the points? Explain.

d) What is the heart rate after climbing 18 stairs? 13 stairs?

e) About how many stairs were climbed when the heart rate was 85 beats/min? 130 beats/min?

f) Suppose you climbed a very long flight of stairs. Would your heart rate change more rapidly near the beginning of your climb or near the end of your climb? Explain.

5. a) Graph each relationship in exercise 1.

b) In each case, describe how one quantity changes as the other changes.

6. Recall that two numbers are reciprocals if their product is 1. Which graph illustrates the relationship between a number and its reciprocal? Explain.

a)

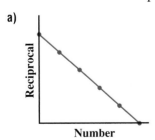

b)

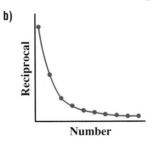

c)

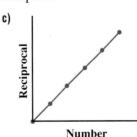

7. Recall that two numbers are opposites if their sum is 0. Draw a graph to illustrate the relationship between a number and its opposite.

8. **Investigation:** **Masses of Textbooks** You will need a set of scales that measures up to 20 kg. Digital bathroom scales are ideal.

a) Measure and record the mass of one copy of *Addison-Wesley Mathematics 9* text.

b) Repeat part a with two and more copies of the same text. Record your results for up to 10 books in a table.

Number of textbooks	Mass (kg)
1	

c) Draw a graph to show the mass of each number of textbooks. Should the points on the graph be joined? Explain.

d) Describe any patterns in the table, and relate them to the graph.

e) Describe your graph to your partner or group. Explain what it represents.

9. **Investigation:** **Paper Tube Relationships** Work with a partner. You will need a paper tube and a tape measure. When you look at a wall through the tube, you can see a region on the wall. When you move closer to the wall or farther from the wall, the height of the region changes.

a) Predict how the height of the region would change if you move:

i) closer to the wall   ii) farther from the wall

b) Measure some distances from the wall and the heights of the regions seen through the tube. Record your measurements in a table.

Distance from the wall (cm)	Height of the region seen through tube (cm)

c) Draw a graph to show the relationship in part b.

d) Suppose you were to use a longer tube. Would the results be the same? Explain.

10. **Academic Focus Investigation:** **Heights and Diameters of Cans**
Measure the heights and the diameters of as many different cans as possible. Try to include some cans whose heights and diameters are equal. Record the results in a table.

Description	Diameter, d (cm)	Height, h (cm)

a) Which can has the greatest value for $h \div d$? Which can has the least value for $h \div d$?

b) Draw a graph of the height against the diameter. How are the results of part a illustrated on the graph?

c) Did you have any cans with the same diameter and different heights? If so, how can you tell this from the graph?

d) Did you have any cans with the same height and different diameters? If so, how can you tell this from the graph?

e) Mark the points on your graph that represent cans whose heights are:

    i) less than the diameter   **ii)** greater than the diameter   **iii)** equal to the diameter

11. **Investigation: Comparing Ounces with Millilitres** The capacities of some cans are marked in both millilitres (mL) and ounces (oz.). Find as many cans as you can like this. Record the results in a table.

Description	Capacity (mL)	Capacity (oz.)

a) Draw a graph of the capacity in ounces against the capacity in millilitres.

b) What kind of relationship is illustrated by the graph? Explain.

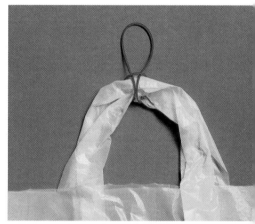

12. **Academic Focus Investigation: Stretching Elastic Bands** Work with a partner or in a group to investigate how far an elastic band stretches when it holds objects with different masses.

You will need a spring balance, a long elastic band, a tack, a plastic bag with handles, a metre stick, and several objects with different masses.

Loop the elastic band through the handles of the plastic bag. Tack the elastic band firmly to a bulletin board so the bag hangs freely. Measure the length of the elastic band.

a) Follow this procedure for each object you are using.

    i) Use the spring balance to measure the mass of the object. Record this mass.

    ii) One person holds the tack firmly as another person places the object in the plastic bag.

    iii) Measure and record the length of the elastic band. Use a table similar to this.

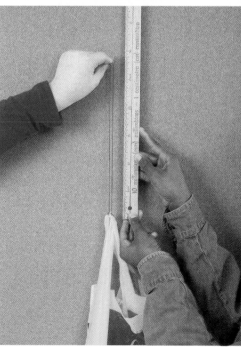

Object	Mass (g)	Length of band (cm)
Empty bag	0	13.7

b) Graph your results. Decide whether you should join the points. Keep these results for later use on page 417.

c) Describe the graph. What does it tell you about your experiment?

d) Compare your graph with those of other students. Describe any similarities or differences you see. Explain the differences.

e) Use your graph. Predict how far the elastic band might stretch when it holds each mass.

   i) 250 g   ii) 750 g   iii) 2 kg

f) **Communicating the Ideas** Write a report to summarize your experiment. Describe what you did and what you found out about the relationship between the length of an elastic band and the masses of the objects it supports. Include your table and your graph in your report.

13. **Investigation:** **Relating the Volume and Mass of Water** Work with a partner.

a) Plan an experiment to determine how the volume of water is related to its mass. You will need to measure the volume and the mass of different amounts of water. For this, you will need some containers to hold the water. You will also need a way to determine the mass of the water without its container.

b) Carry out the experiment. Copy and complete this table to summarize your results.

Volume of water (mL)	Mass of water (g)

c) Graph the data. Is the relation linear or non-linear?

d) Describe how the mass of water is related to its volume.

e) What is the mass of each volume of water?
   i) 1 mL
   ii) 1 L
   iii) 1 m^3

f) **Communicating the Ideas** Write a report to summarize your experiment. Describe what you did and what you found out about the volume and mass of water. Include your table and your graph in your report.

14. Psychologists have experimented to measure how much a person remembers of material that was learned. The results of one experiment are shown in the table.

Time in days	1	5	15	30	60
Percent remembered	84%	71%	61%	56%	54%

a) Draw a graph to show the data.

b) Suppose you graphed the percent forgotten instead of the percent remembered. How would this graph differ from the graph you drew in part a?

15. The chart shows the stopping distances for speeds from 20 km/h to 130 km/h on dry, clean level pavement. This information is used in drivers' education courses. Stopping distance is the sum of the driver reaction distance and the braking distance. Many factors affect stopping distance: road conditions, the incline of the road, tire conditions, and so on.

Speed (km/h)	Average stopping distance (nearest metre)
20	8
30	12
40	17
50	23
60	31
70	41
80	52
90	66
100	81
110	99
120	120
130	143

a) What is meant by "driver reaction distance"?

b) What is meant by "breaking distance"?

c) Graph these data. How did you join the points? Explain.

d) What is the stopping distance for a speed of 65 km/h? 95 km/h?

e) How does a wet road affect stopping distance?

f) Mathematical Modelling Results are sometimes different from those predicted by mathematical models. Refer to your graph in part c. How would the graph change in each situation?
   i) The road is wet.
   ii) The road is not level.
   iii) The road is a gravel road.

g) What other factors affect stopping distance?

PROBLEM SOLVING FOCUS

Is the Fuel Gauge in a Car Accurate?

Every time a person buys gas, she resets the trip odometer to 000. The photographs show the odometer readings and the fuel gauge at different times since the last fill up. Is the fuel gauge giving accurate readings?

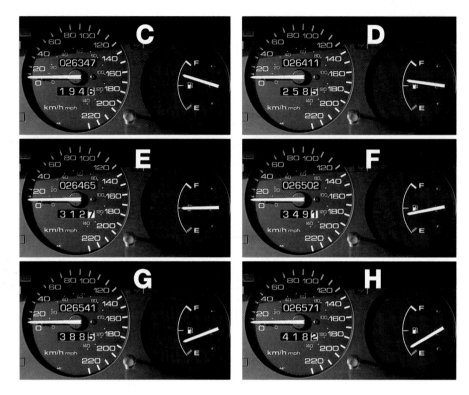

16. a) Clarify the problem. What is an odometer? What is a trip odometer? Discuss with a partner if you're not sure.

b) You can use the information in the photographs to graph the relation between the distance travelled and the fuel gauge reading. If the fuel gauge is accurate, would you expect the relation to be linear or non-linear? Explain.

17. a) Copy and complete this table, then graph the data.

Distance travelled (km)	Fuel gauge reading

b) Examine the table of values and graph. Describe any patterns you observe. Describe whether you think the fuel gauge is accurate, and why.

c) Suppose the gas tank is full and the driver does not stop for gas. About how far will the car have travelled when the gauge reads empty?

d) Ask someone who drives a car to record the odometer reading when the fuel tank is full, and later when the fuel gauge registers $\frac{3}{4}$, $\frac{1}{2}$, and $\frac{1}{4}$. Use the results to repeat this investigation.

18. Select one topic to research and graph.

   a) changes in your height from the time you were born until now

   b) changes in your school population from the year the school opened

   c) changes in the numbers of Internet subscribers

   d) changes in the Canadian population in the 20th century

   e) a topic of your choice

19. **Investigation:** **Sunset Times for Your Location**

   You can use the Internet to help you investigate the relationship between the time of the sunset and the day of the year. To get the sunset times from the Internet, you need to know the latitude of your location.

   a) Determine the latitude of your location. You can refer to an atlas or a map; or try this website: www.indo.com/distance/

   b) Determine the time of the sunset for at least 20 days spread throughout the year. To get the data, try this website: http://riemann.usno.navy.mil/AA/data/docs/RS_OneDay.html#formb Be sure to obtain the times for June 21 and December 21. Use standard times only.

   c) Graph the data you gathered. Describe the relationship.

   d) Daylight savings time usually begins in early April and ends in late October. Describe how the graph would change if daylight savings times were used between April and October.

   e) Describe how the graph would change in each case.
      i) a more northerly location than yours
      ii) a more southerly location than yours

   f) Describe how the graph would change in each case.
      i) locations above the Arctic circle
      ii) locations in the southern hemisphere

COMMUNICATING the IDEAS

In your journal, describe some examples of related quantities in everyday life. Explain how the quantities are related.

On page 59, you considered the problem of comparing the lifetime of an animal with a human lifetime.

Although there is no exact formula, several models have been proposed by veterinarians and scientists. Your task is to make a graph to show how the models relate the lifetime of a cat or a dog to a human lifetime. You will compare the models and determine which model you think is best.

You will need grid paper, some coloured pencils or markers, and a ruler.

1. Prepare a grid with axes as shown. Make the grid as large as possible. You may need to experiment to find the best way to set up the axes and the scales.

   a) The horizontal axis corresponds to the animal's age. Since the expected lifetime for a cat or a dog is slightly less than 20 years, label the horizontal scale from 0 to 20.

   b) The vertical axis corresponds to a person's age. Label the vertical scale from 0 to 100.

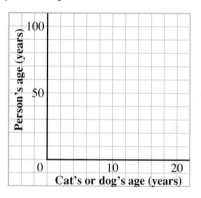

Models Described by a Rule
Model 1

Some people say that one year of a cat's life is equivalent to 7 years of a person's life.

2. a) Make a table to record some ages of cats and humans that satisfy this model.

   b) Graph the data from your table. Decide if it makes sense to join the points on the graph. Make sure your graph reflects your decision. Label your graph.

   c) Do you think this model is reasonable? Explain.

Model 2

This model for cats appeared in an article in *Reader's Digest.*

The first year of a cat's life equals about 21 human years. For each additional year, count 4 human years for each year of the cat's life.

3. a) Make a table to record some ages of cats and humans that satisfy this relationship.

   b) Graph the data on the same grid as Model 1. Label the graph.

4. Compare the graph of this model with the graph of Model 1.

   a) State two important ways in which Model 2 differs from Model 1.

   b) Explain what these differences mean in terms of relating the lifetime of a cat to a human lifetime.

Model 3

This model for dogs appeared in an article in *The Toronto Star*.

The first year of a dog's life equals about 15 human years. The second year adds another 10 years. For each additional year, count 5 human years for each year of the dog's life.

5. a) Make a table to record some ages of dogs and humans that satisfy this relationship.

   b) Graph the data on the same grid as Models 1 and 2. Label the graph.

   c) Describe how Model 3 is similar to Model 2.

   d) Do you think it would be reasonable to use either Model 2 or Model 3 for both cats and dogs? Explain.

Models Described by a Table

The book *The Best Cat Ever*, by Cleveland Amory and Lisa Adams, contains the following models for relating the age of a cat to the age of a human.

Model 4

This model was developed by a veterinarian. Ages are in years.

Cat's age	$\frac{1}{2}$	$\frac{2}{3}$	1	2	4	6	8	10	12	14	16	18	20	21
Person's age	10	13	15	24	32	40	48	56	64	72	80	88	96	100

6. a) Graph these data on the same grid as Models 1 to 3. Label the graph.

   b) Explain how this model compares with Models 1 to 3.

Model 5

This model was developed by using a computer to compare the ages of 480 cats with data obtained from census records on human ages. Ages are in years.

Cat's age	1	2	3	4	5	6	7	8	9	10	11	12	13	14	15	16	17
Person's age	17	28	31	41	45	45	51	58	61	61	66	66	71	76	81	81	89

7. a) Graph these data on the same grid as Models 1 to 4. Label the graph.

   b) What is the unusual property of this model, compared with the others?

   c) Do you think this model is reasonable? Explain.

Comparing the Models

8. In exercise 4a, you considered how Model 2 differed from Model 1. Do the other models differ from Model 1 in the same ways? Explain.

9. Consider the graphs of all the models except Model 1. Look at the parts of these graphs that correspond to about the first $1\frac{1}{2}$ years of the animal's life.

   a) To what significant portion of a person's life does this correspond?

   b) What does this tell you about how the lifetime of a cat or a dog compares with a human lifetime?

10. Model 1 could be modified by replacing 7 with a different number. State an advantage and a disadvantage of replacing 7 with:

   a) a number less than 7
   b) a number greater than 7

11. All models, except the first, suggest that a graph relating a cat's (or a dog's) lifetime to a human lifetime looks like Graph 1 below.

   a) What does the shape of the graph tell you about how a cat's lifetime compares with a human lifetime?

   b) Suppose the graph looked like Graph 2 or Graph 3. How would the lifetime of a cat be different from what it is now? Explain.

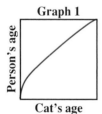
Graph 1
Person's age — Cat's age

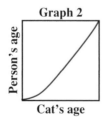
Graph 2
Person's age — Cat's age

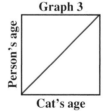
Graph 3
Person's age — Cat's age

COMMUNICATING the IDEAS

Choose the model from these pages that you think is the best one for relating the lifetime of an animal to a human lifetime. In your journal, write to explain your choice.

2.4 Using a Motion Detector to Investigate Relationships

You can use technology to gather data and display how certain quantities are related. To do the investigations in this section, you will need a TI-83 graphing calculator, a Calculator-Based Ranger™ (CBR™) unit, and the connecting cable. The CBR is a sonic motion detector that collects data and displays them on the calculator screen.

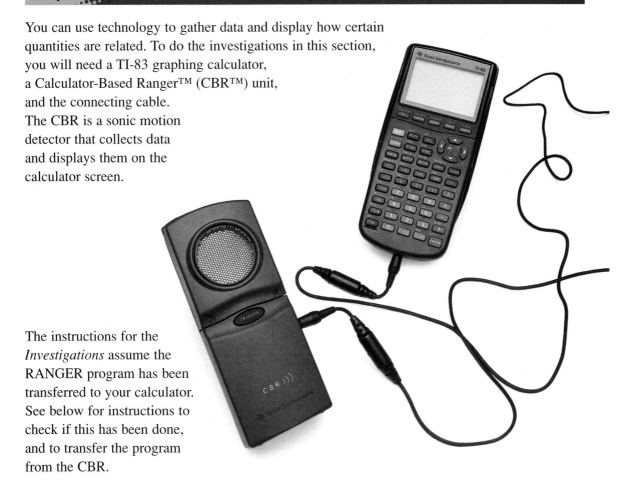

The instructions for the *Investigations* assume the RANGER program has been transferred to your calculator. See below for instructions to check if this has been done, and to transfer the program from the CBR.

Checking for the Ranger program

To check if the RANGER program has been transferred to your calculator, follow these steps:

- Connect the CBR to the calculator with the connecting cable.
- Turn on the calculator, and press `PRGM`. A list of programs stored in memory will appear. If RANGER appears in the list, the program has been transferred. If RANGER does not appear, continue with the following steps.

Transferring the RANGER program to the calculator

- On the calculator, press `2nd` `X,T,θ,n` `▶` `ENTER`. The calculator will indicate that it is waiting to receive the program.
- On the CBR, open the pivoting head and press `82/83`. The CBR will send this program to the calculator.

Distance to a Wall

You will use the CBR to measure its distance from a wall as you move toward the wall or away from the wall. The calculator displays a graph to show how this distance changes as you move.

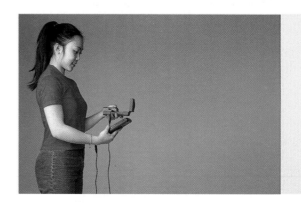

Step 1. Setup

- Work in a space near a large smooth wall. A classroom chalkboard is ideal. The CBR must always be between 0.5 m and 6.0 m from the wall. Make sure there are no objects in the clear zone between the CBR and the wall.

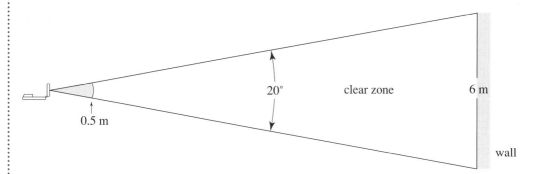

- Connect the CBR to the calculator with the connecting cable. Make sure the connections are secure.
- Turn on the calculator, and press PRGM.
- Choose RANGER.
- Press ENTER ENTER to display the main menu.

MAIN MENU	▶START NOW
REALTIME:	YES
TIME(S):	15
DISPLAY:	DIST
BEGIN ON:	[ENTER]
SMOOTHING:	NONE
UNITS:	METERS

- Press **2** to choose SET DEFAULTS.

- Make sure the cursor is beside START NOW. If it is not, use the arrow keys to move it there.
- Hold the calculator in one hand and the CBR in the other. Aim the sensor directly at the wall.

Step 2. Collect and graph the data.

- When you are ready to start, press ENTER. Follow the instructions on the screen. As you move toward the wall or away from the wall, the calculator displays a distance-time graph recording your distance to the wall.
- To make the calculator redraw the graph in a better position on the screen, press ENTER **1**.
- To repeat, press ENTER **3**.
  Try moving toward the wall at a steady rate.
  Try moving away from the wall at a steady rate.
  Try moving more quickly or more slowly.
  Try different patterns of moving, including standing still.
  Repeat until you are satisfied with the result.
- Leave the graph on the screen while you complete the following exercises. Since the data for this graph are in your calculator, you can disconnect the cable so that someone else can use the CBR.

1. What physical quantity is represented along each axis?

   a) the horizontal axis   **b)** the vertical axis

2. Describe what happens to the plotted points in each case.

   a) You move toward the wall, or away from the wall.

   b) You move more quickly, or more slowly.

   c) You stand still.

3. **a)** Sketch one graph you obtained with the CBR, or use a computer linkup to print it. Label the axes, including units.

   b) Describe what your screen represents in terms of how you moved toward or away from the wall.

Viewing the coordinates

You can view the coordinates of some points on the graph. These correspond to the data the CBR gathered.

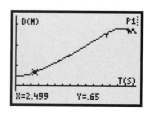

- Press TRACE and the arrow keys to move a flashing cursor along the graph. Its coordinates will appear on the screen.
- To get back to the main menu, press ENTER.

4. In the screen on page 89:

a) How far was the person from the wall when the calculator plotted the point under the flashing cursor?

b) How many seconds after the plotting started did this occur?

c) Was the person moving toward the wall or away from it? Explain.

d) Describe how the person moved during the time the data were collected.

Viewing the data in lists

You can also view the data in lists, but you have to exit the program first.

- Choose QUIT from the main menu.

- Press STAT 1. A screen similar to this one appears. The numbers in the columns are called lists. List L1 contains the times in seconds. List L2 contains the distances to the wall in metres. The calculator used these numbers to plot the points on the graph.

- When you have viewed the data, press 2nd MODE to select QUIT.

5. Two distance-time graphs obtained with the CBR are shown. Describe how the person moved to obtain each graph.

a)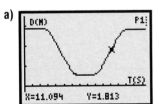

b)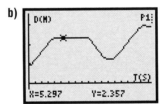

6. a) Describe how you could use the CBR to measure distances.

b) Measure some distances with the CBR. Compare the results with measurements obtained with a tape measure.

c) What are some advantages and disadvantages of using the CBR to measure distances?

Pendulum Experiment

You will use the
CBR to measure its
distance from a
swinging pendulum.
The calculator will
display a graph to
show how this
distance changes as
the weight swings
back and forth.

Work with a partner.

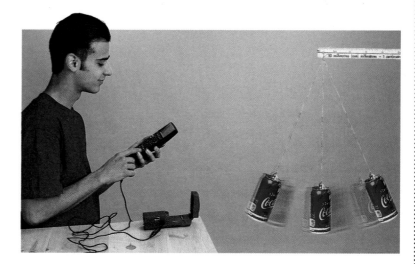

Step 1. Setup

- Set up the pendulum equipment and the CBR as shown above. Use an
  object at least as large as a pop can for the weight. This is necessary so
  the CBR measures the distance to the weight and not to objects beyond
  it. Make the pendulum as long as you can.

- Secure the CBR at least 0.5 m from the closest approach of the weight.

- Run the RANGER program. Press **2** to choose SET DEFAULTS.

- Make sure the cursor is beside START NOW.

- Start the pendulum swinging.

Step 2. Collect and graph the data.

- Press [ENTER] when you are ready to begin. The calculator displays a
  distance-time graph that follows the motion of the pendulum.

- To make the calculator redraw the graph in a better position on the
  screen, press [ENTER] **1**.

- To repeat, press [ENTER] **3**. Repeat until you are satisfied with the result.

- Leave the graph on the screen while you complete the following exercises.
  You can disconnect the cable so that someone else can use the CBR.

1. Sketch the distance-time graph you obtained, or use a computer linkup
   to print it. Label the axes, including units.

2. a) Describe what happens to the plotted points in each case.
   i) The weight is moving toward the CBR.
   ii) The weight is moving away from the CBR.

   b) Describe what happens to the graph as the pendulum slows down.

3. Press TRACE and the arrow keys to move a flashing cursor along the curve. Its coordinates appear on the screen.

   a) What was the maximum distance from the weight to the CBR?

   b) What was the minimum distance from the weight to the CBR?

   c) How many complete swings are represented on the graph?

4. The period of the pendulum is the time for one complete swing. Determine the period of the pendulum as accurately as you can.

5. a) Predict how the distance-time graph will change if you pull the weight farther from the rest position before starting the pendulum.

   b) Use the CBR and your calculator to verify your prediction.

6. a) Predict how the distance-time graph will change if you repeat the experiment with a shorter or a longer pendulum.

   b) Use the CBR and your calculator to verify your prediction.

COMMUNICATING the IDEAS

Choose *Investigation 1* or *2*. In that investigation, the graphs generated by the CBR showed how two physical quantities are related. Describe these two quantities, and explain how they are related. Include sketches of graphs to illustrate your description.

Boggle your MIND

Some species of bamboo, one of the fastest growing plants in the world, can grow 91 cm in a single day. What if a bamboo plant could grow at this rate indefinitely? How long would it take for the plant to grow as high as the CN Tower? Why do you think bamboo plants do not reach such heights?

A small company cuts lawns in the summer and clears driveways and sidewalks of snow in the winter. To become known in the community, the company advertises its services. Two kinds of advertising are being considered. One is to print and distribute flyers to households in the community. The other is to put a display advertisement in the local newspaper.

The company has obtained prices for the two kinds of advertising. Your task is to compare the prices and to recommend which kind of advertising should be used.

You can use a graphing calculator to display graphs that show how certain quantities are related. You can also calculate with the data and display related graphs. To complete the investigations below, you will need a TI-83 graphing calculator. Since other students may have used the calculator previously, you may need to reset it. Ask your teacher or consult the manual for instructions on how to do this.

This graph is an example of a graph that was obtained with the TI-83. It shows how a car's stopping distance is related to its speed (page 81, exercise 15). The data for this graph were given in a table.

To graph data from a table, you must always follow these four steps.

1. Enter the data.
2. Set up the graph.
3. Set up the window.
4. Graph the data.

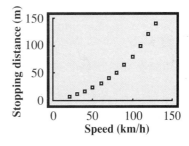

Instructions for each step are provided in *Investigation 1*.

Flyer Advertising Rates

This price list shows the prices charged for printing and distributing different quantities of flyers.

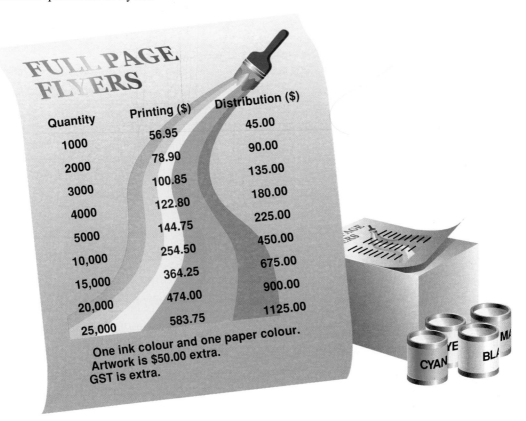

FULL PAGE FLYERS

Quantity	Printing ($)	Distribution ($)
1000	56.95	45.00
2000	78.90	90.00
3000	100.85	135.00
4000	122.80	180.00
5000	144.75	225.00
10,000	254.50	450.00
15,000	364.25	675.00
20,000	474.00	900.00
25,000	583.75	1125.00

One ink colour and one paper colour.
Artwork is $50.00 extra.
GST is extra.

Step 1. Enter the data.

- Press [STAT] **1**. A screen will appear, showing lists L1, L2, and L3. This screen is the *list editor*.

- If there are any numbers in the columns, they must be cleared. Move the cursor into each column heading, and press [CLEAR] [ENTER].

- Move the cursor to the space below L1.

- In list L1, enter the quantities from the table above.

- Move the cursor to the space below L2.

- In list L2, enter the printing costs. When you have finished, your screen should look like this.

L1	L2	L3	2
4000	122.8		
5000	144.75		
10000	254.5		
15000	364.25		
20000	474		
25000	583.75		

L2(10) =

Step 2. Set up the graph.

You must tell the calculator which list to plot along each axis and the type of graph you want.

- Press ⌜2nd⌝ ⌜Y=⌝ to get the STAT PLOT menu. This menu shows the following information for three plots:
   - whether it is turned on or off
   - the type of graph
   - the lists used to create the graph
   - the plotting symbol used

- Press **1** to select Plot 1.
- Press ⌜ENTER⌝ to turn on Plot 1.
- Press ⌜▼⌝ ⌜ENTER⌝ to select the first plot type.
- Press ⌜▼⌝ ⌜2nd⌝ **1** to make sure that L1 is beside Xlist (this will be graphed horizontally).
- Press ⌜▼⌝ ⌜2nd⌝ **2** to make sure that L2 is beside Ylist (this will be graphed vertically).
- Press ⌜▼⌝ ⌜ENTER⌝ to select the first plotting symbol. The screen should look exactly like this.

Step 3. Set up the window.

- Press ⌜WINDOW⌝.
- You want the horizontal axis to show quantities up to 25 000. Enter Xmin = 0, Xmax = 25000, Xscl = 5000.
- You want the vertical axis to show show printing costs up to $583.75. Enter Ymin = 0, Ymax = 600, Yscl = 100.

Step 4. Graph the data.

- Press ⌜GRAPH⌝.

   1. If you have not already done so, follow the steps above to display the graph of printing costs against quantities.

2. Does the relation appear to be linear or non-linear? Explain.

3. You can join the points with line segments.

    a) Press [2nd] [Y=] **1**. Move the cursor to the second graph on the Type line. Press [ENTER] [GRAPH].

    b) Does it make sense to produce a graph with the points joined with line segments? Explain.

    c) Change the graph type back to show points without line segments.

Operating with Lists

Refer to the price list on page 94. Flyers requiring artwork are $50 extra, regardless of size. The calculator can calculate the prices in one step.

- Press [STAT] **1** to go to the list editor. If there are any numbers in L3, move the cursor into the heading of the L3 column, then press [CLEAR] [ENTER].
- Move the cursor into the heading of the L3 column.
- Press [2nd] **2** [+] 50 [ENTER]. The calculator will add 50 to every number in L2 and insert the results in L3.

L1	L2	**L3**	3
1000	56.95	------	
2000	78.9		
3000	100.85		
4000	122.8		
5000	144.75		
10000	254.5		
15000	364.25		

L3 =L2+50

4. a) Predict what the graph of L3 against L1 will look like, compared with the first graph.

    b) To verify your prediction, press [2nd] [Y=] **2** [ENTER] to select Plot 2. Set up this plot in the same way as before, using L3 for Ylist and a different plotting symbol. Press [GRAPH] to see lists L2 and L3 graphed together.

    c) Sketch the graph, or print it using a computer. Label the axes, including units.

    d) Describe how lists L2 and L3 are related, and how the graph shows this relationship.

Turning plots on and off

5. a) Go to the STAT PLOT menu. Turn off Plot 1 and graph Plot 2 alone.

    b) Turn on Plot 1, turn off Plot 2, and graph Plot 1 alone.

    c) Turn on Plots 1 and 2, and graph them together once again before continuing.

Viewing coordinates of points

6. a) Press [TRACE]. You will see a flashing cursor on one of the plotted points, with its coordinates at the bottom of the screen. Use the arrow keys to move the cursor. Find out what happens when you use each of the four arrow keys.

b) Determine the cost for printing 15 000 flyers without art.

Changing the window

7. Try using different values for Xscl, Ymax, or Yscl.

Managing lists

Up to now, you have used lists L1, L2, and L3. The list editor contains three more lists that you can access using the arrow keys.

8. Refer to the price list on page 94. In addition to printing the flyers, you also need to distribute them to potential customers.

a) Clear list L3, then enter the distribution costs in L3.

b) Move the cursor into the L4 column, and clear L4 if necessary. Move the cursor into the heading of the L4 column. Press [2nd] **2** [+] [2nd] **3** [ENTER]. The calculator will add the corresponding costs and insert the results in L4.

c) Predict what the graph of L4 against L1 will look like, compared with the first graph.

d) Go to the STAT PLOT menu. Change Plot 2 to set up the graph of L4 against L1, and verify your prediction. You will need to change some window settings to see the whole graph.

e) Trace to determine the cost for printing and distributing 15 000 flyers.

9. According to the price list, GST is extra.

a) Clear list L5, then move the cursor into the heading of the L5 column. Press [2nd] **4** [×] 1.07 [ENTER]. The calculator will calculate the costs including GST and insert the results in L5.

b) Go to the STAT PLOT menu and change Plot 2 to graph L5 against L1. Press [GRAPH] to obtain a graph that shows how the total cost of printing and distributing the flyers, including GST, is related to the quantity.

c) Trace to determine the total cost, including GST, for printing and distributing 15 000 flyers.

d) Sketch or print the graph, and label the axes.

10. Advertisers are interested in unit costs. The unit cost is the cost of printing and distributing one flyer.

a) Clear list L6, then move the cursor into the heading of the L6 column.

b) Press [2nd] **5** [÷] [2nd] **1** [ENTER]. The calculator will divide the prices in L5 by the quantities in L1 and insert the results in L6.

c) Graph L6 against L1 to show the relationship between the unit costs and the quantity. Be sure to change the window settings.

d) Does the relation appear to be linear or non-linear? Explain.

e) Use the trace key to determine the unit cost for 15 000 flyers.

f) Sketch or print the graph, and label the axes.

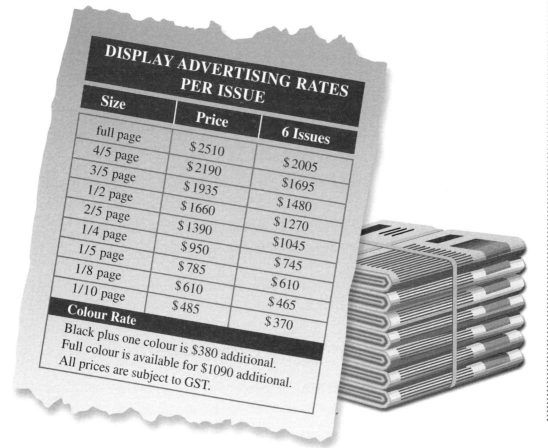

INVESTIGATION 2

Newspaper Advertising Rates

This rate card shows the advertising rates for display advertisements in a weekly newspaper.

DISPLAY ADVERTISING RATES PER ISSUE

Size	Price	6 Issues
full page	$2510	$2005
4/5 page	$2190	$1695
3/5 page	$1935	$1480
1/2 page	$1660	$1270
2/5 page	$1390	$1045
1/4 page	$950	$745
1/5 page	$785	$610
1/8 page	$610	$465
1/10 page	$485	$370

Colour Rate

Black plus one colour is $380 additional.
Full colour is available for $1090 additional.
All prices are subject to GST.

Step 1. Enter the data.

- Follow the steps on page 94 to clear lists L1 and L2.
- Enter the sizes in L1 and the prices in L2. Use 1 for the size of a full page. To enter a fraction such as $\frac{4}{5}$, press 0.8 [ENTER] or 4 [÷] 5 [ENTER].

Step 2. Set up the graph.

- Follow the steps on page 95.

Step 3. Set up the window.

- Follow the steps on page 95. Use appropriate values for the minimum and maximum values on both axes, and for the scales.

Step 4. Graph the data.

- Press [GRAPH].

1. If you have not already done so, follow the steps above to display the graph of prices against sizes.

2. Does the relation appear to be linear or non-linear? Explain.

3. Refer to the rate card on page 98. Advertisements containing one other colour cost $380 more. Full-colour advertisements cost $1090 more.

   a) Use the list editor. Have the calculator calculate and enter prices for one colour in L3 and prices for full colour in L4.

   b) Predict what the graphs of L3 and L4 against L1 will look like, compared with the first graph.

   c) Use your calculator to verify your prediction. Display all three lists on the same graph.

   d) Sketch or print the graph, then label the axes.

   e) Describe how lists L2, L3, and L4 are related, and how the graph shows this relationship.

4. According to the rate card, all prices are subject to GST. Assume the advertisements have no colour.

   a) Change list L3 to represent the prices including GST.

   b) Predict what the graph of L3 against L1 will look like, compared with the first graph. Verify your prediction.

   c) Trace to determine the total cost, including GST, for a quarter-page advertisement.

5. The newspaper has a circulation of approximately 25 000 copies. The unit cost is the cost to have the advertisement in one issue of the newspaper.

a) Use list L4 to calculate the unit cost, including GST, for each size.

b) Graph L4 against L1 to show the relationship between the unit costs and the sizes.

c) Does the relation appear to be linear or non-linear? Explain.

d) Trace to determine the unit cost for a quarter-page advertisement.

e) Sketch or print the graph, then label the axes.

6. The rate card shows the prices if the same advertisement is used in 6 issues of the newspaper.

a) Enter these prices in list L5.

b) Use list L6 to calculate the total price, including GST, for advertisements in 6 issues.

c) Graph the prices. Sketch the graph, or print it using a computer. Label the axes, including units.

d) Determine the total cost for running a quarter-page advertisement in 6 issues.

7. Academic Focus A full-page advertisement measures 25.0 cm by 35.0 cm.

a) Create a graph to show the cost per square centimetre, including GST, of each size of advertisement.

b) Does the relation appear to be linear or non-linear? Explain.

COMMUNICATING the IDEAS

Decide which type of advertisement is the best for the company described on page 93. Be sure to consider the advantages and disadvantages of each kind of advertisement in making your decision. In your journal, write a report to explain the reasons for your decision. Support your answer with data obtained using the calculator.

The graph in *Example 1,* page 74, shows a relationship between two quantities.

- These quantities are related by multiplication and division.
- The points on the graph lie on a straight line through the origin.
- The line goes up to the right.

Any situation that has these properties is called a *proportional situation*. To be an effective problem solver you must be able to recognize proportional situations. When you solve problems in proportional situations, you use multiplication or division, or both.

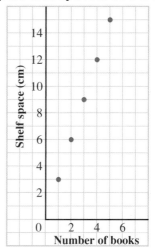

Space used by books on a shelf

Recognizing Proportional Situations

Solve problems 1 to 6, then answer the questions below.

Problem 1

In 3 min, Bob typed 120 words. At this rate, how many words could he type in 15 min?

Problem 2

In 3 min, Bob typed 120 words. At this rate, how long would it take him to type 200 words?

Problem 3

In 3 games, Mary had 10 hits. At this rate, how many hits would she have in 8 games?

Problem 4

In 3 games, Mary had 10 hits. At this rate, how many games would she need to have 100 hits?

Problem 5

Keisha is 15 years old and her brother Jermaine is 10 years old. When Keisha is 30 years old, how old will Jermaine be?

Problem 6

Keisha is 15 years old and her brother Jermaine is 10 years old. When Jermaine is 30 years old, how old will Keisha be?

1. In what ways are these problems similar? In what ways are they different?

2. Did any of the problems seem easier or harder than the others? If so, what is the reason for this?

3. Did you use the same method to solve each problem?

4. Which of these problems represent proportional situations? How do you know? How do you know the other problems do not represent proportional situations?

A problem involving a proportional situation contains data that you must organize to solve the problem.

Example 1

Marcia works in a card store after school. In 4 h of part-time work, Marcia earned $20.

a) At this rate, how much would she earn in 8 h? How many hours would it take to earn $100?

b) Suppose you know the number of hours Marcia worked. Write an equation to determine Marcia's earnings.

c) Suppose you know the amount Marcia earned. Write an equation to determine how long she worked.

d) Draw a graph to show how Marcia's earnings are related to the number of hours she worked.

Solution

a) In 4 h, Marcia earns \$20. Divide by 4 to find the earnings for 1 h.
This is called the *unit rate*.

In 1 h, she would earn $\frac{\$20}{4} = \$5$

To calculate the earnings, multiply the number of hours by the unit rate.
In 8 h, she would earn $8 \times \$5 = \$40$

To calculate the number of hours, divide the amount by the unit rate.

The number of hours to earn \$100 is $\frac{100}{5} = 20$

It would take 20 h to earn \$100.

b) Use E to represent earnings in dollars and n the number of hours. Since you multiply the number of hours by 5 to determine the earnings, the equation is $E = 5n$.

c) Use the same variables. Since you divide the earnings by 5 to determine the number of hours, the equation is $n = \frac{E}{5}$.

d) Use the data in part a. Make a table of values and draw a graph.

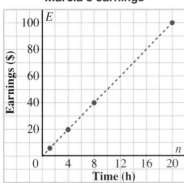

Marcia's earnings

Time, n hours	Earnings, E dollars
4	20
1	5
8	40
20	100

Boggle your MIND

Bombay is the financial and commercial centre
of India. It has one of the highest population densities in
the world. Some parts of the inner city have nearly 40 000 people
per square kilometre. What if the population density in your classroom were the same
as in these parts of Bombay? About how many people would there be in your classroom?

Example 2

At the bulk food store, Jerry bought 188 g of mixed nuts for $2.61.

a) At this price, how much would 450 g of mixed nuts cost?

b) What mass could he buy for $5.00?

c) Show the information above on a graph.

Solution

a) 188 g of mixed nuts cost $2.61.

1 g costs $\frac{\$2.61}{188}$.

> Divide by 188 to find the price for 1 g. This is the *unit price*.

450 g of mixed nuts cost

$450 \times \frac{\$2.61}{188} \doteq \$6.25$

> Multiply the mass by the unit price.

It would cost Jerry $6.25 to buy 450 g of mixed nuts.

b) $2.61 buys 188 g.

$1.00 buys $\frac{188}{2.61}$ g.

> Divide by 2.61 to find the mass you can buy for $1.00.

$5.00 buys $5 \times \frac{188}{2.61}$ g $\doteq 360$ g

> Multiply the number of dollars by the mass you can buy for $1.00.

Jerry could buy 360 g of mixed nuts for $5.00.

c) Summarize the results in a table, then draw the graph.

Mass (g)	Price ($)
188	2.61
450	6.25
360	5.00

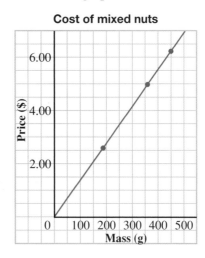

Cost of mixed nuts

Some problems can be solved in more than one way. It does not matter which method you use. One method may seem easier or more obvious to you than another method.

DISCUSSING
*the*IDEAS

1. Why do you use multiplication or division, and not addition or subtraction, to solve problems involving proportional situations?

2. In *Example 1*, what patterns can you find in the table? How are these patterns shown on the graph?

3. In *Example 1*, suppose Marcia's rate of pay increased. How would the graph change?

4. In *Example 2*, suppose the price of mixed nuts decreased. How would the graph change?

5. a) Explain why the plotted points on the graph in *Example 1* were joined with a dotted line, while the plotted points on the graph in *Example 2* were joined with a solid line.

   b) Suggest another way the graph in *Example 1* could have been drawn. Explain.

2.6   EXERCISES

 1. Only one problem below represents a proportional situation. Which problem is it? How do you know this problem represents a proportional situation? How do you know the other problem does not represent a proportional situation?

a) Lil scored 5 goals in 9 games. At this rate, how many goals might she score in 80 games?

b) A tree is 4.0 m high. It is growing at a rate of 1.2 m per year. At this rate of growth, how high will it be in 5 years?

2. One cheeseburger costs $1.29. What is the cost for each number of cheeseburgers?

a) 3   b) 5   c) 7   d) 10   e) 12   f) 20

3. One hockey ball costs $0.72. What is the cost for each number of balls?

a) 2   b) 4   c) 6   d) 13   e) 17   f) 100

4. A case of 24 cans of soda costs $6.96. What is the unit price?

5. Six bottles of motor oil costs $11.34.

a) What is the unit price?

b) Based on the unit price, what is the price for 10 bottles?

6. It takes 45 L to fill Noni's car's gas tank. The cost for the fill-up is $27.86.

  a) What is the price of 1 L of gas? Round your answer to the nearest cent.

  b) Based on the unit price, what is the cost of 35 L of gas?

7. A customer buys 400 g of candy for $2.40. What is the cost of each mass?

  a) 800 g   **b)** 100 g   **c)** 125 g   **d)** 350 g

8. An amount of $42 500 was raised in the first 20 min of the Red Shield Telethon. At this rate:

  a) How much would be raised in 3 h?

  b) How long would it take to raise $1 000 000?

9. In the summer, Tina worked part-time for a landscaping company. In 3.5 h, Tina earned $28.70. At this rate:

  a) How much would she earn in 9 h?

  b) How many hours would it take her to earn $350?

10. a) Taborah had 12 hits in 30 at-bats. About how many at-bats would she need to have 100 hits?

  b) **Mathematical Modelling** In part a, what assumption is being made? Do you think this assumption is realistic? Explain.

11. Refer to *Problem 1* on page 101.

  a) Make a table to show how many words Bob would type in 3 min, 6 min, 9 min, 12 min, and 15 min.

  b) Use the data in the table to draw a graph.

  c) Suppose you knew the number of minutes Bob typed. Write an equation to determine the number of words Bob would type. Test your equation by using some of the number pairs in the table.

  d) How would the table, the graph, and the equation change if Bob typed at a faster rate? If he typed at a slower rate?

  e) **Mathematical Modelling** In parts a to d, what assumption is being made? Do you think this assumption is realistic? Explain.

12. A mass of 5 kg of grass seed covers an area of 300 m². What mass of grass seed would be needed to cover a Canadian football field measuring 150 m by 60 m?

13. Carry out calculations to find out if the unit cost refers to the bottle or the tins.

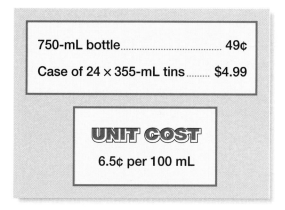

750-mL bottle............................ 49¢

Case of 24 × 355-mL tins $4.99

UNIT COST

6.5¢ per 100 mL

14. The giant sequoia trees on the west coast of North America are among the world's tallest and oldest living things. Some of these trees are 3200 years old. Every 24 h, the average sequoia pumps about 1000 L of water from its roots to its leaves.

a) How much water is pumped by one giant sequoia:
  i) in one year?
  ii) during the tree's lifetime?

b) How long would it take to pump the amount of water that would fill:
  i) a pop can?   **ii)** your classroom?
  (Remember that 1 m³ = 1000 L.)

15. The *International Prices* database from the data disk contains 1982 and 1994 information about salaries and prices in cities around the world.

a) Open the database. Find the records for Athens, Greece. What were the hourly wage and the cost of a typical basket of food in 1982? In 1994?

b) For each year, calculate the number of hours a person in Athens would have to work to buy a basket of food. Were workers in Athens better off in 1982 or 1994? Explain your answer.

c) Find the records for Oslo, Norway, in the database. Make the same comparison as in part b.

d) Add a calculated field to the database that calculates and displays the number of hours a person would have to work to buy a basket of food.

e) Sort by the new field. In which city did people have to work the most hours to buy a basket of food in 1982? In 1994?

f) In which city did people have to work the fewest hours to buy a basket of food in 1982? In 1994?

16. This table is part of a spreadsheet. The spreadsheet shows the cost of peanuts for each 0.5 kg up to 3 kg.

	A	B
1	Kg of peanuts	Price($)
2	0.5	1.48
3	1	2.95
4	1.5	4.43
5	2	5.90
6	2.5	7.38
7	3	8.85

a) Start a new spreadsheet file. Format the cells in column B to show numbers to 2 decimal places. Use formulas to create a table that looks like the one above. Use a formula in every cell except A1, B1, and A2.

b) Explain how you know the table shows a proportional relationship.

c) Use your spreadsheet's charting option to graph the relationship from the table. Does the graph confirm that it is a proportional relationship? Explain.

d) Extend the table to show the cost of 11.5 kg of peanuts.

17. The label on a medicine bottle reads 80 mg/mL. The doctor's medical reference book states that the dosage for this medicine is 20 mg per kilogram of body mass. How many millilitres of the medicine should be given to a 40-kg patient?

18. This label appeared on a package of grass seed.

PLANTING INSTRUCTIONS ENCLOSED

Covers 60 m²

1 kg

The instructions inside the package contained this statement.
* Seed lawn evenly 454 g per 27.8 m² in two directions.

a) Calculate to investigate whether the rate of spreading the seed printed on the package is the same as the rate printed on the instructions inside the package.

b) What improvement would you make in either the label or the instructions?

COMMUNICATING *the* **IDEAS**

In your journal, explain the difference between a proportional situation and a non-proportional situation. Use an example of each to illustrate your answer.

In Section 2.3, you considered some models for relating the lifetimes of cats or dogs to human lifetimes. The fact that cats or dogs become adults earlier in their lifetimes than humans was an important feature of these models. We can use this idea to develop a model for other animals. This model requires making assumptions about the number of years in a lifetime and the number of years to become an adult. For cats or dogs and humans, these assumptions seem reasonable:

	Cat or dog	Human
Years to become an adult	2	20
Years in a lifetime	20	100

On a graph that compares the lifetimes of cats or dogs with humans, the number of years to become an adult is represented by A(2, 20). The number of years in a lifetime is represented by B(20, 100).

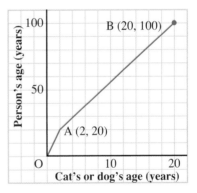

Going from O to A (pre-adult stage)
2 cat years correspond to 20 human years.
1 cat year corresponds to 10 human years.

Going from A to B (adult stage)
18 cat years correspond to 80 human years.
1 cat year corresponds to $\frac{80}{18}$ human years.
This is approximately 4.5 human years.

We can combine these results to describe a rule for relating the lifetime of a cat or a dog to a human lifetime:

For each of the first 2 years, count 10 human years for each cat year.
After that, count about 4.5 human years for each cat year.

1. The table on page 110 shows estimates of the number of years to become an adult and the number of years in a lifetime for four animals.

	Bear	Dolphin	Chimpanzee	Elephant
Years to become an adult	1	10	7	20
Years in a lifetime	25	50	60	70

a) For each animal, draw a graph to show the relationship between the lifetime of the animal and a human lifetime.

b) Use your graph to describe a rule for relating the lifetime of the animal to a human lifetime. Keeping in mind that the numbers in the table are only estimates, make adjustments to your rule that seem reasonable.

2. In exercise 1, compare your graphs with the graph on page 109. Explain how the graph illustrates your answer to each question below.

a) Which animal becomes an adult earlier in its lifetime than humans do?

b) Which animal becomes an adult at about the same time in its lifetime as a human?

c) Which animal becomes an adult later in its lifetime than humans do?

3. Scientists have observed that most mammals (excluding humans) live for about one billion heartbeats.

a) What does this tell you about how the heartbeats of animals with short life spans compare with the heartbeats of animals with long life spans? (The life span is the number of years lived.)

b) Which graph below best shows the relationship between the heartbeats of different kinds of animals and their life spans? Explain.

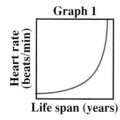
Graph 1

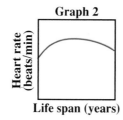
Graph 2

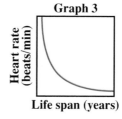
Graph 3

c) Sketch the graph you chose. Make two copies. You will use these in exercises 7 and 8, page 112.

COMMUNICATING the IDEAS

Suppose you have information about the life cycle of a particular animal. In your journal, write to explain how you could determine a rule to relate the lifetime of that animal to a human lifetime. Illustrate your explanation with an example, using an animal that is different from the ones above.

1. Investigation: Tape Counters

Video cassette recorders usually have tape counters to help people locate items on the tape. In this investigation you will look into the relationship between the number on the counter and the playing time. You will need a video cassette recorder (VCR), or an audio tape recorder that has a counter, and a watch or a clock.

a) *For Fast Forward*

   i) Insert a tape into your VCR. Set the counter to 0000. Press the fast forward button, and note the counter numbers after different times until the end of the tape is reached. Copy and complete this table.

Fast forward time (seconds)	Counter number

   ii) Draw a graph to show how the counter number is related to the fast forward time.

   iii) Does the relation between the counter number and the playing time appear to be linear or non-linear?

b) *For Rewind*

   i) Start rewinding the tape, and note the counter numbers after different times until the beginning of the tape is reached. Record the results in a table.

   ii) Draw a graph to show how the counter number is related to the rewind time.

   iii) Compare your graph with the graph in part a) ii. Explain any similarities or differences.

c) *For Regular Playing*

   In part a, suppose you had used the play button instead of the fast forward button.

   i) How would the times to reach the same counter numbers differ from those in the table in part a) i?

   ii) Suppose you graphed the results. How would the graph differ from the graph in part a?

2. Plan and conduct an experiment to investigate the change in temperature as the ice cubes in a glass melt.

a) Draw a graph to show how the temperature changes with time.

b) Describe how the temperature changes as time increases.

3. **Academic Focus** Measure the heights of 6 family members. Record each person's height and age. Combine your data with those of 4 classmates.

   a) Construct a table of values of height against age for 30 people. Does there appear to be a relationship? Explain.

   b) Graph the data. Should you join the points? Explain. Does there appear to be a relationship between height and age? Explain.

4. You will need a thermometer for measuring outdoor temperatures.

   a) Measure and record the outdoor temperature every 4 h from 08:00 to 20:00. Continue taking temperature readings for two days.

   b) Graph your data. Estimate the outdoor temperature at 15:00 the first day, and at 18:00 the second day.

   c) Explain whether you think you can use the graph to estimate the lowest overnight temperature. Give reasons.

5. Refer to *Problem 3* on page 101.

   a) Make a table to show how many hits Mary would get in 3 games, 6 games, 9 games, 12 games, and 15 games, if she continued to hit at the same rate.

   b) Use the data in the table to draw a graph.

   c) Suppose you know how many games Mary played. Write an equation to determine the number of hits Mary would get. Test your equation using some of the number pairs in the table.

6. a) Ms. Ewart is in charge of supplies and equipment for the Hillsview Hockey League. She can buy pucks from Company A at $16.95 per dozen. Company B sells a case of 3 dozen pucks for $45.95. Which is the better price per puck?

   b) After the game, the parents make hot chocolate for the players. Ms. Ewart can buy a box of 20 packets for $3.49 or a case of 300 packets for $41.95. Which has the lower unit price?

7. **Mathematical Modelling** On average, humans live for about 2.5 billion heartbeats. Use a sketch of the graph you chose in exercise 3b, page 110.

   a) Would the point corresponding to humans lie above or below the curve on the graph?

   b) Mark the approximate location of the point corresponding to humans.

8. **Mathematical Modelling** Scientists have also observed that most mammals, including humans, take about one breath for every four heartbeats. Use the other sketch of the graph you chose in exercise 3b, page 110. Draw a curve to represent the relationship between breathing rate and life span.

1. Use the order of operations to evaluate each exercise.
   a) $(-5) + (2)(-3)$
   b) $(-15) \div 3 + (-8)(-2)$
   c) $8 + 5 \times (-2 + 8)$
   d) $28 \div (-4) - (2)(-9)$
   e) $(3)(-5)(-2) + \frac{120}{-40}$
   f) $-5.12 - (-8.36)(2)$

2. Use a calculator to evaluate each expression to 2 decimal places.
   a) $\frac{262.21}{8.6 \times 16.9}$
   b) $\frac{0.095 \times 2250 + 0.125 \times 4229}{5}$

3. A quality-control inspector examines 120 cans of paint. She finds 6 cans substandard.
   a) What percent is substandard?
   b) What percent is acceptable?

4. Look at the stock report on page 34. The second last column lists the highest value of each stock during the previous 52 weeks. Write each number in this column as a fraction, with numerator and denominator as integers.

5. Multiply or divide, as indicated.
   a) $\frac{18}{7} \times \frac{21}{9}$
   b) $\frac{3}{28} \div \frac{9}{7}$
   c) $\frac{9}{48} \div \frac{6}{16}$
   d) $\frac{33}{4} \times \frac{7}{22}$
   e) $(-0.2) \times 0.6$
   f) $(-3.6) \div (-4)$

6. A hiker begins a three-day walk. Each day, she records the time for which she walks and the total distance travelled. The results are shown. Copy the table.

Day	Time (h)	Distance (km)	Daily average speed
1	6.0	24.6	
2	5.1	13.6	
3	9.2	27.0	

   a) Divide each distance by the corresponding time to determine the daily average speed. Enter this amount in the table.
   b) Calculate the total distance and the total time.
   c) Calculate the average speed by dividing the total distance by the total time.
   d) Calculate the mean of the daily average speeds.
   e) Is the average speed the same as the mean of the daily average speeds? Explain.

7. a) The table shows the scoring record of one lacrosse player. Graph the data.

Games played	2	4	8	10	12	14	16	18
Goals scored this season	0	1	2	3	4	4	6	6

   b) Does it make sense to join the points in this graph? Explain.

8. Determine the better buy: 750 mL of dish detergent for $2.09 or 900 mL for $2.39

100 m

100 m
9.84

200 m

200 m
19.32

Who Is the World's Fastest Human?: Part I

At the 1996 Olympic Summer Games, Canadian sprinter Donovan Bailey won the 100-m sprint in a world record time of 9.84 s. He claimed the unofficial title of "The World's Fastest Man."

However, 5 days later, American sprinter Michael Johnson broke the world record in the 200-m sprint with a time of 19.32 s. American sportscasters immediately proclaimed Johnson as the world's fastest man.

In this chapter, you will learn how to compare the two runners. Here are some things to consider:

1. Examine the information above. Is it sufficient for you to decide who was faster at the 1996 Olympic Games?

   2. Is there a calculation you could do to help you decide who is faster?

3. Is there other information that might help you make a decision?

4. Would it be fair to have Bailey and Johnson run a 100-m sprint? Should they run a 200-m sprint?

You will return to this problem in Section 3.4.

FYI Visit www.awl.com/canada/school/connections

For information related to the above problem, click on <u>MATHLINKS</u> followed by <u>AWMath</u>. Then select a topic under Who Is the World's Fastest Human?

This section reviews these skills and topics:

- Graphing
- Integers

1. While travelling in a car, a passenger recorded the odometer reading every minute.

Time (min)	0	1	2	3	4	5	6	7
Odometer reading (km)	123.8	125.4	127.0	128.6	130.2	131.8	133.4	135.0

a) Determine how the numbers in the second row of the table are related. Use this relationship to predict the odometer readings for 8 min, 9 min, and 10 min.

b) Graph the relation.

c) By how much did the distance increase for each elapsed time?

   i) 1 min   **ii)** 2 min   **iii)** 3 min   **vi)** 4 min

d) Describe the car's speed in kilometres per minute.

e) Describe the car's speed in kilometres per hour.

f) The next three odometer readings in the table were 136.0, 137.2, and 138.8. Compare these readings with your predictions in part a. What might have happened to cause the readings to be different from your predictions?

g) In 10 min, how far did the car travel?

h) What was the average speed of the car for these 10 min?

2. a) The temperature is −5°C and it warms up to 3°C. By how much did the temperature increase?

b) The temperature in part a increased over a period of 4 h. At what rate did the temperature increase?

c) The temperature dropped from 3°C to −12°C over the next 5 h. At what rate did the temperature drop?

3. Simplify without using a calculator.

a) $-3 + 5$ b) $3 - 5$ c) $(-3)(-5)$ d) $\frac{-6}{-2}$

e) $-3 - 5$ f) $\frac{-3 + 7}{4 - 5}$ g) $\frac{0 - (-6)}{-9 - 3}$ h) $-3(3 - (-3))$

Slope of a Staircase

1. These diagrams represent two staircases.

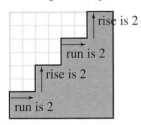

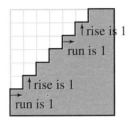

We move 2 blocks right. We say, "The run is 2." We move up 2 blocks. We say, "The rise is 2."

We move 1 block right and 1 block up. The run is 1 and the rise is 1.

a) Suppose we lay a board on each staircase. What do you notice about the steepness of each board?

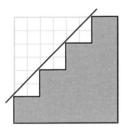

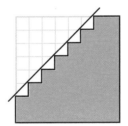

b) Explain where extra blocks could be placed on the first staircase to make the second staircase.

2. a) On grid paper, draw a staircase where each step has rise 6 and run 2.

b) Without changing the steepness, draw additional blocks so that each horizontal step is only 1 block.

c) On the new staircase, as we move 1 block right, how many blocks do we move up? This number is the *slope*. What is the slope of the staircase?

d) i) Draw the board that would lie on the staircase in part a.
   ii) Explain why moving 2 units right and 6 units up has the same steepness as moving 1 unit right and 3 units up.

e) When the rise is 6 and the run is 2, what is the slope?

3. a) On grid paper, draw a staircase where each step has rise 2 and run 4.

b) Shade in blocks and part blocks so that each horizontal step is only 1 block.

c) On the new staircase, as we move 1 block right, how many blocks do we move up?

d) **i)** Draw the board that would lie on the staircase in part a.
ii) Explain why moving 4 units right and 2 units up has the same steepness as moving 1 unit right and 0.5 units up.

e) When the rise is 2 and the run is 4, what is the slope?

4. Compare the steepness of the boards in exercises 1, 2, and 3.

a) In exercise 1, as we moved 1 block right, how many blocks did we move up? What is the slope?

b) In exercise 2, as we moved 1 block right, how many blocks did we move up? What is the slope?

c) In exercise 3, as we moved 1 block right, how many blocks did we move up? What is the slope?

d) How does the slope of a steep board compare with the slope of a board that is more level?

In mathematics, the word *slope* is a number that represents the steepness of a line on a grid. The number always indicates how far we move vertically as we move 1 unit horizontally. The slope of a line indicates how steep the line is.

5. Copy and complete this chart.

		rise	run	slope
a)	1st staircase in exercise 1			
b)	staircase in exercise 2			
c)	staircase in exercise 3			
d)		8	2	
e)		6	3	
f)		1	4	
g)		0	2	

6. Use the patterns in exercise 5. Explain how we determine the slope of a line.

A formula for determining slope is:

$$\text{slope} = \frac{\text{rise}}{\text{run}}$$

The Slope of a Roof

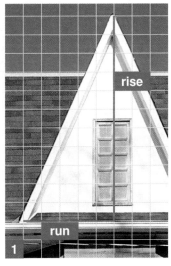

1. a) Which roof is the steepest?

b) Which roof is least steep?

c) List the roofs in order of steepness.

2. The first picture above shows the rise and the run of a roof.

a) Use the grid on each picture. Estimate the rise and the run of each roof. Copy this table. Complete the second and third columns.

House	rise	run	$\dfrac{\text{rise}}{\text{run}}$
1			
2			
3			

b) Divide the rise by the run. Write the results in the fourth column.

c) Compare the numbers in the fourth column with your answers to exercise 1. What do you notice?

The pitch of a roof, the steepness of a ski run, or the gradient of a mountain road are all examples of slope. In each case, the slope is determined by dividing the rise by the run.

The following *Example* shows that we do not need a grid to calculate slope.

Example

These diagrams show how the rise and run of a water wave are defined. Oceanographers have found that a wave tends to fall over, or *break*, when its slope becomes greater than $\frac{2}{7}$. For each wave shown, determine if it would break.

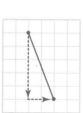

a)

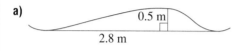

b)

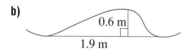

Solution

Determine the slope of each wave.

a) $\text{slope} = \frac{\text{rise}}{\text{run}}$
$= \frac{0.5}{2.8}$
$\doteq 0.179$

b) $\text{slope} = \frac{\text{rise}}{\text{run}}$
$= \frac{0.6}{1.9}$
$\doteq 0.316$

Since $\frac{2}{7} \doteq 0.286$, the wave in part b would break, and the wave in part a would not.

DISCUSSING the IDEAS

1. Suppose we move down (instead of up) as we move from left to right. What type of number could show this?

2. What is the slope of the line segment shown? Explain in two different ways.

3. On grid paper, explain how to draw a line with each slope: $\frac{1}{3}$, −2, 4, −0.5, and 0.

A 1. Copy each staircase on grid paper. For each staircase:

a) Draw the board that would lie on the staircase.

b) Shade in blocks and part blocks so that each horizontal step is only 1 block.

c) State the slope of the staircase.

i) 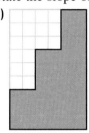   ii) 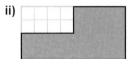   iii)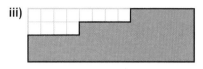

B 2. This diagram represents a roof. Determine its slope.

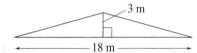

3. A section of a roller-coaster track falls 25 m in a horizontal distance of 15 m. What is the slope of this section of the track?

4. a) Slope is important when an airplane takes off. Explain.

b) What might affect the slope of the plane at takeoff? Explain.

5. a) Measure the rise and the run for the steps in a staircase in your home or at school.

b) Calculate the slope of the staircase.

c) Compare your slope with slopes determined by your classmates. Discuss similarities and differences.

6. This drawing represents the side view of part of a small roller coaster. Each square represents one square metre. The roller coaster moves from left to right.

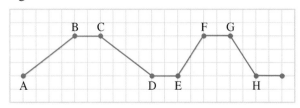

a) Calculate the heights of the two hills. Which hill is higher?

b) Which hill has the steeper climb? Explain.

c) Which hill has the steeper drop? Explain.

d) Explain how two hills can have the same height and yet not have the same steepness.

e) How will the steepness of the track affect the speed of the roller coaster?

7. State the slope of each line segment.

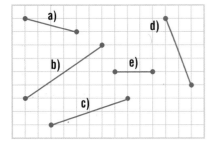

8. The slope of a line segment is 3. What is a possible rise and run?

9. The slope of a line segment is 4. The run is 6. What is the rise?

10. Suppose you were to ski or snowboard down a very steep hill. What would you do to avoid going too fast and losing control?

11. a) There are strict rules about the slopes of highways and train tracks. Why?

b) How do engineers make a road or train track less steep?

12. Copy these line segments in your notebook. Match each segment with the best estimate for its slope: 2, 1, $\frac{1}{4}$, 0, $-\frac{1}{4}$, –1, –2. Assume each segment is drawn on a grid.

13. a) Suggest a way to calculate the slope of the roof of your home.

b) Estimate the slope of the roof of your home.

c) Roofs of new homes in Ontario have a fairly low slope. However, roofs in ski resorts are often quite steep. Why?

Building the Best Staircase

Staircases come in many shapes and sizes. There are circular staircases, wide and narrow staircases, long and short staircases.

All staircases have three main parts.

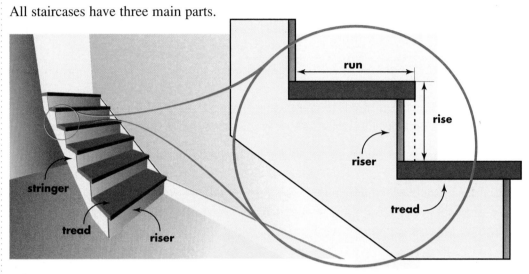

The run or *tread* is the horizontal part of a step.

The rise or *riser* is the vertical part of a step.

The *stringers* are the sloping boards running diagonally between floors. The stringers support the staircase. The rise and run of the steps determine the slope of the staircase.

14. Look at these 3 staircases.

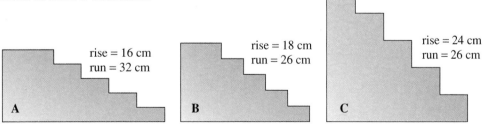

rise = 16 cm
run = 32 cm

A

rise = 18 cm
run = 26 cm

B

rise = 24 cm
run = 26 cm

C

a) How is the number of risers related to the number of treads?

b) Which staircase would most likely be used as the main staircase in a home? Explain your choice.

c) Which staircase is best suited for climbing into an attic? Explain.

d) Most staircase accidents occur when people are walking down. Which staircase do you think would be safest? Explain.

e) How might the safety of a staircase be improved?

15. Over the years, different guidelines have been developed for the design of staircases. Here is one guideline.

- The run plus twice the rise should be 62 cm (a normal stride).

a) Copy and complete this table to show 5 possible runs and rises that satisfy this guideline.

rise	run	slope

b) In exercise 5, you measured the rise and run for a staircase in your home or school. Does this staircase satisfy the guideline? Explain.

16. In a new house, the upstairs floor is 280 cm above the downstairs floor. Use the guideline in exercise 15 to design a staircase to join the floors. Your design should be a diagram that shows the number of steps, the run and rise of each step, and the total amount of horizontal space needed for the staircase.

C **17. a)** Suggest a method to determine the slope of a ski hill.

b) The rating system for a ski hill (for example, Black Diamond) depends partly on its slope. What other factors might be involved? Explain.

COMMUNICATING
the **IDEAS**

In your journal, explain what slope means and why calculating $\frac{\text{rise}}{\text{run}}$ determines slope.

Famous mathematician René Descartes devised *x*- and *y*-axes to plot a point identified by a pair of numbers. This is the *Cartesian plane*, and its invention changed mathematics forever.

INVESTIGATION

Points and Their Coordinates

Setup

- Press [2nd] [Y=] **4** [ENTER]. This will turn off any plots that have been left on.
- Press [Y=]. If there is an expression beside Y1=, press [CLEAR]. If there are any other expressions in the list, press [▼] [CLEAR] to clear them. Your screen should look like the one below left.
- Press [WINDOW], and change the settings to those in the screen below right. To enter the negative sign, be sure to use the change-sign key, [(-)], and not the subtraction key [-].

```
Plot1 Plot2 Plot3
\Y1=
\Y2=
\Y3=
\Y4=
\Y5=
\Y6=
\Y7=
```

```
WINDOW
 Xmin=-4.7
 Xmax=4.7
 Xscl=1
 Ymin=-3.1
 Ymax=3.1
 Yscl=1
 Xres=1
```

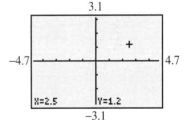

1. Press [GRAPH]. Use the scroll buttons ([▼], [▲], [►], [◄]) to move a cursor around the screen. The coordinates of the cursor's location appear at the bottom of the screen.

2. Find all the points that have $x = 3$. Describe where they are.

3. Find all the points that have $y = -2$. Describe where they are.

4. **a)** Move the cursor to the point $(3, -2)$. Describe its location.

   b) Move the cursor to the point $(-2, 3)$. Describe its location.

   c) Explain why $(-2, 3)$ is different from $(3, -2)$.

5. Move the cursor to the points with these coordinates:

(2, 0), (0, 2), (–4, –1), (3.5, 1)

6. Academic Focus Predict what will happen to the coordinates of the points on the screen if you use these window settings. Use your calculator to confirm your prediction.

a) Xmin = –9.4, Xmax = 9.4, Ymin = –6.2, Ymax = 6.2

b) Xmin = –47, Xmax = 47, Ymin = –31, Ymax = 31

c) Xmin = –10, Xmax = 10, Ymin = –10, Ymax = 10

If we know that a point has x-coordinate 4, then the point could be anywhere on the vertical line through 4 on the x-axis.

If we know that a point has y-coordinate –3, then the point could be anywhere on the horizontal line through –3 on the y-axis.

So, if $x = 4$ and $y = –3$, then there is only one place on the grid where the point could be. It is marked on this grid as point A.

The location of a point is written as an ordered pair:

the x-coordinate⟍ ⟋the y-coordinate
(4, –3)

Example

Plot and label each point: A(–3, 2), B(0, 4), C(–1, 0), D(4.5, $-\frac{5}{3}$).

Solution

To plot A, locate –3 on the x-axis, then visualize a vertical line through this point. Locate 2 on the y-axis and visualize a horizontal line through this point. These lines intersect at A.

Plot the other points in a similar way.

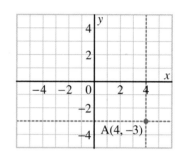

1. Explain what the coordinates of all points on each line have in common.

a) the *x*-axis   **b)** the *y*-axis   **c)** any horizontal line   **a)** any vertical line

2. In the *Example*, explain how point D$(4.5, -\frac{5}{3})$ was plotted.

3.2 EXERCISES

A

1. Write the coordinates of any five points whose first coordinates are –3.
Then plot the points. How are these points related?

2. Write the coordinates of any five points whose second coordinates are –5.
Then plot the points. How are these points related?

3. Name the coordinates for each point shown below.

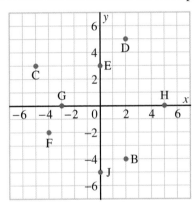

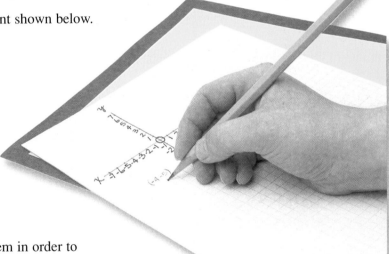

B

4. Plot each set of points and join them in order to
form a quadrilateral. Identify the quadrilateral.

a) A(1, 1), B(1, 5), C(–3, 5), D(–3, 1)

b) J(1, –3), K(5, 1), L(8, 1), M(4, –3)

c) P(–3, 0), Q(–6, –2), R(4, –4), S(10, 0)

5. Plot these points. Connect the points in order.

(1, –1), (2, 1), (1, 3), (–1, 4), (–3, 3), (–4, 1), (–3, –1), (–1, –2), (1, –1)

6. Plot these points. Connect the points in order. What picture do you see?

(2, 1), (5, 5), (1, 2), (0, 5), (–1, 2), (–5, 5), (–2, 1), (–5, 0), (–2, –1), (–5, –5),
(–1, –2), (0, –5), (1, –2), (5, –5), (2, –1), (5, 0)

7. Draw a design on coordinate axes. Ensure that each vertex is at the intersection of grid lines. List the coordinates of the vertices. Exchange coordinates with a partner. Draw the design described by your partner's coordinates. Compare designs.

8. Three lists of points are given. For each list:

a) Plot the points on a grid.

b) Describe any geometrical pattern formed by the points.

c) Explain why the geometrical pattern occurs.

d) Write the coordinates of two other points that fit the pattern.

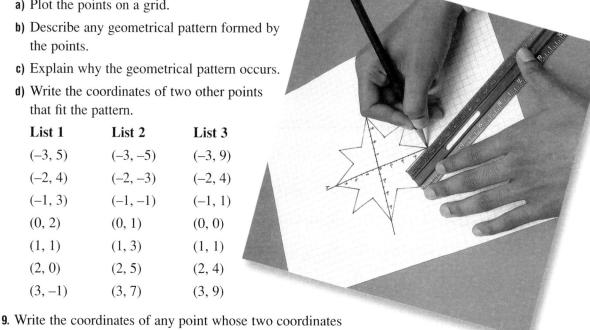

List 1	List 2	List 3
(–3, 5)	(–3, –5)	(–3, 9)
(–2, 4)	(–2, –3)	(–2, 4)
(–1, 3)	(–1, –1)	(–1, 1)
(0, 2)	(0, 1)	(0, 0)
(1, 1)	(1, 3)	(1, 1)
(2, 0)	(2, 5)	(2, 4)
(3, –1)	(3, 7)	(3, 9)

9. Write the coordinates of any point whose two coordinates are equal. Repeat for four more points. Then plot the points. What do these points have in common?

10. Write the coordinates of any point whose two coordinates are opposites. Repeat for four more points. Then plot the points. What do these points have in common?

11. The points S(2, 2) and T(–2, 2) are two vertices of a square. Plot these points on coordinate axes. What are the possible coordinates of the other two vertices? Find as many answers to this question as you can.

C 12. Plot the points A(2, 4) and B(8, 4) on coordinate axes. C is a point so that the area of △ABC is 12 square units. Find at least two possible locations for C.

COMMUNICATING the IDEAS

Sit back-to-back with a partner. Take turns to explain how to plot points such as (–3, 4) and (5, 0). Take turns to choose the coordinates of a point and explain how to plot them.

Line Segments and Slope

You will use a TI-83 calculator to graph line segments. The calculator will determine the slope of each segment. Your task is to determine how the slope is related to the line segment.

The instructions below assume that a program called SLOPE has been transferred to your calculator. If it has not, your teacher can obtain it from the Teacher's Resource Book.

Setup

- Press $\boxed{\text{Y=}}$. Use $\boxed{\text{CLEAR}}$ and the scroll buttons to clear all equations.

- If any of Plot 1, Plot 2, or Plot 3 at the top of the screen are highlighted, use the scroll buttons and $\boxed{\text{ENTER}}$ to remove the highlighting.

1. Press $\boxed{\text{PRGM}}$. Choose SLOPE.

The calculator will display the screen below left, prompting you to enter the *x*-coordinate of a point A. Enter the *x*-coordinate and press $\boxed{\text{ENTER}}$. Enter the *y*-coordinate and press $\boxed{\text{ENTER}}$. Then enter the coordinates of point B. The calculator will graph the line segment AB and calculate its slope (rounded to 3 decimal places). The second screen below shows the result for A(–10, –8) and B(20, 12).

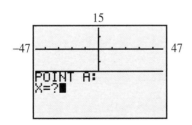

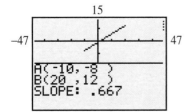

2. Draw 10 line segments on grid paper. As you draw the segments, follow these instructions:

- Use integer coordinates where the *x*-coordinate is between –47 and 47, and the *y*-coordinate is between –15 and 15. This is necessary to match the split screen on the graphing calculator.
- Ensure some line segments are steeper than others, some go up to the right, and some go down to the right. Include horizontal and vertical segments.

3. a) Use the SLOPE program to determine the slope of each segment you drew in exercise 2. Record the slope of each line segment beside the line segment on your grid paper.

b) Describe the slope of each segment.
   i) a line segment that goes up to the right
   ii) a line segment that goes down to the right
   iii) a horizontal line segment
   iv) a vertical line segment

Now that you can plot points on the coordinate plane, you can determine the slope of any line segment when the coordinates of its endpoints are given.

Example 1

Determine the slope of line segment AB.

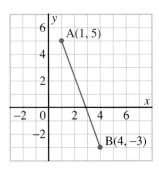

Solution

Determine the slope by counting squares. Moving from A to B, the rise is –8 and the run is 3.

Slope of AB $= \dfrac{\text{rise}}{\text{run}}$

$= \dfrac{-8}{3}$

$= -\dfrac{8}{3}$

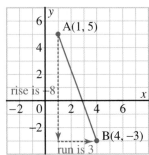

As *Example 1* illustrates, we can determine the slope of a line segment by counting squares. We can also determine the slope of a line segment by visualizing how the *x*- and *y*-coordinates change as we move from one endpoint to the other endpoint.

Example 2

Determine the slope of line segment CD.

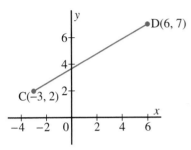

Solution

Think ...

To determine the rise, we want to know how far we move up or down as we move from C to D. Vertical positions are controlled by the *y*-coordinates. To determine the run, we want to know how far we move left or right. Horizontal positions are controlled by the *x*-coordinates.

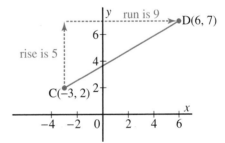

Moving from C to D, the *y*-coordinates change from 2 to 7. This is an increase of 5. Hence, the rise is 5.

Moving from C to D, the *x*-coordinates change from −3 to 6. This is an increase of 9. Hence, the run is 9.

Slope of CD $= \dfrac{\text{rise}}{\text{run}}$

$\qquad\quad = \dfrac{9}{5}$

Example 1 and *Example 2* illustrate two ways to determine the slope of a line segment. Compare these examples with the method in *Example 2*.

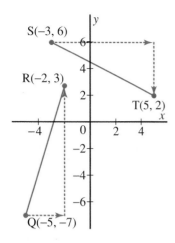

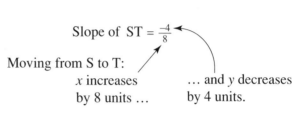

Slope of QR = $\frac{10}{3}$

Moving from Q to R:

x increases by 3 units …

… and y increases by 10 units.

Slope of ST = $\frac{-4}{8}$

Moving from S to T:

x increases by 8 units …

… and y decreases by 4 units.

Example 3

Determine the slope of each line segment.

Solution

Slope of AB = $\frac{\text{rise}}{\text{run}}$

$= \frac{0}{6}$

$= 0$

Slope of CD = $\frac{\text{rise}}{\text{run}}$

$= \frac{8}{0}$

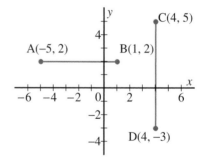

The denominator is 0, and division by 0 is not defined.
We say that the slope of CD is *undefined*.

On a grid:

The slope of any horizontal segment is zero.	The slope of any vertical segment is undefined.	A line segment *rising* to the right has *positive* slope.	A line segment *falling* to the right has *negative* slope.
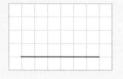		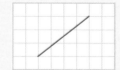	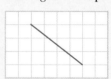

In many situations, a grid has scales on the axes. In this case, we use the scales to determine the coordinates of the endpoints of a line segment before we determine its slope.

Example 4

This is a side view of a water coaster.

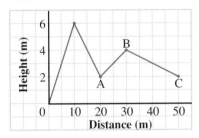

Determine the slope of the sections from A to B and from B to C.

Solution

The section from A to B is a line segment with endpoints A(20, 2) and B(30, 4). Moving from A to B, *x* increases by 10 and *y* increases by 2. Hence, the run is 10 and the rise is 2.

Slope of AB $= \frac{\text{rise}}{\text{run}}$

$= \frac{2}{10}$

$= \frac{1}{5}$

The slope of the section from A to B is $\frac{1}{5}$.

The section from B to C is a line segment with endpoints B(30, 4) and C(50, 2). Moving from B to C, *x* increases by 20 and *y* decreases by 2. Hence, the run is 20 and the rise is –2.

Slope of BC $= \frac{\text{rise}}{\text{run}}$

$= \frac{-2}{20}$

$= -\frac{1}{10}$

The slope of the section from B to C is $-\frac{1}{10}$.

1. **a)** When you determine the slope of a line segment, does it matter whether you find the rise first, or the run first? Explain.

   b) Which do you prefer: to find the rise first or the run first?

2. Refer to the diagram in *Example 1*. Both the rise and the run are shown below segment AB.

   a) Where else could the rise and the run have been shown on this diagram?

   b) Explain why there are two different positions for the rise and the run.

3. In the solution of *Example 1*, we started at A and moved to B.

   a) Determine the rise and the run when we move from B to A.

   b) How would the solution change if this rise and this run were used?

4. Refer to the solution of *Example 2*.

   a) What calculation can you use with the *x*- and *y*-coordinates to determine the rise and the run?

   b) Could a similar calculation be used to determine the slope in *Example 1* and in the examples following *Example 2*? Explain.

5. In *Example 4*, could the slopes of AB and BC be determined by counting squares? Explain.

3.3 EXERCISES

 1. Use the diagram to determine the slope of each line segment.

a)
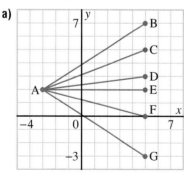

b)
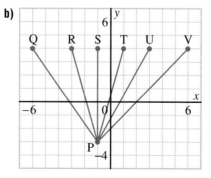

2. Write to explain the method you used to complete exercise 1. Compare your method with that of a classmate. If your classmate's method was different from yours, explain it.

3. Graph each line segment. Determine its slope from the diagram.

    a) A(–2, 7), B(6, –4)   **b)** C(3, –5), D(8, 10)   **c)** E(1, 6), F(5, –4)

    d) G(–3, 7), H(–3, –7)   **e)** J(–4, –3), K(8, 5)   **f)** L(2, –7), M(7, –7)

4. The coordinates of the vertices of triangles are given. Graph each triangle. Determine the slope of each side.

    a) A(5, –1), B(0, 4), C(–2, –5)   **b)** R(–3, 4), S(6, 7), T(2, –3)

    c) L(4, –2), M(–4, 8), N(4, 8)   **d)** E(–2, –1), F(–1, –6), G(5, 6)

5. Have you ever seen the screen saver program where lines are drawn across the screen? Here is how you can make a pattern of lines: Use only the first quadrant of a Cartesian plane. Start at (0, 10), then draw a line segment with slope $-\frac{10}{1}$. The next line segment begins at (0, 9) and has slope $-\frac{9}{2}$. The next line segment begins at (0, 8) and has slope $-\frac{8}{3}$. Continue this pattern until you reach (0, 0). What do you notice?

6. This is a side view of a railway track.

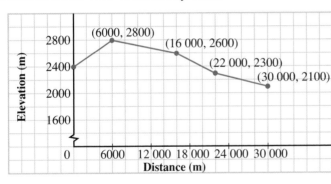

    a) Why is the zigzag mark drawn on the vertical axis?

    b) What is the slope of each section of the railway track?

    c) What is the slope of a railway track that rises 2.2 m for a run of 100 m?

    d) When the slope of a railway track is greater than that calculated in part c, extra locomotives are required to pull a train. In which sections of the above railway track would extra locomotives be required?

7. Here is a side view of a water coaster. The slope of each segment is given. Determine the coordinates of each point A to F.

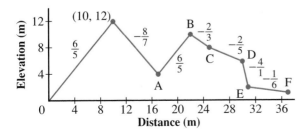

8. Two points on a line segment are G(5, 6) and H(2, –3). Determine the coordinates of two other points on the line segment.

9. a) For each given slope, determine the coordinates of the endpoints of a line segment with that slope.

i) 3   **ii)** –5   **iii)** $\frac{3}{5}$ **iv)** $-\frac{5}{3}$ **v)** –3   **vi)** 5

b) Compare your answers to part a with those of a classmate. Explain any differences.

TECHNOLOGY FOCUS

The CBR Distance Match Activity

In this activity, the calculator displays a distance-time graph similar to this. Distances are measured, in metres, from the CBR unit to a wall. As you move toward or away from the wall, the CBR measures your distance and transfers it to the graph as a series of dots. Your task is to make the dots fit the graph on the screen as closely as possible.

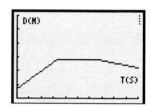

Setup

• Attach the CBR unit to a TI-83 calculator.

• Turn on the calculator, then press PRGM.

• Choose RANGER. (If this program is not present, see page 87.)

• Press ENTER ENTER to display the main menu.

Doing the Activity

• Hold the calculator in one hand and the CBR in the other. Aim the sensor directly at a wall.

• Press **3** to choose APPLICATIONS. Press **1** to choose METERS. Press **1** to choose DIST MATCH.

• Press ENTER. The calculator will display a distance-time graph. Estimate your distance to the wall and stand where you think the graph begins.

• Press ENTER to begin data collection. Walk forward or backward, and try to match the graph as your position is plotted on the screen.

- When the graph is complete, press ENTER. Press **1** to try again. Repeat until your graph nearly matches the one given. Press **2** to try again with a new graph. Repeat as many times as you can. Press **5** when you run out of time.

10. Each graph the CBR makes has three line segments. Explain your answer to each question.

a) What is happening when the slope of a line segment is 0?

b) What is true about the distance between you and the wall in each case?
   i) The slope is positive.   **ii)** The slope is negative.

c) How do you have to walk in each case?
   i) to match a segment that is very steep
   ii) to match a segment that has slope close to 0

After you have quit the program, you can view the data the CBR gathered. To do this, press STAT **1**.

A screen similar to this appears, showing three lists. List L1 contains the times in seconds. List L2 contains the distances to the wall in metres. The calculator used these numbers to plot the points on the screen.

L1	L2	L3	1
00.000	1.00	0.00	
.25	1.02	0.00	
.50	1.06	0.00	
.75	1.11	0.00	
1.00	1.18	0.00	
1.25	1.26	0.00	
1.50	1.33	0.00	

L1(1)=0

11. Think of a graph of a relation as a picture of a roller coaster. You ride from left to right on the graph. Write to describe the ride on a section with each given slope.

a) 3   **b)** $\frac{1}{2}$ **c)** 0   **d)** $-\frac{1}{3}$ **e)** -4

12. This graph shows the heights, in feet, of 3 different helicopters as they climb to their maximum altitudes.

a) Without calculating, rank the helicopters from the least rate of climb to the greatest rate of climb.

b) For each helicopter, estimate its maximum altitude; then calculate its approximate rate of climb.

c) Is the helicopter with the greatest rate of climb the first to reach its maximum altitude? Explain.

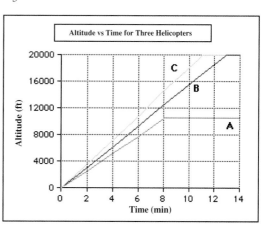

13. Use a Cartesian plane.

a) If possible, draw a triangle so that all three sides have positive slopes.

b) If possible, draw a quadrilateral so that three sides have positive slopes.

c) If possible, draw a quadrilateral so that all four sides have positive slopes.

14. The line segment joining each pair of points has the given slope. Determine each value of x. Draw each segment on a grid.

a) A(-1, 2), B(x, 6)　　slope $\frac{1}{2}$　　　　　**b)** G(0, -2), H(x, 3)　　slope 1

c) R(x, 0), S(-2, 4)　　slope $-\frac{2}{3}$　　　**d)** U(x, -3), V(4, 9)　　slope 3

15. The line segment joining each pair of points has the given slope. Determine each value of y. Draw each segment on a grid.

a) C(1, 3), D(5, y)　　slope $\frac{3}{4}$　　　　　**b)** Q(0, y), R(4, 6)　　slope 2

c) L(-2, 6), M(5, y)　　slope -1　　　　**d)** E(0, y), F(4, -2)　　slope $-\frac{3}{2}$

16. Choose one part of exercise 14 or 15. Write to explain how you determined the value of x or y.

17. Academic Focus Up to now in this chapter, you have used this formula for slope:
$$\text{slope} = \frac{\text{rise}}{\text{run}}$$
The rise and the run are sometimes expressed in different ways. This leads to other formulas for slope.

a) In *Discussing the Ideas,* exercise 4, you learned that the run can be found by subtracting the x-coordinates. Similarly, the rise can be found by subtracting the y-coordinates (in the same order). Suppose A has coordinates (x_1, y_1) and B has coordinates (x_2, y_2). Write a formula for slope in terms of these coordinates.

b) Sometimes, the change in x is written as $\triangle x$. Similarly, the change in y is written as $\triangle y$. Use these symbols to write a formula for slope.

C **18.** One endpoint of a line segment is A(4, 6). The other endpoint is on the x-axis. Determine the coordinates of the endpoint on the x-axis for each given slope.

a) 1　　　　**b)** 2　　　　**c)** 3　　　　**d)** $\frac{1}{2}$　　　　**e)** -2　　　　**f)** $-\frac{1}{2}$

19. Two line segments have a common endpoint N(0, 4). They have slopes 2 and $-\frac{1}{2}$. The other endpoints are on the x-axis. Determine their coordinates.

COMMUNICATING the IDEAS

Your friend missed today's mathematics lesson and telephones you to ask about it. How would you explain to her, over the telephone, how to determine the slope of a line segment when the coordinates of its endpoints are known?

3.4 Who Is the World's Fastest Human?: Part I

On page 115, you considered whether Donovan Bailey or Michael Johnson could claim to be the world's fastest human. You investigated their world-record sprints in the 1996 Summer Olympics. In this section, you will develop some mathematical models to help you decide who is faster.

The Average Speed Model

1. Use the information on page 115. On grid paper, start a distance-time graph. Draw axes with *Time in seconds* along the horizontal axis, and *Distance in metres* along the vertical axis. Label the origin O.

2. a) Plot point D to represent Bailey's time for the 100 m. Join OD.

   b) Calculate the slope of OD. What does this slope represent?

3. a) Plot point M to represent Johnson's time for the 200 m. Join OM.

   b) Calculate the slope of OM. What does this slope represent?

The 100-m Model

4. Michael Johnson ran 200 m. He reached the 100-m mark at 10.12 s. Use the graph in exercise 3.

   a) Plot point N to represent Johnson's time for 100 m. Join ON.

   b) Calculate the slope of ON. What does this slope represent?

   c) How does Johnson's average speed for the first 100 m compare with Bailey's average speed?

The 200-m Model

5. Donovan Bailey ran 100 m. Suppose he ran the second 100 m in the same time as his first 100 m. Use the graph in exercise 4.

a) Plot point E to represent Bailey's time for 200 m. Join OE.

b) Calculate the slope of OE. What does this slope represent?

c) How does Bailey's average speed for 200 m compare with Johnson's average speed?

Comparing the Models

6. In the above models, you used slopes of line segments to model Donovan Bailey's and Michael Johnson's world-record sprints.

a) Are the points between the endpoints of these line segments accurate representations of the positions of the runners during the two races? Explain.

b) For each model, decide if both runners are treated fairly. If you think one runner is not treated fairly, explain.

Modifying the Average Speed Model

7. Academic Focus At the start of the race, it takes a certain time for runners to react to the sound of the starter's pistol. Suppose this time is subtracted from the runners' times for the two races.

a) About how long do you think the reaction time might be?

b) Use your estimate from part a to modify your graphs in exercises 2 and 3. Repeat the slope calculations. Does this change your opinion about who was faster?

c) Explore the effect of using different reaction times. What would the reaction time have to be for this model to favour Donovan Bailey?

d) Do you think this modified model is a fairer way to compare the two runners? Do you still need more information? Explain.

Save your results for use later. We will return to these problems in Chapter 9.

COMMUNICATING the IDEAS

In your journal, write to explain whether you think Donovan Bailey or Michael Johnson was faster at the 1996 Summer Olympics. Include calculations and graphs in your explanation.

Recall, from Chapter 2, that a relationship between a pair of quantities is a
relation. For example, there is often a relation between the number of hours an
employee works and the amount of pay she receives.

Monique has a part-time job at a garden centre. She is paid at a rate of $5.50
per hour. Employees are paid for parts of hours worked.

Monique knows the number of hours she has worked. This is called the *input*.
She multiplies this by $5.50 to determine her total pay. Her total pay is called
the *output*.

We can draw a diagram to show how Monique can calculate her pay:

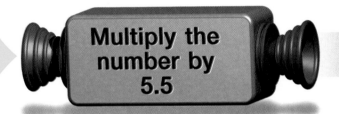

INVESTIGATION 1

Relations as Equations

1. a) How much will Monique earn after each number of hours?

    i) 1   **ii)** 2   **iii)** 3   **iv)** 4   **v)** 5   **vi)** 6   **vii)** 7

   b) Summarize the results of part a in a table.

2. Find as many patterns in the
table as you can.

3. Add a third column to your
table. Complete the third
column by determining how
much more each *y*-coordinate
is than the preceding *y*-
coordinate. What do you
notice about these numbers?

Hours	Earnings ($)	Difference
0	0	
		5.50 (5.50 is 5.50 more than 0)
1	5.50	
2	11.00	
3		
4		
5		

4. a) On grid paper, draw a graph to show how Monique's earnings are
related to the number of hours she worked. Decide whether to join
the points on the graph. Explain your decision.

b) Explain why the points lie on a straight line.

c) Use the graph to estimate Monique's pay when she works 7.25 h.

5. **a)** Label two points on your graph A and B. Determine the slope of AB.

b) Label any other point C on your graph. Determine the slope of BC.

c) Label any other point D on your graph. Determine the slope of CD.

d) Compare these slopes to the numbers in the *Difference* column of your table of values. Explain.

6. Write a short paragraph to describe the graph you drew in exercise 4. State whether it is a linear relation.

7. Suppose *h* represents the number of hours Monique works, and *p* represents her pay in dollars.

a) Write an equation to express *p* in terms of *h*.

b) Test your equation using some numbers from the table.

8. Use your equation to calculate Monique's pay when she works 7.25 h. Compare the result with your estimate in exercise 4c.

9. Suppose Monique's rate of pay increases to $6.00 per hour. Describe how each item would change.

a) the table of values   **b)** the graph   **c)** the equation

10. **Academic Focus** Suppose the manager of the garden centre changes the policy about paying for parts of hours worked. The change is that employees are expected to work for whole numbers of hours only. They will no longer be paid for parts of hours worked. Describe the effect this would have, if any, on each item. Explain your answers.

a) the table of values   **b)** the graph   **c)** the equation

---

In *Investigation 1*, you learned that a relation can be expressed using an equation. For example, the relation between the amount Monique is paid, *p* dollars, and the number of hours she works, *h*, is expressed by the equation $p = 5.50h$. This equation is a model that describes how her pay is calculated.

$$p = 5.50h$$

To determine Monique's pay, *p* dollars … … multiply the number of hours by 5.50.

Other relations have similar equations. For example, suppose *x* and *y* are related by the equation $y = 3x - 1$.

This relation can be expressed as a table of values and a graph.

$$y = 3x - 1$$

To determine the value of *y* … … multiply the value of *x* by 3, then subtract 1.

The Relation $y = 3x - 1$

If you do not have a graphing calculator, complete Part A and Part C.
If you have a graphing calculator, complete Part B and Part C.

Part A

1. Copy this table. Use the rule
below to complete the table.

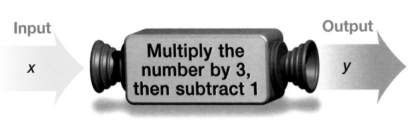

input x	output y
0	
1	
2	
3	
4	
5	
6	

Input

x

Multiply the number by 3, then subtract 1

Output

y

You have made a table of values for the relation defined by
$y = 3x - 1$.

Go on to Part C.

Part B

Setting up an equation

- Press ⬚Y=⬚. Use ⬚CLEAR⬚ and the scroll buttons to
  clear all equations.

- If any of Plot 1, Plot 2, or Plot 3 at the top of the
  screen are highlighted, use the scroll buttons and
  ⬚ENTER⬚ to remove the highlighting.

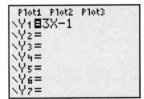

- Make sure the cursor is beside ⬚Y=⬚. Press 3 ⬚X,T,θ,n⬚ ⬚–⬚ 1. You have
  entered the equation $y = 3x - 1$. Your screen should look like the one
  above right. Note that ⬚X,T,θ,n⬚ is the variable key. You always use this key
  to enter the variable x in an equation.

Setting up a table of values

- Press ⬚2nd⬚ ⬚WINDOW⬚ for TBLSET. Make sure that 0 is beside
  TblStart and 1 is beside $\triangle$Tbl. This will set the table so
  that the values of x begin at 0 and increase by 1. Make
  sure that Auto is highlighted in the last two lines. Your
  screen should look like this.

2. a) Press ⌷2nd⌷ ⌷GRAPH⌷ for TABLE. A table of values will appear.

   b) Copy the table in your notebook.

3. How do you think the calculator worked out the values for *y*?

Setting up a graph

- Press ⌷WINDOW⌷, and change the settings so that Xmin = –23.5, Xmax = 23.5, Xscl = 10, Ymin = –15.5, Ymax = 15.5, Yscl = 10.

4. a) Press ⌷GRAPH⌷. The graph of a line appears.

   b) Press ⌷TRACE⌷. Values of *x* and *y* appear. Press ▶ or ◀ to move a cursor along the line. Notice that the values of *x* and *y* change as you move.

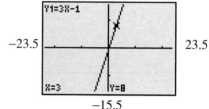

   c) Move the cursor until the value of *x* is the same as one value in the table in exercise 1. Compare the value of *y* with that in the table. Repeat for different values of *x*.

Part C

5. Add a third column to your table. Complete the third column by determining how much more each *y*-coordinate is than the previous *y*-coordinate. What do you notice about these numbers?

x	y	Difference
0	–1	3 (2 is 3 more than –1.)
1	2	
2		
3		
4		
5		
6		

6. a) On grid paper, graph the relation using your table of values.

   b) Explain why it makes sense to connect the points with a straight line.

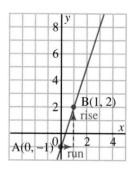

7. a) On your graph, label points A(0, –1) and B(1, 2). Determine the slope of AB.

   b) Plot point C(2, 5) on your graph. Determine the slope of BC.

   c) Continue this process for each point in your table of values.

   d) Compare these slopes to the numbers in the *Difference* column of your table of values. Explain.

Here is a summary of the results of the *Investigations*.

- A relation can be represented by an equation in x and y (or other letters), a table of values, or a graph.
- Suppose the graph of the relation is a straight line. When the values of the x-coordinates increase by 1, the differences in the y-coordinates are equal to the slope of the line.

Example

Draw a graph of the relation described by the equation $y = 8 - 2x$.

Solution

$y = 8 - 2x$

Choose several values of x.

When $x = -2$, $y = 8 - 2(-2)$

$\qquad\qquad = 8 + 4$

$\qquad\qquad = 12$

When $x = 0$, $y = 8 - 2(0)$

$\qquad\qquad = 8$

Continue in this way to determine values of y for other values of x. Make a table of values, then plot the coordinates (x, y) on a grid. Join the points with a straight line, and label it with its equation.

x	y
−2	12
0	8
2	4
4	0
6	−4

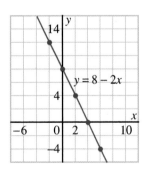

In the *Example*, the equation $y = 8 - 2x$ acts like a formula that relates the values of y to the values of x. That is, if you know a value of x, the value of y is determined by the equation. All the pairs of values of x and y that can be obtained in this way can be plotted on a graph. These points all lie on a straight line. We say that the line is the graph of the equation.

The graph of an equation contains all the points, and only those points, whose coordinates satisfy the equation.

Equation of a Line Property

The coordinates of every point on the line satisfy the equation of the line.

Every point whose coordinates satisfy the equation of the line is on the line.

1. We can describe a relation in different ways. For example, we might describe a relation using a table of values. Is it true that a table of values shows all possible input numbers? Explain.

2. **a)** List at least three other ways to describe a relation.

   b) With a partner, discuss the advantages and disadvantages of each way you listed in part a.

3. Explain each statement. Use examples from your graph in *Investigation 2* to illustrate your explanations.

   a) The coordinates of a point satisfy an equation.

   b) The graph of an equation passes through a point.

4. Suppose a column labelled *Difference* is added to the solution of the *Example*.

   a) What numbers could be in this column?

   b) Are these numbers equal to the slope of the line? Explain.

3.5   EXERCISES

A 1. **a)** Copy and complete each table of values.

   i) $y = 2x + 3$ **ii)** $y = 5 - 3x$ **iii)** $y = -12 + 4x$

x	y
0	
	0

x	y
0	
	0

x	y
0	
	0

   b) Choose one table from part a. Write to explain how you completed it.

B 2. The equation $C = 40n + 20$ represents the total amount charged by an appliance repair company. The amount, C, is in dollars and n is the number of hours the employee spent working on the appliance.

   a) Copy and complete this table.

   b) Of the ordered pairs listed, which satisfy the equation of the relation, and which do not? Explain.
   (1, 60), (4, 160), (2.5, 120), (−2, −60)

n	C
5	
3	
0	
	100

c) In part b, which ordered pair satisfies the equation but does not make sense in terms of the relation? Explain.

3. This diagram illustrates a relation.

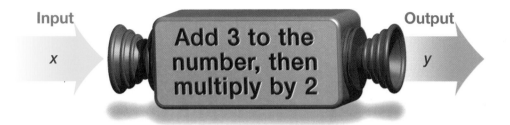

a) Make a table of values with at least 5 different input numbers. Add a *Difference* column to your table. Enter the differences in the *y*-coordinates in this column.

b) Write the equation for the relation.

c) Graph the relation.

4. The cost, *C* cents, to print and bind *n* copies of a manual is modelled by the equation $C = 70 + 20n$.

a) Make a table of values to show the costs for up to 100 copies.

b) Use your table to draw a graph.

c) Use the graph to estimate the cost of 75 copies.

d) Use the graph to estimate how many copies can be made for $10.

5. Three relations are graphed below.

a) Describe how the graphs are similar.

b) Account for the differences in the graphs.

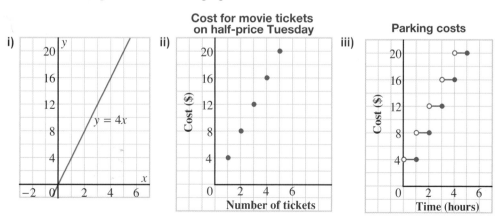

6. a) Graph these relations on the same grid.

Rule 1: Double the number, then add 3 to the result.
Rule 2: Add 3 to the number, then double the result.
Rule 3: $y = 2x - 3$
Rule 4: $y = 2(x - 3)$

b) Account for the similarities and the differences in the graphs.

7. The cost, C dollars, for a school basketball team to play in a tournament is modelled by the equation $C = 300 + 20n$, where n is the number of players.

a) Make a table of values using appropriate values of n.

b) Use your table to draw a graph.

c) Suppose $550 is available for travel costs. How many players can play in the tournament?

d) In the equation $C = 300 + 20n$, what do the numbers 300 and 20 represent? Explain.

e) Mathematical Modelling In part b, the graph represents a model of the cost to play in the tournament.

  i) Does the model consist of the line joining the points, or only the points? Explain.

  ii) Which points are reasonable ones to use for the model? Why?

8. A car travels at a constant speed from Edmonton to Calgary. The distance, d kilometres, from Calgary after t hours of driving is modelled by the equation $d = 280 - 100t$.

a) Make a table of values and draw a graph of d against t.

b) Explain how the graph shows the distance between these two cities. What is the distance?

c) Explain how the graph shows the total travelling time. What is the total travelling time?

d) After 2 h, how far is the car from Calgary? How far is it from Edmonton?

e) Explain why the equation is correct.

9. The thermometer of an old oven is calibrated in Fahrenheit degrees. This formula converts Fahrenheit temperatures to Celsius temperatures.

$$C = \frac{5}{9}(F - 32)$$

a) Make a table of values, then draw a graph of Celsius temperatures against Fahrenheit temperatures.

b) Use your graph to determine the Fahrenheit temperature for each Celsius temperature.

  i) 90°C   **ii)** 120°C   **iii)** 200°C

c) Use your graph to determine the Celsius temperature for each Fahrenheit temperature.

i) 90°F   **ii)** 120°F   **iii)** 200°F

d) Extend the graph to determine the Celsius temperature for each Fahrenheit temperature.

i) 20°F   **ii)** 0°F   **iii)** −10°F   **iv)** −20°F

e) There is only one temperature that is the same in both scales. What temperature is it?

10. Estimation An approximate rule for converting Fahrenheit temperatures to Celsius temperatures is: "Subtract 30, then divide by 2."

a) Use this rule to make a table of values.

b) Draw a graph of estimated Celsius temperatures against Fahrenheit temperatures.

c) Write the equation of the relation.

11. Academic Focus Describe a situation that could be modelled by each linear equation.

a) $p = 6.75h$ **b)** $p = 25 + 6.75h$ **c)** $C = 50n + 30$

d) $C = 45n + 400$ **e)** $d = 500 - 100t$ **f)** $d = 100t$

12. Academic Focus Describe a situation that could be modelled by each linear equation. For each equation, state what x and y represent. Use situations that are different from the ones you used in exercise 11.

a) $y = 3x$ **b)** $y = 20x + 40$ **c)** $y = 65x + 500$

13. a) Graph the relations in exercises 9 and 10 on the same grid.

b) For what range of temperatures do you think the approximate rule would be useful? Explain.

c) Oven temperatures for cooking and baking are generally in the range from 350°F to 450°F. How would you revise the approximate rule in exercise 10 so that it would be useful for these temperatures?

14. Find an example of an equation whose graph is not a straight line. Make a table of values for your equation, then draw the graph to show that it is not a straight line.

COMMUNICATING *the* IDEAS

In your journal, write to explain what it means to say that a line is the graph of an equation. Use an example to illustrate your explanation.

In Section 3.5, you graphed relations from their equations. In that section, all the graphs were straight lines, and all the relations were linear. However, not all equations have graphs that are straight lines. When the graph is not a straight line, the relation is *non-linear*.

INVESTIGATION

The Relation $y = x^2 - 3x$

If you do not have a graphing calculator, complete Part A and Part C.
If you have a graphing calculator, complete Part B and Part C.

Part A

1. Copy this table. Use the equation $y = x^2 - 3x$ to complete the *y*-column.

2. a) Complete the *Difference* column by determining how much more each *y*-coordinate is than the preceding coordinate.

x	y	Difference
−2	10	
−1	4	−6 (4 is 6 less than 10.)
0		
1		
2		
3		
4		

b) What do you notice about the numbers in the *Difference* column?

c) Explain how these differences compare with the differences in *Investigation 2*, page 144.

Go to Part C.

Part B

Setup

• Press $\boxed{Y=}$. Use $\boxed{\text{CLEAR}}$ and the scroll buttons to clear all equations.

• If any of Plot 1, Plot 2, or Plot 3 at the top of the screen are highlighted, use the scroll buttons and $\boxed{\text{ENTER}}$ to remove the highlighting.

- Make sure the cursor is beside [Y=]. Press [X,T,θ,n] [x²] [–] 3 [X,T,θ,n].
  You have entered the equation $y = x^2 - 3x$.
- Press [2nd] [WINDOW] for TBLSET. Set up the table to start at 0 with differences of 1.
- Press [WINDOW], and change the settings so that Xmin = –4.7, Xmax = 4.7, Xscl = 1,
  Ymin = –3.1, Ymax = 3.1, Yscl = 1.

3. Press [2nd] [GRAPH] for TABLE. Use the scroll buttons to scroll up until
   the table shows values of x starting at –2. Compare the values on the
   screen with the table you completed in exercise 1.

4. a) Press [GRAPH]. The graph of a curve appears.

   b) Press [TRACE]. Use the scroll buttons to move left and right on the
   curve. Move the cursor until the value of x is the same as one value
   in the table in exercise 1. Compare the value of y with that in the
   table. Repeat for different values of x.

Part C

5. a) On grid paper, plot the points from your table of values.
   Draw a smooth curve through the points. To make it
   easier to draw the curve, you could determine more
   points using x-coordinates such as 0.5, 1.5, 2.5. Your
   graph should look like this.

   b) On your graph, label points A(–2, 10) and B(–1, 4).
   Determine the slope of AB.

   c) On your graph, label point O(0, 0). Determine the slope
   of OB.

   d) Continue this process for each point in your table of
   values. Compare these slopes to the numbers in the
   Difference column of your table of values. Explain.

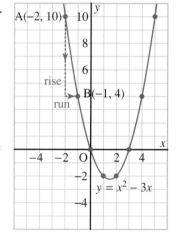

To graph a relation from a table of values,
we plot the points, then draw a line
or curve through the points.

Example

The effectiveness of a sunscreen is indicated by a number called the sunscreen protection factor. When you know the protection factor, s, of a sunscreen, you can determine the percent, p, of the sun's ultraviolet rays that pass through it using this formula: $p = \frac{100}{s}$

a) Some typical sunscreens have protection factors of 2, 8, 15, 25, and 45. Determine the percent of the sun's ultraviolet rays that pass through each sunscreen.

b) Draw a graph to show how the percent of the sun's ultraviolet rays that pass through a sunscreen depends on the protection factor.

Solution

a) Substitute 2, 8, 15, 25, and 45 for s in the formula $p = \frac{100}{s}$ to obtain this table of values.

Sunscreen protection factor, s	Percent of ultraviolet rays passing through, p
2	50.0
8	12.5
15	6.7
25	4.0
45	2.2

b)

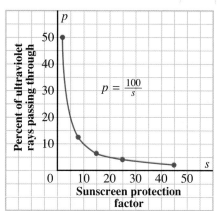

DISCUSSING the IDEAS

1. Suppose the graph of a relation is a straight line.

   a) How many points do you need to graph the line on grid paper?

   b) Why might it be a good idea to plot more points when you graph a line?

2. Explain how you can tell whether a given relation is linear or non-linear.

3. In the graph on page 151, would it be correct to join the plotted points with line segments? Explain.

4. Suppose the graph of a relation is not a straight line. How can you tell how many points you need to graph the relation on grid paper?

B **1.** Copy each table. Calculate the differences. Decide if the graph of the relation is a straight line. If possible, state the equation that relates y and x.

a)

x	y	Difference
−2	5	
−1	2	
0	−1	
1	−4	
2	−7	
3	−10	
4	−13	

b)

x	y	Difference
−2	5	
−1	9	
0	12	
1	14	
2	15	
3	15	
4	14	

c)

x	y	Difference
−2	5	
−1	5	
0	5	
1	5	
2	5	
3	5	
4	5	

2. The rules defining several relations are given below. For each relation:

  i) Make a table of values with a *Difference* column.

  ii) Decide if there are any numbers that cannot be used as input numbers.

  iii) Use the *Difference* column to predict if the graph will be linear.

  iv) Write an equation for the relation.

  v) Graph the relation using a graphing calculator or grid paper. If you use a graphing calculator, sketch each graph in your notebook.

  vi) Write the equation on each graph and state whether it is linear or non-linear.

  a) Add 3 to the input number to get the output number.

  b) To get the output number, divide 12 by the input number.

  c) Divide the input number by 2 to get the output number.

  d) Subtract 2 from the input number, then multiply by the input number to get the output number.

3. a) Graph each equation. Decide if each relation is linear or non-linear.

  i) $y = 5 - 2x$ **ii)** $y = \dfrac{3 + 2x}{5}$ **iii)** $y = x + 3$

  iv) $y = x^3 - 4x^2$ **v)** $y = \dfrac{3}{x}$ **vi)** $y = 0.5x + 3$

  vii) $y = x(x + 5)$ **viii)** $y = 2^x$ **ix)** $y = x^2$

  b) Suppose you are given an equation for a relation. How do you know if the relation is linear without graphing it?

4. Graph each relation on a separate grid.

  a) *Rule 1*: The output number is the opposite of the input number.

  b) *Rule 2*: $y = -1$

  c) *Rule 3*: $y = \dfrac{x(x - 1)}{2}$

5. a) Graph these relations on the same grid.

Rule 1: Square the number, then subtract 2 from the result.

Rule 2: Subtract 2 from the number, then square the result.

Rule 3: $y = x^2 + 2$

Rule 4: $y = (x + 2)^2$

b) Account for the similarities and the differences in the graphs.

6. These graphs were produced by a graphing calculator. The equations of the relations are shown below. Identify the equation that corresponds to each graph.

i)
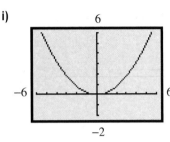

ii)
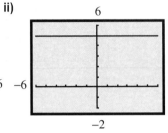

iii)
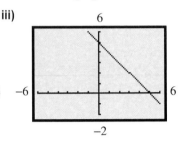

a) $y = 5 - x$ **b)** $y = \frac{x^2}{5}$ **c)** $y = 5$

7. Refer to the graph you drew in 2.2 Exercises, page 80, exercise 14. Calculate the slope of the line segment joining each adjacent pair of points. How do these slopes show that this relation is non-linear?

8. Suppose an object falls from rest. The distance the object falls, d metres, and the time it takes, t seconds, are related by the equation $d = 4.9t^2$.

a) Graph this relation. Use the graph to describe, in as much detail as possible, how an object falls from rest.

b) How long would it take an object to reach the ground when it is dropped from each height?

i) 20 m   ii) 30 m   iii) 40 m

9. Money invested in Guaranteed Investment Certificates (GICs) earns compound interest. The table shows the amounts to which a principal of $1250 grows after various years, at an interest rate of 3.75%.

a) Graph the data. Join the points. Write to explain how you joined them.

b) Estimate the amount after each time.

Number of years	Amount ($)
0	1250.00
1	1296.88
2	1345.51
3	1395.96
4	1448.31
5	1502.62

i) 1.5 years   ii) 2.5 years   iii) 3.5 years   iv) 4.5 years

c) Calculate the differences. Explain why this relation is non-linear.

10. Usually, light does not penetrate below 100 m into an ocean. The table shows the percent of surface light present at various depths.

Depth (m)	Percent of light present
0	100
20	63
40	40
60	25
80	16
100	10

a) Graph the data. Join the points.

b) Use the graph. Estimate the percent of surface light present at a depth of 15 m.

c) Estimate the depth at which 30% of the light is present.

d) Calculate the differences. Explain why this relation is non-linear.

C **11.** The Body Mass Index (BMI) describe a person's physical fitness. This is derived from the equation
$$BMI = \frac{mass\ (kg)}{(height\ (m))^2}$$
The desirable range for the BMI is between 20 and 25 for men and women.

a) Consider people whose mass is 70 kg. Substitute 70 for mass in the equation. This equation then relates the BMI for these people to their height.

b) Graph the relation in part a for some reasonable heights.

c) Describe how the BMI changes as height increases.

d) How would the graph be different for people with a mass less than 70 kg? How would it be different for people with a mass greater than 70 kg?

e) Make a sketch to show BMI relations corresponding to different masses.

12. Mathematical Modelling The Body Mass Index is only a crude measure of physical fitness. In exercise 11, you substituted for mass to relate the BMI to height. You could have substituted for height to relate the BMI to mass. Consider people who are 150 cm tall. In the equation, substitute 1.5 for the height to relate the BMI for these people to their mass. Graph this relation. Why is this different from the relations you graphed in exercise 11?

COMMUNICATING *the* **IDEAS**

In your journal, explain how you know whether a relation is linear or non-linear. Refer to its graph and the differences in its table of values.

1. Copy the staircase (below left) on grid paper. Draw the board that would lie on the staircase. Shade in blocks and part blocks so that each horizontal step is only one block. State the slope of the staircase.

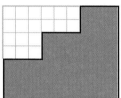
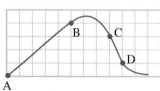

2. The diagram (above right) is a side view of a section of a roller coaster that moves from left to right.

   a) Determine the slope of the section from A to B, and from C to D.

   b) Describe how the roller coaster is moving for each section in part a.

3. On a grid, draw a line segment with each slope: -2, 0, 3, $\frac{-2}{3}$, 0.4.

4. The slope of a line segment is $-\frac{3}{5}$. What is a possible rise and run?

5. a) Plot the points A(3, –2), B(0, 5), C(3, 5), D(–1, –1).

   b) Determine the slope of each segment: AB, AC, BC, CD.

6. Copy each table. Calculate the differences. Decide if the relation is linear or non-linear.

a)

x	y	Difference
–2	–2	
–1	1	
0	4	
1	7	
2	10	
3	13	
4	16	

b)

x	y	Difference
–2	9	
–1	8	
0	6	
1	3	
2	–1	
3	–6	
4	–12	

c)

x	y	Difference
–2	9	
–1	7	
0	5	
1	3	
2	1	
3	–1	
4	–3	

7. **Investigation: The Temperature of Hot Chocolate** You will need a mug, a thermometer, a clock or watch with a second hand, an electric kettle, and hot chocolate powder.

   a) Make a mug of hot chocolate. How do you think its temperature will change in the next 20 min?

   b) Measure and record the temperature every minute for 20 min. Record your results in a table.

c) Draw a graph with *Time* along the horizontal axis and *Temperature* along the vertical axis. Did you join the points? Explain.

d) In your table in part b, add a *Difference* column. Complete this column.

e) Write to explain how the temperature changed as time increased.

f) Did the temperature change as much during the 10th minute as it did during the 1st minute? Explain.

g) Is the relation linear or non-linear? Explain.

h) Do you think you would get different results if you repeated the experiment with hot water? Explain.

8. Graph each relation on a separate grid.

a) *Rule 1*: The output number is the same as the input number.

b) *Rule 2*: The output number is always 3.

9. Graph each equation. State if the relation is linear or non-linear.

a) $y = x^2 - 3$ **b)** $y = -\frac{1}{3}x + 2$ **c)** $y = \frac{10 - x}{2}$ **d)** $y = \frac{12}{x}$

Mathematical MODELLING

The 10-m Model

For Donovan Bailey's world-record sprint in the 100 m at the 1996 Olympics, the time for each 10-m segment of the race was recorded. You can use this information to determine his fastest speed when covering 10 m.

Time (s)	0	1.9	3.1	4.1	4.9	5.6	6.5	7.2	8.1	9.0	9.84
Distance (m)	0	10	20	30	40	50	60	70	80	90	100

10. a) Draw a graph of the distance Bailey ran against the time.

b) Join adjacent points with line segments. Which line segment appears to have the greatest slope?

c) What was Bailey's fastest speed for a 10-m segment?

These are the corresponding times for Michael Johnson.

Time (s)	0	1.9	3.3	4.5	5.5	6.3	7.0	7.7	8.4	9.2	10.12
Distance (m)	0	10	20	30	40	50	60	70	80	90	100

Time (s)		11.1	12.1	13.1	14.0	14.8	15.6	16.4	17.3	18.2	19.32
Distance (m)		110	120	130	140	150	160	170	180	190	200

11. Repeat exercise 10 for Johnson.

BANQUET STYLE
ROUND TABLES

BANQUET STYLE
OBLONG TABLES

THEATRE STYLE
CHAIRS ONLY

Setting Up for a Banquet

People sometimes rent large rooms in hotels or community centres to hold a banquet, a reception, or some other function. The number of people who can attend is determined by the area of the room, and by the way the tables and chairs are arranged. On page 158, there are three possible seating arrangements for one room.

1. Which seating arrangement provides for:

   a) the most people?   **b)** the fewest people?

2. **Estimation** Choose any two seating arrangements. Estimate how many more people can be seated in one arrangement than the other. Write this difference as a fraction of the number in the arrangement that seats fewer people. Express this fraction as a percent.

3. How many people do you think could be accommodated in your classroom for each seating arrangement?

In Section 4.4, you will use mathematical models to estimate the number of people who can be seated in each arrangement. You will apply the models to your classroom, other rooms in your school, and some hotel rooms.

FYI Visit www.awl.com/canada/school/connections

For information related to the above problem, click on MATHLINKS followed by AWMath. Then select a topic under Setting Up for a Banquet.

This section reviews these concepts:
- Slope
- Linear relations
- Non-linear relations

1. The diagram shows a square formed using toothpicks. Each side of the square uses 3 toothpicks. Suppose many squares are constructed, using different numbers of toothpicks along each side.

a) Copy and complete this table.

b) Describe the patterns in the table.

c) Suppose n represents the number of toothpicks on one side. Write an equation to relate T, the total number of toothpicks, to n.

Number of toothpicks on one side	Total number of toothpicks in the square
1	
2	
3	12
100	

d) Graph the relation. Should you connect the points with line segments? Explain.

e) Determine the slope of the line segment joining any two points on your graph.

f) Repeat part e for a different pair of points. What do you notice?

2. The product of two numbers is 36. Suppose the numbers are represented by x and y.

a) Copy and complete this table.

b) Describe the patterns in the table.

c) Graph the relation. Explain how you did this.

d) Choose any two points on your graph. Determine the slope of the line segment joining them.

e) Repeat part d for a different pair of points. What do you notice?

x	y
1	
2	
3	
6	
9	
12	
18	
36	

3. A table of values for a relation is given.

a) Copy the table. Complete the *Difference* column.

b) How do we know that this relation is linear?

c) How can we use the table to determine the slope of the graph of this relation? Explain.

d) Write to describe the graph of this relation.

x	y	Difference
−1	−4	
0	−2	
1	0	
2	2	
3	4	

Patterns occur everywhere in mathematics. When we have a table of values for two quantities, we often use patterns to find out how the quantities are related. For example, this table shows some values of x and y. You can tell at a glance that each y-value is 1 more than the corresponding x-value. We express this relationship by writing $y = x + 1$.

x	y
1	2
2	3
3	4
4	5
5	6

INVESTIGATION 1

Matching Points with an Equation

You will use a TI-83 calculator to graph points. You will graph equations of lines and try to graph the line that passes through the points. Then you will know that its equation is the equation you entered.

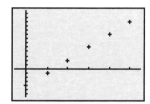

Setup

- Press [Y=]. Use [CLEAR] and the scroll buttons to clear all equations and plots.

- Press [2nd] [Y=] to select STAT PLOT. Then press **1** to select Plot 1. Use the scroll buttons and [ENTER] to make sure the settings for Plot 1 are as shown.

- Press [STAT] **1** to get the list editor. If there are any numbers in the first two columns, they must be cleared. Move the cursor into each column heading, then press [CLEAR] [ENTER].

- Move the cursor to the space below L1. Enter the numbers 0, 1, 2, 3, 4, 5 in list L1. Press 0 [ENTER] 1 [ENTER], and so on.

- Move the cursor to the space below L2. Enter the numbers –4, –1, 2, 5, 8, 11 in list L2. Press [(-)] 4 [ENTER] [(-)] 1 [ENTER], and so on.

You have entered these ordered pairs: (0, –4), (1, –1), (2, 2), (3, 5), (4, 8), and (5, 11) as a table of values in the calculator.

- Press [ZOOM] **9**. The graph at the top of this page appears. When you press these buttons, the calculator automatically resets the window to contain all the plotted points.

1. Press [Y=], and make sure the cursor is beside
   [Y₁=]. Press 2 [X,T,θ,n] [−] 1 [GRAPH]. You have entered
   the equation $y = 2x - 1$. The screen shows that
   this is not correct because the line does not pass
   through all the points.

   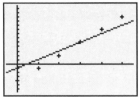

   a) Press [Y=]. Adjust the equation, then press [GRAPH]
      until you have the line that passes through all the points.

   b) Write the equation of this line. You will use it in exercise 4.

2. a) When you pressed [ZOOM] **9**, the calculator changed the window
      settings. To find out what they are, press [WINDOW]. Record Xmin, Xmax,
      Ymin, and Ymax.

   b) To see your graph again, press [GRAPH]. Sketch the graph on plain
      paper (show the axes, the plotted points, and the line). Use the
      window settings you recorded in part a to label the endpoints of the
      axes on your graph. Write the equation of the line on your graph.

   c) Choose two points on the graph. Mark their coordinates on your
      sketch. Verify that their coordinates satisfy the equation.

3. Repeat exercises 1 and 2 for each set of ordered pairs.

   a) $(0, -5)$, $(1, -3)$, $(2, -1)$, $(3, 1)$, $(4, 3)$, $(5, 5)$

   b) $(0, 9)$, $(1, 7)$, $(2, 5)$, $(3, 3)$, $(4, 1)$, $(5, -1)$

   c) $(0, 20)$, $(1, 15)$, $(2, 10)$, $(3, 5)$, $(4, 0)$, $(5, -5)$

4. Look at your results in exercises
   1 to 3.

   a) Compare each equation
      with its ordered pairs.

   b) By looking at the ordered
      pairs, how can you
      determine the slope
      of the line?

The Human Calculator

No calculators are allowed.

1. Work with a partner. One of you will be the "Calculator" and the other the "Player."

2. Calculator: Think of a simple, single operation you can perform mentally, then write it on a slip of paper without letting the Player see it. For example, add 5, or multiply by 3, or square the number, and so on. Avoid choosing difficult operations.

3. Player: You must guess the operation the Calculator is performing by asking only two questions as often as you like. But each time you ask, you lose points.
   - If the input number is ☐, what is the output number? (You may only use numbers between –10 and 10.)
   - Is the operation " ☐ "?
   Write down everything you ask and the answers the Calculator gives. At the end of the game, you should check these answers.

4. Calculator: Keep score as follows. The Player starts with 100 points. Each time the Player asks you a question, subtract 10 points. Each time the Player guesses the operation incorrectly, deduct 20 points. When you make a mistake, the Player gets 100 points.

5. Change the roles, and repeat steps 1 to 4.

6. For the second round, the Calculator chooses two operations in a row (for example, add 3, then multiply by 2), and the Player starts with 200 points.

Example

For each table of values, determine a rule relating x and y.

a)

x	y
0	0
1	5
2	10
3	15
4	20
5	25

b)

x	y
0	2
1	3
2	4
3	5
4	6
5	7

c)

x	y
0	5
1	4
2	3
3	2
4	1
5	0

Solution

a) More than one rule can be seen in the table.

Rule 1
Each y-value is 5 times the corresponding x-value. For example, $20 = 5(4)$
One rule is $y = 5x$.

Rule 2
The differences in the x-column are 1. The differences in the y-column are 5.
Another rule is: Start with $y = 0$ when $x = 0$.
When x increases by 1, y increases by 5.

b) More than one rule can be seen in the table.

Rule 1
Each y-value is 2 more than the corresponding x-value. For example, $6 = 4 + 2$
One rule is $y = x + 2$.

Rule 2
The differences in the x-column are 1. The differences in the y-column are 1.
Another rule is: Start with $y = 2$ when $x = 0$.
When x increases by 1, y increases by 1.

c) More than one rule can be seen in the table.

Rule 1
Corresponding pairs of x-values and y-values add to 5. For example, $4 + 1 = 5$
One rule is $x + y = 5$.

Rule 2
The differences in the x-column are 1. The differences in the y-column are -1.
Another rule is: Start with $y = 5$ when $x = 0$.
When x increases by 1, y decreases by 1.

1. In the solutions to the *Example*, two rules were given for each table.

   a) Consider Rule 1 in each part. What do these rules have in common?

   b) Consider Rule 2 in each part. How are these rules different from Rule 1?

2. Choose one table in the *Example*. Suppose you needed *y*-values for other values of *x*.

   a) Would one rule be easier to use than the other? Explain.

   b) Would your answer to part a depend on the values of *x*? Explain.

4.1 EXERCISES

A 1. Determine three different rules that give an output number of 4 when the input number is 2.

2. Determine a rule for each table of values.

a)

x	y
1	2
2	4
3	6
4	8
5	10
6	12

b)

x	y
0	1
1	3
2	5
3	7
4	9
5	11

c)

x	y
0	2
2	6
4	10
6	14
8	18
10	22

d)

x	y
0	8
1	7
2	6
3	5
4	4

e)

x	y
0	−2
1	−3
2	−4
3	−5
4	−6

f)

x	y
0	0
1	1
2	4
3	9
4	16

B 3. When two people were playing the Human Calculator game, they had a disagreement. The Calculator had reported the output numbers shown when the input numbers were 2 and 3:

Input number	Output number
2	4
3	9

The operation the Calculator had used was "multiply by 5, then subtract 6." However, the Player came up with a different rule that also worked.

a) Describe another rule that would produce the same output numbers for these two input numbers.

b) Describe at least two rules that produce the output numbers shown for the given input numbers.

i)

Input number	Output number
2	5
3	10

ii)

Input number	Output number
2	4
3	8

4. Determine a rule for each table of values.

a)

x	y
0	2
1	3
2	4
3	5
4	6

b)

x	y
0	−1
1	1
2	3
3	5
4	7

c)

x	y
0	−3
1	−1
2	1
3	3
4	5

d)

x	y
0	0
1	2
2	6
3	12
4	20

C 5. A relation is defined by this equation:
$$y = 2x + 0.1(x − 1)(x − 2)(x − 3)(x − 4)(x − 5)$$

a) Use the equation to determine the values of y for $x = 1, 2, 3, 4, 5,$ and 6. Show the results in a table.

b) How does your table compare with the table in exercise 2a?

c) Are the rules for the two tables the same? Explain.

COMMUNICATING the IDEAS

When we try to find the rule for a relation, we do not simply guess. In your journal, write tips to help a person make a reasonable suggestion for the equation of a relation. How would you know if your suggestion is correct?

Graphing Earnings

1. **a)** Sara earns $6 baby-sitting for 2 h. Suppose she is paid the same rate for any time she works. Copy and complete this table.

Hours worked	Earnings ($)	Difference ($)
0		
1		
2	6	
3		
4		
5		
6		

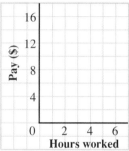

b) Graph the relation on a grid. Draw a line through the points.

c) What is the slope of the line? How does this compare with the differences in the table?

d) What happens to Sara's earnings when the number of hours increases by 1?

e) Draw the staircase for this graph. Explain how this illustrates your answer to part d.

f) What point on the graph shows what Sara earns when she works 0 h?

2. **a)** Copy and complete this table.

   b) How might this set-up of the table confuse someone?

   c) Use the first two rows of the table to determine the slope of the line.

   d) Compare the slope with the numbers in the *Difference* column. What do you notice?

Hours worked	Earnings ($)	Difference ($)
1		
4		
5		
7		

3. a) Copy and complete this table.

  b) Why are the differences constant?

  c) Why are the differences not the same as the slope?

  d) How are the differences related to the slope? Explain.

Hours worked	Earnings ($)	Difference ($)
1		
4		
7		
10		

4. Explain your answer to each question.

  a) Does every table of values for a linear relation have constant differences?

  b) When the differences are constant, what must be true about the table of values?

In Chapter 3, we determined the slope of a line segment using the coordinates of its endpoints. Suppose several line segments with the same slope are connected. For example, start at A(1, 3), then move 2 units up and 3 units right to point B. Then move 2 units up and 3 units right to C. Continue in this way to D and E. Observe that A, B, C, D, and E all lie on a line.

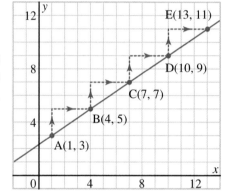

Choose any two segments of this line; for example, AB and BD, or AD and CE. Determine their slopes.

Slope of AB $= \frac{5-3}{4-1}$ Slope of BD $= \frac{9-5}{10-4}$

         $= \frac{2}{3}$ $= \frac{4}{6}$

                               $= \frac{2}{3}$

Slope of AD $= \frac{9-3}{10-1}$ Slope of CE $= \frac{11-7}{13-7}$

         $= \frac{6}{9}$ $= \frac{4}{6}$

         $= \frac{2}{3}$ $= \frac{2}{3}$

The fact that all these slopes are $\frac{2}{3}$ suggests that the slope of every segment of the line is $\frac{2}{3}$. Similar results apply for other lines.

The slopes of all segments of a line are equal. The slope of a line is the slope of any segment of the line. For example, the slope of the line shown above is $\frac{2}{3}$.

Example 1

When you exercise, it is recommended that you do not allow your pulse rate to exceed a given maximum. This maximum pulse rate (*m* beats per minute) is related to your age (*a* years) by this equation: $m = 220 - a$

a) Make a table of values for this equation, for people between the ages of 18 and 50.

b) Draw a graph of *m* against *a*.

c) Determine the slope of the line.

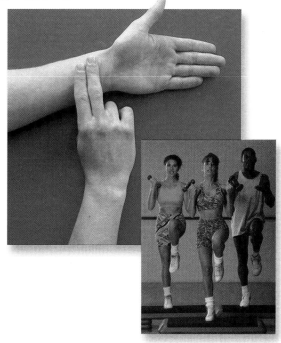

Solution

a) Choose some values of *a*. Substitute them into the equation $m = 220 - a$
Determine the corresponding values of *m*.
For example, when $a = 18$, $m = 220 - 18$
$= 202$

Age, *a* years	Maximum pulse rate, *m* beats per minute
18	202
25	195
40	180
50	170

b)

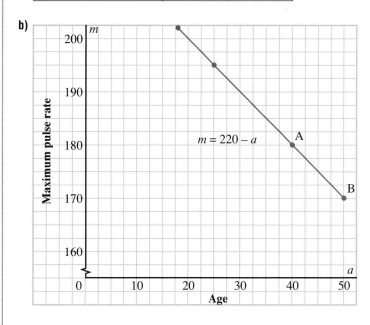

c) The graph in part b is a straight line.
Choose any two points on the line,
such as A(40, 180) and B(50, 170).

Slope of AB = $\frac{\text{rise}}{\text{run}}$

$= \frac{170 - 180}{50 - 40}$

$= -1$

The slope of the line is -1.

Example 2

On a grid, draw a line through K(4, −2) with slope $-\frac{1}{3}$.

Solution

Start at K(4, −2). Move 1 unit up and 3 units left
(or, 1 unit down and 3 units right). Repeat two or
three times to obtain several points on the line.
Then draw the line through these points.

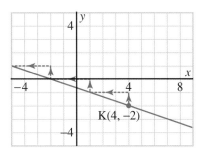

DISCUSSING
the IDEAS

1. **a)** On page 168, the slopes of four line segments were calculated. Choose any two of these segments. Explain how the rises and the runs of these segments are related.

   b) Repeat with a different pair of line segments.

2. What do you think would happen to a line if the slope was different on different sections of the line?

3. Refer to the graph in the solution of *Example 1*.

   a) What does the jagged line at the base of the vertical axis indicate?

   b) Suppose the graph were drawn without the jagged line. Explain how it would compare with this graph.

4. In *Example 1*, we found that the slope of the line is -1. What does this tell you about how the maximum pulse rate changes as a person's age increases?

A 1. State the slope of each line.

a)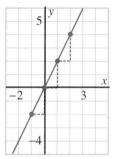

b)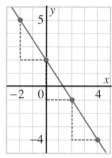

c)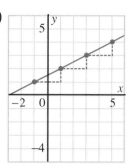

2. a) On the same axes, draw a line through E(0, 4) with each given slope. Then determine the coordinates of two more points on each line.

   i) 3   **ii)** 1   **iii)** $\frac{1}{2}$ **iv)** 0

   v) −2   **vi)** $-\frac{1}{4}$ **vii)** not defined by a real number

   b) Choose one slope from part a. Write to explain how you determined the coordinates of two points.

B 3. Suppose a parent decides that her children should receive a weekly allowance from age 6 to 16. The amount is 75¢ the first year and increases by 75¢ each year. Let *a* dollars represent the allowance of a child whose age is *n* years.

   a) Make a table of values and draw a graph of *a* against *n*.

   b) Explain why the points on the graph lie on a straight line.

   c) Does it make sense to join the points? Explain.

   d) Determine the slope of the line. What does the slope represent?

4. On a grid, draw a line with each given slope. Determine the coordinates of two points on the line.

   a) 3   **b)** $\frac{4}{3}$ **c)** −2   **d)** $-\frac{2}{5}$ **e)** $-\frac{3}{4}$

5. Choose one slope from exercise 4. Compare the coordinates of the two points you determined with those of a classmate. Do your points lie on your classmate's line? Do your classmate's points lie on your line? If your answer to either of these questions is no, explain why the points lie on different lines.

6. On a grid, draw a line through each point with each given slope. Then determine the coordinates of two more points on each line.

   a) A(0, 3) with slope 1   **b)** R(2, 1) with slope $\frac{2}{3}$

   c) L(1, −3) with slope $-\frac{1}{2}$ **d)** C(5, 4) with slope 0

7. After finishing a roll of film, you take it for processing.

Number of exposures	Cost
12	$9.18
24	$13.38
36	$17.58

a) Let *n* represent the number of exposures. Let *C* dollars represent the processing cost. Draw a graph of *C* against *n*.

b) Explain why the points on the graph lie on a straight line.

c) Does it make sense to join the points? Explain.

d) Determine the slope of the line. What does the slope represent?

e) Sometimes, it is possible to take an extra picture at the end of the roll of film. Use your graph to estimate the cost for: 13 exposures; 25 exposures; 37 exposures.

f) Sometimes, a few pictures on a roll may not turn out. The customer is usually not charged for such photographs. Make a table that sales staff in the store could use to show the costs for other numbers of exposures.

8. Turkeys should be cooked at an oven temperature of 165°C. The cooking time depends on the turkey's mass. For turkeys between 3 kg and 8 kg, the recommended cooking time is 30 min per kilogram.

a) Let *m* kilograms represent the mass of a turkey. Let *t* hours represent the time to cook it. Draw a graph of *t* against *m* for reasonable values of *m*.

b) What does the slope of the graph represent?

c) Larger turkeys require slightly less cooking time per kilogram. How would the graph change if you made this adjustment?

d) Turkeys that contain stuffing require an extra 10 min per kilogram. How would the graph change if the turkey were stuffed?

e) Many American cookbooks use pounds instead of kilograms. One pound is slightly less than half a kilogram. How would the graph change if *m* were measured in pounds instead of kilograms?

9. Transport Canada still uses feet as the units to describe the position of an aircraft. After take-off, a Beechcraft 19-passenger aircraft climbs 40 ft vertically for every 250 ft travelled horizontally until it reaches cruising altitude. The coordinates of the aircraft after 1 s are shown in the graph.

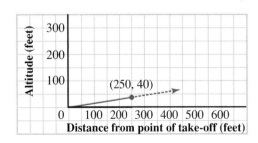

a) Copy the graph. Show the coordinates of the aircraft after 2 s, 3 s, 4 s, and 5 s.

b) What is the slope of the path of the aircraft?

c) How high is the aircraft when it has travelled a horizontal distance of 60 000 ft?

d) How long does it take to reach a cruising altitude of 20 000 ft?

10. On its approach to landing, a Beechcraft 19-passenger aircraft descends 32 ft vertically for every 500 ft of horizontal movement.

a) Draw a graph to show the aircraft's position for horizontal distances of up to 10 000 ft from the runway.

b) What is the slope of the path of the aircraft?

c) How high is the aircraft when its horizontal distance is 7500 ft from the runway?

d) Compare the slope of the graph in this exercise with the slope of the graph in exercise 9. Why do you think these slopes are so different?

11. Each pair of points lies on a line. Determine the coordinates of two more points that lie on each line.

a) E(2, 3) and F(1, 7)

b) G(−4, 7) and H(1, 0)

c) J(−6, −2) and K(5, 8)

d) L(−3, −7) and M(−4, −6)

12. Graph each set of three points. Determine the slopes of segments AB, BC, and AC. Compare their slopes. What do you notice?

a) A(0, 1), B(3, 3), C(9, 7)

b) A(−6, 1), B(−2, −1), C(4, −4)

c) A(8, 5), B(−4, 1), C(3, 4)

13. Points that lie on the same line are *collinear* points. In the diagram, three points, A, B, and C appear to be collinear.

a) Determine the slopes of AB, BC, and AC.

b) Determine whether the three points are collinear.

c) Find another way to determine if the points are collinear.

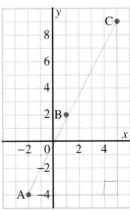

14. Are the points in each set collinear?

a) D(−4, 4), E(0, 2), F(6, −1)

b) J(5, 9), K(1, 4), L(−2, 1)

c) R(−3, −3), S(2, 1), T(11, 8)

15. Points M(1, −1), N(3, −5), and Q(d, 5) lie on the same line. What is the value of d?

16. a) A line has slope 4. It passes through the points A(3, 8) and B(2, *k*). What is the value of *k*?

b) Write to explain how you determined the value of *k*.

17. A line has slope −1. It passes through the points C(−*q*, 3) and D(4, −2). What is the value of *q*?

18. Refer to exercise 7. You can use a spreadsheet to determine the mean cost per exposure for different numbers of exposures.

a) Set up this spreadsheet. Copy the formulas in row 3 down to row 39.

	A	B	C
1	Number of exposures	Cost	Mean cost per exposure
2	0	$4.89	
3	=A2+1	=B2+0.35	=B3/A3

b) Explain the formula in each cell.
 i) A3 **ii)** B3 **iii)** C3

c) What happens to the mean cost per exposure as the number of exposures increases? Explain your answer.

d) Use the spreadsheet to draw a graph to show how the mean cost per exposure relates to the number of exposures.

e) Explain why the relation is not linear.

19. a) On April 14, 1981, the first American space shuttle, *Columbia*, returned to Earth. At one point in its reentry, it was travelling at approximately 1080 km/h and dropping at 4200 m/min. What was the slope of the reentry path to 2 decimal places?

b) Mathematical Modelling When you determined the slope of the reentry path in part a, you assumed that the space shuttle followed a path that is a straight line.
 i) Give a reason why the reentry path may not be a straight line.
 ii) As the space shuttle approaches the ground, how would you expect the slope of the reentry path to change?

COMMUNICATING *the*IDEAS

In your journal, explain the meaning of the slope of a line and how it is related to linear relations.

The Equation $y = mx + b$

1. The graphs below were drawn using the same equations but different window settings.

a) Which screen shows a more accurate graph?

b) What are the advantages and disadvantages of using these two window settings?

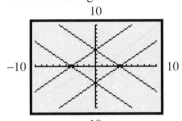 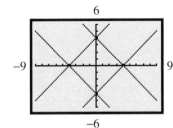

2. a) On the same screen, graph each equation in the lists below left.

b) Describe the pattern in the graphs. Explain how the numbers in the equations account for the pattern.

c) Visualize how the graph of $y = mx + 1$ changes as m varies. What special case occurs when $m = 0$?

$y = 2x + 1$	$y = -0.5x + 1$	$y = 0.5x + 5$	$y = 0.5x - 1$
$y = x + 1$	$y = -x + 1$	$y = 0.5x + 3$	$y = 0.5x - 3$
$y = 0.5x + 1$	$y = -2x + 1$	$y = 0.5x + 1$	$y = 0.5x - 5$

3. a) On the same screen, graph each equation in the lists above right.

b) Repeat exercise 2b.

c) Visualize how the graph of $y = 0.5x + b$ changes as b varies. What special case occurs when $b = 0$?

4. Based on your investigations, describe how the values of m and b affect the graph of the equation $y = mx + b$.

5. Predict what the graph of each equation would look like. Sketch each graph on paper, then use your calculator to check your answer.

a) $y = 2x + 3$ **b)** $y = -2x + 3$ **c)** $y = -x - 4$

6. What equations were used to make the graphs on the screens above?

Using Grid Paper to Investigate $y = mx + b$

One way to graph the equation of a straight line is to make a table of values. Another way to graph an equation depends on obtaining information about the graph from the numbers in the equation.

Equations of the Form $y = mx$

1. a) Use a table of values to graph each equation on the same axes.

$y = x$ $\qquad$ $y = 2x$ $\qquad$ $y = \frac{1}{2}x$ $\qquad$ $y = 0x$

$y = -x$ $\qquad$ $y = -2x$ $\qquad$ $y = -\frac{1}{2}x$

b) Compare the graphs in part a. How are they the same? How are they different?

2. a) Determine the slope of each line in exercise 1.

b) Compare each slope with the corresponding equation. What do you notice?

3. Each equation you graphed in exercise 1 has the form $y = mx$.

> What does this number tell you about the graph?

Equations of the Form $y = mx + b$

4. a) Use a table of values to graph each set of equations on the same axes.

i) $y = 2x + 5$ $\qquad$ $y = -\frac{1}{2}x + 5$ $\qquad$ **ii)** $y = 2x + 5$ $\qquad$ $y = 2x - 1$

$\quad\;\; y = x + 5$ $\qquad\;\;\; y = -x + 5$ $\qquad\qquad\;\; y = 2x + 3$ $\qquad\;\; y = 2x - 3$

$\quad\;\; y = \frac{1}{2}x + 5$ $\qquad\; y = -2x + 5$ $\qquad\qquad\;\; y = 2x + 1$ $\qquad\;\; y = 2x - 5$

$\quad\;\; y = 0x + 5$

b) Compare the graphs in part a. How are they the same? How are they different?

5. a) Determine the slope of each line in exercise 4.

b) Compare each slope with the corresponding equation. What do you notice?

6. Each equation you graphed in exercise 4 has the form $y = mx + b$.

> What does this number tell you about the graph?

> What does this number tell you about the graph?

Consider the equation $y = 2x + 3$ and the table of values below.
Plot the points on a grid. Join the points with a straight line.

x	y
−1	1
0	3
1	5
2	7
3	9

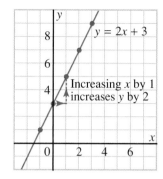

The table and graph suggest another method for graphing a linear
equation. This method is based on two numbers in the equation:

The slope

This is the value of m when the
equation has the form $y = mx + b$.
In the case of $y = 2x + 3$, the
slope is 2.

The y-intercept

It is the value of b when the
equation has the form $y = mx + b$.
It is also the y-coordinate of the
point where the line crosses the
y-axis. In the case of $y = 2x + 3$,
the y-intercept is 3.

$$y = 2x + 3$$

slope | y-intercept

> The graph of the equation $y = mx + b$ is a straight line
> with slope m and y-intercept b.

The equation $y = mx + b$ is called the *slope y-intercept form* of the
equation of a line. We can draw the graph of an equation in this
form without making a table of values.

Boggle your MIND

The train trip from Myrdal to Flåm in Norway takes 50 min. It passes through a
narrow mountain valley to a fjord 865 m below. The track is so steep that the
train is equipped with 5 different braking systems, each of which is capable of
stopping the train. In one section, the track descends from 669 m to 556 m in
1.94 km. What is the slope of this section?

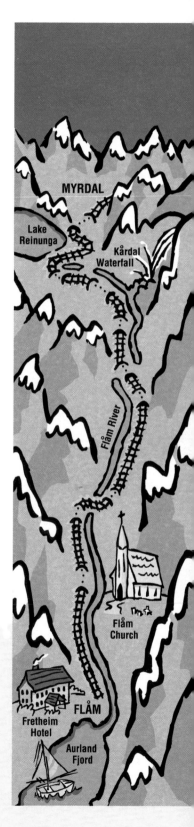

Example 1

Graph the line represented by each equation.

a) $y = \frac{2}{3}x - 5$ **b)** $y = -2x + 4$

Solution

a) $y = \frac{2}{3}x - 5$

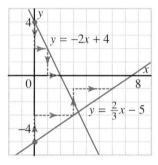

The slope is $\frac{2}{3}$.

The y-intercept is −5. The corresponding point has coordinates (0, −5).

Begin at (0, −5). Move 2 up and 3 right. This is a point on the line. Other points on the line can be obtained by continuing in this way, or by moving 2 down and 3 left.

b) $y = -2x + 4$

The slope is −2, or $\frac{-2}{1}$.

The y-intercept is 4. The corresponding point has coordinates (0, 4). Begin at (0, 4). Move 2 down and 1 right. This is a point on the line. Other points on the line can be obtained by continuing in this way, or by moving 2 up and 1 left.

We can also determine the equation of a line in the slope y-intercept form when its graph is given.

Example 2

Determine the equation of each line on this grid.

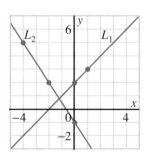

Solution

The slope and the y-intercept of each line can be read from its graph.

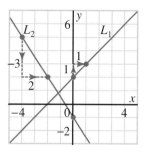

L_1 has a slope of 1 and a y-intercept of 2.

Its equation is $y = 1x + 2$, or $y = x + 2$.

L_2 has a slope of $-\frac{3}{2}$ and a y-intercept of -1.

Its equation is $y = -\frac{3}{2}x - 1$.

DISCUSSING the IDEAS

1. Describe the line you think each equation represents.

    a) $y = x$ **b)** $y = 5$ **c)** $x = -3$

2. Use an example to explain why the value of b in the equation $y = mx + b$ is the y-coordinate of the point where the line crosses the y-axis.

3. Does every line have an equation that can be written in the form $y = mx + b$? Explain.

4.3 EXERCISES

1. State the slope and the y-intercept for the line represented by each equation.

  a) $y = 3x + 5$ **b)** $y = -2x + 3$ **c)** $y = \frac{2}{5}x - 4$ **d)** $y = -\frac{1}{2}x + 6$

  e) $y = -4x - 7$ **f)** $y = \frac{3}{8}x - \frac{5}{2}$ **g)** $y = \frac{4}{3}x - 2$ **h)** $y = \frac{9}{5}x + 1$

2. Write the equation of each line with the given slope and y-intercept.

  a) $m = 2$, $b = 3$ **b)** $m = -1$, $b = 4$ **c)** $m = \frac{2}{3}$, $b = -1$

  d) $m = -\frac{4}{5}$, $b = 8$ **e)** $m = -3$, $b = \frac{5}{2}$ **f)** $m = 0$, $b = 3$

3. For each line, state the slope, the y-intercept, and the equation.

  a) 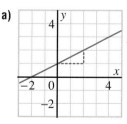   **b)** 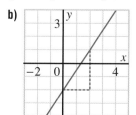   **c)**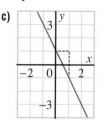

4. a) Determine the equation of each line.

i)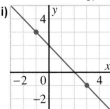

ii)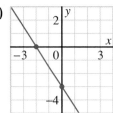

iii)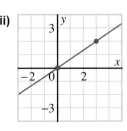

b) Choose one line from part a. Write to explain how you determined its equation.

B **5. a)** Graph the line represented by each equation.

i) $y = \frac{2}{5}x + 3$ **ii)** $y = \frac{3}{4}x - 2$ **iii)** $y = -\frac{1}{2}x + 1$ **iv)** $y = -\frac{3}{2}x - 1$

v) $y = 2x - 3$ **vi)** $y = -x + 5$ **vii)** $y = -3x + 2$ **viii)** $y = 0x - 4$

b) Choose one equation from part a. Write to explain how you graphed the line.

6. a) Graph the line represented by $y = -\frac{1}{2}x + 3$.

b) What are the coordinates of the point where the line in part a intersects the x-axis?

c) Shade in the triangle formed by the line and the x- and y-axes. Determine its area.

7. The equations $y = 2x + 4$ and $y = -x + 7$ are given.

a) Graph the line represented by each equation. Determine the coordinates of the point of intersection.

b) Shade in the triangle formed by the two lines and the x-axis. Determine the area of this triangle.

8. The equations of the three sides of a triangle are $y = 2x - 4$, $y = -\frac{1}{2}x + 6$, and $y = -3x + 1$. Graph these lines on the same axes. Determine the coordinates of the vertices of the triangle.

9. $P(x, y)$ is any point on the line in *Example 1a*. Visualize what happens as P begins to move along the line in the direction shown.

a) As P moves along the line, what happens to:
   i) the size and shape of $\triangle$PQR?
   ii) the rise from Q to P?
   iii) the run from Q to P?
   iv) the slope of QP?

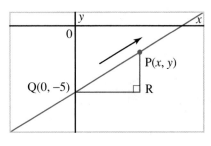

b) Do the answers to part a change if P moves in the opposite direction? Explain.

c) Write a formula for the slope of QP in terms of x and y.

10. **Investigation: Patterns in** $y = mx + b$

  a) Identify the patterns in the values of m and b in each list of equations.

  i) $y = 2x + 4$
  $y = x + 3$
  $y = 0x + 2$
  $y = -x + 1$
  $y = -2x + 0$

  ii) $y = 2x - 6$
  $y = x - 3$
  $y = 0.5x - 1.5$
  $y = -0.5x + 1.5$
  $y = -x + 3$
  $y = -2x + 6$

  iii) $y = x + 1$
  $y = 2x + 0.5$
  $y = 0.5x + 2$
  $y = -x - 1$
  $y = -2x - 0.5$
  $y = -0.5x - 2$

  b) Plot the graphs in each list on the same grid. Describe what you see.

  c) Explain how the patterns in the equations account for the patterns on the graphs.

11. a) The equation of a line is $y = 3x + b$. Determine the value of b when the line passes through each point.

  i) R(2, 1)   ii) K(-1, 4)   iii) A(3, -2)   iv) B(-2, 2)

  b) Choose one point from part a. Write to explain how you determined the value of b.

12. The equation of a line is $y = mx + 2$. Determine the value of m when the line passes through each point.

  a) D(12, 5)   b) S(1, -3)   c) E(-2, 6)   d) A(-5, 1)

13. a) Identify the pattern in the values of m and b in these equations.

  $y = x + 1$
  $y = 2x + 0.5$
  $y = 0.5x + 2$

  $y = -x - 1$
  $y = -2x - 0.5$
  $y = -0.5x - 2$

  b) Plot the graphs of all six equations on the same grid. Describe what you see.

  c) Explain how the patterns in the equations account for the patterns on the graphs.

C 14. Predict what the graphs of the equations in each list would look like. Use your calculator to check your prediction.

  a) $y = x + 3$
  $y = 10x + 3$
  $y = 100x + 3$
  $y = 1000x + 3$

  b) $y = x + 3$
  $y = 10x + 30$
  $y = 100x + 300$
  $y = 1000x + 3000$

Suppose your friend telephones you to discuss tonight's homework. How would you explain, over the telephone, how to graph an equation of the form $y = mx + b$? How would you explain what the graph represents? Use examples to illustrate your explanations.

4.4 Setting Up for a Banquet

On page 159, you considered the problem of setting up tables and chairs for a banquet, a reception, or some other function. One company uses approximate rules to estimate the number of chairs and tables needed. These are mathematical models for estimating the number of people. To use these models, the area of the room must be in square feet. (One square metre is approximately 10 square feet.) The models do not allow for problems caused by wide traffic aisles, locations of columns, service doors, or different room shapes. The models are useful for a quick general approximation.

Gathering Data

1. Estimate or measure the area, in square metres, of one or more of these rooms in your school.

   a) your classroom   **b)** the cafeteria

   c) the gymnasium   **d)** the auditorium

2. The dimensions of some rooms in the Royal York Hotel in Toronto are given to the nearest foot. Calculate the area of each room.

   a) Canadian Room   length: 187 ft   width: 71 ft

   b) Imperial Room   length: 96 ft   width: 63 ft

   c) Manitoba Room   length: 55 ft   width: 22 ft

3. Multiply the areas of the rooms in exercise 1 by 10.76 to convert the areas to square feet. Copy this table. Complete the *Area* column.

Room	Area (sq. ft)	Number of people		
		Theatre style	Oblong table	Round table
Classroom				
Cafeteria				
Gymnasium				
Auditorium				
Canadian Room				
Imperial Room				
Manitoba Room				

The Theatre Style Model

Approximate rule for theatre style:
For the number of people, divide the room area (in square feet) by 6.

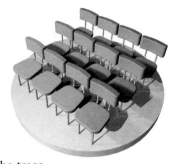

4. a) Let x represent the room area in square feet. Let y represent the number of people who can be seated. Use the approximate rule to write an equation for y in terms of x for this model.

b) Graph the equation. Use a graphing calculator if you have one.

5. a) Determine how many people can be seated in each room. (Use the trace button on a graphing calculator if you have one. When tracing, you can make the cursor jump to the location you want by entering the number and pressing ENTER.) Enter the results in the table.

b) Are the results for the room in your school reasonable? Explain.

The Oblong Table Model

Approximate rule for oblong tables:
For the number of people, divide the room area (in square feet) by 8.

6. a) Write an equation for y in terms of x for this model.

b) Graph the equation. (Use the second line in the Y= list.) Display the graphs for both models.

7. a) Determine how many people can be seated at oblong tables in each room (if possible). Enter the results in the table.

b) Are the results for the rooms in your school reasonable? Explain.

The Round Table Model

Approximate rule for round tables:
For the number of people, divide the room area (in square feet) by 10.

8. a) Write an equation for y in terms of x for this model.

b) Graph the equation. (Use the third line in the Y= list.) Display the graphs for all three models.

9. a) Determine how many people can be seated at round tables in each room (if possible). Enter the results in the table.

b) Are the results for the rooms in your school reasonable? Explain.

COMMUNICATING the IDEAS

In your journal, write to explain how approximate rules can be used to determine the number of people who can be seated at a banquet.

Many relationships in business, industry, science, and medicine can be represented by linear relations. The slope and the intercepts can represent different things. Variables other than x and y may be used.

Example 1

To hold a banquet, it costs $1000 to rent the hall, plus $25 for every person attending. Let C dollars represent the total cost and let n represent the number of people attending.

a) Write an equation for the relation between the total cost, C, and the number of people attending, n.

b) Graph the relation.

c) Determine the slope and C-intercept of the graph.

d) What do the rise, the run, and the slope represent?

e) What does the C-intercept represent?

Solution

a) C dollars represents the total cost and n represents the number of people attending. The equation is $C = 25n + 1000$.

b) *Using a TI-83 graphing calculator*

Choose the window settings. Assume a maximum of 100 people attend.
When $n = 100$, $C = 25(100) + 1000$
$= 3500$
Press WINDOW. Insert Xmin = 0,
Xmax = 100, Xscl = 10, Ymin = 0,
Ymax = 4000, Yscl = 1000.
Press Y= 25 X,T,θ,n + 1000.
Press GRAPH to display the graph below.

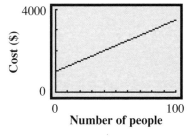

b) *Using grid paper*

Choose two values of n.
When $n = 0$, $C = 25(0) + 1000$
$= 1000$
When $n = 100$, $C = 25(100) + 1000$
$= 3500$
Draw axes on grid paper. Label the horizontal axis n and the vertical axis C. Plot the points (0, 1000) and (100, 3500). Join the points with a straight line. Label the graph with its equation.

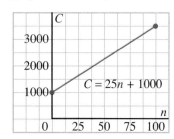

c) Use the equation $C = 25n + 1000$. The slope is 25 and the C-intercept is 1000.

d) The rise is the change in cost. The run is the change in the number of people attending the banquet. The slope represents how much the cost increases when one more person attends.

e) The C-intercept represents the cost when 0 people attend the banquet. This is the fixed cost, such as hall rental.

In *Example 1*, the cost increases by $25 every time another person attends. We say that the *rate of change* of the cost is $25 per person. Since this is also the slope of the line, we say that the rate of change of the cost is constant.

Example 2

A second banquet hall charges $40 per person for a reception. Let C dollars represent the total cost and n represent the number of people attending.

a) Write an equation to model this relation.

b) Graph the relation.

c) Determine the slope and the C-intercept.

d) What does the slope represent?

e) What does the slope indicate about the rate of change of C?

Solution

a) The total cost is $40 multiplied by the number of people attending.
The equation is $C = 40n$.

b) *Using a TI-83 graphing calculator*
Use the window settings for *Example 1*.
Press [Y=] [CLEAR] 40 [X,T,θ,n] [GRAPH].
The graph is shown.

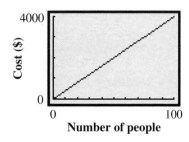

Using grid paper

Choose two values of n.

When $n = 0$, $C = 40(0)$
$$= 0$$
When $n = 100$, $C = 40(100)$
$$= 4000$$

Draw and label the axes as in *Example 1*. Plot the points $(0, 0)$ and $(100, 4000)$. Join the points with a straight line. Label the graph with its equation.

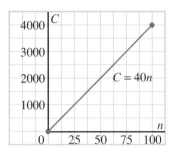

c) Since the equation is $C = 40n$, the slope is 40 and the C-intercept is 0.

d) The slope represents the cost per person, $40.

e) The rate of change of C is constant. It increases by $40 every time another person attends.

In *Example 2*, we say that C *varies directly* with n. The graph of a direct variation relationship is a straight line through the origin. The equation of the relation has the form $y = mx$ or, in this case, $C = 40n$.

In *Example 1*, we say that C *varies partially* with n. The graph of a partial variation relationship is a straight line that does not pass through the origin. The equation of the relation has the form $y = mx + b$ or, in this case, $C = 25n + 1000$.

Example 3

Sam sells computers and earns commission on her sales. Her commission, C dollars, varies directly with her sales, S dollars.
Sam earned a commission of $150 for sales of $3000.

a) Create a table of values for the relation.

b) Graph the relation.

c) Use the graph.
   i) Determine Sam's commission on sales of $8000.
   ii) Sam earns $200 commission. What are her sales?

Solution

a) C varies directly as S, so when $S = 0$, $C = 0$.
Include the given values of $S = 3000$
and $C = 150$ in the table.

S ($)	C ($)
0	0
3000	150

b) Extend the graph to include $S = 8000$
because that value is needed in part c.

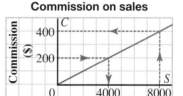

Commission on sales

c) i) When $S = 8000$, $C = 400$; Sam earns \$400
commission on sales of \$8000.
ii) When $C = 200$, $S = 4000$; Sam has sales of
\$4000 to earn a commission of \$200.

Commission on sales

DISCUSSING the IDEAS

1. Refer to *Example 1*. Explain how the graph would change in each case.

   a) The constant term, 1000, increases or decreases.

   b) The coefficient, 25, increases or decreases.

2. In the solution of *Example 1d*, would it be correct to say that the slope represents the cost per person? Explain.

3. Refer to *Example 2*. Explain how the graph would change if the cost per person increases or decreases.

4. Compare the costs of the two halls in *Example 1* and *Example 2*. If you were planning the banquet, which would you choose? Explain.

5. In *Example 2*, the slope represents the cost per person. Does the slope in *Example 1* represent the cost per person? Explain.

6. Explain why the slope represents the rate of change in the cost per person in both *Example 1* and *Example 2*.

B 1. Quenchables Soft Drinks Inc. has been increasing its production each day, as shown in the table. Its aim is to produce 10 000 cans daily. The number of cans produced, C, is related to d, the number of days of production.

Day, d	Number of cans produced, C
1	4000
2	4200
3	4400
4	4600
5	4800

a) Graph this relation. Should you join the points? Explain.

b) How many cans will be produced on day 10?

2. Some candies are placed in a box. The mass of the empty box is 20 g. The mass of each candy is 5 g. Let t grams represent the total mass of the box and the candies. Let n represent the number of candies.

a) Write an equation for the relation between the total mass, t, and the number of candies, n.

b) Graph the relation. Should the points be joined? Explain.

c) Determine the slope and t-intercept of the graph.

d) What does the t-intercept represent?

e) What does the slope represent? What are the units for slope?

f) What does the slope tell you about the rate of change of t?

3. In exercise 2, describe how the graph would change in each situation. Explain.

a) The mass of each candy is 7 g.   b) The mass of the box is 30 g.

4. A tanker truck on a weigh scale contains crude oil. The mass of an empty truck is 14 000 kg. The mass of one barrel of oil is 180 kg. Let T kilograms represent the total mass of the truck and the oil. Let b represent the number of barrels of oil.

a) Write an equation for the relation between the total mass and the number of barrels of oil.

b) Graph the relation. Should the points be joined? Explain.

c) Determine the slope and T-intercept of the graph.

d) What does the T-intercept represent?

e) What does the slope represent? What are the units for slope?

f) What does the slope tell you about the rate of change of T?

5. **Academic Focus** Describe a situation that could be modelled by each linear equation. For each equation, state what x and y represent.

a) $y = 5x$ b) $y = 5x + 100$ c) $y = 15x + 1200$

6. Volcanoes and geysers provide spectacular evidence that Earth's interior is hotter than its surface. Suppose the surface temperature is 20°C. For every kilometre below the surface, the temperature increases by 10°C. Let T°C represent the temperature at a depth of d kilometres.

   a) Write an equation for the relation between the temperature and the depth below the surface.

   b) Graph the relation. Should the points be joined? Explain.

   c) Determine the slope and T-intercept of the graph.

   d) What does the T-intercept represent?

   e) What does the slope represent? What are the units for slope?

   f) What does the slope tell you about the rate of change of T?

   g) **Mathematical Modelling** Do you think the relationship between depth and temperature is exact? Give some reasons to support your answer.

7. In exercise 6, how would the graph change in each situation? Explain.

   a) The surface temperature is 5°C.   b) The surface temperature is 40°C.

8. The boiling point of water, T°C, depends upon H, the height in kilometres above sea level. The boiling point at sea level is 100°C. For every kilometre above sea level, the boiling point decreases by about 3.4°C.

   a) Write an equation for the relation between the boiling point and the height above sea level.

   b) Graph the relation. Should the points be joined? Explain.

   c) Determine the slope and T-intercept of the graph.

   d) What does the T-intercept represent?

   e) What does the slope represent? What are the units for slope?

   f) What does the slope tell you about the rate of change of T?

   g) The highest mountain in the world is Mt. Everest at 8848 m. Use the trace feature of a graphing calculator to determine the temperature at which water boils at the top of Mt. Everest.

9. The amount of pancake batter mix required varies directly with the number of people who eat breakfast. It takes 4 cups of batter mix to serve 6 people.

   a) Create a table of values, then graph the relation.

   b) How many cups must be prepared for 30 people?

   c) How many people can be served with 12 cups of batter?

   d) Suppose a different batter mix is used. The new mix requires 5 cups of batter mix for 8 people. Visualize the graph for this relation. Describe how this graph is different from the graph in part a.

10. For the production of yearbooks, there is a fixed cost of $8000 to set up the press. There is also a variable cost of $4 to print and bind each book. The production company prints yearbooks in batches of 50.

Number of books, n	Total cost, C dollars
0	
50	

a) Copy and complete this table, for values of n up to 300.

b) Graph the relation.

c) Use the graph to determine the cost of 500 yearbooks.

d) Determine the slope and C-intercept. What do they represent?

e) Suppose the cost for each book was reduced to $3.00, and the set-up costs increased to $8400. Visualize the graph for this relation. Describe how this graph is different from the graph in part b.

11. In exercise 1, suppose the trend continues.

a) How many cans will be produced on day 20?

b) On which day will 10 000 cans be produced?

12. A local promoter is organizing a concert in the park, at a cost of $12 000. People attending the concert pay $25 for each ticket. Let t represent the number of tickets sold, and let P dollars represent the promoter's profit.

a) Write an equation for the relation between the promoter's profit, P, and the number of tickets sold, t. Graph the relation.

b) How many tickets must be sold for the promoter to break even? How is this shown on the graph?

13. The yearbook club wants to choose a company to print the school yearbooks. Blue Heron Yearbooks charges $8000 for set up and $4 per copy. Miles Ahead Yearbooks charges $8400 for set up and $3 per copy.

a) Graph the relations that represent these costs on the same grid.

b) Where do the lines intersect? What does this point represent?

c) Suppose 300 yearbooks are printed. Which company charges less? Suppose 800 yearbooks are printed. Which company charges less? Explain your answers.

COMMUNICATING the IDEAS

In your journal, explain why all examples of direct variation are linear relations, but not all linear relations are examples of direct variation. Use examples in your explanation.

What Did the Calculator Do?

You will enter numbers in a TI-83 calculator, and it will calculate other numbers. Your job is to determine what the calculator is doing.

The instructions below assume that a program called GUESRULE has been transferred to your calculator. If it has not, your teacher can obtain it from the Teacher's Resource Book. When you run the program, the calculator asks for an input number. It uses these two steps to calculate the output number:

• It multiplies the input number by an integer.

• Then it adds an integer to the result.

The game can be played at four levels of difficulty. Two examples from one game are shown below. When the input number was 3, the output number was 8, and when the input number was 7, the output number was 20. Can you tell how the calculator determined the output numbers? Explain.

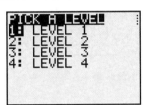
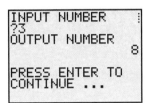
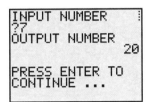

Each game starts with two screens similar to those above right. Then you have a choice:

1. Choose another input number.

2. Guess the rule.

3. See a graph of the ordered pairs.

4. See a table of the input and output numbers.

5. Start again with a different game.

6. End the game.

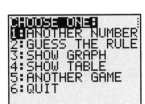

The following screens show the solution to the game above.

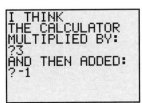
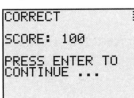

Scoring

Each time you play a new game, you start with 100 points. Each time you choose another number, the calculator deducts 10 points. For each incorrect guess, the calculator deducts 10 points. Your job is to try to get 100 points every time.

1. To play the game, press $\boxed{\text{PRGM}}$. Choose GUESRULE. Choose one level of difficulty.

2. Try to win 100 points every time at each level before moving to the next level.

3. Write to explain a strategy to get 100 points every time at each level.

   a) Levels 1 or 2   b) Level 3   c) Level 4

4. For a particular rule, an input of 3 produces an output of 9.

   a) What are two possible rules?

   b) An input of 7 produces an output of 21. What do you think the rule is?

   c) When the input is x, what is the output?

5. To calculate a student's mark as a percent, the teacher divides the mark by 80, then multiplies by 100.

   a) Determine a mark of 66 as a percent.

   b) Let m represent the mark and p the percent. Write an equation for p in terms of m. Graph the relation.

6. Scott's pay varies directly with the number of hours he works. When Scott works 20 h, he earns $130.00.

   a) Determine the amount Scott earns for each time worked.
      i) 30 h   ii) 10 h   iii) 17 h

   b) Write to explain how to determine Scott's pay when you know the number of hours Scott worked.

   c) Let h represent the number of hours Scott works and P dollars Scott's total pay. Write an equation for his pay in terms of the hours worked.

   d) Graph the relation.

7. A car begins a trip with an odometer reading of 237.5 km. The car travels 1.5 km every minute.

   a) Create a table to show the odometer reading, r kilometres, for each of the first 15 min of the trip. Include a *Difference* column.

b) Graph the relation.

c) What is the slope of the line?

d) What is the *r*-intercept of the line?

e) Write the equation of the line.

f) What does the slope of the line represent?

g) What will the odometer reading be after 1 h?

8. Match each line with its corresponding equation.

a) $y = -2$

b) $y = \frac{1}{2}x + 2$

c) $y = -x + 2$

d) $y = \frac{1}{2}x - 2$

e) $y = 2x + 2$

f) $y = -2x + 2$

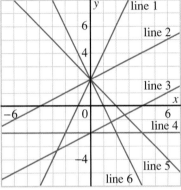

9. Mathematical Modelling Several rectangular tables are arranged in a room. Eight people can sit at each table: 3 on each side and 1 at each end.

a) Suppose the tables are arranged end-to-end. How many people could be seated for each number of tables?

i) **ii)** **iii)**

iv) **v)**

b) Let *t* represent the number of tables and let *p* represent the number of people who can be seated. Make a table of values for *t* and *p*.

c) Graph the relation. Should you join the points? Explain.

d) Determine the slope of the line. What does the slope represent?

e) What does the slope tell you about the rate of change of *p*?

f) Write the equation of the relation.

10. Mathematical Modelling Suppose the tables are arranged side-by-side, as shown. Repeat exercise 9 using this arrangement.

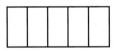

11. Mathematical Modelling Suppose the tables in exercise 9 were square. Each table seats 2 people on each side.

a) How would the graph in exercise 9c change? Explain.

b) How would the equation of the relation in exercise 9f change? Explain.

1. Use the order of operations to evaluate each exercise.

   a) $(-2) + \frac{(-10)}{2} + 2(5-8)$

   b) $(3)(-2) - (-10) \div 5$

   c) $3(5 + (-10)) \div 2$

   d) $\left(-\frac{100}{2}\right) + (-41)(2)$

2. Use a calculator. Complete each calculation using as few key strokes as possible. Record the keying sequences as well as the answers.

   a) $8.62 \times (37.11 - 51.21)$

   b) $\frac{(21.3 - 8.8) \times (65.3 - 39.7)}{3.6 \times (68.5 - 31.2)}$

   c) $\frac{181.001}{21.315 \times 2.321} - 2$

3. In Ontario, the provincial sales tax (PST) is 8% and the goods and services tax (GST) is 7%. The price of a sweatshirt is $42.00. Determine the GST and PST. What is the total price of the sweatshirt?

4. Evaluate.

   a) $\left(-\frac{9}{8}\right) + \left(-\frac{2}{3}\right)$

   b) $\left(-\frac{3}{5}\right) - \left(-\frac{8}{9}\right)$

   c) $\left(-\frac{3}{5}\right) \times \left(\frac{45}{2}\right)$

   d) $\left(-\frac{9}{13}\right) \div \left(-\frac{2}{39}\right)$

5. a) A car is travelling at a constant speed on a highway. It increases its speed to pass a second car, then returns to its original speed. Which graph best describes this motion? Explain.

   i) 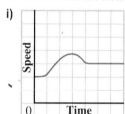 ii) 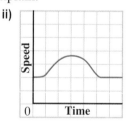 iii)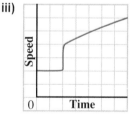

   b) Choose one graph from part a that does not describe the motion. Write to explain why it does not describe the motion. Describe a situation that could be represented by that graph.

6. For each graph, describe a practical situation it could represent.

   a) 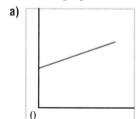 b) 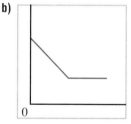 c)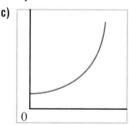

7. A laser printer can print 4 pages of text per minute.

   a) At this rate, how many pages could it print in 5 min?

   b) How long would it take to print a 50-page report?

8. Plot each pair of points. Determine the slope of the line segment joining each pair of them.

  a) A(2, 7), B(−5, −5)   **b)** C(−1, 6), D(8, −3)

9. a) Graph each relation on a separate grid.

  i) *Rule 1*: The output number is the opposite of the input number.
  ii) *Rule 2*: $y = -1$
  iii) *Rule 3*: $y = \dfrac{x(x-1)}{2}$

  b) Which functions from part a are linear? How do you know? Explain.

10. Determine a rule for each table of values.

a)

x	y
0	−4
2	−2
4	0
6	2
8	4

b)

x	y
2	5
3	8
4	11
5	14
6	17

c)

x	y
4	10
3	7
−5	−17
1	1
−3	−11

11. On a grid, draw a line through A(5, −2) with slope $\dfrac{2}{3}$.

12. A line has slope $\dfrac{1}{2}$. It passes through M(1, 9) and N(p, 3). What is the value of p?

13. Are the points in each set collinear? Write to explain how you know.

  a) A(1, 1), B(3, 0), C(7, −2)
  b) G(2, 7), H(4, 16), I(0, −2)

14. State the slope and y-intercept for the line represented by each equation.

  a) $y = -x + 1$ **b)** $y = \dfrac{2}{3}x - 8$

15. a) Graph the line represented by each equation.

  i) $y = 2x - 1$ **ii)** $y = -\dfrac{1}{2}x + 3$
  iii) $x = 4$ **iv)** $y = -3$

  b) Choose one equation from part a. Write to explain how you graphed the line.

16. The equation of a line is $y = mx + b$. The line passes through (1, 4) and (0, −6). Determine the values of m and b.

17. A supertanker travelling at 25 km/h needs 5 km to come to a complete stop. Suppose stopping distance varies directly as speed.

  a) Graph the relation.

  b) Determine the stopping distance for a supertanker travelling at 12 km/h.

  c) Determine the slope. What does it represent?

  d) Determine the speed a supertanker was travelling if the stopping distance was 3.5 km.

How Thick Is the Pile of Paper?

Visualize folding a piece of paper in half, forming 2 layers. Visualize folding it in half again, forming 4 layers. Suppose you were to continue folding in half as long as possible.

1. Try to do this with a sheet of paper. How many times can you fold the paper before it is impossible to make another fold?

2. After you have made the last fold, what prevents your making the next fold?

3. Would it make a difference if you started with a thinner sheet or a larger sheet? Try it to find out.

4. As you fold the paper, more and more layers of paper pile up. Suppose it were possible to fold the paper 50 times. About how high do you think the pile of paper would be? Record your estimate for use later.

You will return to this problem in Section 5.4.

FYI Visit www.awl.com/canada/school/connections

For information related to the above problem, click on MATHLINKS followed by AWMath. Then select a topic under How Thick Is the Pile of Paper?

This section reviews these concepts:

- Powers with positive exponents
- Powers of ten
- Scientific notation
- Ordered pairs on a coordinate grid

A computer monitor can display an image that looks like a photograph. An image combines different tones of red, green, and blue. The computer provides 256 different tones of red, 256 different tones of blue, and 256 different tones of green. So, the number of different colours a monitor can display is $256 \times 256 \times 256$, which we write as 256^3. We say, "256 to the exponent 3," or "256 cubed." The number 256^3 is a *power*. The number 256 is the base. The number 3 is the exponent.

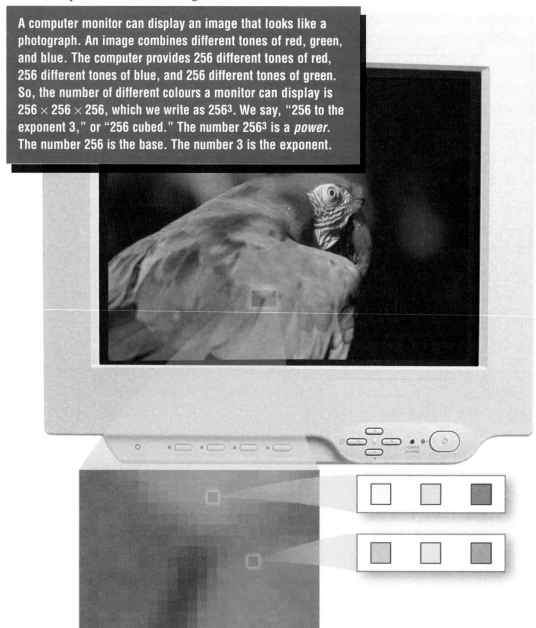

1. a) Use a calculator to multiply $256 \times 256 \times 256$.

   b) Find out how to use the calculator to evaluate 256^3 as a power. Check that the result matches your answer to part a. Record the key strokes you used.

2. a) What does 2^3 mean?

   b) What does 3^2 mean?

   c) Explain how these pictures illustrate 2^3 and 3^2.

3. Sketch and label a cube or square to represent each power.

   a) 5^2 b) 5^3 c) 10^2 d) 10^3

4. Explain what each power means. Evaluate each power.

   a) 5^4 b) 7^3 c) 3^2 d) 10^5

5. To display the colour red, a computer needs 8 bits of information. There are 2^8 ways the computer can store 8 bits of information. The computer also needs 8 bits of information to display blue, and 8 bits of information to display green.

   a) What does 2^8 mean? Check that $2^8 = 256$.

   b) What does the product $2^8 \times 2^8 \times 2^8$ mean?

   c) Explain how the product in part b relates to the information on page 198.

6. Write as a power of 10.

   a) 100   b) 1000   c) 10 000

   d) one million   e) one billion   f) one trillion

7. Each number is in scientific notation. Write each number in decimal form.

   a) 1.4×10^1 b) 1.4×10^2 c) 1.4×10^3

   d) 2.54×10^2 e) 3.26×10^3 f) 1.75×10^5

8. Write in scientific notation.

   a) 280   b) 2800   c) 28 000

   d) 6 hundred   e) 6 thousand   f) 60 thousand

9. a) Plot and join each set of points.

   i) A(2, 1), B(2, 5), C(6, 5), D(6, 1)   ii) P(3, 6), Q(1, 8), R(3, 10), S(5, 8)

   b) What figures are formed? Explain how you know.

A power represents repeated multiplication. In each *Investigation* you will examine patterns that occur when powers are multiplied or divided. You can use these patterns to multiply and divide powers efficiently.

INVESTIGATION 1

Multiplying Powers

1. Copy and complete this table.

	Product of powers	Product form	Power form
	$10^2 \times 10^3$	$(10 \times 10) \times (10 \times 10 \times 10)$	10^5
a)	$10^3 \times 10^4$		
b)	$10^2 \times 10^6$		
c)	$5^4 \times 5^5$		
d)	$5^3 \times 5^1$		
e)	$2^2 \times 2^9$		

2. Extend the table. Make up five more examples of your own. Include them in the table.

3. Look at the completed table.

   a) State a rule for multiplying two powers of 10. Explain why your rule works.

   b) State a rule for multiplying two powers of 5.

   c) State a rule for multiplying two powers of the same number.

4. Can you use your rule to multiply: $2^3 \times 3^5$? Explain.

In the *Investigation*, you discovered a pattern that will now be explained.

Multiplying Powers

Since x^3 means $x \times x \times x$ and x^4 means $x \times x \times x \times x \times x$, then
$$x^3 \times x^4 = (x \times x \times x) \times (x \times x \times x \times x \times x)$$
$$= x^7$$
The powers x^3 and x^4 have the same base.

We can obtain the product $x^3 \times x^4$ by adding the exponents: $x^3 \times x^4 = x^{3+4}$
$$= x^7$$

Dividing Powers

1. Copy and complete this table.

Quotient of powers	Product form	Power form
$10^5 \div 10^3$	$\dfrac{10 \times 10 \times 10 \times 10 \times 10}{10 \times 10 \times 10}$	10^2
a) $10^8 \div 10^5$		
b) $10^7 \div 10^3$		
c) $5^{10} \div 5^4$		
d) $5^5 \div 5^4$		
e) $9^8 \div 9^3$		

2. Extend the table. Make up five more examples of your own. Include them in the table.

3. Look at the completed table.

    a) State a rule for dividing two powers of 10. Explain why your rule works.

    b) State a rule for dividing two powers of 5.

    c) State a rule for dividing two powers of the same number.

4. Can you use your rule to divide: $5^7 \div 6^4$? Explain.

In the *Investigation*, you discovered a pattern that will now be explained.

Dividing Powers

Since x^5 means $x \times x \times x \times x \times x$ and x^3 means $x \times x \times x$, then
$$x^5 \div x^3 = \frac{x \times x \times x \times x \times x}{x \times x \times x}$$
$$= x^2$$
The powers x^5 and x^3 have the same base.

We can obtain the quotient $x^5 \div x^3$ by subtracting the exponents: $x^5 \div x^3 = x^{5-3}$
$$= x^2$$

1. We multiplied: $x^3 \times x^4$.

   a) Suppose the exponents 3 and 4 were different. Would the adding method still work? Explain.

   b) Suppose the base x was different. Would we get similar results? Explain.

2. We divided: $x^5 \div x^3$.

   a) Suppose the exponents 5 and 3 were different. Would the subtraction method still work? Explain.

   b) Suppose the base x was different. Would we get similar results? Explain.

We can generalize the *Investigation* results.

Exponent Law for Multiplying Powers

To multiply powers with the same base, keep the base and add the exponents.

$x^n \times x^m = x^{n+m}$, where n and m are natural numbers

Exponent Law for Dividing Powers

To divide powers with the same base, keep the base and subtract the exponents.

$x^n \div x^m = x^{n-m}$, where $x \neq 0$, n and m are natural numbers, and $n > m$

Example 1

Evaluate each power.

a) 1.2^5 **b)** $(-2.3)^3$ **c)** $\left(\frac{3}{5}\right)^4$ **d)** $\left(-\frac{7}{4}\right)^4$

Solution

The keystrokes are for a scientific calculator.

a) $1.2^5 = 1.2 \times 1.2 \times 1.2 \times 1.2 \times 1.2$ Key in: 1.2 $\boxed{y^x}$ 5 $\boxed{=}$
       $= 2.488\ 32$

b) $(-2.3)^3 = (-2.3) \times (-2.3) \times (-2.3)$ Key in: 2.3 $\boxed{+/-}$ $\boxed{y^x}$ 3 $\boxed{=}$
       $= -12.167$

c) $\left(\frac{3}{5}\right)^4 = \frac{3}{5} \times \frac{3}{5} \times \frac{3}{5} \times \frac{3}{5}$ Key in: (3 ÷ 5) y^x 4 =

     $= 0.1296$

d) $\left(-\frac{7}{4}\right)^4 = \left(-\frac{7}{4}\right) \times \left(-\frac{7}{4}\right) \times \left(-\frac{7}{4}\right) \times \left(-\frac{7}{4}\right)$ Key in: (7 ÷ 4 +/-) y^x =

     $= 9.378\ 906\ 25$

Example 2

Write each expression as a single power. Then evaluate the power.
Write each power to 3 decimal places.

a) $3.2^5 \times 3.2^4$ **b)** $(-4.8)^5 \div (-4.8)^2$

Solution

a) $3.2^5 \times 3.2^4 = 3.2^{5+4}$ **b)** $(-4.8)^5 \div (-4.8)^2 = (-4.8)^{5-2}$

          $= 3.2^9$ $= (-4.8)^3$

          $\doteq 35\ 184.372\ 09$ $= -110.592$

          $\doteq 35\ 184.372$

5.1   EXERCISES

1. Express each number as a power of 10.

   a) 1000   **b)** 10 000   **c)** 100 000 000

   d) 1 000 000   **e)** 100 000   **f)** 1 000 000 000 000

2. Express each number as a power of 2.

   a) 8   **b)** 32   **c)** 256   **d)** 16   **e)** 1024   **f)** 64

3. Write each fraction so the denominator is a power of 2.

   a) $\frac{1}{8}$ **b)** $\frac{1}{32}$ **c)** $\frac{1}{256}$ **d)** $\frac{1}{16}$ **e)** $\frac{1}{1024}$ **f)** $\frac{1}{64}$

4. Use a calculator. Write each fraction as a decimal.

   a) $\frac{1}{2^3}$ **b)** $\frac{1}{2^5}$ **c)** $\frac{1}{3^4}$ **d)** $\frac{1}{3^2}$ **e)** $\frac{1}{2^2}$ **f)** $\frac{1}{2}$

5. Evaluate each power.

   a) 3^6 **b)** $(-5)^9$ **c)** 2.1^5 **d)** $(-8)^3$

   e) $(-1.7)^4$ **f)** $\left(\frac{2}{5}\right)^4$ **g)** $\left(-\frac{3}{11}\right)^3$ **h)** 0.2^2

6. Write each product as a single power.

   a) $3^4 \times 3^6$

   b) $7^4 \times 7^7$

   c) $(-5)^{16} \times (-5)^9$

   d) $2.1^5 \times 2.1^5$

   e) $(-8)^5 \times (-8)$

   f) $(-1.7)^4 \times (-1.7)^3$

7. Write each quotient as a single power.

   a) $3^8 \div 3^3$

   b) $2^{16} \div 2^7$

   c) $(-8)^{20} \div (-8)^5$

   d) $\dfrac{1.5^{18}}{1.5^6}$

   e) $\dfrac{(-6)^8}{(-6)^2}$

   f) $\dfrac{(-2.3)^7}{(-2.3)^3}$

8. a) A rectangular wheat field is 10^5 m long and 10^3 m wide. What is its area?

   b) Another rectangular field is 10 000 m wide. Its area is 10^9 m². How long is the field?

9. a) The tallest tree in the world is about 10^2 m tall. The highest mountain is about 10^4 m. About how many times as high as the tree is the mountain?

   b) Earth's diameter is about 10^7 m. The diameter of the largest known star is 10^{12} m. About how many times as great as the diameter of Earth is the diameter of the largest star?

B **10.** Write each expression as a single power. Then evaluate each power.

   a) $3^3 \times 3^2$

   b) $9^4 \div 9^2$

   c) $(-8)^7 \div (-8)^4$

   d) $(-2)^4 \times (-2)^3$

   e) $5^4 \div 5$

   f) $2^2 \times 2^3 \times 2$

   g) $4^5 \div 4^3$

   h) $7^5 \div 7^3$

11. Choose one part of exercise 10. Write to explain how you completed the exercise.

12. Mental Math Explain how the subtraction method for dividing powers can help you evaluate an expression mentally. Create some examples to show this.

13. Write each expression as a power. Then evaluate each power. Write each product or quotient to 3 decimal places.

   a) $4.6^2 \times 4.6^4$

   b) $(-1.7)^5 \div (-1.7)^2$

   c) $8.3^7 \div 8.3^4$

   d) $(-3.7)^4 \times (-3.7)^3$

   e) $0.2^4 \div 0.2$

   f) $0.1 \times 0.1^2 \times 0.1^4$

14. Evaluate each expression.

   a) 30×2^4

   b) 100×2^3

   c) $12 \times \left(\dfrac{1}{2}\right)^6$

   d) $256 \times \left(\dfrac{1}{2}\right)^4$

15. a) List the powers of 2 up to 2^8. Evaluate each power.

   b) Use your answers from part a. Evaluate each expression without multiplying or dividing.

   i) 16×16

   ii) 32×4

   iii) $256 \div 8$

   iv) $128 \div 32$

16. In the Exponent Law for Dividing Powers:

   a) Why is $n > m$?

   b) Why is $x \neq 0$?

17. a) List the powers of -2 up to $(-2)^8$. Evaluate each power.

b) Describe when $(-2)^n$ will be positive.

c) Describe when $(-2)^n$ will be negative.

d) Explain why the results you described for parts b and c occur.

18. Evaluate each power.

a) $(-3)^2$ **b)** -3^2 **c)** $-(-3)^2$ **d)** 3^2

19. Write to explain the results of exercise 18.

20. Make up an exercise similar to exercise 18. Exchange exercises with a student. Complete the other student's exercise. Complete your own exercise. Compare answers.

21. Write each expression as a single power.

a) $\dfrac{10^5 \times 10^2}{10^3}$ **b)** $\dfrac{2^7 \times 2^3}{2^4}$ **c)** $\dfrac{3^{12}}{3 \times 3^6}$

d) $\dfrac{(-5)^9 \times (-5)}{(-5)^4}$ **e)** $\dfrac{6^7 \times 6^{11}}{6^8 \times 6^2}$ **f)** $\dfrac{(-1)^{10}}{(-1)^5 \times (-1)}$

22. Astronomers estimate that there are about 10^{11} galaxies in the universe. They also estimate that each galaxy contains about 10^{11} stars. About how many stars are in the universe?

PROBLEM SOLVING FOCUS

Good News Travels Fast

In the 1970s, there was a shampoo commercial that used the idea of doubling. In the commercial, a woman described how she was so pleased with her new shampoo that she told two friends about it. Each of these people told two friends, who told two friends, and so on.

What if it really happened? How many days would it take until more than one million people had used the shampoo?

23. Simplify the problem by making some assumptions. Suppose each step of the process takes one day. On day 1, the first woman used the shampoo. On day 2, she told two friends, who used the shampoo the same day. On day 3, each friend told two friends, who used the shampoo the same day, and so on. How many people are told about the shampoo on day 3? On day 4?

24. Start with the least number and look for a pattern. Organize your work in a table.

a) Copy and complete this table.

b) Describe a pattern in the second column.

c) Examine each number in the third column: it should be one less than a power of 2. Express each number in the third column in this form. How is the exponent in the power of 2 related to the day number?

d) What is the smallest power of 2 that is greater than 1 000 000?

e) On what day does the number in the third column exceed 1 000 000?

Day	Number who hear about the shampoo that day	Total number who have used the shampoo
1	1	1
2	2	1 + 2 = 3
3	$2^2 = 4$	3 + 4 = 7
4	$2^3 = 8$	7 + 8 = 15
5		
6		
7		
8		
9		
10		

25. Describe how exercise 24 solves the problem of how many days it takes for one million people to have used the shampoo.

26. Look back at the problem and its solution. It is probably not realistic to expect that the number of people using a product would double each day. What pattern would you expect? Write to explain your ideas.

G 27. a) Add any row, column, or diagonal. What is the magic sum for this magic square?

b) Change this magic square so that the products of the numbers in any row, column, and diagonal are the same. What is the magic product for your square?

COMMUNICATING the IDEAS

To multiply two powers with the same base you add the exponents. What are some other examples in mathematics where you complete one operation by performing a different operation? In your journal, list your ideas, with examples.

Suppose we apply the exponent law to $2^3 \div 2^3$.

We obtain $2^{3-3} = 2^0$.

Suppose we apply the exponent law to $2^2 \div 2^5$.

We obtain $2^{2-5} = 2^{-3}$.

Powers are defined using repeated multiplication: 2^3 means $2 \times 2 \times 2$.

Powers such as 2^0 and 2^{-3} have no meaning according to this definition.

We cannot multiply 0 twos together.

We cannot multiply -3 twos together.

To give meaning to powers such as 2^0 and 2^{-3}, we will look at some number patterns.

INVESTIGATION

Descending Powers

1. The table shows descending powers of 2. Copy the table. Evaluate each power down to 2^1. Write your answers in the *Number* column. Look at this column. What pattern do you see?

Power	Number
2^4	
2^3	
2^2	
2^1	
2^0	
2^{-1}	
2^{-2}	
2^{-3}	
2^{-4}	

2. Continue the pattern from exercise 1 to complete the *Number* column.

3. Did you use fractions or decimals to complete the *Number* column? If you used decimals, write each decimal as a fraction.

4. Write the denominator of each fraction as a power of 2. What do you notice?

5. Use your results from exercise 4.

  a) Write 2^{-5} as a fraction.   **b)** Write 2^{-6} as a fraction.

6. Copy each table. Use the method of exercises 1 to 4 to complete each table.

a)

Power	Number
3^4	
3^3	
3^2	
3^1	
3^0	
3^{-1}	
3^{-2}	
3^{-3}	
3^{-4}	

b)

Power	Number
10^4	
10^3	
10^2	
10^1	
10^0	
10^{-1}	
10^{-2}	
10^{-3}	
10^{-4}	

7. Use the results from exercise 6. Write each power as a fraction.

a) 3^{-5} **b)** 3^{-6} **c)** 10^{-5} **d)** 10^{-6}

8. Write each power as a fraction.

a) 2^{-a} **b)** 3^{-a} **c)** 10^{-a} **d)** n^{-a}

9. a) Write each power as a number: 2^0, 3^0, 10^0

b) Write n^0 as a number.

The patterning exercises in the *Investigation* suggest we can assign meaning to zero and negative exponents. We define zero and negative exponents, as follows.

Zero Exponent

x^0 is defined to be equal to 1; that is, $x^0 = 1$ ($x \neq 0$)

Negative Integer Exponent

x^{-n} is defined to be the reciprocal of x^n; that is, $x^{-n} = \frac{1}{x^n}$ ($x \neq 0$ and n is an integer)

Using these two definitions, we can evaluate a power with any integer exponent.

Example 1

Evaluate each power.

a) 5^{-2} **b)** $(-3)^{-1}$ **c)** $\dfrac{1}{5^{-2}}$

Solution

a) $5^{-2} = \dfrac{1}{5^2}$

$\quad\quad = \dfrac{1}{25}$

b) $(-3)^{-1} = \dfrac{1}{(-3)^1}$

$\quad\quad\quad\quad = \dfrac{1}{-3}$

$\quad\quad\quad\quad = -\dfrac{1}{3}$

c) $\dfrac{1}{5^{-2}} = 5^2$

$\quad\quad = 25$

Example 2

Use a calculator to evaluate each power. Explain each result.

a) 2^{-4} **b)** $(-3)^{-4}$ **c)** $-\dfrac{1}{2^{-4}}$

Solution

The keystrokes are for a scientific calculator.

a) For 2^{-4}, press: 2 $\boxed{y^x}$ 4 $\boxed{+/-}$ $\boxed{=}$ to display 0.0625

2^{-4} is the reciprocal of 2^4.

That is, $2^{-4} = \dfrac{1}{2^4}$

$\quad\quad\quad = \dfrac{1}{16}$

$\quad\quad\quad = 0.0625$

b) For $(-3)^{-4}$, press: 3 $\boxed{+/-}$ $\boxed{y^x}$ 4 $\boxed{+/-}$ $\boxed{=}$ to display 0.012345679

$(-3)^{-4}$ is the reciprocal of $(-3)^4$, which is 81.

That is, $(-3)^{-4} = \dfrac{1}{(-3)^4}$

$\quad\quad\quad\quad\quad = \dfrac{1}{81}$

$\quad\quad\quad\quad\quad = 0.012\ 345\ 679$

c) For $-\dfrac{1}{2^{-4}}$, press: 1 $\boxed{+/-}$ $\boxed{\div}$ 2 $\boxed{y^x}$ 4 $\boxed{+/-}$ $\boxed{=}$ to display -16

$-\dfrac{1}{2^{-4}}$ is the reciprocal of -2^{-4}.

That is, $-\dfrac{1}{2^{-4}} = -2^4$

$\quad\quad\quad\quad\quad = -16$

At the beginning of this section, we supposed the exponent laws were true and obtained powers of 2^0 and 2^{-3}.

However, we cannot assume the exponent laws apply to negative exponents and zero exponents. We shall use the definitions of a negative exponent and a zero exponent to show these laws can be applied.

Consider these two ways to evaluate $2^3 \div 2^3$.

By applying the law for dividing powers:

$$\frac{2^3}{2^3} = 2^{3-3}$$
$$= 2^0$$

By evaluating the powers first:

$$\frac{2^3}{2^3} = \frac{8}{8}$$
$$= 1$$

Comparing these results: $2^0 = 1$

Consider these two ways to evaluate $2^2 \div 2^5$.

By applying the law for dividing powers:

$$\frac{2^2}{2^5} = 2^{2-5}$$
$$= 2^{-3}$$

By evaluating the powers first:

$$\frac{2^3}{2^5} = \frac{8}{32}$$
$$= \frac{1}{8}$$
$$= \frac{1}{2^3}$$

Comparing these results: $2^{-3} = \frac{1}{2^3}$

Since both methods produce the same results, we can use the exponent laws with negative and zero exponents.

Example 3

Write each expression as a single power. Then evaluate the power.

a) $4^{-5} \times 4^3$　　　　b) $\dfrac{6^2}{6^{-1}}$　　　　c) $\dfrac{3^4 \times 3^{-1}}{3^{-2}}$

Solution

a) $4^{-5} \times 4^3 = 4^{-5+3}$
$$= 4^{-2}$$
$$= \frac{1}{4^2}$$
$$= \frac{1}{16}$$

b) $\dfrac{6^2}{6^{-1}} = 6^{2-(-1)}$
$$= 6^3$$
$$= 216$$

c) $\dfrac{3^4 \times 3^{-1}}{3^{-2}} = \dfrac{3^{4+(-1)}}{3^{-2}}$
$$= \frac{3^3}{3^{-2}}$$
$$= 3^{3-(-2)}$$
$$= 3^5$$
$$= 243$$

1. In *Example 2b*, explain the keystrokes used.

2. In *Example 3b*, explain the steps in the Solution.

3. Look at the powers in *Example 1a* and *c*. How are the powers related?

4. Look at the powers in *Example 2a* and *c*. How are the powers related?

5. Explain the meanings of each pair of powers. How are these powers similar? How are they different?

   a) 4^3 and 4^{-3} b) 4^3 and -4^{-3} c) $(-4)^3$ and -4^{-3}

5.2 EXERCISES

A 1. Write each power with a positive exponent. Then evaluate each power.

   a) 3^{-1} b) 2^{-2} c) 7^{-1} d) 5^{-1} e) 3^{-3} f) 6^{-2}

2. Evaluate each power.

   a) -3^{-1} b) -2^{-2} c) -7^{-1} d) -5^{-1} e) -3^{-3} f) -6^{-2}

   g) $(-3)^{-1}$ h) $(-2)^{-2}$ i) $(-7)^{-1}$ j) $(-5)^{-1}$ k) $(-3)^{-3}$ l) $(-6)^{-2}$

3. Look at the results of exercise 2. Write to explain any patterns you see.

4. Evaluate.

   a) 2^4 b) 2^{-4} c) -2^4 d) -2^{-4}

   e) $(-2)^4$ f) $(-2)^{-4}$ g) $-(-2)^4$ h) $-(-2)^{-4}$

5. Look at the results of exercise 4. Write to explain any patterns you see.

6. Write each power with a positive exponent. Then evaluate.

   a) $\frac{1}{2^{-1}}$ b) $\frac{1}{3^{-2}}$ c) $\frac{1}{5^{-2}}$ d) $\frac{1}{2^{-3}}$ e) $\frac{-1}{4^{-2}}$ f) $\frac{-1}{10^{-4}}$

7. Use a calculator to evaluate each power. Explain each result.

   a) 0.2^{-1} b) 0.25^{-2} c) 0.5^{-3} d) $(-2)^0$ e) 1.5^{-1} f) $(-1.2)^{-2}$

B 8. Write each expression as a single power. Then evaluate each power.

   a) $10^3 \times 10^{-2}$ b) $2^{-6} \times 2^2$ c) $(-7)^{-2} \times (-7)^5$

   d) $5^{-1} \times 5^{-2}$ e) $3^{-4} \times 3^5$ f) $3^2 \div 3^{-2}$

   g) $2^{-1} \div 2^3$ h) $(-3)^{-4} \div (-3)^{-2}$ i) $10^{-2} \div 10^2$

   j) $3^{-3} \times 3^2 \times 3^{-1}$ k) $\frac{2^5}{2^{-1}} \times \frac{2^{-3}}{2^2}$ l) $\frac{2^2}{2^{-4}} \times \frac{2^{-2}}{2^2}$

9. Evaluate each power. Write to explain any patterns you see.

a) 1^1 b) 1^{-1} c) $(-1)^1$ d) $(-1)^{-1}$

e) -1^1 f) -1^{-1} g) $-(-1)^1$ h) $-(-1)^{-1}$

10. Determine which power in each pair is greater. Explain your answer.

a) $2^{-3}, 3^{-2}$ b) $2^{-4}, 4^{-2}$ c) $2^{-5}, 5^{-2}$

11. Evaluate each power.

a) -3^3 b) 3^2 c) -3^1 d) 3^0

e) -3^{-1} f) 3^{-2} g) -3^{-3} h) 3^{-4}

12. Look at the results of exercise 11. Write to explain any patterns you see.

13. Evaluate each power.

a) $(-4)^3$ b) $-(-4)^2$ c) $(-4)^1$ d) $-(-4)^0$

e) $(-4)^{-1}$ f) $-(-4)^{-2}$ g) $(-4)^{-3}$ h) $-(-4)^{-4}$

14. Look at the results of exercise 13. Write to explain any patterns you see.

15. Write each power as a decimal.

a) 10^3 b) 10^2 c) 10^1 d) 10^0

e) 10^{-1} f) 10^{-2} g) 10^{-3} h) 10^{-4}

16. Use a calculator to evaluate each power to 6 decimal places.

a) 4^{-5} b) 5^{-4} c) $(-5)^{-6}$ d) $(-6)^{-3}$ e) 1.2^{-10}

17. Write each expression as a single power, then evaluate. Explain any patterns.

a) $2^3 \times 2^3$ b) $2^3 \times 2^2$ c) $2^3 \times 2^1$ d) $2^3 \times 2^0$

e) $2^3 \times 2^{-1}$ f) $2^3 \times 2^{-2}$ g) $2^3 \times 2^{-3}$ h) $2^3 \times 2^{-4}$

18. Write each expression as a single power, then evaluate. Explain any patterns.

a) $\dfrac{2^3}{2^3}$ b) $\dfrac{2^3}{2^2}$ c) $\dfrac{2^3}{2^1}$ d) $\dfrac{2^3}{2^0}$

e) $\dfrac{2^3}{2^{-1}}$ f) $\dfrac{2^3}{2^{-2}}$ g) $\dfrac{2^3}{2^{-3}}$ h) $\dfrac{2^3}{2^{-4}}$

19. Evaluate.

a) $4^0 \times 4^{-3}$ b) $11^3 \div 11^{-1}$ c) $9^0 \div 9^{-4}$

d) $6^{-5} \times 6^3$ e) $3^{-1} \div 3^{-4}$ f) $5^{-7} \times 5^{10}$

20. Use the laws of exponents to evaluate each expression.

a) $3^2 \times 3^{-1}$ b) $5^3 \times 5^{-2}$ c) $10^{-3} \times 10^{-2}$

d) $4^2 \times 4^{-2} \times 4^3$ e) $2^{-6} \times 2^{-2} \times 2^5$ f) $(-1)^1 \times (-1)^2 \times (-1)^3$

g) $\dfrac{7^{-1}}{7^3}$ h) $\dfrac{6^{-2}}{6^{-3}}$ i) $(-3)^0 \div (-3)^{-1}$

Growth of Bacteria

Scientists grow bacteria for medical research.
The bacteria "garden" is called a "culture."
By counting the bacteria in a culture at
regular time intervals, scientists can learn
how bacteria grow under controlled
conditions. The table shows a typical
bacteria count every hour starting with a
count of 1000 at noon. The number of
bacteria doubles every hour.

Time	Elapsed time (h)	Number of bacteria
noon	0	1000
1:00 P.M.	1	2000
2:00 P.M.	2	4000
3:00 P.M.	3	8000

21. How many bacteria are in the culture at each elapsed time?

    a) 4 h   b) 5 h   c) 6 h

22. Write a formula for the number of bacteria in the culture
    when the elapsed time is n hours. Explain your formula.

In exercise 22, you should have found that the number of
bacteria after n hours is 1000×2^n. You can use this formula
if n is negative. For example, if $n = -1$, the question would
be: "How many bacteria were there 1 h *before* noon?"

23. How many bacteria were in the culture at each time?

    a) 1 h before noon   b) 2 h before noon

    c) 3 h before noon

24. At 12:30 P.M., there were about 1400 bacteria in the culture. About how
    many bacteria would there be at each time?

    a) 1 h later   b) 2 h later   c) 3 h later

    d) 1 h earlier   e) 2 h earlier   f) 3 h earlier

25. a) Use information from the previous exercises and their answers. Draw a
       large graph to show the number of bacteria for $-3 \le n \le 3$, where n
       represents the number of hours relative to noon. Plot as many points as
       you can. Draw a smooth curve through the plotted points.

b) Use your graph to estimate the number of bacteria at each time.

i) 12:15 P.M. **ii)** 1:15 P.M. **iii)** 2:15 P.M.

iv) 11:45 A.M. **v)** 10:45 A.M. **vi)** 9:45 A.M.

26. **Mathematical Modelling** In exercises 21 to 25, you modelled how to determine the number of bacteria in a culture at different times.

   a) Give as many reasons as you can to explain why the actual numbers of bacteria present at these times could be different from the numbers predicted by the model.

   b) Do you think the growth could continue indefinitely? Explain.

27. Use guess and check. Determine each value of n.

   a) $n^{-2} = \frac{1}{9}$ **b)** $n^{-4} = \frac{1}{625}$ **c)** $n^{-5} = \frac{1}{32}$

   d) $3^n = \frac{1}{27}$ **e)** $4^n = \frac{1}{16}$ **f)** $7^n = \frac{1}{343}$

28. Evaluate.

   a) $\frac{8^5 \times 8^{-11}}{8^{-3}}$ **b)** $\frac{3^{-3}}{3^5 \times 3^{-2}}$ **c)** $\frac{4^{-3} \times 4^{-4}}{4^{-5}}$

29. Use guess and check. Determine each value of n.

   a) $n^{-2} = \frac{1}{25}$ **b)** $n^{-3} = \frac{1}{8}$ **c)** $n^{-4} = \frac{1}{81}$

   d) $2^n = \frac{1}{4}$ **e)** $2^n = \frac{1}{64}$ **f)** $5^n = \frac{1}{625}$

30. **Mental Math** Explain how the meaning of a zero exponent can help you evaluate an expression mentally. Make up some examples to show this.

C 31. There is only one integer n so that $n^n = \frac{1}{4}$. What is the integer?

32. There are only two different positive integers m and n so that $m^{-n} = n^{-m}$. What are these integers?

COMMUNICATING the IDEAS

Is a power with a negative exponent always negative? Is it always positive? Or, is it sometimes negative and sometimes positive? Make up some examples to investigate these questions. Write your answers in your journal and include your examples.

5.3 Powers of Powers

We can use the meanings of exponents to extend the exponent laws of Section 5.1.

An expression such as $(2^4)^3$ is a power of a power.

$(2^4)^3$ means $2^4 \times 2^4 \times 2^4$.

Hence, $(2^4)^3 = 2^4 \times 2^4 \times 2^4$

$$= 2^{4+4+4}$$

$$= 2^{12}$$

The exponent of 2^{12} is the product of the exponents in the expression $(2^4)^3$.

That is, $(2^4)^3 = 2^{4 \times 3}$

We would get similar results if we used other exponents or another number for the base. We can write an exponent law for a power of a power.

Exponent Law for a Power of a Power

$(x^m)^n = x^{mn}$, where m and n are integers

We can use the exponent laws to simplify expressions involving powers. Since powers involving negative exponents were defined to satisfy the exponent laws, we can use these laws for any integer exponents.

Example

Write as a power with a single exponent.

a) $(4^2)^5$ b) $(2^{-2})^3$ c) $(45^3)^{-2} \times (45^2)^{-1}$

Solution

a) $(4^2)^5 = 4^{2 \times 5}$

$$= 4^{10}$$

b) $(2^{-2})^3 = 2^{(-2) \times 3}$

$$= 2^{-6}$$

c) $(45^3)^{-2} \times (45^2)^{-1} = 45^{3 \times (-2)} \times 45^{2 \times (-1)}$

$$= 45^{-6} \times 45^{-2}$$

$$= 45^{-6+(-2)}$$

$$= 45^{-8}$$

DISCUSSING the IDEAS

1. In the solution to the *Example*, parts *b* and *c*, write each power with a positive exponent.

A 1. Write as a power with a single exponent.

   a) $(2^3)^{-2}$ **b)** $(3^{-2})^4$ **c)** $(4^{-3})^2$ **d)** $(5^2)^{-4}$ **e)** $(8^{-5})^0$ **f)** $(7^{-2})^{-1}$

B 2. Write each expression as a power with a single exponent.

   a) $(4^3)^2$ **b)** $(7^4)^2$ **c)** $(3^6)^2$ **d)** $(10^3)^4$ **e)** $(3^2)^6$ **f)** $[(-10)^2]^3$

   g) $(2^3)^{-2}$ **h)** $(5^2)^{-1}$ **i)** $(3^{-5})^{-2}$ **j)** $(4^0)^{-2}$ **k)** $[(-2)^2]^{-3}$ **l)** $[(-4)^3]^{-2}$

3. Use a calculator. Evaluate each expression in two different ways:

   • Complete the operations in brackets first.

   • Use the exponent laws, then evaluate.

   Compare the results to confirm they are equal.

   a) $(3^2)^4$ **b)** $[(-2)^6]^2$

ACADEMIC FOCUS

Powers of 2

Use only the table of powers of 2. Complete exercises 4 to 9.

$2^{25} = 33\ 554\ 432$	$2^8 = 256$	$2^{-9} = 0.001\ 953\ 125$
$2^{24} = 16\ 777\ 216$	$2^7 = 128$	$2^{-10} = 0.000\ 976\ 562\ 5$
$2^{23} = 8\ 388\ 608$	$2^6 = 64$	$2^{-11} = 0.000\ 488\ 281\ 25$
$2^{22} = 4\ 194\ 304$	$2^5 = 32$	$2^{-12} = 0.000\ 244\ 140\ 625$
$2^{21} = 2\ 097\ 152$	$2^4 = 16$	$2^{-13} = 0.000\ 122\ 070\ 312\ 5$
$2^{20} = 1\ 048\ 576$	$2^3 = 8$	$2^{-14} = 0.000\ 061\ 035\ 156\ 25$
$2^{19} = 524\ 288$	$2^2 = 4$	$2^{-15} = 0.000\ 030\ 517\ 578\ 125$
$2^{18} = 262\ 144$	$2^1 = 2$	$2^{-16} = 0.000\ 015\ 258\ 789\ 062\ 5$
$2^{17} = 131\ 072$	$2^0 = 1$	$2^{-17} = 0.000\ 007\ 629\ 394\ 531\ 25$
$2^{16} = 65\ 536$	$2^{-1} = 0.5$	$2^{-18} = 0.000\ 003\ 814\ 697\ 265\ 625$
$2^{15} = 32\ 768$	$2^{-2} = 0.25$	$2^{-19} = 0.000\ 001\ 907\ 348\ 632\ 812\ 5$
$2^{14} = 16\ 384$	$2^{-3} = 0.125$	$2^{-20} = 0.000\ 000\ 953\ 674\ 316\ 406\ 25$
$2^{13} = 8192$	$2^{-4} = 0.062\ 5$	$2^{-21} = 0.000\ 000\ 476\ 837\ 158\ 203\ 125$
$2^{12} = 4096$	$2^{-5} = 0.031\ 25$	$2^{-22} = 0.000\ 000\ 238\ 418\ 579\ 101\ 562\ 5$
$2^{11} = 2048$	$2^{-6} = 0.015\ 625$	$2^{-23} = 0.000\ 000\ 119\ 209\ 289\ 550\ 781\ 25$
$2^{10} = 1024$	$2^{-7} = 0.007\ 812\ 5$	$2^{-24} = 0.000\ 000\ 059\ 604\ 644\ 775\ 390\ 625$
$2^9 = 512$	$2^{-8} = 0.003\ 906\ 25$	$2^{-25} = 0.000\ 000\ 029\ 802\ 322\ 387\ 695\ 312\ 5$

4. Use powers. Determine each answer without doing the arithmetic.

   a) 4096×256
   b) $256 \times 128 \times 64$
   c) $65\ 536 \div 2048$

   d) $\dfrac{262\ 144 \times 8192 \times 512}{16\ 384 \times 64}$
   e) 64^3
   f) 4^{10}

5. Choose one part of exercise 4. Write to explain how you completed it.

6. a) Find as many patterns as you can in the final digits of the powers of 2.

   b) Explain why the patterns occur.

7. Determine each answer without doing the arithmetic.

   a) 0.125×0.0625
   b) $131\ 072 \times 0.007\ 812\ 5$

   c) $256 \times 0.003\ 906\ 25$
   d) $0.015\ 625 \div 0.0625$

   e) $16\ 384 \div 0.031\ 25$
   f) $0.003\ 906\ 25 \div 4096$

   g) 0.25^5
   h) 0.125^4

8. a) Use the table of powers of 2 to create a table of powers of 4.

   b) Create a table of powers of 8.

9. a) **Estimation** Find a power of 2 that is very close to a power of 10. Write the result in the form $2^m \doteq 10^n$.

   b) Estimate each power below as a power of 10. Use a calculator to check your results.

   i) 2^{30}
   ii) 2^{40}
   iii) 2^{50}

10. Simplify.

    a) $(3^2)^3 \times (3^4)^2$
    b) $(6^5)^2 \div (6^2)^3$
    c) $(7^3)^2 \times (7^8)^2$

    d) $(15^3)^4 \div (15^{-6})^{-2}$
    e) $(8^{-5}) \times (8^{13})^{-4}$
    f) $(4^{-2})^{-3} \div (4^{-6})^{-2}$

    g) $(51^{-3})^{-5} \div (51^{-4})^6$
    h) $(29^{-6})^3 \times (29^7)^{-2}$
    i) $(101^{-8})^{-4} \div (101^{-7})^{-5}$

11. Use guess and check to determine each value of n.

    a) $(n^2)^2 = 81$
    b) $(n^2)^3 = 64$
    c) $(n^2)^2 = 625$
    d) $(5^2)^n = 15\ 625$

C 12. Write these numbers in order from least to greatest.

   2^{5555} 3^{4444} 4^{3333} 5^{2222}

COMMUNICATING the IDEAS

In your journal, explain why you add the exponents when you write $2^4 \times 2^3$ as a power, and why you multiply the exponents when you write $(2^4)^3$ as a power.

On page 197, you considered this situation: a piece of paper is folded in half, then in half again, and again. It is folded in half as many times as possible.

You will need a sheet of blank paper and a ruler.

1. Fold the paper in half, forming 2 layers of paper. Fold it in half again, forming 4 layers. Continue to fold in half as long as you can.

2. Copy this table. Record your results. Use your folded paper to help you begin the entries in each column. Extend the table at least as far as the maximum number of folds you were able to make.

Number of folds	Number of layers
0	1
1	
2	
3	

3. **Estimation** As you fold, the pile of paper becomes thicker. At some point, it will be about 1 mm thick.

   a) How many layers of paper are there when the pile is about 1 mm thick?

   b) Use the result of part a to estimate the thickness of the sheet of paper with which you started.

4. Suppose you could fold the paper 10 times.

   a) How many layers of paper would there be?

   b) About how thick would the pile of paper be?

5. Suppose you could fold the paper 50 times.

   a) How many layers of paper would there be?

   b) About how thick would the pile of paper be? Express your answer in the most appropriate unit of measurement.

   c) Compare your answer in part b with the distances in the chart that follows. Which of these distances is closest to the thickness of the pile of paper that is folded 50 times?

Height of an adult	2 m
Height of a 2-storey house	10 m
Height of a 10-storey apartment building	50 m
Height of the CN Tower	550 m
Height of jet aircraft in flight	12 000 m
Height of the space shuttle in orbit	200 km
Distance to the moon	380 000 km
Distance to the sun	150 000 000 km

6. As you fold, the area of paper on the top layer becomes smaller.

   a) Measure the length and the width of the piece of paper with which you started, in millimetres.

   b) Calculate the area of the paper in square millimetres.

   c) Add another column to your table for the area of the top layer. Write your answer from part a in the first row. Calculate the area of the top layer after each number of folds. Enter the results in the new column.

Number of folds	Number of layers	Area of top layer (mm^2)
0	1	
1		
2		
3		

7. Suppose you could fold the paper 10 times.

   a) How many layers of paper would there be?

   b) What would the area of the top layer be?

8. Suppose you could fold the paper 50 times.

   a) How many layers of paper would there be?

   b) What would the area of the top layer be?

   c) Compare your answer in part b with the areas in the chart below. Which of these areas is closest to the area of the top layer of the pile of paper that is folded 50 times?

Area of one face of a sugar cube	100 mm^2
Area of this circle •	1 mm^2
Area of the dot in this letter: i	0.01 mm^2
Area of a pollen grain	0.001 mm^2
Area of a pit in a CD track	10^{-5} mm^2

9. Mathematical Modelling Your table in exercise 6 is a mathematical model. It represents the number of layers and the area of the top layer when the piece of paper is folded over and over again.

a) Like most mathematical models, certain assumptions are made in making the model. List as many assumptions as you can for this model.

b) Like most mathematical models, this model has limitations.

i) For how many folds does the model apply for predicting the number of layers in the pile?

ii) For how many folds does the model apply for predicting the area of the top layer?

c) You may have tried to get more folds by using a thinner sheet of paper or a larger sheet. Were you able to get more folds by doing this? Explain.

When you folded the paper, you probably found that the greatest number of folds you could make was about 7. One reason for this is that some of the paper gets in the way at the sides of the pile. This difficulty could be overcome by cutting the paper instead of folding.

Visualize cutting a piece of paper in half and placing one half on top of the other. Visualize cutting the two pieces in half again and placing one half on top of the other. Visualize doing this over and over again. In the exercises below, we will make the following assumptions.

- The piece of paper with which we start measures 256 mm by 256 mm.
- 16 sheets of paper form a layer 1 mm thick. That is, the thickness of the paper is $\frac{1}{16}$ mm.
- If we are careful, it should be possible to cut a tiny piece of paper measuring 1 mm by 1 mm. That is, the smallest piece of paper that could be cut has an area of 1 mm^2.

10. a) Copy the table that follows. Extend the table until the area of the top layer becomes 1 mm^2. Keep this table for use on page 249.

b) How many layers are there when the area of the top layer is 1 mm^2?

c) How thick is the pile of paper when the area of the top layer is 1 mm^2? Express your answer in the most appropriate unit of measurement. Visualize how high the pile of paper would be.

Number of cuts	Number of layers	Thickness of the pile (mm)	Area of top layer (mm²)
0	1	$\frac{1}{16}$	65 536

11. a) In exercise 10, describe some difficulties you might encounter if you tried to cut and pile the paper until the pieces were as small as 1 mm by 1 mm.

b) Estimation Based on your experience with folding the paper, estimate how many layers you might be able to make if you were to cut the paper instead of folding it.

12. Use the first few rows of data in your table in exercise 10 to draw three different graphs, described below. Try to include as many data points on your graph as you can.

a) a graph to show the number of layers against the number of cuts

b) a graph to show the thickness of the pile of paper against the number of cuts

c) a graph to show the area of 1 layer against the number of cuts

13. Choose one graph from exercise 12.

a) The points on one graph should appear to lie on a curve. Is it meaningful to draw a curve through these points? Explain.

b) Explain why it is not possible to draw a graph to show all the data in your table.

14. Mathematical Modelling Your table in exercise 10 is a mathematical model that represents the number of layers, the thickness of the pile, and the area of the top layer when the piece of paper is folded many times.

a) List as many assumptions as you can that were made in this model.

b) i) For how many cuts does the model apply for predicting the number of layers in the pile?

ii) For how many cuts does the model apply for predicting the area of the top layer?

COMMUNICATING the IDEAS

Choose one graph from exercise 12. In your journal, write to explain:

a) why the points do not lie on a straight line

b) why it is not possible to plot all the points on the graph

5.5　Scientific Notation

In an earlier grade, you used scientific notation to express very large numbers more simply. Now that you've had some practice using negative powers of 10, you will learn how to express very small numbers in scientific notation.

To write a number in scientific notation, write it as the product of:

- a number greater than -10 and less than -1 or greater than 1 and less than 10 and
- a power of 10

Scientists tell us that there are about 120 000 000 000 stars in our galaxy, the Milky Way. The zeros in this number are place holders to show the position of the decimal point. When a decimal point occurs at the end of the number, as in this case, we don't usually show it. To express the number of stars in our galaxy using scientific notation, we write:

$$120\ 000\ 000\ 000 = 1.2 \times 100\ 000\ 000\ 000$$
$$= 1.2 \times 10^{11}$$

The number of stars in our galaxy is about 1.2×10^{11}.

Hydrogen is the most abundant element in the universe. The mass of a hydrogen atom is about 0.000 000 000 000 000 000 000 001 67 g. As before, the zeros are place holders to show the position of the decimal point. To express the mass of a hydrogen atom using scientific notation, we write:

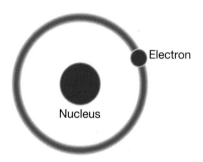

Diagram of a hydrogen atom

$$0.000\ 000\ 000\ 000\ 000\ 000\ 000\ 001\ 67 = 1.67 \times 0.000\ 000\ 000\ 000\ 000\ 000\ 000\ 001$$
$$= 1.67 \times 10^{-24}$$

The mass of a hydrogen atom is about 1.67×10^{-24} g.

Example 1

The mass of Earth is about 6.0×10^{24} kg.

a) The mass of the sun is about 3.3×10^{5} times as great as the mass of Earth. What is the mass of the sun?

b) The mass of the sun is about 2.7×10^{7} times as great as the mass of the moon. What is the mass of the moon?

Solution

The keystrokes are for a scientific calculator.

a) Multiply 3.3×10^5 by 6.0×10^{24}.

Press: 3.3 [Exp] 5 [×] 6.0 [Exp] 24 [=] to display 1.98^{30}

Do not clear the display.

$(3.3 \times 10^5) \times (6.0 \times 10^{24}) = 1.98 \times 10^{30}$

The mass of the sun is approximately 2.0×10^{30} kg.

b) The mass of the moon is about 2.7×10^7 times as small as the mass of the sun.

Divide 1.98×10^{30} by 2.7×10^7. Use the display from part a.

Press: [÷] 2.7 [Exp] 7 [=] to display 7.333333333^{22}

$\dfrac{1.98 \times 10^{30}}{2.7 \times 10^7} \doteq 7.33 \times 10^{22}$

The mass of the moon is approximately 7.3×10^{22} kg.

Example 2

Diatoms are a primary source of food in the sea. They are tiny one-celled plants that live in shells. A diatom measures about 5×10^{-4} mm across. Suppose diatoms were placed side by side. How many diatoms would be needed to stretch along Lake Ontario's shoreline, which measures about 1146 km?

Solution

Express 1146 km in millimetres.

$$1 \text{ km} = 1000 \text{ m} \qquad\qquad 1146 \text{ km} = 1146 \times 10^6 \text{ mm}$$
$$= 1\,000\,000 \text{ mm} \qquad\qquad = 1.146 \times 10^3 \times 10^6 \text{ mm}$$
$$= 10^6 \text{ mm} \qquad\qquad = 1.146 \times 10^9 \text{ mm}$$

To calculate how many diatoms are needed to stretch this far, divide the distance by the width of a diatom. Divide 1.146×10^9 by 5×10^{-4}.

Press: 1.146 [Exp] 9 [÷] 5 [÷] [Exp] 4 [+/-] [=] to display 2.292^{12}

$\dfrac{1.146 \times 10^9}{5 \times 10^{-4}} = 2.292 \times 10^{12}$

It would require about 2.3×10^{12} diatoms to stretch along Lake Ontario's shoreline.

Example 3

All matter is made up of atoms. Atoms are so small that 6.022×10^{23} gold atoms have a mass of approximately 200 g. You could hold this many atoms of gold in the palm of your hand. The same number, in grains of sand, takes up the top 2 m of sand in the Sahara Desert. How many atoms of gold are in a 1-kg gold bar?

Solution

Convert 1 kg to grams: 1 kg = 1000 g

200 g contain 6.022×10^{23} atoms.

So, 1000 g contain $\frac{1000}{200} \times (6.022 \times 10^{23})$ atoms $= 5 \times 6.022 \times 10^{23}$ atoms
$$= 30.11 \times 10^{23} \text{ atoms}$$
$$= 3.011 \times 10^{24} \text{ atoms}$$

A 1-kg bar of gold contains 3.011×10^{24} atoms of gold.

Boggle
your MIND

Canada produces 6.5 million tonnes of toxic waste each year. How much is this for every person living in Canada? How much is this per person, per day?

1. When writing a very large number in scientific notation, how can you tell which power of 10 to use? Illustrate your answer with examples.

2. When writing a very small number in scientific notation, how can you tell which power of 10 to use? Illustrate your answer with examples.

3. Do you think that every number can be written in scientific notation? Explain your answer.

4. Can you think of a reason to write numbers such as 880 and 0.025 in scientific notation? Explain.

5.5 EXERCISES

1. What numbers complete this table?

	Item	Decimal	Scientific Notation
a)	Temperature of the sun's interior	1 300 000 °C	
b)	Thickness of a plastic film	0.000 01 m	
c)	Mass of an electron		9.2×10^{-28} g
d)	Number of galaxies in the universe		1.2×10^{11}
e)	Estimated age of Earth	4 500 000 000 years	
f)	Diameter of a hydrogen atom	0.000 000 005 cm	
g)	Land area of Earth		1.5×10^{8} km^2

2. Scientific calculators may display results differently. What do you think each display means?

a) Calculator 1

i)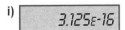
2.5^{12}

ii) 6.25^{-10}

b) Calculator 2

i)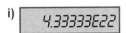
$3.125E-16$

ii) $4E24$

c) Calculator 3

i) $4.33333E22$

ii) $5.E-40$

3. Write in scientific notation.

a) 1200 b) 270 000 c) 430 d) 0.24

e) 0.0037 f) 0.000 014 8 g) −13 600 h) −0.000 018 8

i) 18×10^2 j) 142×10^5 k) 16×10^{-2} l) 236×10^{-6}

4. Write as a numeral.

a) 1.8×10^5 b) 2.9×10^4 c) 3.3×10^7 d) 4.4×10^9

e) 1.6×10^{-1} f) 8.4×10^{-2} g) 2.24×10^{-4} h) 1.88×10^{-5}

i) -2.41×10^{-10} j) -1.87×10^6 k) -3.02×10^{-3} l) -2.16×10^{-1}

5. Refer to *Example 2*. Calculate the number of diatoms needed to cover each distance. Explain each answer.

a) a line 1 mm long

b) a line 1 km long

c) Canada's ocean coastline, 241 402 km

6. Express each number in this news item in scientific notation.

A new fingerprinting method uses gold particles to bind to the proteins every finger leaves behind. The amount of protein is tiny—only one billionth of a gram per print. The gold particles are about two thousandths of a millimetre in diameter.

7. When asked to express 1500 in scientific notation, Kimi replied 15×10^2. Why is this not correct?

B **8.** The smallest hole ever made in solid material is so small that 4 000 000 of them side by side are needed to make a line 1 cm long. Calculate how many of these holes could be made in a square with each side length.

a) 1 cm b) 1 m c) 1 mm

9. Write the keystrokes you would use to evaluate each expression on your calculator.

a) $(5.9 \times 10^5) \times (4.7 \times 10^{-8})$ b) $(3.5 \times 10^9) \div (8.7 \times 10^{-5})$

c) $(2.4 \text{ million}) \times (6.5 \text{ million})$ d) $1 \div (5 \text{ billion})$

10. Simplify.

a) $3 \times 10^7 \times 4 \times 10^8$ b) $1.4 \times 10^{10} \times 3.7 \times 10^{14}$

c) $9.8 \times 10^{11} \times 1.3 \times 10^4$ d) $3.6 \times 10^{23} \times 5.9 \times 10^6$

e) $1.2 \times 10^{13} \times 4.7 \times 10^9$ f) $4.1 \times 10^{26} \times 3.2 \times 10^9$

11. Simplify.

a) $\dfrac{3.72 \times 10^{10}}{1.47 \times 10^8}$ b) $\dfrac{9.3 \times 10^{12}}{3.3 \times 10^7}$ c) $\dfrac{2.43 \times 10^{-7}}{2.3 \times 10^{-4}}$ d) $\dfrac{2.55 \times 10^{-9}}{3.0 \times 10^{-15}}$

12. When Mark wrote a number in scientific notation, he made a mistake. He wrote 6.2×10^4 instead of 6.2×10^{-4}. How many times as large as the correct number was Mark's number?

13. On a television program about sea otters, the following statements were made:
   - One square centimetre of a sea otter's fur contains about 20 000 hairs.
   - A sea otter has about 8 billion hairs.
   a) Write these two numbers in scientific notation.
   b) Calculate the area of a sea otter's body, in square centimetres.
   c) Express your answer to part b in square metres. Does the result seem reasonable? Explain.

SCIENCE FOCUS

Chemistry and the Mole

In *Example 3*, we considered 200 g of gold that contain approximately 6.022×10^{23} atoms. The number 6.022×10^{23} is an important number in chemistry. Just as one dozen is a counting tool in measuring quantities, one *mole* is a counting tool in chemistry. One mole is 6.022×10^{23}.

One mole of atoms is 6.022×10^{23} atoms. Depending on the element, one mole of atoms has a particular mass.

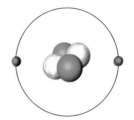

Helium Atom

14. One mole of helium atoms has a mass of about 4 g.
   a) Make a table of values to show the number of atoms in 0 g, 2 g, 4 g, 6 g, 8 g, and 10 g of helium.
   b) Graph the data in part a. What type of graph is it? Explain.

15. Suppose you had a balloon filled with 4 g of helium.
   a) How many moles of helium atoms would it contain?
   b) How many helium atoms would the balloon contain?

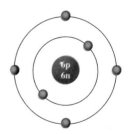

Carbon Atom

16. One mole of carbon atoms has a mass of about 12 g. Repeat exercise 14, replacing helium with carbon.

17. Graphite is made up of carbon atoms and is commonly used in industry. For example, the lead in pencils is graphite. Suppose a length of graphite has a mass of 36 g.

Carbon Atom

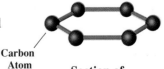

Section of Graphite Molecule

   a) How many moles of carbon atoms does it contain?
   b) How many carbon atoms does it contain?

18. A magazine article reported that about 100 billion aluminum beverage cans are made each year in North America. Suppose these cans are piled one on top of another. Carry out measurements and calculations to determine how high this stack would be.

19. Use the *Moon and Planets* database from the data disk. Find the information you need to answer each question.

a) The nearest star is about 2.7×10^5 times as far from the sun as Earth is. How far is the nearest star from the sun?

b) The mass of the heaviest known star, Eta Carinae, is about 6.23×10^8 times as great as the mass of Mars. What is the mass of Eta Carinae?

c) The diameter of the largest known star, Betelgeuse, is about 1.35×10^4 times as great as the diameter of Uranus. What is the diameter of Betelgeuse?

20. In 1977, two spacecraft named Voyager 1 and Voyager 2 were launched to visit the outer planets in the 1980s. These spacecraft have now travelled so far they have left the solar system. Voyager 2 is travelling at 58 000 km/h, and 296 000 years from now it will reach Sirius, the brightest star in the sky. How far away is Sirius?

21. Gold and silver are bought as investments. The prices of gold and silver are quoted per ounce, and these quotes change daily. Look at today's newspaper for the current prices of gold and silver. Use these data:

1 pound = 16 ounces; 1 pound $\doteq$ 454 g

One mole of gold atoms has a mass of 197 g.
One mole of silver atoms has a mass of 108 g.

a) Determine the number of gold atoms and silver atoms in one ounce of each metal.

b) Suppose you had 8 ounces of gold and 8 ounces of silver.

  i) What would be the value of each metal?

  ii) How many gold and silver atoms would you have?

COMMUNICATING the IDEAS

Suppose two numbers in scientific notation are multiplied, and their product is written in scientific notation. How is the power of 10 in the product related to the powers of 10 in the two original numbers? Answer this question in your journal, and illustrate your answer with some examples.

Graphing Squares

Consider a sequence of squares that have side lengths increasing by 1 cm.

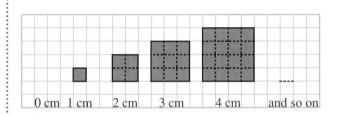

Side length (cm)	Area (cm^2)
0	0
1	1
2	4
3	9

1. Make a table of values to show side lengths and corresponding areas of squares. Extend the table for squares with side lengths up to 20 cm.

2. Graph the data. Draw the graph as large as possible. Construct the graph so that *Area* is on the vertical axis and *Side length* is on the horizontal axis.

3. Is it reasonable to connect the points with a smooth curve? Explain.

4. Use the graph. Estimate, to 1 decimal place, the length of a side of a square with each area.

    a) 30 cm^2 **b)** 57 cm^2 **c)** 183 cm^2 **d)** 350 cm^2

5. Use the graph. Estimate, to the nearest whole number, the area of a square with each side length.

    a) 7.5 cm   **b)** 12.5 cm   **c)** 15.25 cm   **d)** 18.75 cm

6. Graph the equation $y = x^2$. Compare the graph of $y = x^2$ to the graph you drew in exercise 2. How is the equation $y = x^2$ related to the formula for the area of a square?

7. Look at each pair of numbers in the table in exercise 1.

    a) How is the second number related to the first number?

    b) How is the first number related to the second number?

8. Use a calculator to check your answers to exercises 4 and 5.

The *Investigation* reviewed squares and square roots.
When you square a number, you multiply it by itself:

$$15^2 = 225$$
$$(-15)^2 = 225$$

Since $15 \times 15 = 225$, we say that 15 is a square root of 225, and we write $\sqrt{225} = 15$.
Since $(-15) \times (-15) = 225$, another square root of 225 is -15.
When the radical sign, $\sqrt{}$, is used, it indicates only the positive square root.

All positive numbers have square roots.
Perfect squares are numbers with square roots that are integers; 64 is a perfect
square because its square roots are 8 and -8.

Example 1

The photograph on the right is an enlargement of the one on the left — its
area is exactly twice as large. Without measuring, and without using a
calculator, estimate the side length of the photograph on the right.

5.0 cm

5.0 cm

Solution

The photograph on the left has side length 5 cm. So, its area is 25 cm^2.
The area of the photograph on the right is twice the area of the photograph
on the left. So, its area is 50 cm^2.
The side length of the photograph on the right is $\sqrt{50}$ cm.

Method 1

Use the graph from the *Investigation*, exercise 2, to estimate $\sqrt{50}$.
Draw a horizontal line through $A = 50$. Draw a vertical line through the point where the horizontal line meets the graph. This line meets the x-axis close to 7.

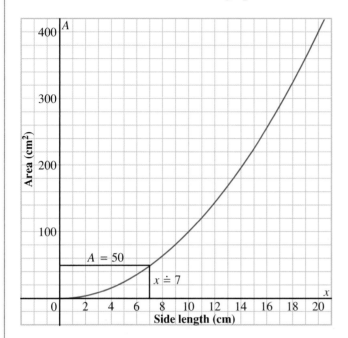

From the graph, $\sqrt{50}$ is about 7.

Method 2

Use a number line. Think of the perfect squares closest to 50.

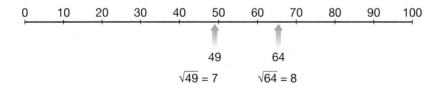

50 is between 49 and 64, and much closer to 49.
Hence, $\sqrt{50}$ is between 7 and 8, and much closer to 7.
Estimate $\sqrt{50}$ to be about 7.1.

The larger photograph has a side length of about 7.1 cm.

To simplify an expression that contains square roots, we use the order of operations.

Example 2

Simplify each expression. Give each answer to 2 decimal places if necessary.

a) $\sqrt{81} + \sqrt{25}$ **b)** $\sqrt{81 + 25}$ **c)** $\sqrt{\sqrt{81} + \sqrt{25}}$

Solution

a) $\sqrt{81} + \sqrt{25}$

Find each square root, then add.

$\sqrt{81} + \sqrt{25} = 9 + 5$
$= 14$

b) $\sqrt{81 + 25}$

Add, then find the square root.

$\sqrt{81 + 25} = \sqrt{106}$ Use a calculator.
$\doteq 10.30$

c) $\sqrt{\sqrt{81} + \sqrt{25}}$

Find each square root, then add.

$\sqrt{\sqrt{81} + \sqrt{25}} = \sqrt{9 + 5}$
$= \sqrt{14}$ Use a calculator.
$\doteq 3.74$

DISCUSSING *the* IDEAS

1. In *Example 1*, the area of the larger photo is twice the area of the smaller photo.

   a) Explain why the side length of the larger photo is not twice the side length of the smaller photo.

   b) Suppose the side length of the larger photo was twice the side length of the smaller photo. How would the areas of the photos compare?

2. *Example 1* presents two methods to estimate a square root. Another method is to use a calculator to calculate $\sqrt{50}$. Use a calculator to calculate $\sqrt{50}$ to confirm the results of *Example 1*. State an advantage of each method.

3. In *Example 1*, measure a diagonal of the smaller square. What do you notice? Explain.

A Use the graph you drew in the *Investigation* to complete exercises 1 to 5.

1. Find a square root of each number. Which square roots are estimates, and which are exact?

   a) 170   b) 225   c) 360   d) 80

2. For each number in exercise 1, there is another square root. State what the other square root is.

3. Which square roots are between 8 and 9? Explain how you know.

   $\sqrt{67}$, $\sqrt{91}$, $\sqrt{78}$, $\sqrt{62}$, $\sqrt{84}$, $\sqrt{80}$

4. Estimate each square root to 1 decimal place.

   a) $\sqrt{20}$ b) $\sqrt{60}$ c) $\sqrt{120}$ d) $\sqrt{280}$

5. Estimate the square of each number to the nearest whole number.

   a) 9.5   b) 12.5   c) 17.5   d) 19.5

6. Write to explain what is meant by the square root of a number.

7. What are the square roots of each number?

   a) 4   b) 9   c) 49   d) 81   e) 121   f) 64

8. What are the square roots of each number?

   a) $\frac{1}{16}$ b) $\frac{1}{25}$ c) $\frac{16}{25}$ d) $\frac{4}{9}$ e) $\frac{25}{49}$ f) $\frac{64}{81}$

9. Which of the square roots listed below are between each pair of numbers?

   a) 3 and 4   b) 7 and 8   c) 11 and 12

   d) 10 and 11   e) 13 and 14   f) 18 and 19

   $\sqrt{11}$, $\sqrt{52}$, $\sqrt{61}$, $\sqrt{14}$, $\sqrt{330}$, $\sqrt{360}$, $\sqrt{320}$, $\sqrt{257}$, $\sqrt{190}$,
   $\sqrt{140}$, $\sqrt{171}$, $\sqrt{118}$, $\sqrt{110}$, $\sqrt{130}$, $\sqrt{80}$, $\sqrt{35}$

10. Estimate each square root to 1 decimal place.

   a) $\sqrt{76}$ b) $\sqrt{86}$ c) $\sqrt{117}$ d) $\sqrt{140}$ e) $\sqrt{45}$ f) $\sqrt{105}$

11. Determine each square root.

   a) $\sqrt{144}$ b) $\sqrt{14\ 400}$ c) $\sqrt{1\ 440\ 000}$

   d) $\sqrt{1.44}$ e) $\sqrt{0.0144}$ f) $\sqrt{0.000\ 144}$

12. Calculate the length of the side of a square with each area. Round to 1 decimal place where necessary.

   a) 400 cm²   b) 0.25 m²   c) 90 cm²

   d) 150 cm²   e) 300 cm²   f) 25 000 m²

13. Explain why each answer in exercise 12 involves only the positive square root.

14. Simplify each expression. Give the answer to 2 decimal places where necessary.

a) $\sqrt{64} + \sqrt{36}$ **b)** $\sqrt{64 + 36}$ **c)** $64 + \sqrt{36}$

d) $\sqrt{64} \times \sqrt{36}$ **e)** $\sqrt{64 + \sqrt{36}}$ **f)** $\sqrt{\sqrt{64} + \sqrt{36}}$

15. A square garden has area 230 m².

a) How long is each side of the garden, to the nearest centimetre?

b) How much fencing would be needed to enclose the entire garden?

16. A student drew a sketch on a 16-cm square piece of paper. She wants to mount the sketch on a piece of poster board twice the area of the paper. How would you estimate the length of each side of the poster board? What is your estimate?

17. Suppose the sketch in exercise 16 is enlarged so that its area is 3 times as great as the original. Estimate the length of each side of the enlargement.

APPLIED
FOCUS

Make One Large Square from Two Small Squares

You will need a pair of scissors and two congruent squares with side length 5 cm.

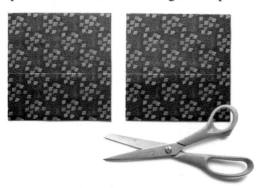

18. Cut the squares into smaller pieces. Arrange all the pieces to form one large square.

a) Write to explain how you formed the large square. Include the number of pieces you cut and the shape of each piece.

b) Could you have made fewer cuts and still formed one large square? Explain.

c) Measure the side length of the large square.

d) Compare this activity with *Example 1*, page 230. How could you use the results of this activity to complete *Example 1* a different way?

19. Simplify each expression. Estimate the result where necessary.

a) $\sqrt{25} + \sqrt{49}$ b) $25 + \sqrt{49}$ c) $\sqrt{25} + 49$

d) $\sqrt{25} \times \sqrt{49}$ e) $\sqrt{25 + 49}$ f) $\sqrt{25 \times 49}$

g) $\sqrt{25 + \sqrt{49}}$ h) $\sqrt{\sqrt{25} + 49}$ i) $\sqrt{\sqrt{25} + \sqrt{49}}$

20. You can use a graphing calculator to determine square roots.

Setup On the TI-83, set the graphing window to Xmin = 0, Xmax = 94, Xscl = 10, Ymin = −1, Ymax = 10, Yscl = 1. Press ⌐Y=⌐ and clear any equations or statplots.

Move the cursor to the Y1 line, and press ⌐√⌐ ⌐X,T,θ,n⌐ ⌐)⌐. Your screen will look like the screen below left. Press ⌐TRACE⌐ to obtain a screen similar to the screen below right.

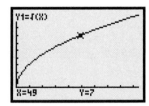

a) On the screen above right, values of *x* and *y* are shown at the bottom of the screen. How is the value of *y* related to the value of *x*?

b) On your calculator, press ⌐▶⌐ or ⌐◀⌐ several times. Observe how the values of *x* and *y* change. Is the relationship you observed in part a still true?

c) Use the arrow keys to determine each square root.

i) $\sqrt{45}$ ii) $\sqrt{50}$ iii) $\sqrt{75}$ iv) $\sqrt{34}$

d) You can make the cursor jump to any value of *x* by entering the number and pressing ⌐ENTER⌐. Use this method to determine each square root.

i) $\sqrt{17.5}$ ii) $\sqrt{38.2}$ iii) $\sqrt{84.25}$ iv) $\sqrt{7.625}$

e) Your graphing calculator screen shows the graph of $y = \sqrt{x}$. Explain why the graph is a curve and not a straight line.

21. A square carpet in a room covers 60% of the hardwood floor area. The room is 5 m by 5 m.

a) What are the dimensions of the carpet?

b) What is the area of the floor not covered by the carpet?

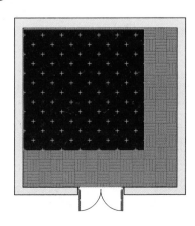

22. a) Use a calculator to find each square root.

    i) $\sqrt{3}$ **ii)** $\sqrt{300}$ **iii)** $\sqrt{30\,000}$

    iv) $\sqrt{3\,000\,000}$ **v)** $\sqrt{0.03}$ **vi)** $\sqrt{0.0003}$

  b) Look at the results in part a. Write to explain the pattern.

23. a) A square has one vertex at (0,0) and an area of 49 square units. Find possible coordinates of the other vertices of the square.

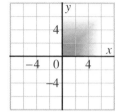

  b) A square has one vertex at (0, 0) and an area of 64 square units. Find possible coordinates of the other vertices of the square.

  c) A square has one vertex at (2, 3) and an area of 16 square units. Find possible coordinates of the other vertices of the square.

24. What happens when you try to use a calculator to find the square root of a negative integer such as −3? Explain.

25. Determine two values that satisfy each equation. Give the answers to 2 decimal places where necessary.

  a) $n^2 = 81$ **b)** $k^2 = 0.25$ **c)** $x^2 = 96$ **d)** $z^2 = \dfrac{4}{49}$ **e)** $y^2 = 38$

26. Solve each equation. Give the answers to 2 decimal places where necessary.

  a) $x^2 = 100$ **b)** $8.1 = k^2$ **c)** $m^2 + 5 = 30$ **d)** $q^2 - 10 = 90$

27. a) Suppose you know the diameter of a circle. How could you find its area?

  b) Write a formula for the area, A, of a circle in terms of its diameter, d.

  c) Graph the area, A, against the diameter, d.

  d) Suppose you know the area of a circle. How could you find its diameter?

  e) Write a formula for the diameter of a circle in terms of its area.

  f) Find the diameter of the circle with each area. Give each answer to 1 decimal place.

    i) 22 cm^2 **ii)** 33 cm^2 **iii)** 40 cm^2 **iv)** 5 m^2

COMMUNICATING the IDEAS

Look at the square roots in these exercises. Some of the square roots are less than the original numbers, while others are greater than the original numbers. How can you tell if the square root of a number is greater than or less than the number? Record your ideas in your journal, with examples.

The Pythagorean Theorem relates the areas of the squares on the sides of a right triangle. Ancient texts reveal that many centuries ago, different civilizations knew this property of right triangles.

Egypt, 2000 B.C.

The ancient Egyptians may have constructed square pyramids using a knotted rope to form a triangle with sides of lengths 3, 4, and 5 units.

Babylonia, 1700 B.C.

Clay tablets show that the ancient Babylonians knew how to calculate the length of the diagonal of a square.

Greece, 540 B.C.

Although it had been known for centuries, the Pythagorean Theorem is named after the Greek philosopher, Pythagoras, who was the first to prove that this theorem applies to all right triangles.

China, 200 B.C.

About the time of the Han period, the Chinese text Chòu-peï contains a discussion of the Pythagorean Theorem based on the diagram at the right.

The Pythagorean Theorem is important because people use it to calculate the length of a side of a right triangle if they know the lengths of the other two sides.

The side opposite the right angle is the *hypotenuse*.
The two shorter sides are the *legs*.

For the right triangle shown,

Area of square on AB = Area of square on BC + Area of square on AC

That is, $AB^2 = BC^2 + AC^2$

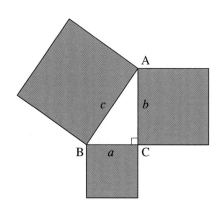

The area of this square ....

... is equal to the sum of the areas of these two squares

The Pythagorean Theorem

Draw any right triangle and the squares on its sides. Make the diagram as large as possible.

Cut the smaller squares to produce pieces that fit together on the largest square. Compare your cuts and pieces with those of your classmates. Describe the most efficient way to make the cuts.

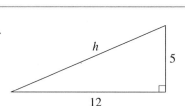

Example 1

Determine the length of the hypotenuse in this right triangle.

Solution

Use the Pythagorean Theorem.

$h^2 = 12^2 + 5^2$
$\quad = 144 + 25$
$\quad = 169$
$h = \sqrt{169}$
$h = 13$

The hypotenuse is 13 units long.

Example 2

The bottom of a 7.0-m extension ladder is 2.0 m from the base of a wall.
How high up the wall does the ladder reach?

Solution

Let w metres represent the height at which
the ladder touches the wall.

Use the Pythagorean Theorem.

$$w^2 + 2^2 = 7^2$$
$$w^2 = 7^2 - 2^2$$
$$= 49 - 4$$
$$= 45$$
$$w = \sqrt{45}$$
$$w \doteq 6.7082$$

The ladder reaches 6.7 m up the wall.

The Pythagorean Theorem can be used on a coordinate grid because the grid
defines right angles.

Example 3

A line segment joins the points $P(-1, 3)$ and $Q(4, 6)$. Calculate the length of
the line segment PQ. Express the length to 1 decimal place.

Solution

Plot P and Q on a grid. Draw a right triangle under PQ. Let
h units represent the length of the hypotenuse. Count squares
to find the lengths of the legs.
They are 5 units and 3 units.

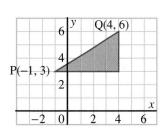

Use the Pythagorean Theorem.

$$h^2 = 5^2 + 3^2$$
$$= 25 + 9$$
$$= 34$$
$$h = \sqrt{34}$$
$$h \doteq 5.8$$

Line segment PQ is approximately 5.8 units long.

1. Look at the Babylonian clay tablets on page 237. Explain the connection between the Pythagorean Theorem and the diagonal of a square.

2. Look at the solution for *Example 2*. Use the areas-of-squares description of the Pythagorean Theorem to explain why $w^2 = 7^2 - 2^2$.

3. Explain how you could use the Pythagorean Theorem to calculate the distance between any two points on a coordinate grid. Describe situations where the Pythagorean Theorem cannot be used to find the distance.

4. Do you think you can use the Pythagorean Theorem to calculate the distance between any two points? Explain your thinking. Consider examples such as these:

   a) The distance between your chair and the door to your classroom

   b) The distance between Ottawa and Hong Kong

5.7   EXERCISES

 1. Calculate the length of the third side of each triangle. Give each answer to 1 decimal place, where necessary.

a)
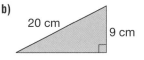
3 cm   4 cm

b)
20 cm   9 cm

c)
7 cm
9 cm

2. Determine the length of each line segment.

a)
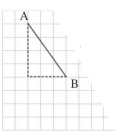
A
B

b)
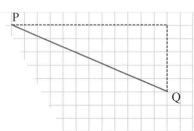
P
Q

3. Calculate the length of the third side of each triangle. Round each answer to 1 decimal place.

a)

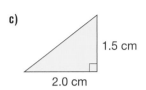

b)

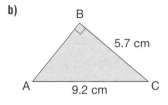

c)

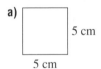

d)

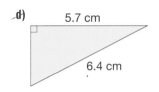

4. Calculate the length of a diagonal of each rectangle. Give each answer to 1 decimal place, where necessary.

a)

5 cm
5 cm

b)

5 cm
10 cm

c)

5 cm
15 cm

5. The dimensions of a computer monitor are 28 cm by 21 cm. Monitors are sold according to the length of the diagonal. How would an advertiser quote the size of this monitor?

6. Calculate the length of each line segment.

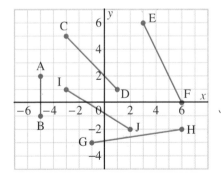

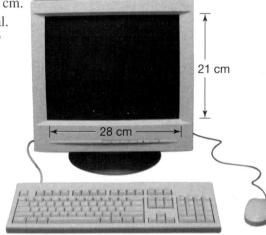

21 cm

28 cm

7. Refer to *Example 1*, page 230.

   a) Calculate the length of the diagonal of the smaller photograph. What do you notice?

   b) Explain how the Pythagorean Theorem relates to *Example 1*.

8. Plot each pair of points. Calculate the distance between them.

   a) A(1, 3), B(5, 5)   **b)** C(6, 0), D(8, 2)   **c)** E(−3, 2), F(1, −3)

   d) G(−4, 2), H(−1, 3)   **e)** J(−1, −4), K(2, −1)   **f)** L(−3, 1), M(0, −1)

9. A triangle has vertices $J(-3, 2), K(2, 3)$, and $L(4, -1)$. Draw the triangle on grid paper. Calculate the lengths of its sides.

10. A rectangle has vertices $P(-3, -2), Q(1, 2), R(3, 0)$, and $S(-1, -4)$.

   a) Draw the rectangle on grid paper. Calculate the lengths of its sides.

   b) Calculate the area of the rectangle.

   c) Calculate the lengths of the diagonals of the rectangle.

FOCUS

The Body Diagonal of a Rectangular Prism

11. a) Get a cardboard box. Measure its length, width, and height.

   b) Calculate the length of the diagonal of each face of the box.

   c) Calculate the length of the body diagonal.

   d) Check part c by measuring the body diagonal.

   e) Suppose you had to fit a metal rod in the box. What is the length of the longest rod that would fit? Explain.

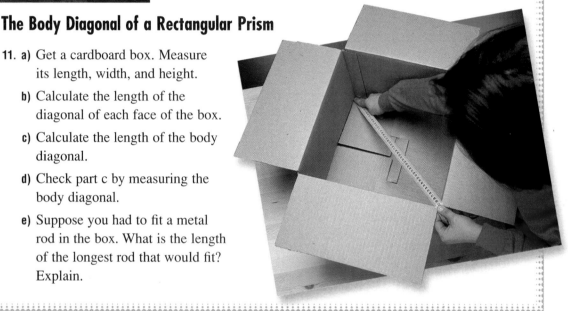

12. A triangle has shorter sides lengths a units and b units; and the longest side c units.

   a) Choose values of a, b, and c for which $a^2 + b^2 = c^2$. Sketch the triangle.

   b) Choose values of a, b, and c for which $a^2 + b^2 > c^2$. Sketch the triangle.

   c) Choose values of a, b, and c for which $a^2 + b^2 < c^2$. Sketch the triangle.

   d) Describe the triangles you drew in parts a, b, and c.

13. A computer store advertises a 14-inch monitor. What are possible dimensions of this monitor? What do you think are the most reasonable dimensions?

14. Look at these numbers:

   $$\sqrt{0.25}, \quad \sqrt{1}, \quad \sqrt{1.44}, \quad \sqrt{2}, \quad \sqrt{3.5}, \quad \sqrt{4}, \quad \sqrt{6.25}, \quad \sqrt{9}$$

   Find a sorting rule that excludes two of these numbers. Describe your rule.

15. In exercise 4, all three rectangles have width 5 cm. Visualize other rectangles like these, which have different lengths but whose widths are all 5 cm. Let x centimetres represent the length of such a rectangle.

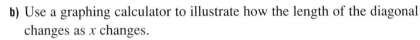

5 cm

x cm

a) Use the Pythagorean Theorem to write an equation for the length, y, of the diagonal of the rectangle.

b) Use a graphing calculator to illustrate how the length of the diagonal changes as x changes.

Setup On the TI-83, set the graphing window to Xmin = 0, Xmax = 18.8, Xscl = 5, Ymin = −1, Ymax = 10, Yscl = 1. Press [Y=] and clear any equations or statplots. Move the cursor to the Y1 line. Enter the equation you obtained in part a, and press [TRACE]. Trace along the curve to verify your answers to exercise 4.

c) Describe how the length of the diagonal changes as x gets closer and closer to 0. Explain why this is reasonable.

d) Describe how the length of the diagonal changes as x gets larger and larger. Explain why this is reasonable.

e) Explain why the graph is a curve and not a straight line.

16. Consider all the points that have integer coordinates and are 5 units from $(0, 0)$.

a) How many such points are there? What are their coordinates? Plot the points on grid paper.

b) Choose four of these points that form a rectangle with diagonals 10 units long. How many different rectangles like this can you make? To justify your answer, draw the rectangles on grid paper in a systematic way.

c) What is the area of each rectangle?

17. For a sloping ladder to be safe, the distance from the wall to the base of the ladder must be $\frac{1}{4}$ of the vertical distance from the ground to the top of the ladder. A 12-m ladder is placed safely against a wall. How far up the wall does the ladder reach?

COMMUNICATING the IDEAS

Identify three different situations where you could apply the Pythagorean Theorem. Record your ideas in your journal.

Earlier in your study of mathematics, you encountered these sets of numbers.

Natural numbers, N

1, 2, 3, 4, 5,...

Integers, I

... –3, –2, –1, 0, 1, 2, 3,...

Rational numbers, Q

Numbers that can be expressed in fractional form

Examples:

$\frac{2}{3}$ $\frac{-9}{4}$ $\frac{5}{-7}$ $\frac{-1}{-2}$ 1.82   5.8   –2

We will now investigate another set of numbers.

INVESTIGATION

Sets of Numbers

1. Express each rational number in decimal form.

   Use a calculator if necessary.

   a) $\frac{3}{8}$ b) $\frac{7}{12}$ c) $\frac{-23}{16}$ d) $\frac{7}{-8}$

   e) $\frac{37}{11}$ f) $\frac{53}{99}$ g) $\frac{17}{222}$ h) $\frac{22}{7}$

2. Look at the results for exercise 1 a and b. Explain why the decimals in the quotients always terminate or repeat. Look at these paper-and-pencil division calculations for ideas.

   In exercise 1a,
   the remainders
   must be less than 8.

   $$\begin{array}{r} 0.375 \\ 8\overline{)3.000} \\ \underline{24} \\ 60 \\ \underline{56} \\ 40 \\ \underline{40} \\ 0 \end{array}$$

   In exercise 1b,
   the remainders
   must be less than 12.

   $$\begin{array}{r} 0.583 \\ 12\overline{)7.000} \\ \underline{60} \\ 100 \\ \underline{96} \\ 40 \\ \underline{36} \\ 4 \end{array}$$

   One of these two cases will occur when any rational number is expressed in decimal form. Therefore, from exercise 2, when a rational number is expressed in decimal form, the digits either terminate or repeat.

3. Only three of the numbers that follow are rational numbers.

   a) Which ones do you think they are? Explain.

   b) Why are the others not rational numbers? Do you think they are numbers? Explain.

i) 1.010203040506070809010011012013 01…

ii) −238.418773

iii) 3.141592653589793238462643383 27950288419…

iv) 88175.47547547547547547547547 5475475…

v) 47.444444438383838383838222097 4449072…

vi) −0.07921883675849200078397839 78397839…

4. Recall that we use *bar notation* to indicate a repeating decimal. For example, 2.4$\overline{35}$ means 2.435353535353535353535…

   a) Write a few digits of each number without using bar notation.

      i) 4.$\overline{9}$ ii) 17.$\overline{02}$ iii) −8.51$\overline{273}$

   b) Write the two repeating decimals in exercise 3b using bar notation.

   c) What are two advantages of bar notation?

If you use a calculator to calculate $\sqrt{2}$, you will obtain something like 1.414 213 562. To check this, you can multiply 1.414 213 562 by 1.414 213 562. But the product has more digits than most calculators can handle. Using a computer, the exact value of this product is:

1.414 213 562 × 1.414 213 562 = 1.999 999 998 944 727 844

Since the product is not exactly 2, we say that 1.414 213 562 is an *approximation* to $\sqrt{2}$.

We write $\sqrt{2} \doteq 1.414\ 213\ 562$

Using a computer, we can calculate more accurate approximations to $\sqrt{2}$, such as:

$\sqrt{2} \doteq 1.414\ 213\ 562\ 373\ 095\ 048\ 801\ 688\ 724\ 209\ 698\ 078\ 569\ 671\ 875\ 376\ 94$

No matter how many digits we calculate for $\sqrt{2}$, we will never determine its exact value, and we will never find a pattern of digits that repeats. This means that $\sqrt{2}$ cannot be expressed in fractional form $\frac{m}{n}$, where m and n are integers.

That is, $\sqrt{2}$ is not a rational number. $\sqrt{2}$ is an irrational number.

Any number that cannot be expressed in the form $\frac{m}{n}$, where m and n are integers ($n \neq 0$), is an *irrational number*. In decimal form, the digits of an irrational number neither terminate nor repeat. The set of numbers is denoted $\overline{Q}$.

Examples of rational numbers	**Examples of irrational numbers**
Terminating decimals	Decimals that neither terminate nor repeat

Terminating decimals		Decimals that neither terminate nor repeat
–2.875	3.0	–2.718 281 818 459 045 235 36...
7.231 875 622 945	8.45×10^{-7}	1.010 010 001 000 010 000 010...
Repeating decimals		–357.575 757 575 757 877 233...
–2.333 333 333 333 333 333 33...		$\sqrt{5} \doteq 2.236\ 067\ 977\ 499\ 789\ 696\ 41$
$0.\overline{7}$		$-\sqrt{31.5} \doteq -5.612\ 486\ 080\ 160\ 912\ 078\ 38$
$3.\overline{142\ 857}$		$\pi \doteq 3.141\ 592\ 654...$
5.121 212 121 212 121 212 12...		
$-23.059\ 723\ 116\ \overline{894\ 5}$		

All the numbers above are *real numbers*. The set of real numbers consists of all the rational numbers and all the irrational numbers—that is, all numbers that can be expressed in decimal form.

DISCUSSING the IDEAS

1. A calculator was used to approximate $\sqrt{3}$. It displayed 1.732 050 8.

   a) Is 1.732 050 8 rational or irrational?

   b) Is $\sqrt{3}$ rational or irrational?

   c) Can a number be both rational and irrational? Explain.

2. A student wrote the formula for the circumference of a circle in the form $\pi = \dfrac{C}{d}$. The student claimed that this proved that π is a rational number. Do you agree with this reasoning? Explain.

5.8 EXERCISES

1. Does each number appear to be rational or irrational? Why is the phrase "appear to be" used in this question?

   a) 1.253 253 253 253 253 253 253 253...

   b) 0.147 474 747 474 747 457 883 312...

   c) 72.041 000 000 019 875 198 751 987...

   d) –0.121 232 123 432 123 454 321 234...

2. Classify each number as natural, integer, rational, or irrational. Explain your reasoning. (Some numbers may belong to more than one set.)

a) $\frac{1}{4}$ b) -4 c) 4.99 d) $-5\frac{3}{8}$ e) 8 f) 3^{-2}

3. Which of these numbers appear to be rational?

a) 2.547 483 271... b) 27.216 216 2... c) −13.478 197 435...

d) 43.304 004 00... e) −7.428 f) −0.453 562 571 0...

4. Give examples of two rational numbers between each pair of numbers.

a) 3.0, 3.5 b) −6.5, −6.1 c) −4.17, −4.1$\overline{7}$ d) 7.$\overline{45}$, 7.45

5. Which of these numbers are not rational?

a) $\sqrt{5}$ b) $\sqrt{5} + \sqrt{11}$ c) $\sqrt{5 + 11}$ d) $\sqrt{11 - 5}$

6. Which of these numbers are irrational?

a) $\sqrt{21}$ b) $\sqrt{64}$ c) $\sqrt{135}$ d) $\sqrt{1.44}$ e) $\sqrt{0.9}$ f) $\sqrt{0.04}$

B

7. Classify each number as natural, integer, rational, or irrational. Some of the numbers will belong to more than one set.

a) $\frac{3}{5}$ b) $0.\overline{25}$ c) -7 d) 23 517 e) $\sqrt{25}$ f) 2^{-1}

g) 3×10^9 h) 2.4×10^{-6} i) $-2\frac{1}{4}$ j) $\sqrt{7}$ k) 3.14 l) $-875.0\overline{297}$

8. Which of these numbers are irrational?

a) $\sqrt{3}$ b) $-\sqrt{3}$ c) $6 + \sqrt{3}$ d) $6 - \sqrt{3}$ e) $\sqrt{6 + 3}$ f) $\sqrt{36}$

COMMUNICATING the IDEAS

Suppose you have a number with many decimal places.

a) If you see a repeating pattern, can you be certain that the number is a rational number? Explain.

b) If you do not see a repeating pattern, can you be certain that the number is an irrational number? Explain

Record your ideas in your journal. Include some examples to illustrate your conclusions.

Nesting Numbers

1. You can use envelopes to show how different sets of
numbers are related. You will need five envelopes of
different sizes, and 30 small pieces of cardboard or paper.

   Natural numbers, N

   Write each of these numbers on a small piece of cardboard.

   6, 0, −2, −99, $\frac{2}{3}$, 2^{10}, 3×10^6, 2.4×10^9, $\sqrt{2}$, $\frac{12}{7}$, π, $\sqrt{900}$,

   2.13, 2^{-1}, −1, 5.8×10^{-6}, $-\sqrt{2}$, 75%, 10^{-3}, 0.762, $32.\overline{6}$, $-\frac{1}{2}$,

   $-17.0\overline{298}$, 22^{22}, 3 355 432, 63.172 844,

   1.212 211 222 111 222 211 111..., 150 million, 2.5 billion,

   −17.002 900 290 029 002 900 290 029…

   Integers, I

   Rational numbers, Q

   Irrational numbers, $\overline{Q}$

   Label each of four envelopes with one description at the right.
   Think carefully about the size of each envelope as you label it.
   Place the numbers in the envelopes.

   Follow this rule:

   Each number must be inside every envelope
   containing a set of numbers to which it belongs.

   For example, since −2 is an integer, −2 must be
   inside envelope I. Since $-2 = \frac{-2}{1}$, −2 is a rational
   number, and must also be inside envelope Q.

   Label the fifth envelope *Real Numbers, R*. Place
   all the numbers in this envelope!

2. Write each product and quotient as a power.

   a) $3^5 \times 3^2$ b) $(-2)^4(-2)^3$ c) $-2^3 \times 2^5$ d) $15^3 \times 15^2$

   e) $4^5 \div 4^3$ f) $3^8 \div 3^6$ g) $\frac{12^8}{12^8}$ h) $\frac{16^3}{16^2}$

3. a) Can you apply the laws of exponents to simplify $5^4 \times 4^5$? Explain.

   b) Can you apply the laws of exponents to simplify $9^2 \div 27^2$? Explain.

4. Which is the greater number in each pair? Explain.

   a) 8^3, 5^4 b) 8^{-3}, 5^{-4} c) 6^3, 4^4 d) 6^{-3}, 4^{-4} e) 9^2, 2^6

5. There is only one power of 5 between 1000 and 10 000. Which number is it?

6. Use the laws of exponents to write each expression as a single power.

a) $(5^2)^2$ **b)** $(8^3)^4$ **c)** $(12^5)^2$ **d)** $(9^3)^{-1}$ **e)** $[(-5)^2]^3$

7. One grain of grass pollen has an estimated mass of 5×10^{-9} g. How many pollen grains are there in 1 g of grass pollen?

8. Mathematical Modelling Use the table you completed in exercise 10, page 220. Choose any row in the table except the first row. Predict what the answer should be in each case below. Explain.

a) You divide the thickness of the pile by the number of layers.

b) You multiply the area of one layer by the number of layers.

9. Mathematical Modelling In exercise 10, page 220, you should have noticed that, except for the numbers in the first column, all the numbers in the table are powers of 2.

a) Make a copy of your table, writing all these numbers in power form.

b) Let n represent the number of cuts. Write an expression for:

  i) the number of layers   **ii)** the thickness of the pile in millimetres

  iii) the area of the pile in square millimetres

c) Use your expressions in part b to prove that your predictions in exercise 9 are correct.

10. One light-year is the distance light travels in one year. The speed of light is 3×10^8 m/s.

a) Calculate the approximate number of metres in one light-year.

b) Calculate the approximate number of kilometres in one light-year.

11. Every atom contains negatively charged particles called electrons and positively charged particles called protons. Each electron has a mass of 9.11×10^{-28} g and each proton has a mass of 1.67×10^{-24} g.

a) A hydrogen atom contains one electron and one proton. What is the mass of a hydrogen atom?

b) How many times as heavy as an electron is a proton?

12. a) Find the perimeter of a square with area 49 cm^2.

b) Find the approximate perimeter of a square with area 150 cm^2.

13. a) Calculate the area of each square, at the right.

b) Calculate the lengths of the sides of each square.

c) What patterns can you find in the results?

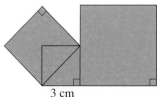
3 cm

14. Look at the diagram from Chòu-peï on page 237. Suppose the smaller square in the middle has area 1 cm^2. Without using the Pythagorean Theorem, calculate the side length of the large square.

Designing Mixtures

Marika owns and operates a bulk food store. She frequently mixes different kinds of foods, and needs to solve this problem.

Peanuts sell at $5/kg and pecans sell at $20/kg. Marika wants to make 30 kg of a mixture of peanuts and pecans that will sell at $10/kg. How many kilograms of peanuts and pecans should she use?

In this chapter, you will develop mathematical models to solve problems like this. You will apply the models to solve similar problems that involve other prices or foods in the bulk food store, and to other situations that involve mixtures of two quantities.

1. Why might Marika want to make a mixture of peanuts and pecans?

2. Solve the problem using any method.

3. Suppose the prices were different. Would you be able to use your method to solve a similar problem? Explain.

You will return to this problem in Sections 6.6 and 6.8.

 FYI Visit www.awl.com/canada/school/connections

For information related to the above problem, click on <u>MATHLINKS</u> followed by <u>AWMath</u>. Then select a topic under Designing Mixtures.

This section reviews these concepts:

- The concept of a variable
- Solving simple equations
- Order of operations

Suppose this pattern of figures continues. One figure will have 20 blue squares. How many green squares will it have?

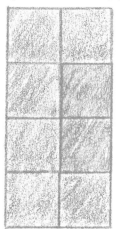  

To solve this problem, we could continue to draw the figures until we reach the figure with 20 blue squares. This could be tedious.

An alternative method is to write an equation that relates the numbers of blue and green squares in each figure.

Look at the figures.

In each figure, there are 4 more blue squares than green squares.
Let g represent the number of green squares.
Let b represent the number of blue squares.

The equation is $b = 4 + g$.

For 20 blue squares, $b = 20$

The equation becomes $20 = 4 + g$.

To solve this equation, we think: What number added to 4 makes 20? The number is 16.

$$g = 16$$

There will be 16 green squares in the figure with 20 blue squares.

1. **a)** Identify the variables on page 252.

   b) Do you think it is correct to say that a variable represents "an unknown number"? Explain.

   c) Do you think you could use symbols other than letters as variables? Explain.

2. **a)** Can an expression contain more than one variable?

   b) Can a variable occur more than once in an expression?

   Give examples to illustrate your answers.

3. Write an equation to represent each sentence.

   a) Five more than a number is 21.

   b) A number decreased by 11 is 15.

   c) Four times a number, added to 6, is 14.

   d) A number divided by 3 is 18.

4. Solve each equation in exercise 3 to find each number.

5. Let *n* represent the number of fish in Linda's aquarium.

   a) **i)** John's aquarium has 3 more fish than Linda's. Write an expression for the number of fish in John's aquarium.
   ii) Suppose John's aquarium has 11 fish. Write an equation. Use it to find the number of fish in Linda's aquarium.

   b) **i)** Adriana's aquarium has twice as many fish as Linda's. Write an expression for the number of fish in Adriana's aquarium.
   ii) Suppose Adriana's aquarium has 24 fish. Write an equation. Use it to find the number of fish in Linda's aquarium.

   c) **i)** Brett's aquarium has one-third as many fish as Linda's. Write an expression for the number of fish in Brett's aquarium.
   ii) Suppose Brett's aquarium has 4 fish. Write an equation. Use it to find the number of fish in Linda's aquarium.

6. Solve each equation.

   a) $x + 3 = 8$ **b)** $11 + 5z = -4$ **c)** $2y - 3 = 5$

7. Choose one equation from exercise 6. Write to explain how you solved it.

8. Simplify. Use the order of operations.

   a) $3 \times 5 - 2 \times 7$ **b)** $3(5 - 2 \times 7)$ **c)** $(3 \times 5 - 2)7$

   d) $3 - 5 \times 2 + 7$ **e)** $(3 - 5)(2 + 7)$ **f)** $3 - 5(2 + 7)$

The Distributive Law

You are planting both flowers and vegetables in a rectangular garden. To buy fertilizer for the garden, you need to know its area. You can calculate the area in two ways.

Method 1

Total area = width × length

Method 2

Total area = area with flowers + area with vegetables

1. Calculate the area of the garden using both methods. Are the two results the same?

2. Repeat exercise 1 using a rectangular garden with different measurements. Use positive rational numbers. Are the two results the same for this garden?

4 m

6 m

5 m

Since you calculated the area of the garden in *Investigation 1* using *Method 1* and *Method 2*, you can write:

$$5(4 + 6) = 5 \times 4 + 5 \times 6$$

You get similar results with other numbers:

$$3(7 + 2) = 3 \times 7 + 3 \times 2$$
$$4.5(2.4 + 6.3) = 4.5 \times 2.4 + 4.5 \times 6.3$$

In arithmetic, you write equations such as those above. In algebra, you use variables and write only one equation: $a(b + c) = ab + ac$. This equation is called the *distributive law* for multiplication over addition. In *Investigation 1*, exercise 2, you found that the variables a, b, and c can be positive rational numbers. Do you think the variables could be negative?

An Equation for the Distributive Law

1. **a)** Substitute some negative numbers for a, b, and c in the left side of
   $a(b + c) = ab + ac$.
   Substitute the same numbers in the right side.
   Do you get the same result on both sides?

   b) Repeat part a with other negative numbers. What kinds of numbers can a, b, and c represent in this equation?

2. There is also a distributive law for multiplication over subtraction. Make up some examples to illustrate this law.

Distributive Law

$a(b + c) = ab + ac$
$a(b - c) = ab - ac$ where a, b, and c can be any real numbers

---

We can use algebra tiles to represent algebraic expressions.

This tile is a 1-tile.
It represents one unit, or 1.

To represent -1, flip the tile.

This tile is a variable-tile. It represents a variable. For example, if you are using s, you can call this tile an s-tile. If you are using w, you call it a w-tile.

To represent the opposite of s, or $-s$, flip the tile.

To represent the expression $s + 4$ with algebra tiles, use one s-tile and four 1-tiles.

To represent $2w + 10$, use two w-tiles and ten 1-tiles.

To represent $2(w + 5)$, form two equal groups of tiles. Each group contains one w-tile and five 1-tiles.

The algebra tiles demonstrate an example of the distributive law:
$2(w + 5) = 2w + 10$

Algebra Tiles and the Distributive Law

1. What expression does each group of algebra tiles represent?

   a)    b)

2. Use algebra tiles to represent each expression.

   a) $2x + 1$ b) $3y - 5$

   c) $2 - n$ d) $-4x + 3$

3. Use algebra tiles to represent each expression. Then use the tiles to write the expression without brackets.

   a) $2(x + 4)$ b) $3(2x - 1)$

   c) $6(2 - a)$ d) $-2(2m - 3)$

4. In each part of exercise 3, compare the algebraic expression with the algebra-tiles expression.

   a) What patterns can you find?

   b) Without using the algebra tiles, how can you write an expression without brackets?

   c) Make up some examples to illustrate your method. Check with the algebra tiles.

Example 1

a) Use algebra tiles to represent the expression $5 - 2x$.

b) What is the value of this expression for each value of x?

    i) $x = 6$ **ii)** $x = -3$

c) Use algebra tiles to represent the expression $-(5 - 2x)$.

Solution

a) Use five 1-tiles and two flipped x-tiles.

b) i)

> ***Think ...***
>
> If each x-tile represents 6, each flipped x-tile represents -6. Replace each flipped x-tile with six flipped 1-tiles.

Since a 1-tile represents $+1$ and a flipped 1-tile represents -1, a pair of opposite tiles add to 0. Remove five 0-pairs, leaving seven flipped 1-tiles, or -7.

In symbols, substitute 6 for x and write:

$$5 - 2x = 5 - 2 \times 6$$
$$= 5 - 12$$
$$= -7$$

ii)

> ***Think ...***
>
> If each x-tile represents -3, each flipped x-tile represents 3. Replace each flipped x-tile with three 1-tiles. This gives eleven 1-tiles, or 11.

In symbols, substitute -3 for x, and write:

$$5 - 2x = 5 - 2(-3)$$
$$= 5 + 6$$
$$= 11$$

c) Just as $-x$ represents the opposite of x, so $-(5 - 2x)$ represents the opposite of $5 - 2x$. Start with the expression in the brackets (which is the same as in part a), and flip the tiles.

$-(5 - 2x) = -5 + 2x$, or $2x - 5$

Example 2

Use algebra tiles to represent each expression. Use the result to write the expression without brackets.

a) $2(3x - 4)$ **b)** $-3(p - 3)$

Solution

a)

> ***Think ...***
>
> 2 equal groups of tiles

Each group has three x-tiles and four flipped 1-tiles.

In all, there are six x-tiles and eight flipped 1-tiles.
This means that $2(3x - 4) = 6x - 8$

b)

> ***Think ...***
>
> 3 equal groups of tiles

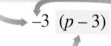

Each group has one p-tile and three flipped 1-tiles.

The negative sign means flip all the tiles.

There are three flipped p-tiles and nine 1-tiles.
This means that $-3(p - 3) = -3p + 9$

Instead of using algebra tiles, we can use the distributive law to write an expression without brackets. This process is called *expanding*.

Example 3

Expand using the distributive law.

a) $6(3n + 4)$

b) $-3(4b - 7)$

Solution

a) $6(3n + 4) = 6 \times 3n + 6 \times 4$
$= 18n + 24$

b) $-3(4b - 7) = (-3)(4b) + (-3)(-7)$
$= -12b + 21$

DISCUSSING the IDEAS

1. Decide if each statement is always true, sometimes true, or never true. Explain your answers.

   a) A 1-tile is positive and a flipped 1-tile is negative.

   b) A variable-tile is positive and a flipped variable-tile is negative.

   c) x is positive and $-x$ is negative.

2. Could a variable tile have a value of 0? Could it represent a rational number? Explain your answers.

3. How could you represent the number 0 using algebra tiles?

4. Can the distributive law be extended to the sum or difference of more than two terms? Explain.

6.1 EXERCISES

1. Write two expressions for the total area of the gardens.

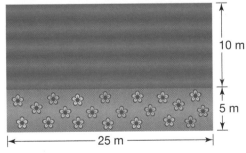

2. Use the distributive law to expand each product.

   a) $3(5 + 7)$

   b) $6(19 - 9)$

   c) $5(-4 + 6)$

   d) $6(2 + 7 + 1)$

   e) $3(2 - 1 + 9)$

   f) $5(-4 - 5 + 2)$

3. Which statement is equivalent to $3(2y - 5)$? Explain your choice.

   a) $2y - 15$ **b)** $6y - 15$ **c)** $2y + 15$ **d)** $6y - 5$

4. What expression does each group of algebra tiles represent?

   a)    **b)**

   c)    **d)**

5. Suppose you flipped all the tiles in exercise 4. What expression would each group of algebra tiles then represent?

6. Determine the value of each expression in exercise 4 when the variable represents 4, and when it represents −3.

7. **a)** Determine the value of each expression in exercise 5 when the variable represents 4, and when it represents −3.

   b) Compare your answers with those for exercise 6. What do you notice?

8. Expand using the distributive law.

   a) $3(5 + 8)$ **b)** $5(6 - 4)$ **c)** $11(5 - 7)$ **d)** $-6(8 - 4)$

   e) $12(5 - 6)$ **f)** $-4(7 - 9)$ **g)** $13(1 + h)$ **h)** $8(11 - d)$

   i) $4(k + 5)$ **j)** $-9(8 - x)$ **k)** $3(6 + m)$ **l)** $-5(f + 9)$

9. Expand using the distributive law.

   a) $5(4 + 10 + 2)$ **b)** $4(11 - 5 - 2)$ **c)** $9(4 + 5 - 8)$ **d)** $-8(9 - 2 + 8)$

B 10. Use algebra tiles to represent each expression. Determine the value of the expression when the variable represents 3, and when it represents −1.

   a) $3a + 5$ **b)** $-4c - 6$ **c)** $-2e + 4$ **d)** $-1 - 6g$

   e) $4q + 7$ **f)** $-6 - 3k$ **g)** $7 - 2t$ **h)** $-3 + 5s$

   i) $4z - 6$ **j)** $-3 + 2a$ **k)** $-3x + 5$ **l)** $-7 - k$

   m) $8 + 6c$ **n)** $-p - 4$ **o)** $6x + 1$ **p)** $-7 - 4t$

11. Use algebra tiles to represent each expression. Use the tiles to write the expression without brackets.

   a) $5(k + 1)$ **b)** $2(3 - 2w)$ **c)** $4(2m + 1)$ **d)** $-1(4 + 5y)$

   e) $-3(2 - p)$ **f)** $3(1 - 3b)$ **g)** $-2(4t - 5)$ **h)** $-4(2s + 2)$

12. Determine the value of each expression in exercise 11 when the variable represents −8.

13. Only two expressions in each set below are equal. Which ones are they? Use algebra tiles to justify your answer.

a) $3x + 2$ $3x − 2$ $2 + 3x$ $2 − 3x$

b) $−4g + 5$ $−5g + 4$ $−5g − 4$ $4 − 5g$

c) $2j − 7$ $7 − 2j$ $−7 − 2j$ $−2j + 7$

d) $−5b + 3$ $−3 − 5b$ $−5 + 3b$ $−5b − 3$

14. Expand using the distributive law.

a) $6(2.5y − 9.3)$ b) $1.4(2x + 7.5)$ c) $\frac{1}{2}(6 + 8z)$

d) $9(6.8x − 3.1)$ e) $−3.5(2 + 3m)$ f) $\frac{1}{3}(4 − 6z)$

15. Which of the following expressions is equal to $5(m + 3) − 16$? Explain.

a) $5(m + 3 − 16)$ b) $5m + 15 − 16$ c) $5m + 15 − 80$

16. Which of the following expressions is equal to $\frac{x + 4}{5}$? Explain your choice.

a) $5(x + 4)$ b) $\frac{1}{5}(x + 4)$ c) $x + 4 ÷ 5$

17. Which of the following expressions is equal to $\frac{2x − 3}{7}$? Explain.

a) $2(x − \frac{3}{7})$ b) $\frac{2}{7}(x − 3)$ c) $\frac{1}{7}(2x − 3)$

18. Expand using the distributive law.

a) $3(x + 2y − 7)$ b) $−2(a − 5b + 2)$ c) $−(6m − 7n)$

d) $4(9p + q − 9r)$ e) $5(x + 6y − 4)$ f) $3(7c − 9 + d)$

19. Expand each expression.

a) $2.5(n + 2)$ b) $3.2(2 − 1.5r)$ c) $2(x − 2)$ d) $2\pi(R − r)$

e) $−1.1(2c − 9)$ f) $3(3 + b)$ g) $13(\pi − 2y)$ h) $0.1(100d − 25)$

C 20. Do you think it is possible to illustrate expansions like those in exercise 18, parts e and f with the algebra tiles you have been using? If so, describe how you would do this. If not, describe a set of tiles for which it would be possible.

COMMUNICATING the IDEAS

What do you think the word "distribute" means? Look up this word in a dictionary. Why do you think the law $a(b + c) = ab + ac$ is called the distributive law? Write your ideas in your journal.

In arithmetic, you learned to add, subtract, multiply, and divide numbers.

In algebra, you will learn to add, subtract, multiply, and divide algebraic expressions.

When you use algebra tiles, the terms that are represented by the same type of tile are called *like* terms. All the terms represented by variable tiles are like terms. The terms represented by the 1-tiles are also like terms.

When you add or subtract expressions using algebra tiles, you use the Zero Principle.

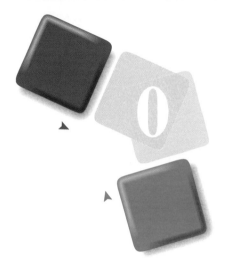

The Zero Principle

You know that a 1-tile and a flipped 1-tile add to 0. In fact, any two opposite tiles add to 0. This means that you can add or remove pairs of opposite tiles without changing an expression.

You see: or

You think:
The sum of each pair is 0.

You use the Zero Principle when you combine groups of tiles. For example, here are three groups of tiles that represent $4x$, $-2x$, and 5.

You think:
To combine them, you can use the Zero Principle to remove two pairs of opposite tiles. Two variable tiles and five 1-tiles remain. You cannot combine the variable tiles and 1-tiles since they are not the same type.

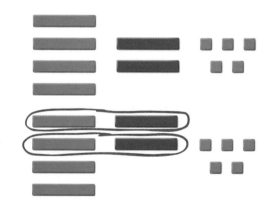

You write: $4x - 2x + 5 = 2x + 5$

The terms $4x$ and $-2x$ are like terms because they contain the same variable. Similarly, 7 and -3 are like terms. They contain no variables. They are called *constant* terms. The terms $2x$ and 5 are not like terms and cannot be combined.

When you combine like terms, you make the expression simpler than it was originally.

Example 1

a) Use algebra tiles to simplify the expression $4a + 3 + 2a - 4$.

b) What is the value of this expression for each value of a?

    i) $a = 8$ **ii)** $a = -2$

Solution

a)

> ***Think ...***
>
> four a-tiles   three 1-tiles
>
>   and two a-tiles   and four flipped 1-tiles
>
> $$4a + 3 + 2a - 4$$

From the tiles, $4a + 3 + 2a - 4 = 6a - 1$

b) **i)** When $a = 8$, the value of the expression is $6 \times 8 - 1 = 48 - 1$, or 47.

    ii) When $a = -2$, the value of the expression is $6 \times (-2) - 1 = -12 - 1$, or -13.

We could have simplified the expression in *Example 1* without using algebra tiles. We do this in *Example 2*.

Example 2

Simplify the expression $4a + 3 + 2a - 4$ by combining like terms.

Solution

$$4a + 3 + 2a - 4 = 4a + 2a + 3 - 4$$
$$= 6a - 1$$

Example 3

Use algebra tiles to combine like terms: $2(x + 2) - 3(2 - x)$

Solution

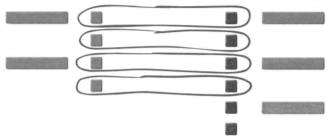

Think ...

Combine two groups of these tiles ...   ... and flip three groups of these tiles.

$$2(x + 2) \ - \ 3(2 - x)$$

two x-tiles and four 1-tiles   Flip six 1-tiles and three flipped x-tiles

From the tiles, $2(x + 2) - 3(2 - x) = 5x - 2$

When we do not use algebra tiles, we use the distributive law.

Example 4

Simplify the expression $2(x + 2) - 3(2 - x)$.

Solution

$$2(x + 2) - 3(2 - x) = 2x + 4 - 6 + 3x$$
$$= 2x + 3x + 4 - 6$$
$$= 5x - 2$$

DISCUSSING the IDEAS

1. At the bottom of page 262, we said that the terms $2x$ and 5 cannot be combined. Explain how algebra tiles can be used to show this.

2. In *Example 1*, we could have found the value of the expression without combining like terms. What advantage is there to combining like terms before substituting?

A **1.** Which are like terms?

a) $5x, -2x$ b) $3a, 7$ c) $2x, -1$ d) $4, 8$

e) $2x, 3y$ f) $-5c, c$ g) $-x, 4x$ h) $3, 3s$

i) $8k, -4k, 3$ j) $9p, -4, 7p$ k) $2s, 2t, 2u$ l) $-82, 6w, -8v$

2. There are ten pairs of like terms below. Find all ten pairs.

$2x$ $-3y$ $5x$ $-y$ 3 $-x$ 5 $4x$ -1

3. Combine like terms.

a)    b)    c)

4. Use algebra tiles to combine like terms.

a) $6s + 3s$ b) $4v - 2v$ c) $-5b + 2b + 4b$

d) $7p - p + 3p$ e) $-6c - 2c - c$ f) $6t + 5 + 2t$

g) $5 - 2a - 3a$ h) $11n - 12n + 6$ i) $9 - 4d + 3d$

j) $4u - 6 + u + 3$ k) $-k + 2k - 3k + 4k$ l) $-6q - 2q + q - 7$

5. Use algebra tiles to combine like terms. Determine the value of each simplified expression when $x = -2$, and when $x = 0$.

a) $3(x - 2) + 4$ b) $-x - 5 + 2(1 + 3x)$ c) $-3 + 4(1 - x) + 5x$

d) $-8(-x - 1) - 3x - 5$ e) $2(x + 3) - (5 - x)$ f) $-3(2 + 3x) + 8x - 3$

B **6.** Combine like terms. Use algebra tiles if you like.

a) $3x + 4x - 3x$ b) $-3a + 2a - a$ c) $-8 + 5c - 3c$

d) $3k - 2 - k + 6$ e) $5(2b + 1) + 3b$ f) $-4u + 8 - (2 + 3u)$

7. Simplify each expression. Determine its value when $x = 1$, and when $x = -1$.

a) $-7x + 12 - 2x$ b) $8x + 3 - 11x - 7$ c) $10(x - 5) + 7x - 2$

d) $9 + 3x - (8x - 12)$ e) $5x + 3(4x - 2) - 12$ f) $2(3x + 2) + 4(2 + x)$

8. Simplify each expression. Determine its value when $x = 4$, and when $x = -3$.

a) $4x + 2x - 2$ b) $5x - 6x - 2$ c) $11x - 5 - 7x - 4$

d) $9 + 3x - (8x - 12)$ e) $2x + 3(4x - 2)$ f) $-8(3 - 2x) - 7 - 6x$

9. Simplify each expression. Determine its value when the variable has the given value.

a) $4a + 7a - 3$ for $a = 3$ b) $-3m + 21 + 7m$ for $m = -7$

c) $15(s + 2) - s$ for $s = 0$ d) $20x - 3 - 6x$ for $x = 2.5$

10. Simplify each expression. Determine its value when $x = 7$, $x = -5$, and $x = 0$.

   a) $9x - 5 - 6x - 2x + 4$ **b)** $8x - 2 - 6x - 6$ **c)** $-3(x - 1) - (2x - 3)$

   d) $5x - 3(x - 4)$ **e)** $-(x - 2) + 4(3 - x)$ **f)** $7(1 - x) - 2(3x - 2)$

11. Simplify each expression.

   a) $7a + 3a + 2b - 5b$ **b)** $-3m + 2n - 7n + 4m$

   c) $45s + 15t - 7 - 5t - 5s$ **d)** $4x - 3y - (x - y)$

   e) $48p - 16q - 3r - 18p - 3r$ **f)** $-32g + 10 - 15g + 4h - 3$

   g) $-2(11 - 3c) + 2d - 9c$ **h)** $7(1 - x) - 3(1 - 2x)$

12. Simplify each expression.

   a) $m - 2n + 5m - n$ **b)** $2a + 3b - c - 3a - b + 5c$

   c) $3x - y + 7 - x + 6y - 7$ **d)** $13s - 16r - 4s - 6 + 3r + 10$

   e) $7(-2d - 3e - d + 4) - 6e - 8$ **f)** $5(q - 7m + 6q) - (11n + m + 7q)$

   g) $-(a - 5) - 2(3b - 5) + 3(2c - 5)$ **h)** $3(11x - 10y - 6x - 6y) - (2x - y)$

C **13.** Write expressions for the perimeter and the area of each figure.

   a)

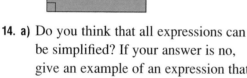

   b)

14. a) Do you think that all expressions can be simplified? If your answer is no, give an example of an expression that cannot be simplified.

   b) Which of these expressions do you think is the simpler? Explain.

      $7(x + y + z)$ $7x + 7y + 7z$

   c) Without using the words "simple," "simpler," or "simplest," explain what the word "simplify" means.

COMMUNICATING the IDEAS

Your friend phones you for help to simplify this expression: $3a - 2(a - 1)$

To simulate that you are talking on the telephone, sit back-to-back with another student. Provide that student with verbal instructions to simplify the expression.

Write another expression and reverse roles.

6.3　Solving Equations Algebraically

On page 253, you solved equations by inspection. That is, you looked at an equation and calculated the solution. Some equations cannot be easily solved this way. They must be solved algebraically.

When you have solved an equation, you can check your solution by following these steps:

- Substitute your solution for the variable in both sides of the original equation.
- Simplify both sides of the equation separately. If both sides simplify to the same number, your solution is correct.

Example 1

Solve each equation algebraically. Check your solutions.

a) $3x - 17 = 28$

b) $4 - 5k = 8 + k$

Solution

a)
$$3x - 17 = 28$$
Add 17 to each side.
$$3x - 17 + 17 = 28 + 17$$
$$3x = 45$$
Divide each side by 3.
$$\frac{3x}{3} = \frac{45}{3}$$
$$x = 15$$
Check: Substitute 15 for x in each side of the equation.
Left side $= 3(15) - 17$　Right side $= 28$
$$= 45 - 17$$
$$= 28$$
Since both sides are equal, $x = 15$ is correct.

b)
$$4 - 5k = 8 + k$$
Add $5k$ to each side.
$$4 - 5k + 5k = 8 + k + 5k$$
$$4 = 8 + 6k$$
Subtract 8 from each side.
$$4 - 8 = 8 + 6k - 8$$
$$-4 = 6k$$
Divide each side by 6.
$$\frac{-4}{6} = \frac{6k}{6}$$
$$k = -\frac{2}{3}$$
Check: Substitute $-\frac{2}{3}$ for k in each side of the equation.
Left side $= 4 - 5\left(-\frac{2}{3}\right)$　Right side $= 8 + \left(-\frac{2}{3}\right)$
$$= \frac{12}{3} + \frac{10}{3} \qquad\qquad = \frac{24}{3} - \frac{2}{3}$$
$$= \frac{22}{3} \qquad\qquad\quad = \frac{22}{3}$$
Since both sides are equal, $k = -\frac{2}{3}$ is correct.

Example 2

The grade 9 students from Loyalist Collegiate and Vocational Institute are planning a weekend trip to Toronto. The bus company charges $1416.16 for all transportation costs, including the driver's salary and accommodations. The cost for accommodations and admission to the various attractions the students will visit is $62.50 per student.

a) Write an equation to relate the total cost of the trip, C dollars, to the number of students, n, who go on the trip.

b) The total cost for a group of students was $3978.66. Substitute 3978.66 for C to get an equation in n. Solve the equation for n to determine how many students went.

c) **Academic Focus** Rearrange the equation in part a so you can figure out how many students went on the trip by looking at the total cost.

Solution

a) The number of students who go on the trip is n.
There is a fixed cost of $1416.16.
There is a cost of $62.50 for each student.
This is $62.5n$ dollars for all students.
Thus, the total cost of the trip, in dollars, is
$C = 1416.16 + 62.5n$

b) $C = 1416.16 + 62.5n$
Substitute 3978.66 for C.
$3978.66 = 1416.16 + 62.5n$
To solve for n, subtract 1416.16 from each side.
 $2562.5 = 62.5n$
Divide each side by 62.5.
     $41 = n$
Thus, 41 students went on the trip.

c) Rearrange the equation in part a to solve for n.
Subtract 1416.16 from each side of the equation.
$$C - 1416.16 = 1416.16 + 62.5n - 1416.16$$
$$C - 1416.16 = 62.5n$$
Divide each side by 62.5.
$$\frac{C - 1416.16}{62.5} = \frac{62.5n}{62.5}$$
$$\frac{C - 1416.16}{62.5} = n$$
You can use this formula: $n = \frac{C - 1416.16}{62.5}$

1. In the solution to *Example 1a*:

   a) Explain why you add 17 to each side.

   b) Explain why you divide each side by 3.

2. In the solution to *Example 1b*:

   a) Explain why you add $5k$ to each side.

   b) Explain why you subtract 8 from each side.

   c) Explain why you divide each side by 6.

3. The equation $C = 1416.16 + 62.5n$ was used in the solution to *Example 2a*. Explain what this equation means.

4. Explain how you could check the answer in the solution to *Example 2b*.

5. In the solution to *Example 2c*, the equation $n = \dfrac{C - 1416.16}{62.5}$ was obtained.

   a) Explain what this equation means.

   b) Explain how you could check that this equation is correct.

6.3 EXERCISES

1. Solve each equation. Check your solution.

   a) $5j = 15$ b) $4p = -20$ c) $x + 5 = 9$ d) $c - 5 = -2$

   e) $15 - p = 12$ f) $a + 6 = 8$ g) $-\dfrac{v}{2} = -2$ h) $\dfrac{t}{7} = 1$

   i) $3t = 27$ j) $8 = 15 - s$ k) $-6 = 3b$ l) $-3s = 9$

2. Solve each equation. Check your solution.

   a) $4v = 12$ b) $j + 27 = 30$ c) $24 - p = 20$ d) $-4c = -28$

   e) $q + 7 = 11$ f) $36 = -4h$ g) $-5g = 3$ h) $\dfrac{c}{7} = 6$

3. Refer to *Example 2* on page 268.

   a) How much would it cost for a group of 31 students to go on the trip?

   b) How much would it cost for a group of 24 students to go on the trip?

   c) The total cost for a group of students was $3728.66. How many students went?

4. Lester has $53 in savings. Each week he saves another $16. He represents his total savings with the equation $S = 53 + 16n$, where S is his savings in dollars, and n is the number of weeks.

   a) To determine how much money Lester will have after 3 weeks, substitute 3 for n.

b) Lester wants to buy a pair of in-line roller skates that cost $165, including all taxes. To determine how many weeks it will take him to save $165, substitute $165 for S. Solve the equation for n.

5. Nasmin has $15 and saves $4.25 per week. Mayumi has $20 and saves $3.50 per week.

a) For each girl, write an equation to show how much money she will have after n weeks.

b) Use the equations to determine how much each girl will have after 5 weeks.

c) Use the equations to determine which girl will be the first to have enough money to buy a computer game that costs $49.

6. Write an exercise similar to exercise 5. Prepare a solution for your exercise. Exchange exercises with a partner. Complete the exercise your partner wrote. Compare your solutions.

B 7. To rent a certain model of car for one day, a company charges $28.50 plus an additional charge of 15¢ for every kilometre driven. You can represent this cost with the equation $C = 28.50 + 0.15d$, where C is the cost, in dollars, and d is the distance driven, in kilometres.

a) To determine the cost for driving 200 km, substitute 200 for d.

b) Your budget allows you $75 to spend on a rental car for a day. To determine how far the car could be driven for $75, substitute 75 for C then solve the equation for d.

c) Why do you think the rental cost depends on the distance the car is driven?

8. Solve each equation.

a) $2x - 15 = 27$ b) $3a - 1 = 20$ c) $12 + 5y = -13$

d) $7p + 11 = -17$ e) $8z - 42 = 2z$ f) $3f = 12f + 21$

g) $-3 + x = -4x - 43$ h) $12m - 25 = 4m + 7$ i) $2e - 6 = -5 - 4e$

j) $24 - 4c = 15 - c$ k) $6b - 8 = 4 - 3b$ l) $-5p + 9 = 3p - 15$

9. **Mental Math** Look at exercises 1 to 8. Identify 4 equations that you solved using only mental calculations. Explain how you solved them.

10. Solve each equation. Check your solution.

a) $7 = 23 - 4x$ b) $3a - 10 = 10$ c) $8 - 2z = 5 + 3z$

d) $4m + 9 = 2m$ e) $12x + 17 = 10 - 2x$ f) $5 - 3k = -4$

g) $5x + 4 = 40$ h) $9 - 2a = a + 5$ i) $2 - 4x = 1 - x$

j) $3 + 7c = 2c - 3$ k) $2 = 9a - 3$ l) $5 - 6n = 2n + 5$

11. The cost, C dollars, to produce a school yearbook is given by the equation $C = 8000 + 9n$, where n is the number of yearbooks printed.

a) What does each term on the right side of the equation represent?

b) The yearbook committee has a budget of $10 000. To determine the number of yearbooks that can be produced for $10 000, substitute 10 000 for C then solve the equation for n.

c) How many yearbooks can be produced for $20 000?

12. Volcanoes and geysers illustrate that Earth's interior is very hot. The formula $T = 10d + 20$ is used to estimate the temperature, T degrees Celsius, at a depth of d kilometres.

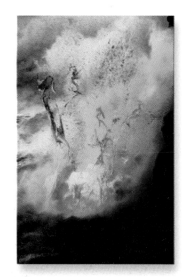

a) What does each term on the right side of the equation represent?

b) To estimate the depth where the temperature is 50°C, substitute 50 for T then solve the equation for d.

c) At what depth is the temperature 100°C?

13. The formula for the perimeter P of a rectangle with length l and width w is $P = 2l + 2w$. A rectangular field is 135 m long and requires 450 m of fencing to enclose it.

a) To determine the width of the field, substitute 450 for P, 135 for l, then solve the equation for w.

b) Another field is 45 m wide and requires 380 m of fencing. How long is the field?

Hockey Standings

14. In hockey standings, 2 points are given for a win, and 1 point is given for a tie.

a) For each team in the list, check that the points scored are correct.

b) Suppose you know the number of wins and ties that a hockey team has in a season. How could you determine the team's total points?

c) Write an equation to determine a team's total points.

Eastern Conference Northeast Divison

	W	L	T	Pts
Buffalo	19	7	5	43
Toronto	19	13	2	40
Boston	15	12	6	36
Ottawa	15	13	4	34
Montreal	9	18	7	25

15. Use the equation from exercise 14.

a) A team had 28 wins and 6 ties. How many points did it have?

b) A team had 83 points. It had 37 wins. How many ties did it have?

c) A team had 79 points. It had 11 ties. How many wins did it have?

16. One side of a rectangle is 6 cm long. The perimeter of the rectangle is numerically equal to its area.

a) What do you think "numerically equal" means?

b) Determine the lengths of the other sides of the rectangle.

c) Verify your answer by calculating the perimeter and area of the rectangle.

C **17.** In exercise 16, one side of the rectangle was 6 cm long.

a) Suppose one side of the rectangle was 1 cm long. Would it still be possible for the perimeter to be numerically equal to the area? Explain.

b) For what lengths of the given side could the perimeter be numerically equal to the area?

COMMUNICATING the IDEAS

Your friend phones you to solve this equation: $3x + 7 = x - 5$

To simulate talking on the phone, sit back-to-back with another student. Tell that student how to solve the equation. Write another equation and reverse roles.

Later in this chapter you will learn how to use equations to solve problems. The equations are usually slightly more complicated than the equations you have been working with up to now. Before you solve these equations, you need to simplify them by performing the same operations on each side.

INVESTIGATION

Solving Equations That Need Simplifying

1. What do you think is the first step to solve each equation?
   Complete this step, then continue the solution.

   a) $4x + 3x = 35$ **b)** $6n - 7 - 2n = 21$ **c)** $4 = 2w + 16 + w - 5$

2. Create one equation similar to those in exercise 1, then solve it.

3. What do you think is the first step to solve each equation?
   Complete this step, then continue the solution.

   a) $2(x + 3) = 14$ **b)** $2(3m - 4) = 11$ **c)** $9 = -3(2t - 7)$

4. Create one equation similar to those in exercise 3, then solve it.

ACADEMIC FOCUS

5. Solve each equation. Your first step should be to multiply every term by a common denominator.

   a) $\frac{12}{x} = 6$ **b)** $\frac{b}{3} = 4 + b$ **c)** $\frac{1}{4}n + \frac{1}{2} = 3$

6. Create one equation similar to those in exercise 5, then solve it.

In the *Investigation*, you should have found that the equations were simplified by:

- combining like terms
- using the distributive law, or
- eliminating the denominators

When solving an equation, simplify each side before applying the same operation to each side.

Example 1

Solve: $3(a - 3) + 4a + 7 = 5a - 3$

Solution

$3(a - 3) + 4a + 7 = 5a - 3$
Simplify the left side.

$3a - 9 + 4a + 7 = 5a - 3$

$7a - 2 = 5a - 3$

Add 2 to each side.

$7a - 2 + 2 = 5a - 3 + 2$

$7a = 5a - 1$

Subtract $5a$ from each side.

$7a - 5a = 5a - 5a - 1$

$2a = -1$

Divide each side by 2.

$\quad \frac{2a}{2} = \frac{-1}{2}$

$a = -\frac{1}{2}$

When an equation contains fractions, multiply each side by a common denominator.

Example 2   Academic Focus

Solve and check: $\frac{x}{2} + 1 = \frac{2x}{3} - 3$

Solution

$\frac{x}{2} + 1 = \frac{2x}{3} - 3$

Multiply each side by a common denominator, 6.

$6\left(\frac{x}{2} + 1\right) = 6\left(\frac{2x}{3} - 3\right)$

$(6)\left(\frac{x}{2}\right) + (6)(1) = (6)\left(\frac{2x}{3}\right) - (6)(3)$

$3x + 6 = 4x - 18$

Subtract 6 from each side.

$3x + 6 - 6 = 4x - 18 - 6$

$3x = 4x - 24$

Subtract $4x$ from each side.

$3x - 4x = 4x - 4x - 24$

$-x = -24$

Multiply each side by −1.

$$x = 24$$

Check: Substitute 24 for x in each side of the equation.

Left side $= \frac{24}{2} + 1$ Right side $= \frac{2(24)}{3} - 3$

$\qquad\qquad = 12 + 1 \qquad\qquad\qquad = \frac{48}{3} - 3$

$\qquad\qquad = 13 \qquad\qquad\qquad\qquad = 16 - 3$

$\qquad\qquad\qquad\qquad\qquad\qquad\qquad = 13$

Since both sides are equal, $x = 24$ is correct.

DISCUSSING the IDEAS

1. The solution to *Example 1* shows one way to solve the equation algebraically. Explain some other ways the equation could have been solved algebraically.

2. **Academic Focus** In the solution to *Example 2*, the first step was to multiply each side by a common denominator, 6.

   a) What other step could have been done first?

   b) Which step do you think is easier to do first? Explain.

   c) Could other common denominators be used? Explain.

6.4 EXERCISES

1. Solve each equation. Check your solution.

   a) $4b - 8b = 24$ **b)** $-27 = -9t + 6t + 3$ **c)** $13 + 4q = -2q + 12 + q$

   d) $24 - 6j = 36$ **e)** $7 + 7k = 2k - 8$ **f)** $6s - 30 = 24$

   g) $30 = 6 - 30w$ **h)** $4x + 4 = 14x - 6$ **i)** $9k - 12 = 3k$

2. **Mental Math** Which equations in exercise 1 were you able to solve using only mental math? What makes them easier to solve without pencil and paper? Explain.

3. Solve and round the answers to the nearest tenth.

   a) $2.5x - 4 + 1.2x = 3.5$ **b)** $-7.2 = 1.9 - 3.2x - 0.9 - 2.1x$

   c) $5.9 - (3x + 2.4) = 0.5x$ **d)** $1.2x + 3.2(2.5 - x) = 40$

4. Academic Focus Solve each equation.

a) $7x - 3x + 5 = 7$ b) $6 = 4x - x + 9$ c) $3(n + 2) = 21$

d) $2(x + 13) = 3(5 - x)$ e) $-(3d + 4) = 5(2 - d)$ f) $4(1 - 2j) = 7(2j + 10)$

g) $\frac{4}{3}d = 12$ h) $\frac{3}{7}p = \frac{1}{2}$ i) $\frac{x}{5} = 2 + \frac{x}{3}$

5. Academic Focus For each equation, decide which of the other two equations is equivalent to it. Explain your choice.

a) $\frac{3x}{2} + \frac{9}{5} = 12$ b) $5 = \frac{9}{4} - \frac{r}{3}$

      $3x + 9 = 120$ $60 = 27 - 4r$

      $15x + 18 = 120$ $5 = 27 - 4r$

6. Solve each equation. Check your solution.

a) $4x + 6x = -20$ b) $5c + 2c + 6 = 34$

c) $4y - 7y = 18$ d) $50 = 8x - x + 1$

e) $12 = 2x - 7x - 8$ f) $-10 = -n + 2 - 2n$

g) $3x - 2 + x = 5 + 7x - 3$ h) $2.5x + 1.5x = 6$

7. Solve each equation.

a) $2(x - 4) = 10$ b) $5(x - 6) = -15$ c) $2(4 - 3m) = 13$

d) $-3(n + 2) = 12$ e) $7 = -2(-3 - y)$ f) $3(2t + 6) = 0$

8. Find the equations you created in the *Investigation*. Exchange equations with another student. Solve the student's equations. Compare your solution with the student's solutions. Explain any differences.

9. Solve each equation.

a) $9x - 1 - 7x - 4 = 5x$ b) $3(1 - 2y) + y = 2$ c) $4 = 6 - 2(x + 1)$

d) $-3(2 - a) - a = 1$ e) $-2(3n - 1) + 2n = 4$ f) $2(p + 1) = 3(p - 1)$

10. Academic Focus Solve each equation.

a) $\frac{1}{7}x = -8$ b) $13 = \frac{-4}{x}$ c) $1 - \frac{y}{5} = 3$ d) $\frac{3}{2} = \frac{7}{8}k$

e) $\frac{x}{2} - 1 = 4$ f) $2 + \frac{n}{3} = 10$ g) $\frac{x}{4} - \frac{2}{3} = 2$ h) $\frac{a}{3} - 3 = \frac{5}{6}$

11. Keyboarding speed, S, is measured in words per minute. It is calculated using the equation $S = \frac{w - 10e}{5}$, where w is the number of words input in 5 min and e is the number of errors. In keyboarding, a word is 5 characters. So, to determine the number of words input, count the number of characters and divide by 5.

a) A person input 275 words in 5 min and made 8 errors. What was the speed?

b) A person input 1250 characters in 5 min and had a speed of 40 words/min. How many errors were made?

c) A person made 3 errors in 5 min and had a speed of 30 words/min. How many words were typed?

12. Canada started using the Celsius scale for temperatures in the 1970s. Suppose a tourist from the United States wants to convert a Celsius temperature to Fahrenheit. Let C represent a temperature reading in degrees Celsius. Let F represent the equivalent reading in degrees Fahrenheit.

a) An approximate rule for converting Celsius to Fahrenheit is "to double and add 30." Write a corresponding equation for F.

b) Recall the approximate rule for converting a Fahrenheit temperature to Celsius, on page 149. Express this rule as an equation.

c) The exact equation for converting Celsius temperatures to Fahrenheit is $F = 1.8C + 32$. Choose some values of C. Determine how closely the approximate rule gives the correct Fahrenheit temperatures.

d) Determine an exact equation for converting a Fahrenheit temperature to Celsius.

13. Set up the spreadsheet below. It compares the approximate and exact conversions in exercise 12 parts a and c. Adjust the Celsius values by entering new numbers in cell A4. Include some negative values among those you try. When are the results of the approximate equation closest to those of the exact equation?

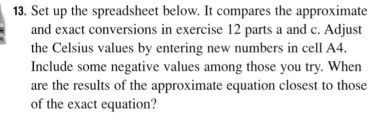

	A	B	C	D
1	Celsius to Fahrenheit Converter			
2				
3	Celsius	Approximate	Exact	Difference
4	0	=A4*2+30	=A4*1.8+32	=C4-B4

COMMUNICATING the IDEAS

You could check the solution of an equation by repeating the steps you used to solve it. In your journal, explain whether you think it is better to substitute your solution into the original equation. Why should each side be simplified separately when checking? Use an example in your explanation.

Consider this problem:

A plane left Halifax, bound for Vancouver. The plane landed in Ottawa and Winnipeg. In Ottawa, 43 passengers left the plane and 5 others came on. In Winnipeg, half the passengers left the plane and 64 came on. There were 130 passengers on the plane when it left Winnipeg. How many were on the plane when it left Halifax?

INVESTIGATION

How Many on the Airplane?

Solve the problem above using systematic trial.

1. Assume 120 passengers were on the plane when it left Halifax.

   a) How many passengers were on the plane when it left Ottawa?

   b) How many passengers were on the plane when it left Winnipeg?

2. How does your answer to exercise 1b compare with the number of passengers (130) in the problem?

3. Choose another number for the number of passengers on the plane when it left Halifax. Do you choose a number greater than 120 or less than 120? Explain.

4. Repeat exercises 1 and 2 for the number you chose.

5. Continue to repeat exercise 3, then exercises 1 and 2. Refine your estimates until you get 130 passengers leaving Winnipeg.

6. How many passengers were on the plane when it left Halifax?

To complete the *Investigation*, you probably had to repeat exercises 1 to 3 several times. You can solve this problem quicker with a spreadsheet.

Planning a spreadsheet

Use this diagram to help you plan your spreadsheet. The formulas you need have been provided.

	A	B
1	Plane Problem	
2		
3		Passengers
4	Halifax	120
5	Ottawa	=B4-43+5
6	Winnipeg	=0.5*B5+64

Using the computer

Start your spreadsheet program.
Input the information from the spreadsheet above.

Move to cell B4 and change the number to 200. What happens to the numbers in cells B5 and B6? Keep changing the number in cell B4 until 130 appears in cell B6.
How many passengers were on the plane when it left Halifax?

Solving a problem by systematic trial with a spreadsheet involves three steps:

Step 1 Plan the cells you need to solve the problem.

This is the most important step, because you are designing the spreadsheet to solve your problem. In the example, this step involves deciding that you need a cell for each number of passengers on the plane when it leaves Halifax, Ottawa, and Winnipeg.

Step 2 Enter numbers and formulas in the cells.

To complete this step, you must know how to calculate the numbers in the cells. For example, in the example you must know that the number in cell B5 is found by subtracting 43 from the number in cell B4, then adding 5.

Step 3 Solve the problem by changing the number in one cell.

By changing the number in cell B4, you were able to solve the problem.

Refer to the spreadsheet on page 279.

1. a) Why was 120 entered in cell B4?

b) Could other numbers have been used in cell B4? Explain.

c) Explain the formulas in cells B5 and B6.

2. In the problem on page 278, half the passengers got off the plane in Winnipeg. Suppose the following fractions of the passengers got off instead. For each fraction, explain how the formula in cell B6 would change. Then solve the new problem.

a) $\frac{1}{3}$ **b)** $\frac{2}{3}$ **c)** $\frac{1}{4}$ **d)** $\frac{3}{4}$

6.5   EXERCISES

1. A vending machine contains $3.50 in dimes and quarters. There are 23 coins in all. How many dimes and how many quarters are there?

a) Explain the formulas in columns B and C.

	A	B	C
1	Dimes and Quarters		
2		Number	Value
3	Dimes		=0.1*B3
4	Quarters	=23-B3	=0.25*B4
5	Total	=B3+B4	=C3+C4

b) In cell B3, enter any natural number between 1 and 23.

c) By entering different numbers in cell B3, solve the problem.

Create your own spreadsheet to complete each of exercises 2 to 7.

2. The length of a rectangular pool is 28.5 m greater than its width. The perimeter of the pool is 143.0 m. What are the dimensions of the pool?

3. Find four consecutive integers so that if the first is increased by 2, the second decreased by 2, then the third multiplied by 2, and the fourth divided by 2, then the sum of the four resulting numbers is 200.

4. There are 44 cm of trim to put around the edge of a triangular sign. Two sides of the triangle must be 8 cm shorter than the third side. All the trim is used. What must the side lengths of the sign be?

5. A hamburger and a large order of fries cost $4.20. The hamburger cost 40¢ more than the fries. How much did the hamburger cost?

6. There are equal numbers of nickels, dimes, and quarters. Their total value is $4.00. How many of each kind of coin are there?

7. A 72-cm piece of wire is cut into two pieces. One piece is twice as long as the other. How long is each piece?

8. Choose one exercise from exercises 2 to 7. Write to explain how you completed it using a spreadsheet.

Estimating Heights

There are formulas that relate the sizes of some parts of the human body. These formulas are approximately the same for all people. For example, suppose you know only the length of a person's radius bone, r centimetres. The formulas to estimate the height, h centimetres, are given below. Substitute the value for r in the appropriate formula, then solve for h.

Radius

Female: $h = 3.34r + 81.2$ Male: $h = 3.27r + 85.9$

9. Set up this spreadsheet.

	A	B	C	D
1	Estimating heights			
2				
3	Length of radius	Height of female	Height of male	Difference
4		=3.34*A4+81.2	=3.27*A4+85.9	=C4-B4
5	=A4+0.5	=3.34*A5+81.2	=3.27*A5+85.9	=C5-B5

Copy the formulas in row 5 to row 6, and beyond. Describe what each formula does. Use this spreadsheet to complete exercises 10 to 12.

10. A radius bone 24.5 cm long was found. Estimate the height if the bone was from a female and if the bone was from a male.

11. For a female, choose 7 values of r between 20 cm and 30 cm. Estimate the corresponding values of h. Make a table of values, then draw a graph.

12. Repeat exercise 11 for a male. Choose values of r between 22 cm and 35 cm.

When you solve a problem, is it easier to use a spreadsheet or write an equation? Explain in your journal and give at least one example to support your comments.

6.6 Designing Mixtures

On page 251, you considered the following problem encountered by Marika, who owns a bulk-food store.

Peanut-Pecan Problem

Peanuts sell at $5/kg and pecans sell at $20/kg. Marika wants to make 30 kg of a mixture of peanuts and pecans that will sell at $10/kg. How many kilograms of peanuts and pecans should she use?

In this section, you will consider some models for solving this problem. Since Marika may need to solve similar problems involving other prices or foods, you will also consider how the model could be applied to similar problems. To avoid duplicating these problems later, they are stated here.

Other Peanut-Pecan Problems (same unit prices)

How many kilograms of peanuts and pecans should Marika use if she wants each mixture?

i) 60 kg of a mixture to sell at $10/kg

ii) 30 kg of a mixture to sell at $8/kg

iii) 20 kg of a mixture to sell at $12/kg

Another Peanut-Pecan Problem (different unit prices)

Peanuts sell at $4.29/kg and pecans sell at $22.79/kg. Marika wants 100 kg of a mixture to sell at $9.49/kg. How many kilograms of peanuts and pecans should Marika use?

Candy Problem

Marika has two grades of candy that she plans to mix to make packages of assorted candy. The price for one candy is $7.50/kg. The price for the other candy is $5.00/kg. Marika wants to make 10 kg of assorted candy to sell at $6.00/kg. How many kilograms of each kind of candy should Marika mix?

Hamburger Problem

Ground chuck is made by combining cuts of beef and fat trim. The amount of fat in ground chuck is limited by government regulations to no more than 25%. A butcher has a supply of beef with fat content 20%. He also has a supply of fat trim with fat content 100%. He wants to make 20 kg of ground chuck with a fat content of 25%. How much beef and how much fat should he use?

Systematic Trial Model

Consider the Peanut-Pecan Problem on page 282.

1.

> **Think ...**
>
> You want 30 kg of the mixture to have a total value of $300.
> You could guess the masses of peanuts and pecans that add to 30 kg.
> You could calculate how much these are worth and compare that money with $300.

a) Estimate masses of peanuts and pecans that you think might be reasonable.

b) What is the total value? Compare with $300 and revise your estimates.

c) Repeat parts a and b until you have a combination of peanuts and pecans worth $300. What is the answer to the problem?

A spreadsheet is an ideal tool for solving problems using systematic trial.

2. Use a spreadsheet program.

Setup Enter the data in the cells as shown. Format the cells in columns B and D to show numbers to 2 decimal places.

	A	B	C	D
1		Unit price	Mass	Value
2		$/kg	kg	$
3	Peanuts	5.00		=B3*C3
4	Pecans	20.00	=30-C3	=B4*C4
5	Total value			=D3+D4

a) Explain the formulas in columns C and D.

b) Enter your estimate for the number of peanuts in cell C3. Change the number in cell C3 until the total value in cell D5 is $300.00. What is the answer to the problem?

3. Would systematic trial be a useful way to solve any of the Other Peanut-Pecan Problems on page 282? Explain.

Algebraic Model

Consider the Peanut-Pecan Problem on page 282.

4.

> **Think ...**
>
> Suppose you know the mass of the peanuts in kilograms.
> How would you find the mass of the pecans?
> How would you find the value of the peanuts?
> How would you find the value of the pecans?

Let x represent the mass of the peanuts in kilograms. Use your answers to the above questions to write an expression in x for:

- the mass of pecans
- the value of the peanuts
- the value of the pecans
- the total value of the peanuts and pecans

You know that the total value is $300. Use this information to write an equation in x. Solve the equation. What is the mass of the peanuts? What is the mass of the pecans? What is the answer to the problem?

Note: Save your solution to this problem for use later (page 296, exercise 9c).

5. Modify your equation in exercise 4 so that you can use an equation to solve these problems on page 282.

   a) Other Peanut-Pecan Problems (same unit prices)

   b) Another Peanut-Pecan Problem (different unit prices)

6. Is the algebraic model a useful model to solve these kinds of problems? Explain.

Reasoning Model

Consider the Peanut-Pecan Problem on page 282.

7.

> **Think ...**
> You want 30 kg of the mixture to have a total value of $300.
> Suppose all 30 kg were peanuts.

   a) What is the value of 30 kg of peanuts?

   b) How much more is the desired mixture worth? Where does this extra value come from?

   c) How much more value comes from each kilogram of pecans? What mass of pecans must there be?

   d) What mass of peanuts must there be? What is the answer to the problem?

   Note: Save your solution to this problem for use later (page 296, exercise 11).

8. Use reasoning to solve these problems on page 282.

   a) Other Peanut-Pecan Problems (same unit prices)

   b) Another Peanut-Pecan Problem (different unit prices)

9. Is the reasoning model a useful model to solve these kinds of problems? Explain.

Recommending a Model

Marika often combines two foods selling at different prices to make a mixture selling at a third price.

10. Explain why the third price should be between the first two prices.

11. Marika could use any of the three models described above.

a) List some advantages and disadvantages of each model.

b) Which model would you recommend to Marika? Explain.

12. Consider the Candy Problem and the Hamburger Problem on page 282. Use the model you recommended in exercise 11b to solve each problem.

Extending the Model

Consider these two problems.
A vending machine contains $3.50 in dimes and quarters. There are 23 coins in all. How many dimes and how many quarters are there?

When Nigel exercises, he jogs at 10 km/h and cycles at 25 km/h. In one week, he exercised for 23 h and covered 350 km. How much time did he spend jogging that week? How much time did he spend cycling?

13. a) Use any model from pages 283-284 to solve each problem above.

b) Compare the two problems.

　i) In what ways are they similar? In what ways are they different?

　ii) In what ways are they similar to the Peanut-Pecan problem?

Varying the Data

14. Academic Focus Consider the Peanut-Pecan Problem on page 282. Describe how the answer to this problem changes in each case.

a) The price of peanuts is higher or lower.

b) The price of pecans is higher or lower.

We will return to these kinds of problems in Section 6.8.

COMMUNICATING *the* IDEAS

In your journal, write a set of instructions for Marika to determine the masses of two foods to mix together to form a mixture to sell at a certain price. Illustrate your instructions with an example different from the problems above.

Every October, Canine Visions Canada sponsors a national Walk-a-dog-a-thon. The money raised provides blind and visually-impaired Canadians with a free 26-day dog guide handling course.

Last year, Ashok Krishnan and Lisa Crosbie took part in the walk-a-thon. Lisa twisted her ankle during the walk and had to drop out. Ashok completed the walk. Ashok walked 6 km farther than Lisa. Together they walked a total distance of 14 km. How far did Lisa walk?

INVESTIGATION

Problem Solving

1. Try to solve the problem above.

2. Several methods for solving problems are described on pages 283-284. Did you use one of these methods? Explain.

3. Compare your solution to the problem with the solutions from other students. Did every student solve the problem in the same way?

4. If you haven't done so already, try to solve the problem using an equation.
Suppose you know how far Lisa walked.
How would you determine how far Ashok walked?
What is the total distance they both walked?
Let x kilometres represent the distance Lisa walked.
Write an expression to represent the distance Ashok walked.
Since you know the total distance, write an equation.
Solve the equation to obtain the answer to the problem.
Check that your answer is correct.

You can solve a problem in many ways. One method is to use an equation. When you use an equation to solve a problem, follow these steps.

- Use a variable to represent the unknown quantity.
- Express any other unknown quantities in terms of this variable, if possible.
- Write an equation, then solve it.
- State the answer to the problem.
- Check the answer by substituting in the problem. Also check that the solution is reasonable.

Example

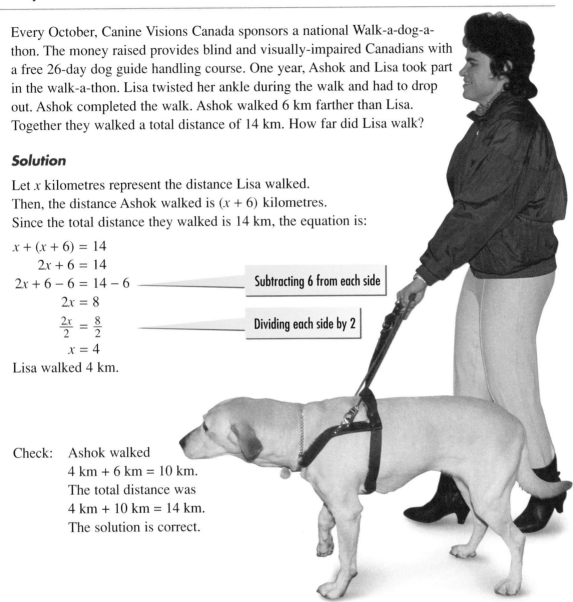

Every October, Canine Visions Canada sponsors a national Walk-a-dog-a-thon. The money raised provides blind and visually-impaired Canadians with a free 26-day dog guide handling course. One year, Ashok and Lisa took part in the walk-a-thon. Lisa twisted her ankle during the walk and had to drop out. Ashok completed the walk. Ashok walked 6 km farther than Lisa. Together they walked a total distance of 14 km. How far did Lisa walk?

Solution

Let x kilometres represent the distance Lisa walked.
Then, the distance Ashok walked is $(x + 6)$ kilometres.
Since the total distance they walked is 14 km, the equation is:

$$x + (x + 6) = 14$$
$$2x + 6 = 14$$
$$2x + 6 - 6 = 14 - 6 \qquad \text{— Subtracting 6 from each side}$$
$$2x = 8$$
$$\frac{2x}{2} = \frac{8}{2} \qquad \text{— Dividing each side by 2}$$
$$x = 4$$

Lisa walked 4 km.

Check: Ashok walked
4 km + 6 km = 10 km.
The total distance was
4 km + 10 km = 14 km.
The solution is correct.

DISCUSSING the IDEAS

1. Suppose the *Example* had asked how far Ashok walked. The solution to the *Example* provides an answer. Solve the problem by letting y kilometres represent the distance Ashok walked, then use an equation. Compare your equation with the equation in the *Example*. How are the equations similar? How are they different?

For each of exercises 1 to 4, write algebraic expressions to complete parts a and b. Use these expressions to write an equation for part c. Solve the equation. Check that your answer satisfies the conditions of the problem.

A 1. Ravi is 8 years older than Natasha. Let Natasha's age be a years.

 a) Ravi's age is ☐ years.

 b) The sum of Ravi's and Natasha's ages is ☐ years.

 c) The sum of their ages is 42. Find their ages.

2. The ages of Kirsten and Victor total 27 years. Let y years represent Kirsten's age.

 a) Victor's age is ☐ years.

 b) Twice Kirsten's age is ☐ years.

 c) Victor's age plus twice Kirsten's age is 43. Find Kirsten's and Victor's ages.

3. The combined mass of a dog and a cat is 28 kg. Let the cat's mass be m kilograms.

 a) The dog's mass is ☐ kilograms.

 b) Three times the cat's mass is ☐ kilograms.

 c) The dog is three times as heavy as the cat. Find the mass of the dog and of the cat.

4. Sydney's mass is 7.5 kg less than her twin brother Shelby's. Let s kilograms represent Shelby's mass.

 a) Sydney's mass is ☐ kilograms.

 b) The sum of their masses is ☐ kilograms.

 c) The sum of their masses is 116.5 kg. Find the mass of Sydney and of Shelby.

B 5. a) What do you think is the answer to this problem? A bottle and a cork cost $1.10. The bottle costs $1 more than the cork. How much does the cork cost?

 b) Solve the problem using an equation, and by reasoning out the solution.

6. Members of the school band sold chocolate bars to raise money. Livio sold twice as many bars as Shaun. They sold a total of 48 bars. How many did each boy sell?

7. Marisa and Sandy ran as far as they could in 30 minutes. Sandy ran 2.5 km farther than Marisa. They ran a total distance of 9.5 km. How far did each girl run?

8. Jaquie and her brother Michel entered a weekend fishing derby. The mass of fish Jaquie caught was four times the mass of Michel's catch. Their total catch was 59 kg. What mass of fish did each person catch?

9. Choose one exercise from exercises 6 to 8. Write to explain how you used an equation to complete it.

Keeping Ships Afloat

To keep an oil tanker balanced and stable, the crew replaces the cargo that is offloaded at each port with sea water. This water is used as ballast.

The mass of cargo offloaded is measured in kilograms. The volume of water taken on is measured in litres. To compare the mass of the cargo with the mass of the water, we use density.

Density is the mass of a unit volume of a substance. A material with its molecules packed tightly together, like metal, has a greater density than a material with more space between its molecules, like wood. Density varies with temperature.

The density, D, of a substance is the quotient of its mass, M, and volume, V. The formula is $D = \frac{M}{V}$.
The mass, M, is the product of density, D, and volume, V. The formula is $M = DV$.
The volume, V, is the quotient of mass, M, and density, D. The formula is $V = \frac{M}{D}$.

In this example, the mass is measured in tonnes (t) and the density in kilograms per litre (kg/L). Recall that 1 t = 1000 kg.

10. A tanker is to be loaded with 140 000 t of Kuparuk crude oil from the Alaska North Slope.

   a) The temperature in port when the oil is loaded is 21°C. At this temperature, the density of sea water is 1.030 kg/L. What volume of sea water must be dumped to allow for this cargo to be loaded?

   b) When the oil is offloaded at its destination, the temperature is only 15°C. At this temperature, the density of sea water is 1.025 kg/L. What volume of sea water must be taken on as ballast to replace the offloaded oil?

11. a) Kuparuk crude oil has a density of 0.9150 kg/L at 21°C. What is the volume of the oil loaded in exercise 10a?

   b) The density of Kuparuk crude oil at 15°C is 0.8862 kg/L. What is the volume of the oil offloaded in exercise 10b?

12. Find two consecutive numbers with a sum of 273.

13. One number is 0.25 less than another number. The sum of the two numbers is 7.25. What are the numbers?

14. A package deal for skis and boots costs $225. The skis cost $60 more than the boots. How much do the skis cost?

15. There are 500 cm of trim to frame a banner. The banner is 22 cm wide. How long can it be?

22 cm

16. A macramé cord with a length of 118 cm is cut into three pieces. One piece is 18 cm longer than the shortest piece. The third piece is three times as long as the shortest piece. How long are the three pieces of cord?

17. An airplane travels eight times as fast as a car. The difference in their speeds is 420 km/h. How fast is each vehicle travelling?

18. Mental Math Were there any exercises you could complete using mental math, without writing an equation? If so, explain how you performed the calculations mentally.

19. Make up a problem to solve using an equation. Solve your problem. Exchange problems with a classmate. Solve your classmate's problem, then compare solutions to the same problem.

C **20.** There are 500 cm of trim to frame a banner. The banner must be between 20 cm and 35 cm wide.

   a) What are the possible lengths of the banner?

   b) Suppose the width increases by 1 cm. What happens to the length?

   c) Draw a graph of the length of the banner against the width.

21. The difference between two numbers is 96. One number is nine times the other. How many pairs of numbers can you find that satisfy these conditions? What are the numbers?

COMMUNICATING *the* IDEAS

Using an equation is only one method to solve a problem. What are some of the advantages and disadvantages of using an equation? Write your ideas in your journal.

6.8 Mixtures and Linear Relations

On pages 283-284, you developed some mathematical models to solve this problem:

Peanut-Pecan Problem

Peanuts sell at $5/kg and pecans sell at $20/kg. Marika wants to make 30 kg of a mixture of peanuts and pecans that will sell at $10/kg. How many kilograms of peanuts and pecans should she use?

A graphical model to solve the problem is described below.

Graphical Model

Think ...

Since peanuts cost $5/kg, the graph of the value of the peanuts against mass is a straight line through the origin, with slope 5.

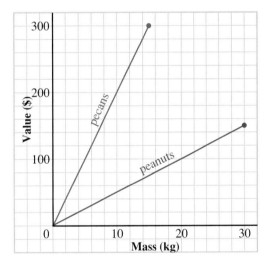

We can write 5 as $\frac{100}{20}$. From the origin, move right 20, then up 100. Mark a point. Draw a line through this point and the origin.

Think ...

Since pecans cost $20/kg, the graph of the value of the pecans against mass is a straight line through the origin, with slope 20.

We can write 20 as $\frac{200}{10}$. From the origin, move right 10, then up 200. Mark a point. Draw a line through this point and the origin.

We can draw these lines on another graph in a different way to solve the problem.

Visualize an empty container. The origin (0, 0) represents the mass and value of its contents.

Suppose Marika starts putting peanuts in the container. Draw a line through (0, 0) with slope 5 to represent the value of the peanuts. Adding peanuts corresponds to moving along this line. Since we do not know the mass of peanuts Marika needs to add, we do not know how far along this line to go.

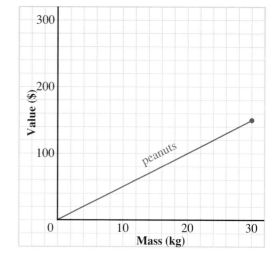

However, we do know that when we start adding pecans, the cost increases from $5/kg to $20/kg. So, the slope of the graph will change from 5 to 20. Also, we want to have 30 kg of a mixture that is worth $300.

Draw a line through B(30, 300) with slope 20. That is, start at B(30, 300), move down 200, then left 10. Mark a point. Draw a line through this point and B.

The lines intersect at the point A(20, 100). This means that there should be 20 kg of peanuts worth $100.

Visualize moving along the first line from O to A, then along the second line to B(30, 300). This corresponds to adding peanuts at $5/kg until there are 20 kg of peanuts, then adding pecans at $20/kg until there are 30 kg in all.

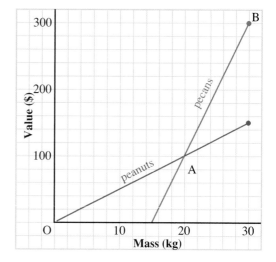

1. **a)** What mass of peanuts should Marika use? What is the value of the peanuts? How can this information be read from the graph?

   b) What mass of pecans should Marika use? What is the value of the pecans? How can this information be read from the graph?

2. The graphs on page 292 were drawn assuming that Marika starts by putting the peanuts in the container. Suppose she puts the pecans in first instead.

a) Draw a graph similar to the second graph on page 292, but starting with pecans.

b) What mass of pecans should Marika use? What is the value of the pecans? How can this information be read from your graph?

c) What mass of peanuts should Marika use? What is the value of the peanuts? How can this information be read from the graph?

3. Each graph below shows a way in which Marika could add peanuts and pecans to the container.

a) Describe the way Marika fills the container, according to each graph.

b) Why might Marika combine the peanuts and pecans in these ways?

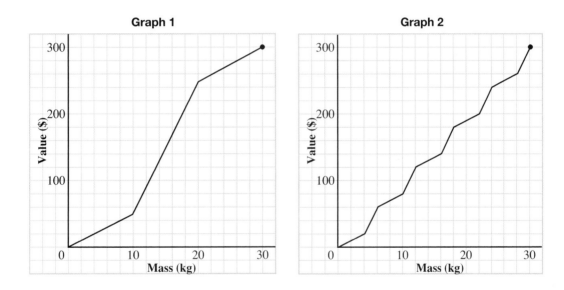

4. **Academic Focus** Suppose the price of peanuts changes, but the price of pecans does not. Visualize how this affects the graphs.

a) Suppose the price of peanuts increases or decreases. Describe how the answer to the Peanut-Pecan Problem changes.

b) Is there any limit to the price of peanuts? Explain.

5. **Academic Focus** Suppose the price of pecans changes, but the price of peanuts does not. Visualize how this affects the graphs.

a) Suppose the price of pecans increases or decreases. Describe how the answer to the Peanut-Pecan Problem changes.

b) Is there any limit to the price of pecans? Explain.

Marika may need to solve similar problems involving other prices. For example, she might want 30 kg of the peanut-pecan mixture to sell at $8/kg, or she might want 20 kg of the peanut-pecan mixture to sell at $12/kg. You can solve these problems by modifying the model.

You will need a sheet of paper thin enough to see through. Follow the steps below to solve the Peanut-Pecan Problem using this modified model.

Step 1 On grid paper, draw a graph to represent the value of the peanuts.

Step 2 Place the thin paper on the grid paper. Draw a graph to represent the value of the pecans.

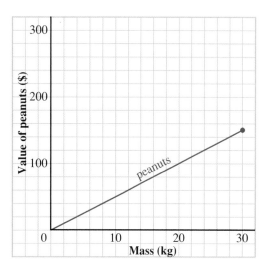

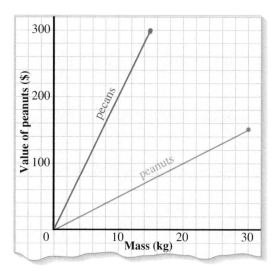

Step 3 Remove the thin paper. Label and number the axes.

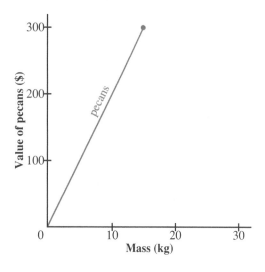

Step 4 Replace the thin paper on top of the first graph. Rotate the thin paper 180° and adjust it so that its origin is on the point (30, 300) on the grid paper. Check that its vertical axis passes through (30, 0) on the first graph, and that its horizontal axis passes through (0, 300) on the first graph. Read the coordinates of the point where the lines on the two graphs intersect.

If you followed Steps 1 to 4, you now have a graph of the peanut values on grid paper and a graph of the pecan values on thin paper.

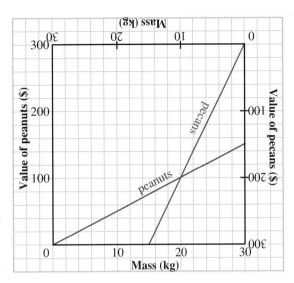

6. Use the graphs in Step 4 to solve the Other Peanut-Pecan Problems (same unit prices), parts b and c, page 282.

7. **Academic Focus** Use your graphs to answer each question.

   a) Suppose the mass of the mixture changes, but its value does not. How does the answer to the Peanut-Pecan Problem change? Is there any limit to the mass of the mixture? Explain.

   b) Suppose the value of the mixture changes, but its mass does not. How does the answer to the Peanut-Pecan Problem change? Is there any limit to the value of the mixture? Explain.

8. Use a graphical model to solve each problem.

   a) Another Peanut-Pecan Problem (different unit prices) on page 282

   b) the Candy Problem on page 282

   c) the Hamburger Problem on page 282

   d) the vending machine problem on page 285

   e) the exercise routine problem on page 285

Comparing the Models

9. Refer to the second graph on page 292.

a) The line OA passes through (0, 0) and has slope 5. Write the equation of this line.

b) The line AB passes through (30, 300) and has slope 20. Write the equation of this line.

c) Recall, from page 283, the algebraic model to solve the Peanut-Pecan Problem. In exercise 4 on that page, you solved this equation: $5x + 20(30 - x) = 300$. Explain how this equation is related to your answers in parts a and b.

10. Choose one problem in exercise 8.

a) Write the equations of the two lines you used to determine the solution.

b) Use the two equations in part a. Write a single equation that could be solved to determine the solution.

11. Recall, from page 284, the reasoning model to solve the Peanut-Pecan Problem. Explain how the steps in the reasoning model can be illustrated on the first graph on page 292.

12. a) List the advantages and disadvantages of the graphical model.

b) Compare the graphical model with the models on pages 283–284. Which model do you think is best? Explain.

COMMUNICATING the IDEAS

Write a set of instructions for Marika to use graphs to determine the masses of two foods to form a mixture to sell at a certain price. Illustrate your instructions in your journal with an example that is different from the problems above.

Boggle your MIND

Some sources estimate that recycling one aluminum can saves the energy equivalent of 1.9 L of gasoline. What if all the students in your school recycled all the aluminum cans they use in one year? How many litres of gasoline would this represent?

Calendar Math

1. Take a calendar for any month. Choose any 3 by 3 square of 9 dates. Add the numbers in the four corners. How does the sum compare with the number in the middle? Repeat with other 3 by 3 squares on the same month. Repeat on calendars for other months.

2. Suppose you know the number in the middle of a 3 by 3 square on the calendar for any month. How would you find the sum of the numbers in the four corners?

3. Let n represent the number in the middle of a 3 by 3 square. Write an expression for the sum of the numbers in the four corners. What are the possible values of n?

august/août

M/L	T/M	W/M	T/J	F/V	S/S	S/D
1	2	3	4	5	6	7
8	9	10	11	12	13	14
15	16	17	18	19	20	21
22	23	24	25	26	27	28
29	30	31				

4. A horse paddock has a width of 10 m.

   a) Calculate the perimeter of the paddock when the length is 15 m.

   b) Calculate the perimeter of the paddock for five other lengths. Record the results in a table.

   c) Suppose you know the length of a paddock with width 10 m. How would you find its perimeter?

   d) Let l represent the length of the paddock. Write an expression to represent its perimeter. What kind of a number is l? What are the possible values of l?

   e) Suppose the perimeter of the paddock is 74 m. Use the expression to determine its length.

5. Expand using the distributive law.

a) $3(2x + 7)$ **b)** $-5(4 + 3n)$ **c)** $12(4s - 5)$

d) $-2(4b - 3)$ **e)** $-(6p + 10)$ **f)** $\frac{1}{2}(4 - 2t)$

g) $-6(-3c - 5)$ **h)** $1.1(-20 + 4k)$ **i)** $2(-a + 2)$

6. Combine like terms and simplify each expression.

a) $2x + 7 + 3x - 5$ **b)** $3m - 12 - 7m + 2$ **c)** $5a + 3b + 8a - 10b$

d) $4y - 11 - 9y + 16$ **e)** $6s + 5t - 2(3s + 9t)$ **f)** $-2(4m - 7n) + 3(m - 13n)$

g) $-3(2q - 5) + 8q - 9$ **h)** $4(-k + \frac{3}{4}) - (5k + 4)$ **i)** $-(-7.4v - 3.2) - 1.4v - 3.5$

7. Simplify each expression then determine its value when $x = 4$, $x = -3$, and $x = -1$.

a) $5x + 2x$ **b)** $8x - 3 + 4x + 9$ **c)** $2x - 7 - 6x + 3$

d) $3x - 2 + 4(x - 5)$ **e)** $-3(4x + 1) - (-7x - 5)$ **f)** $2x + 11 - 4(3x + 7)$

g) $5(2x - 3) + 10 - 3x$ **h)** $-3(2 - x) + 2(5x - 4)$ **i)** $7(2x - 3) - 3(5 - 2x)$

8. Solve each equation.

a) $3x + 2 = 8$ **b)** $2x - 3 = 1$ **c)** $7 - 4x = -5$

d) $3x + 4 = 2x - 3$ **e)** $2x - 5 = 6x + 7$ **f)** $3x - 1 = 5x - 9$

g) $12 + 4x = 5x + 8$ **h)** $-3x + 4 = -5x + 10$ **i)** $-7 - 3x = 8 + 2x$

9. Solve each equation. Check your solution.

a) $2x + 7 = 17$ **b)** $3 - 2x = 15$ **c)** $-40 = -4 + 4x$

d) $3x - 2 = 5x + 8$ **e)** $7 - 5x = 6 + x$ **f)** $-11 + 6x = -6x + 13$

g) $5x - 3 = 2x + 6$ **h)** $-3x + 5 = 2x - 10$ **i)** $-4x + 12 = 2x + 18$

10. When an object falls freely from rest, its approximate speed, v metres per second after t seconds, is given by the formula $v = 9.8t$. This is because acceleration due to Earth's gravity is 9.8 m/s^2.

a) Find the speed of an object after each time.
  i) 2 s **ii)** 5 s **iii)** 8 s

b) Find the time required for the object to reach each speed.
  i) 29.4 m/s **ii)** 88.2 m/s **iii)** 137.2 m/s

c) If the object were on the moon, the formula would be $v = 1.63t$. Repeat parts a and b using this formula.

Give the answers to 1 decimal place.

11. **Academic Focus** Solve each equation.

   a) $5(2x - 3) = 10$ b) $6(-2 - x) = -5(2x + 4)$ c) $-2(1 - x) = -3(2 - x)$

   d) $\frac{72}{x} = 8$ e) $\frac{x}{5} = 12$ f) $\frac{3}{4}x = 15$

   g) $\frac{x}{3} + 2 = -7$ h) $\frac{x}{6} - 5 = \frac{1}{2}x$ i) $\frac{1}{2}x + \frac{1}{3}x = 10$

12. A parking meter accepts only quarters and dollars. There are 31 coins with a value of $20.50. How many quarters and how many dollars are there?

13. For two consecutive integers, the sum of the smaller and twice the larger is 38. What are the integers?

14. A Jaguar travelled 1.2 times as fast as a Mercedes. The difference in their speeds was 24 km/h. Find the speed of each car.

15. The length of a rectangle is 5 cm longer than the width. The perimeter is 54 cm. Find the dimensions of the rectangle.

16. An apple orchard is selling baskets of Macintosh and Delicious apples. The orchard has 8 times as many baskets of Macintosh apples as Delicious apples. The orchard has a total of 153 baskets of apples. How many baskets of each type are there?

17. **Mathematical Modelling** Standard quality coffee sells for $18.00/kg. Prime quality coffee sells for $24.00/kg. What mass of each coffee should be included in 40 kg of a blend that sells for $22.50/kg?

18. **Mathematical Modelling** Oil that costs $22.50/barrel is mixed with oil that costs $35.00/barrel. How many barrels of each oil should be included in 1250 barrels of mixture that sells for $27.50/barrel?

19. **Mathematical Modelling** A car uses gasoline at a rate of 7.5 L/100 km in the city and 5.0 L/100 km on the highway. When the car travelled 300 km, it used 17.5 L of fuel. How far did the car travel on the highway? How much fuel did it use?

6 Cumulative Review

1. Use the order of operations to evaluate each expression.

   a) $3(-8) + 5(18 - 9)$

   b) $7(-8 + 10) - 6(-11 + 5)$

   c) $\left(-\frac{3}{5}\right) \times \frac{2}{5} + \frac{1}{5} \div \left(-\frac{5}{9}\right)$

   d) $(-3)^2 + 5(2)^3$

2. A car's gas tank can hold 51.4 L of fuel.

   a) The tank is $\frac{1}{2}$ full. What volume of fuel does it contain?

   b) The tank is $\frac{3}{4}$ full. What volume of fuel does it contain?

   c) Gas costs 54.9¢/L. You buy half a tank. How much will you pay?

3. In Saskatchewan, the provincial sales tax (PST) is 9% and the goods and services tax (GST) is 7%. The price of a calculator is $83.99. Determine the GST and PST. What is the total price of the calculator?

4. Jorge bought 120 g of candies at the bulk food store for $1.65.

   a) At this price, how much would 70 g cost?

   b) How much could he buy for $3.80?

5. Write a rule for each table of values.

   a)

x	y
0	10
1	9
2	8
3	7
4	6

   b)

x	y
-2	1
-1	2
0	3
1	4
2	5

6. The cost, C dollars, for a school basketball team to play in a tournament is given by $C = 300 + 20n$, where n is the number of players.

   a) Graph this relation.

   b) What is the slope of the graph? What are its units? What does the slope represent?

   c) What is the C-intercept of the graph? What does it represent?

7. What does each power mean? Evaluate each power.

   a) 5^3
   b) 3^{-5}
   c) $(-5)^3$
   d) $(-3)^{-5}$
   e) 3^0

8. Use guess and check. Determine each value of n.

   a) $n^3 = 27$
   b) $n^6 = 64$
   c) $n^2 = 0.25$
   d) $(-2)^n = -32$
   e) $3^n = 81$
   f) $(-3)^n = -27$

9. Simplify.

a) $(6^2)^3 \times (6^4)^5$ b) $(15^3)^2 \div (15^{-2})^{-4}$ c) $(8^{-2})^3 \times (8^4)^{-3}$

d) $(3^4)^{-2} \div (3^5)^4$ e) $(11^{-5})^{-2} \div (11^3)^{-3}$ f) $(-7)^3 \times (-7)^{-2}$

10. The mass of Earth is about 6.0×10^{24} kg.

a) The mass of the sun is about 3.3×10^5 times the mass of Earth. Calculate the mass of the sun.

b) The mass of Earth is about 81 times the mass of the moon. Calculate the mass of the moon.

11. Use this graph to complete this exercise.

a) For each year, estimate the percent of the Canadian population that are visible minorities: 1991, 1996, 2001, 2006, 2011, 2016

b) Use the graph on page 70, exercise 11. For each year in part a, estimate the population of Canada.

c) Use the results of parts a and b. For each year in part a, determine the population of visible minorities in Canada.

d) Show the results of part c on a graph.

Visible Minorities

12. The bottom of a 8.0-m extension ladder is 2.0 m from the base of a building. How high up the building does the ladder reach?

13. Expand using the distributive law.

a) $3(a + 2b - 3c)$ b) $0.1(3.9x + 2y)$

c) $-3(m + 5n - p)$ d) $-(-5d + 6e)$

14. Simplify each expression. Determine its value when the variables have the given value.

a) $3(4a - 2) - (a + 3)$ for $a = 5$

b) $4 + 2(x - 1) - 6x$ for $x = -3$

c) $(b - 3c) - 2(4b + c)$ for $b = 2$ and $c = 1$

15. Solve each equation.

a) $8x = -2$ b) $4a - 40 = 15$ c) $2 - y = 16$ d) $8m + 27 = 3$

Could a Giant Survive?

People have always been interested in the gigantic. For example, in *Gulliver's Travels*, written in the 1700s, Gulliver discovered the Brobdingnag giants. The Brobdingnagians were 12 times as tall as Gulliver.

The Guinness Book of Records reports some real-life examples of exceptionally tall people. The tallest person ever, Robert Wadlow, was 272 cm tall. Wadlow died at 22. The tallest woman, Zeng Jinlian, was 248 cm tall. She died at 18.

In this chapter, you will develop a mathematical model to help you understand what happens to the body if all the body's dimensions become much larger than normal.

Think about how your life would be affected if you were over 2 m tall.

1. What special requirements would you have because of your height?

2. How might people treat you differently? How would that affect you?

3. How might your exceptionally tall size affect your health?

You will return to this problem in Section 7.4.

FYI Visit www.awl.com/canada/school/connections

For information related to the above problem, click on <u>MATHLINKS</u> followed by <u>AWMath</u>. Then select a topic under Could a Giant Survive?

This section reviews these concepts:

- Factoring
- The distributive law
- Like terms
- Exponent laws for multiplying and dividing powers

All the cans on a supermarket shelf arrived at the store in cartons. Cans of tuna are sometimes packaged in cartons of 24. The cans are arranged in 2 layers. Each layer is 4 cans long and 3 cans wide.

Recall that 2, 3, and 4 are factors of 24. One way to express 24 as a product of 3 factors is $2 \times 3 \times 4 = 24$.

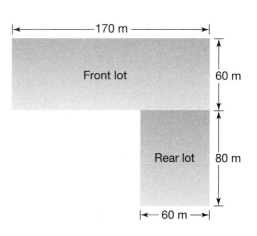

1. a) List as many other ways as you can to express 24 as a product of three factors.

   b) Choose one way from part a. Describe the ways the cans of tuna could be arranged.

2. Other cans of tuna are packaged in cartons of 48. Consider the different sized cartons that could fit 48 cans. List as many sets of three factors of 48 as you can.

3. List all the factors of each number.

   a) 36   b) 13   c) 25   d) 15   e) 16

4. Recall that 24 can be written as a product of its prime factors: $2 \times 2 \times 2 \times 3$. Write each number in exercise 3 as a product of its prime factors.

5. This diagram represents a parking lot. Use the distributive law. Write two expressions for the total area of the parking lot.

6. The tennis court used for singles play is a rectangle with length about 24 m and width about 8 m. The doubles court is a little wider but it has the same length and an area of 264 m².

a) Determine the difference in widths of the singles and doubles courts.

b) Use the distributive law. Write the perimeter of the singles court in two ways.

7. Expand using the distributive law.

a) $6(4x + 9)$

b) $-3(5c + 3)$

c) $11(3 - 8z)$

d) $-10(-2 + 7y)$

e) $5(6z + 2)$

f) $-(3y - 6)$

8. Which are like terms? Explain how you know.

a) $3, -8$

b) $5j, 6g$

c) $11b, -7$

d) $-6, -6v$

e) $12x, 5x, -9x$

f) $-4x, 7x, -8y$

9. Combine like terms.

a) $2x + 4x - 3 + 5$

b) $9x - 5 + 7 - 6x$

c) $-x + 2 - 3x - 4$

d) $5a - 2(a - 4)$

e) $3(2 - x) - 2(3 - x)$

f) $2(5a - 1) - 3(2a - 2) + 4(a - 3)$

g) $-5(a + 3) + 3(1 - a) - (12a - 6)$

h) $6 + 4(2a - 1) - (11 - 7a)$

10. Use the exponent law for multiplying powers. Simplify each expression.

a) $2^4 \times 2^2$

b) $(-3^2) \times 3^2$

c) $(-2^4) \times 2^2$

11. Use the exponent law for dividing powers. Simplify each expression.

a) $\dfrac{2^4}{2^2}$

b) $\dfrac{-3^2}{3^2}$

c) $\dfrac{-2^4}{2^2}$

12. Use the exponent law for a power of a power. Simplify each expression.

a) $(2^2)^4$

b) $\dfrac{(-3^2)^3}{(3^3)^2}$

c) $(4^2)^4 \times (-4)^2$

d) $\dfrac{(2^2)^2 \times (-2)^2}{2}$

Jennifer brought some money home from her vacation in the United States. She had some Canadian and some U.S. bills.

To calculate the amount of money she has, Jennifer adds the U.S. money: $20 + $10 + $10 + $5 + $1 = $46 U.S. and the Canadian money: $10 + $5 + $5 = $20 Can

All the terms that represent Canadian money are like terms. They can be combined into a single value. Similarly, all the terms that represent U.S. money are like terms. However, a term that represents Canadian money and a term that represents U.S. money are unlike terms. They cannot be combined into a single value.

We can say only that Jennifer has $46 U.S. and $20 Can.

In Chapter 6, you worked with like and unlike terms in the form of algebra tiles.

Recall:

This tile is a 1-tile.

It measures 1 unit on each side.
It has an area of 1 square unit.

This tile is a variable-tile.
We call it an x-tile.

It measures 1 unit by x units.
It has an area of x square units.

We now add a new algebra tile:

This tile is a square measuring
x units on each side.
It has an area of $x \times x$, or
x^2 square units.
It is an x^2-tile.

Forming Rectangles with Algebra Tiles

1. Arrange 4 green 1-tiles to form a rectangle.

   a) What is the length of the rectangle?

   b) What is the width of the rectangle?

   c) What is the area of the rectangle?

   d) What is the perimeter of the rectangle?

2. Use the tiles from exercise 1. Arrange the tiles to form a different rectangle. Repeat exercise 1a to d for the new rectangle.

3. Compare your answers to exercises 1 and 2. What do you notice about the perimeter and area?

4. Arrange 4 green x-tiles to form a rectangle.

   a) How many different rectangles can you make?

   b) For each rectangle in part a, repeat exercise 1a to d.

5. Use the tiles from exercises 1 and 4 together. Repeat exercise 4a and b.

6. When you arrange algebra tiles to form different rectangles:

   a) What do you notice about the areas of the rectangles?

   b) What do you notice about the perimeters of the rectangles?

Since x is a variable, we cannot combine the areas of a 1-tile, an x-tile, and an x^2-tile to form a single term. That is, these tiles represent unlike terms.

To represent these tiles:

We think: 3 x^2-tiles + 2 x-tiles + 5 1-tiles

We write: $3x^2 + 2x + 5$

There are special names for terms and combinations of terms. Look at the table below. Answer each question in the last column.

All of these are monomials.	None of these is a monomial.	Which of these is a monomial?
$3x^2$ $4x$ $-6m^3$ $7x^2y$	$3x + 4$ $4y^2 - y$ $\frac{-2}{z}$	$3x + 2$ $\frac{-5y^2}{x}$ $-6xy$

All of these are binomials.	None of these is a binonomial.	Which of these is a binomial?
$3x + 7$ $2y^2 - y$ $4 - x^4$	$3x^5$ $x^2 - 5x + 7$ $+1$ $\frac{1}{a} + \frac{1}{b}$	$x^2 - 4xy$ $-2x^2y^3$ $3a^2 - 2a + 4$

All of these are trinomials.	None of these is a trinomial.	Which of these is a trinomial?
$3x^4 + 7x - 6$ $4ab - 2bc + c^3$ $1 - 4x - 3y^2$	$5x^4 - 2xy$ $3a + 7$ $6x^3 - \frac{2}{y^2} + 2z$	$1 - 2x^5 + \frac{1}{x}$ -4 $x^2 - 3a^2 + 4$

All of these are polynomials.	None of these is a polynomial.	Which of these is a polynomial?
$-3xy$ $3a^3 - 5z^2 - 14$ $11 - d^2$ $3x^3 - 5x + y - 7$	$4a^2 - \frac{2}{b} + 1$ $-\frac{2}{z}$	$2x^2 + \frac{3y}{x} - 4y^3$ $\frac{-5y^2}{-x}$ $3x + 2$

A *monomial* is a mathematical expression with one term.
A term is a coefficient and one or more variables.
A *polynomial* is one term or the sum of two or more terms.
A *binomial* is a polynomial with two terms.
A *trinomial* is a polynomial with three terms.

The term $3x^2$ has *coefficient* 3.
The trinomial $3x^2 - 2x + 5$ contains coefficients 3 and -2; the number 5 is a *constant term*.
The variable is x.

In a polynomial, exponents that occur with variables are whole numbers. Since $\frac{1}{x} = x^{-1}$, then $\frac{1}{x}$ is not a polynomial, because the exponent -1 is not a whole number.

We represented the polynomial $3x^2 + 2x + 5$ using algebra tiles. This polynomial has terms that have positive coefficients. We can also represent a polynomial such as $3x^2 - 2x + 5$, which has a term with a negative coefficient. We do this by flipping the two x-tiles.

We see: $3x^2 - 2x + 5$
We think: 3 x^2-tiles, 2 flipped x-tiles, and 5 1-tiles

THESE ARE ZONKS

THESE ARE NOT ZONKS

ONE OF THESE IS A ZONK

We display:

As you discovered in the *Investigation*, we can combine algebra tiles to form a rectangle. We can write the area and the perimeter of the rectangle as a polynomial.

Example

Write polynomials that represent the perimeter and area of each rectangle.

a)

b)

Solution

a) The rectangle comprises 5 x-tiles.
   Its length is 5.
   Its width is x.
   The perimeter is $x + 5 + x + 5 = 2x + 10$
   The area is $5 \times x = 5x$

b) The rectangle comprises 3 x^2-tiles.
   Its length is $3x$.
   Its width is x.
   The perimeter is $x + 3x + x + 3x = 8x$
   The area is $3x \times x = 3x^2$

DISCUSSING the IDEAS

1. Explain how adding money in the same currency is similar to adding like terms.

2. a) Is a monomial a binomial? Explain.   **b)** Is a monomial a trinomial? Explain.

   c) Is a monomial a polynomial? Explain.

3. a) Is a binomial a trinomial? Explain.   **b)** Is a binomial a polynomial? Explain.

4. Is a trinomial a polynomial? Explain.

A **1.** How much money is represented?

10 Can	10 U.S.	1 U.S.
10 Can	5 Can	2 Can
10 U.S.	5 U.S.	1 U.S.
10 Can	5 U.S.	5 U.S.

2. Which expressions are polynomials? Give reasons.

a) $5x - 3$ **b)** $6x + 7x^2 - 1$ **c)** $2x + 3y - x^2$

d) $2 + \frac{1}{x}$ **e)** 3 **f)** $-\frac{4}{y^2}$

3. Is each expression a monomial, a binomial, or a trinomial? Give reasons.

a) $3x + 4$ **b)** $-x^2$ **c)** $-2 - y^2$ **d)** 10

e) $5 - 2x + 3y$ **f)** $4x$ **g)** $5x^2 + 4y^2 + x$ **h)** $-3 - y$

4. For each display of tiles, state a polynomial that represents the total area.

a)

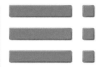

b)

c)

d)

5. Use algebra tiles to represent each polynomial.

a) $x^2 + 3x + 2$ b) $2x^2 + x + 7$ c) $-2x^2 - 3$ d) $2x^2 - 5x - 4$

e) $-x^2 - 3x + 2$ f) $x^2 - 4x$ g) $6 - x$ h) 5

6. State the coefficient in each term.

a) $14x$ b) $7y^2$ c) a d) $-b^2$ e) πr^2 f) $\sqrt{3}m^3 n$

7. State the constant term in each polynomial.

a) $5x^2 - 2x + 6$ b) $-x^2 y - 5$ c) $7 - 3x - 2y$

d) $\frac{1}{2}m^2 - \frac{2}{5} + 5m$ e) $7x^2 - 5y^2$ f) $\frac{x}{2}$

8. State the coefficients in each polynomial. Identify the constant term.

a) $6p + 2q + 3$ b) $a - 2b + 9c$ c) $1.8C + 32$

d) $2\pi r$ e) $7x^2 - 3xy - 9$ f) $4.9s^3 - 1.2s^2 - 0.5s + 2$

9. State the like terms in each group.

a) $5a, 3b, 5c, a^2, -a, 3d, 3e$ b) $4x, 3y^2, 4z, 2y, y^2, 4w$

c) $9g, 6h, 9g^2, \frac{1}{9}g, \frac{1}{6}h^2, g^2$ d) $16, d^2, d, f, -8, 0.5d, 7d^3$

 10. Evaluate $3n + 4$ for each value of n.

a) 1   b) 3   c) 4   d) -1

11. Evaluate $3x - 5$ for each value of x.

a) 0   b) 1   c) -1 d) 7

12. Write a polynomial to represent the perimeter of each rectangle.

a)    b)    c)

13. Write a polynomial to represent the area of each rectangle in exercise 12.

14. Represent each rectangle using algebra tiles.

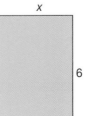

15. For each rectangle in exercise 14, write a polynomial to represent its perimeter and a polynomial to represent its area.

16. a) Write an algebraic expression that is *not* a polynomial.

  b) Write a polynomial that does not use the variable x.

17. Write a polynomial to represent the perimeter of each rectangle.

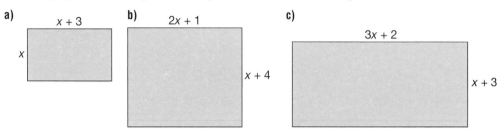

a) $x + 3$ x

b) $2x + 1$ $x + 4$

c) $3x + 2$ $x + 3$

18. For exercise 17, determine the perimeter of each rectangle when $x = 4$ cm and when $x = 1.5$ m.

19. a) Write a polynomial to represent the area of a square of side length $2s$.

  b) Write a polynomial to represent the area of:

    i) the large square   **ii)** the small square   **iii)** the shaded region

  c) Determine the area of each figure in part b when $s = 2.5$ cm.

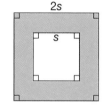

20. The formula, $T = -n^2 + 30n + 20$, gives the approximate temperature in an oven, T degrees Celsius, n minutes after it has been turned on. The formula applies for the first 14 min. Estimate each temperature.

  a) 7 min after the oven was turned on

  b) 10 min after the oven was turned on

21. The formula, $d = 0.20v + 0.015v^2$, gives the approximate stopping distance, d metres, for a car travelling at v kilometres per hour. Estimate the stopping distance for a speed of 50 km/h and a speed of 100 km/h.

PROBLEM SOLVING FOCUS

Polynomials that Generate Prime Numbers

A prime number is any whole number, greater than 1, that is divisible by only itself and 1. Since the discovery of prime numbers, mathematicians have attempted to find a polynomial to generate them.

In 1772, the Swiss mathematician, Leonhard Euler, used the polynomial $n^2 - n + 41$ to generate primes.

We will use a spreadsheet to check that this polynomial does generate primes.

22. Set up this spreadsheet.

    In cell A2, enter different numbers, up to 10.

    In cell B2, are all the numbers generated primes?

	A	B
1	N	Euler's polynomial
2		=A2*A2-A2+41

23. In cell A2, enter several other numbers, up to 40. Use a calculator to check that each number in cell B2 is prime.

24. a) Enter 41 in cell A2.   b) What is 41^2?

    c) Does Euler's polynomial generate a prime number when $n = 41$?

In 1879, E.B. Escott used the polynomial $n^2 - 79n + 1601$.
Insert this polynomial on the spreadsheet beside Euler's polynomial.

	A	B	C
1	N	Euler's polynomial	Escott's polynomial
2		=A2*A2-A2+41	=A2*A2-79*A2+1601

25. Test Escott's polynomial for several values of N. Use a calculator to check if each number in cell C2 is prime.

26. Compare the numbers in column C with those in column B.

    a) Do you notice any similarities?

    b) What patterns can you find in the numbers in column C?

27. a) Enter 80 in cell A2. Show that the number in cell C2 is *not* prime.

    b) Find another value of N for which the number in cell C2 is not prime.

28. Adapt the spreadsheet. Find a value of n for which each polynomial does *not* produce a prime number.

    a) $n^2 + n - 1$ b) $n^2 - n + 17$ c) $n^2 - n + 41, n \neq 41$

COMMUNICATING the IDEAS

In your journal, write the meanings of the prefixes mono-, bi-, tri-, and poly-. List some other words that contain these prefixes. Then use a dictionary to extend your list to 10 words. In this list, are there any words that surprise you? Explain. Is the use of poly- in English the same as poly- in mathematics? Explain.

Polynomials, like numbers, can be added and subtracted. To add two polynomials, we combine like terms. You combined like terms in Section 6.2. The only difference now is that we include x^2-tiles.

INVESTIGATION

Adding and Subtracting Polynomials

1. Use algebra tiles to add $3x^2 + 2x + 1$ and $-2x^2 + 3x - 5$. Sketch the tiles you used. Write to explain how you found the sum.

2. Use algebra tiles to subtract $-2x^2 + 3x - 5$ from $3x^2 + 2x + 1$. Recall that to subtract, you flip the tiles representing the polynomial that is subtracted. Sketch the tiles you used. Write to explain how you found the difference.

We can use algebra tiles to add polynomials.
Suppose we add $2x^2 + 3x + 1$ and $-x^2 + 2x - 4$.

We write: We display:

$(2x^2 + 3x + 1) + (-x^2 + 2x - 4)$

We think:
Combine like terms. Use the Zero Principle.
Each pair of opposite tiles forms a 0-pair.
1 x^2-tile, 5 x-tiles, and 3 flipped 1-tiles remain.
From the tiles, $(2x^2 + 3x + 1) + (-x^2 + 2x - 4) = x^2 + 5x - 3$

Polynomials that have a sum of 0 are called *opposites*.
Flipping the tiles representing $-2x^2 + x - 9$ gives its opposite, $2x^2 - x + 9$.
We can use this to subtract one polynomial from another.

Suppose we subtract $-2x^2 + x - 9$ from $3x^2 + 5x - 6$.
We write: $(3x^2 + 5x - 6) - (-2x^2 + x - 9)$

We think: We display:
Flip the tiles representing $(-2x^2 + x - 9)$.
Combine like terms.
Use the Zero Principle.
5 x^2-tiles, 4 x-tiles, and 3 1-tiles remain.
From the tiles,
$(3x^2 + 5x - 6) - (-2x^2 + x - 9) = 5x^2 + 4x + 3$

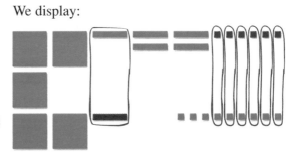

To add polynomials algebraically, we group like terms, then simplify.

Example 1

Simplify. $(-2x^2 + 6x - 7) + (3x^2 - x - 2)$

Solution

$$(-2x^2 + 6x - 7) + (3x^2 - x - 2) = -2x^2 + 6x - 7 + 3x^2 - x - 2 \qquad \text{Removing brackets}$$

$$= -2x^2 + 3x^2 + 6x - x - 7 - 2 \qquad \text{Grouping like terms}$$

$$= x^2 + 5x - 9$$

When we subtract a polynomial from itself, we get zero.
For example, $(x^2 - 2x - 4) - (x^2 - 2x - 4) = 0$

We get the same result if we add the polynomial and its opposite.
For example, $(x^2 - 2x - 4) + (-x^2 + 2x + 4) = 0$

So, to subtract a polynomial, we add its opposite.

Example 2

a) Simplify. $(3x^2 + 5x - 6) - (-2x^2 + x - 9)$

b) Determine the value of the polynomial for each value of x.

   i) $x = 2$ ii) $x = -1$

Solution

a) $(3x^2 + 5x - 6) - (-2x^2 + x - 9)$

   $= (3x^2 + 5x - 6) + (2x^2 - x + 9)$ Adding the opposite of $-2x^2 + x - 9$

   $= 5x^2 + 4x + 3$

b) i) When $x = 2$, the value of the polynomial is: $5(2)^2 + 4(2) + 3 = 5(4) + 8 + 3$

$$= 20 + 11$$
$$= 31$$

  ii) When $x = -1$, the value of the polynomial is: $5(-1)^2 + 4(-1) + 3 = 5(1) - 4 + 3$

$$= 5 - 1$$
$$= 4$$

Some polynomials cannot be represented with algebra tiles. We use the above principles to combine these polynomials.

Example 3

Simplify. $(3x^4 - 2x^2 + 3x - 9) - (x^2 - 4x + 2)$

Solution

$(3x^4 - 2x^2 + 3x - 9) - (x^2 - 4x + 2) = (3x^4 - 2x^2 + 3x - 9) + (-x^2 + 4x - 2)$
$$= 3x^4 - 3x^2 + 7x - 11$$

DISCUSSING the IDEAS

1. What is the sum of a polynomial and its opposite? Explain.

2. Is there a polynomial that is equal to its opposite? Explain.

3. a) State the opposite of the polynomial $3x^2 - 2x - 1$.
   b) Then state the opposite of your answer.
   c) What do you notice?
   d) Do you think this is true for all polynomials? Explain.

4. a) Suppose you have a display of algebra tiles representing a polynomial. How do you obtain the tile display for the opposite polynomial?
   b) How do you determine the opposite of a polynomial without using algebra tiles?

5. Explain how 0-pairs are used with algebra tiles to simplify two polynomials.

6. Explain why the polynomials in *Example 3* cannot be represented with algebra tiles.

7.2 EXERCISES

1. Use algebra tiles to add.
   a) $(x^2 + 2x - 1) + (2x^2 + 3x + 3)$ b) $(3x^2 - x + 5) + (x^2 - 2x - 4)$
   c) $(-2x^2 - 3x - 4) + (-2x^2 - 5x - 1)$ d) $(x^2 - 2x - 4) + (-x^2 + 2x + 4)$

2. a) How are the polynomials in exercise 1d alike?
   b) How are these polynomials different?

3. Use algebra tiles to represent, then simplify, this expression. Explain how you did it.

$(x^2 - 2x + 3) + (4x - 2)$

4. a) What polynomial sum do these tiles represent?

   b) Explain how to use algebra tiles to find the sum of the polynomials in part a.

5. Simplify.

   a) $(6x + 2) + (3x + 4)$

   b) $(5a - 3) + (2a + 7)$

   c) $(8 - 4m) + (-3 - 2m)$

   d) $(-x + 4) + (7x - 2)$

   e) $(4n^2 - 3n - 1) + (2n^2 - 5n - 3)$

   f) $(3x^2 + 6x - 8) + (-5x^2 - x + 4)$

   g) $(2 - 3c + c^2) + (5 - 4c - 4c^2)$

   h) $(8 - 2n - n^2) + (-3 - n + 4n^2)$

   i) $(ab + 3b - 5) + (2ab - 4b - 6)$

   j) $(mn - 5m - 2) + (-6n + 3m + 7)$

6. Show each polynomial using algebra tiles. Then flip the tiles and state its opposite.

   a) $3x^2 + 7$

   b) $2x^2 - 5x + 3$

   c) $-4n^2 + 3n - 5$

7. Use algebra tiles to subtract.

   a) $(-x^2 + 5x + 4) - (2x^2 + 3x + 3)$

   b) $(3x^2 + 4) - (x^2 + 2)$

8. Write to explain why the two polynomials in each pair are not opposites.

   a) $5x^2 - 3x - 2$
      $5x^2 + 3x + 2$

   b) $x^2 + 7x - 9$
      $-x^3 - 7x + 9$

   c) $-4y + y^2 + 11$
      $4y - y^2 + 11$

   d) $x^3 - 4x^2 + 9$
      $-x^3 + 4x^2 - x$

9. State the opposite of each polynomial.

   a) $5x + 2$

   b) $2 - 3a$

   c) $7x^2 - 5x + 4$

   d) $5 - 2m - 4m^2$

   e) $6n^2 - 3n + 1$

   f) $-\frac{1}{2}x - 5$

10. Write each subtraction statement as an addition statement.

   a) $(3x^2 + 5) - (2x^2 + 1)$

   b) $(x^2 + 2x) - (-x - 1)$

   c) $(x^2 + 3x - 2) - (-x^2 - x + 1)$

11. Simplify.

   a) $(-2x + 3) - (3x + 2)$

   b) $(4 - 5n) - (-6n + 2)$

   c) $(8a^2 + 2a - 3) - (-6a^2 + 4a + 7)$

   d) $(-6x^2 + 5x + 1) - (4x^2 + 5 - 2x)$

   e) $(3 - 2m - n^2) - (7 - 6m + n^2)$

   f) $(2 + 6x^2) - (7 - 3x^2)$

   g) $(5 - 6t^2) - (3 - t^2)$

   h) $(5x^2 - 3x) - (-3x + 5x^2)$

12. Simplify.

a) $(3x - 2) - (x - 1)$ **b)** $(2a + 3) + (6a - 1)$

c) $(5x^2 - 3x) - (x^2 + 2x)$ **d)** $(5t - 4) + (3t - 1)$

e) $(3 - 4x + x^2) - (2x - x^2)$ **f)** $(3n^2 - 6n + 5) - (3n^2 - 2n - 1)$

B **13. a)** Use algebra tiles to represent this difference of polynomials.

$(3x^2 - 2x + 5) - (x^2 - 3x - 1)$

b) Explain how you use algebra tiles to simplify the expression in part a.

14. Simplify.

a) $(3x^2 - 2x + 4) + (x^2 + 3)$ **b)** $(3x^2 - 2x + 4) - (x^2 + 3)$

c) $(5m - 2m^2) + (m^2 - 6)$ **d)** $(5m - 2m^2) - (m^2 - 6)$

15. Simplify $(2x^5 + 3x^4 + 4x^3 + 5x^2) + (-2x^3 + 3x^2 - 7)$.
Explain why you cannot use algebra tiles to simplify.

16. Simplify. Then determine the value of the polynomial when $x = 1$ and $x = -2$.

a) $(1 - 2x^2 - x) + (2x - 3x^2 - 7)$ **b)** $(3 - 2x^2 - x) - (2x - 3x^2 - 7)$

17. Each rectangle is divided into squares and rectangles. Write one polynomial for the area of each piece and one polynomial for the area of the entire rectangle.

a)

b)

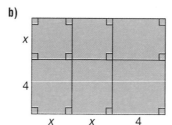

c)

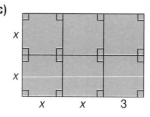

18. Simplify.

a) $(3x^2 - 7x + 4) + (5x - 7x^2 + 6)$ **b)** $(6 - 3x + x^2) + (9 - x)$

c) $(1 - 7x^2 + 2x) + (x^3 - 3x^2 + 7)$ **d)** $(5x - x^2) + (3x + x^2 - 7)$

19. Simplify.

a) $(5x^2 + 7x + 9) - (3x^2 + 4x + 2)$ **b)** $(11m^2 - 5m + 8) - (7m^2 + m - 3)$

c) $(4a^2 - 3a^3 - 7) - (a^2 - 2a^3 - 13)$ **d)** $(-6x^2 + 17x - 4) - (3x^2 + 12x + 8)$

20. Simplify. Then determine the value of the polynomial when $x = -2$ and $x = 3$.

a) $(3x^2 - 8x + 6) - (-2x^2 + 7x + 3)$ **b)** $(x^2 - 4x + x^3) - (3x + 5 - x^3)$

21. a) Simplify.

i) $(5 - 2m - m^2) - (7m + 4 - 5m^2)$ **ii)** $(2m^2 - 5m + 3) - (4 - 3m)$

b) Determine the value of each polynomial in part a when $m = 0$ and $m = -2$.

22. a) Simplify.

    i) $(y^2 - 2y) - (5 - 2y)$ **ii)** $(8y - 5) - (y - 4) + (3y + 1)$

  b) Determine the value of each polynomial in part a when $y = 4$ and $y = 1$.

23. Mental Math Look back at the polynomials you simplified. Were there any exercises you completed using only mental math? If so, identify 3 examples and explain why you could complete them that way.

24. Choose any month on a calendar. Then choose a 3 by 3 square of 9 dates. Let x represent the date at the centre of the square.

  a) Write a polynomial for:

    i) the date one week before x

    ii) the date one week after x

    iii) the sum of the dates in each column

    iv) the sum of all 9 dates

  b) Suppose you know the sum of all 9 dates. How could you determine the value of x?

August

Sun	Mon	Tue	Wed	Thur	Fri	Sat
		1	2	3	4	5	6
7	8	9	10	11	12	13
14	15	16	17	18	19	20
21	22	23	24	25	26	27
28	29	30	31			

one week before

x

one week after

25. When the terms of a polynomial in x are arranged from the highest to the lowest powers of x, the polynomial is in *descending* powers of x.

  a) Simplify. Write the polynomial in descending powers of x.

    $7 - (3x^2 + 2x) - (5x + x^2 - 6) - (3x + 3x^2 - 12)$

  b) Determine the value of the polynomial in part a when $x = -0.5$.

COMMUNICATING the IDEAS

Look through this text. In your journal, record three expressions that cannot be represented with algebra tiles. Explain why they cannot be represented this way.

7.3 Multiplying and Dividing Monomials

In the previous section, we added and subtracted polynomials.

We will investigate the products and quotients of polynomials with one term. Recall that a polynomial with only one term is a monomial.

Recall the exponent laws for multiplying powers, dividing powers, and raising a power to a power. These laws can be applied to multiply and divide monomials.

How would we simplify the product $(3x^2)(5x^3)$?

Recall the meaning of the exponents.

$$(3x^2)(5x^3) = (3 \cdot x \cdot x)(5 \cdot x \cdot x \cdot x)$$

| Writing each term as a product of factors |

$$= (3)(5)(x \cdot x \cdot x \cdot x \cdot x)$$

| Rearranging the factors |

$$= 15x^5$$

| Writing $x \cdot x \cdot x \cdot x \cdot x$ as x^5 |

This example and others like it illustrate this rule for multiplying monomials:

> To multiply two monomials, multiply their coefficients and multiply their variables.

If the variables are the same, add their exponents.

For example, to multiply $3x^2$ by $5x^3$:

Multiply the coefficients: $3 \times 5 = 15$

$$(3x^2)(5x^3) = 15x^5$$

Add the exponents: $2 + 3 = 5$

Similarly, to simplify the quotient, $\dfrac{18x^6}{3x^2}$:

$$\frac{18x^6}{3x^2} = \frac{2 \cdot 3 \cdot 3 \cdot x \cdot x \cdot x \cdot x \cdot x \cdot x}{3 \cdot x \cdot x}$$

| Writing each term as a product of factors |

$$= \frac{2 \cdot 3 \cdot \cancel{3}^1 \cdot x \cdot x \cdot x \cdot x \cdot \cancel{x}^1 \cdot \cancel{x}^1}{\cancel{3}^1 \cdot \cancel{x}^1 \cdot \cancel{x}^1}$$

| Dividing common factors |

$$= 6x^4$$

| Writing $x \cdot x \cdot x \cdot x$ as x^4 |

This example and others like it illustrate this rule for dividing monomials:

To divide two monomials, divide their coefficients and divide their variables.

If the variables are the same, subtract their exponents.

For example, to divide $18x^6$ by $3x^2$:
Subtract the exponents: $6 - 2 = 4$

$$\frac{18x^6}{3x^2} = 6x^4$$

Divide the coefficients: $18 \div 3 = 6$

Sometimes we multiply monomials that are powers. For example, to simplify $(3x^2)^2(2x^3)^3$, we think of its meaning: $(3x^2)(3x^2)(2x^3)(2x^3)(2x^3)$

This expression is the product of five monomials. To determine the product, we multiply the coefficients and multiply the variables.
The product of the coefficients is
$(3)(3)(2)(2)(2) = 72$
The product of the variables is
$(x^2)(x^2)(x^3)(x^3)(x^3) = x^{2+2+3+3+3}$
$$= x^{13}$$
So, $(3x^2)^2(2x^3)^3 = 72x^{13}$

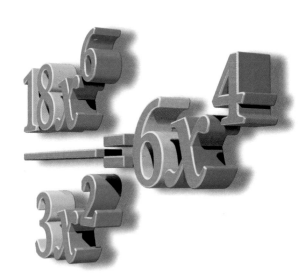

Example 1

Simplify.

a) $(3x^2)(-2x^3)$

b) $8x^4y \div 6x^2y$

Solution

a) $(3x^2)(-2x^3) = (3)(-2)(x^2)(x^3)$
$\quad\quad\quad\quad\quad\quad = -6x^{2+3}$
$\quad\quad\quad\quad\quad\quad = -6x^5$

b) $8x^4y \div 6x^2y = \dfrac{8x^4y}{6x^2y}$

$\quad\quad\quad\quad\quad\quad = \dfrac{8}{6} \cdot \dfrac{x^4}{x^2} \cdot \dfrac{y}{y}$

$\quad\quad\quad\quad\quad\quad = \dfrac{4}{3}x^{4-2}$

$\quad\quad\quad\quad\quad\quad = \dfrac{4}{3}x^2$

Example 2

Simplify.

a) $(2a^2)^4(-5a^3)$

b) $\dfrac{(2b^2)^4}{(-b)^2}$

Solution

a) $(2a^2)^4(-5a^3) = (2a^2)(2a^2)(2a^2)(2a^2)(-5a^3)$
$= -80a^{11}$

b) $\dfrac{(2b^2)^4}{(-b)^2} = \dfrac{(2)^4(b^2)^4}{(-b)(-b)}$
$= \dfrac{16b^8}{b^2}$
$= 16b^{8-2}$
$= 16b^6$

DISCUSSING the IDEAS

1. On page 320, we multiplied $(3x^2)(5x^3)$ to obtain $15x^5$. Explain why we multiply the coefficients but not the exponents.

2. Can the method for multiplying monomials be used to add monomials? Use an example to explain your answer.

3. **Academic Focus** Can the method for multiplying monomials be used to multiply binomials? Use an example to explain your answer.

7·3 EXERCISES

1. Write as a product of factors.

a) $3x^2$ b) $4x^3$ c) $-x^2$ d) $2x^6$

e) $-\dfrac{1}{2}a^4$ f) $9x^2y$ g) $-6a^2b^2$ h) $5m^2n^3$

2. State each product.

a) $(3x^2)(4x^3)$ b) $(-x^2)(2x^6)$ c) $\left(-\dfrac{1}{2}a^2\right)\left(-\dfrac{1}{2}a^4\right)$ d) $(-5a)(6a^2)$

3. State each quotient.

a) $\dfrac{5m^5}{2m^3}$ b) $\dfrac{-25x^5}{10x^2}$ c) $\dfrac{30x^6}{-6x^2}$

4. Name a pair of monomials that will satisfy each equation. Is there only one possible answer for each equation? Explain.

a) $\square \times \square = 3x^6$ b) $\square \times \square = -5b^3$ c) $\square \times \square = -6x$

d) $\square \div \square = 2x^2$ e) $\square \div \square = \dfrac{3}{2}x^3$ f) $\square \div \square = \dfrac{1}{4}$

5. Determine each product.

   a) $4(3b)$ b) $(-7)(2k)$ c) $5(4t)$ d) $(-2)(8p)$

   e) $a(5b)$ f) $p(-3q)$ g) $n(4m)$ h) $x(-2y)$

6. Determine each product.

   a) $(3a)(2a)$ b) $(-2c)(5c)$ c) $(-2a)(-5a)$

   d) $(7x)(3x)$ e) $(5x)(2x)$ f) $(8y)(-7y)$

   g) $(-x)(-5x)$ h) $(3a)(-2a)$ i) $(-2a)(-3a)$

7. Simplify.

   a) $(12x)^2$ b) $(-3xy)^3$ c) $-(5ab)^2$ d) $(2a)^2$

   e) $(9m^5n)^2$ f) $(-3x)^2$ g) $(-5ab^2)^3$ h) $(3mn^4)^2$

8. Determine each quotient.

   a) $\frac{12x^3}{3}$ b) $\frac{32y^4}{16}$ c) $\frac{18y^4}{2y}$ d) $\frac{27m^3}{-9m}$

   e) $(-45y^6) \div (-5y^4)$ f) $3n^6 \div 5n^4$ g) $25x^4 \div (-5x^4)$ h) $36c^5 \div 24c^2$

9. Determine each product.

   a) $(x^3)(-x^2)$ b) $(2p^2)(3p^3)$ c) $(6y^3)(-2y)$

   d) $(3a^2b)(2ab^2)$ e) $(3x^2)^2(2y)^2$ f) $(-2x)^2(-y^2)^3$

B 10. **Academic Focus** The base area and height of each solid are given. State the volume of each solid.

   a)   b)   c)   d)

11. Determine each quotient.

   a) $15x^3 \div 3x$ b) $(-6y^2) \div 2y$ c) $20a^3 \div (-4a^2)$

   d) $\frac{6b^3n^2}{2b^2n}$ e) $\frac{15m^5a^3}{3m^2a}$ f) $\frac{21y^6x^2}{7y^3x^2}$

12. **Academic Focus** The volume, V, and base area of each solid are given. State the height of each solid.

   a)    b) 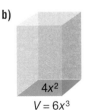   c)   d)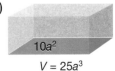

13. Determine each product.

  a) $(3m^4)(7m^5)$ **b)** $(2x^2)(4x^3)$ **c)** $(8a^3)(7a^{11})$ **d)** $(-5b^3)(2b^4)$

  e) $(6x^5)(-3x^3)$ **f)** $(-8p^4)(-6p^2)$ **g)** $\left(\frac{2}{3}y^4\right)\left(\frac{3}{5}y^7\right)$ **h)** $\left(-\frac{5}{8}s^5\right)\left(-\frac{3}{10}s^3\right)$

14. Determine each quotient.

  a) $\frac{-28a^7}{4a^2}$ **b)** $\frac{20s^3}{-5s}$ **c)** $\frac{-32c^8}{-8c^2}$ **d)** $45x^9 \div 9x^3$ **e)** $18y^4 \div 3y^2$

  f) $42m^{12} \div 6m^4$ **g)** $36k^4 \div 9k^3$ **h)** $\frac{49z^7}{7z^4}$ **i)** $\frac{56a^4b^4}{8a^3b^2}$ **j)** $\frac{60x^3y^5}{15x^3y^3}$

15. Multiply or divide.

  a) $(2m^3)(5m^2)$ **b)** $(-x^4)(3x)$ **c)** $\frac{2x^5}{3x^3}$ **d)** $\frac{-9m^8}{12m^5}$ **e)** $(-x)^4(3x)$

  f) $(3a^2b^3)(2ab^4)$ **g)** $\frac{15x^3y^4}{-5xy^3}$ **h)** $(3x^4)^2(-2x)^3$ **i)** $(5a^2)^3 \div 15a^5$ **j)** $\left(\frac{2}{5}a^2b^4\right)\left(\frac{10}{3}ab^3\right)$

16. a) Write the volume of the cube
   as a product of monomials.

   b) Write the volume of the cube
   as a monomial.

   c) Simplify. $(2x^2)(3x^3)(7x^4)$

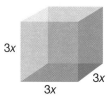

$3x$

$3x$

$3x$

17. Multiply or divide.

  a) $(2d^3)(5d^4)$ **b)** $(-30m^2n^5) \div (-6mn^3)$ **c)** $(-x^2)(5x)$

  d) $\frac{12x^3}{2x}$ **e)** $\frac{-25a^7}{15a^2}$ **f)** $\left(-\frac{3}{5}ab^2\right)\left(-\frac{10}{9}a^3\right)$

18. Simplify, then evaluate for $x = -2$.

  a) $-x^2$ **b)** $(-x)^2$ **c)** $(2x^3)(-3x)$ **d)** $(5x^2)(4x^3)$ **e)** $\frac{12x^5}{3x^2}$ **f)** $\frac{-9x^7}{2x^3}$

C **19.** Simplify, then evaluate for $a = 3$ and $b = 1$.

  a) $(2a^2b^3)^2$ **b)** $(-3ab^3)(5a^2b)$ **c)** $(-4a^3b) \div 2ab$ **d)** $7a^5b^{10} \div (-3b^5)$

COMMUNICATING the IDEAS

In your journal, write a brief answer to each question. Provide examples.

  a) When is the sum or difference of two monomials a monomial?

  b) When is the product of two monomials a monomial?

  c) When is the quotient of two monomials a monomial?

7.4 Could a Giant Survive?

See page 303 for some examples of fantasy giants and exceptionally tall people. The giants in the land of Brobdingnag were 12 times as tall as a normal adult. Could these giants survive?

To model this situation, visualize a continuing sequence of cubes like this:

   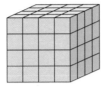

1. Make and complete a table for larger and larger cubes.

Edge length (cm)	Volume (cm³)	Surface area (cm²)	Volume / Surface area
1			
2			
3			
:			
10			

2. a) As the edge length increases, which grows more rapidly, surface area or volume?

   b) As the edge length increases, what happens to the fraction of volume to surface area?

3. Let x centimetres represent the length of the edge of a cube.

   a) Write an equation in terms of x for:

   i) the volume, V, of the cube

   ii) the surface area, A, of the cube

   iii) the ratio $\frac{V}{A}$

   b) Use grid paper or a graphing calculator. Graph the relations in part a.

   c) Explain how the graphs support your answers to exercise 2.

4. Suppose you multiply each dimension of a person by 12.

   a) Approximately how many times as great would the surface area and the volume be for the giant than for the person?

   b) How would the giant's ratio of volume to surface area compare with this ratio for a person?

5. In the movie *Honey, I Blew Up the Kid*, an inventor accidentally enlarges his two-year-old. The child eventually grows from 1 m to 32 m tall, terrorizing Las Vegas until the change is reversed. Suppose you multiply each dimension of a person by 32. Repeat parts a and b of exercise 4.

6. Choose one of the biological systems described below. What health problems might the giants in the land of Brobdingnag have, or the giant child in the movie *Honey, I Blew Up the Kid*?

   Transpiration system Your body generates heat according to its volume. But the rate of cooling depends on the area of your skin, since one way to cool down is perspiration. As the water on your skin evaporates, it helps to keep you cool.

   Respiratory system All the cells in your body require oxygen. The number of cells depends on volume, but the amount of oxygen absorbed by your lungs depends on the surface area of your lungs.

   Skeletal system Your mass depends on volume, but the strength of your bones depends on the area of their cross-section.

7. See page 303 for two real-life examples of the gigantic. Jinlian suffered from severe scoliosis, or curvature of the spine. Wadlow died of an infected blister on his ankle, caused by a poorly fitting brace.

   a) Do you think that Jinlian's and Wadlow's ailments might have been related to their size? Explain.

   b) How do you think their exceptional heights may have contributed to their early deaths?

8. On the preceding page you modelled a giant using a sequence of cubes. A cube may not be the best model because it does not represent the shape of a person well.

a) Try a similar model using a sequence of rectangular prisms. What changes, if any, would there be in your answers to exercise 4b and exercise 5? Explain.

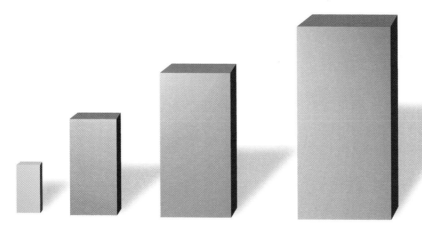

b) Suppose you use a model that more closely resembles the shape of a person. Would your answers to exercise 4b and exercise 5 be different? Explain.

COMMUNICATING
the **IDEAS**

What is your answer to the question "Could a Giant Survive?" In your journal, write to explain how mathematical modelling supports your answer.

In Section 6.2, you expanded a product such as $3(x + 4)$ using the distributive law. You can represent this product using algebra tiles by combining 3 sets of tiles like this:

We can represent a product such as 3×5:
with a rectangle and...   with algebra tiles arranged in a rectangle

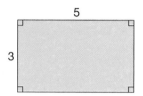   

In each case, the area is $3 \times 5 = 15$

In a similar way, we can represent the product $2(x + 4)$ with algebra tiles to form a rectangle.

The area is $2(x + 4) = 2x + 8$

Instead of writing the length and width as algebraic terms, we use algebra tiles.

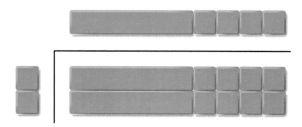

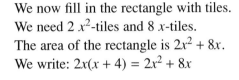

Using Algebra Tiles to Multiply

In exercises 1 and 2, represent each product with algebra tiles.

For each product, sketch the tiles you used.

1. a) $3(x + 2)$ **b)** $4(2x + 3)$ **c)** $2(3x + 1)$

2. a) $3x(x + 2)$ **b)** $4x(2x + 3)$ **c)** $2x(3x + 1)$

3. Look at the sketches and products in exercises 1 and 2. Write to describe any patterns you see.

To represent the product $2x(x + 4)$ with algebra tiles, we make a rectangle that is $2x$ units wide and $(x + 4)$ units long. We place tiles to represent the length and the width.

We now fill in the rectangle with tiles. We need 2 x^2-tiles and 8 x-tiles. The area of the rectangle is $2x^2 + 8x$. We write: $2x(x + 4) = 2x^2 + 8x$

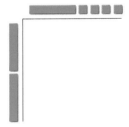

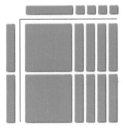

This table compares the distributive law in arithmetic and in algebra.

To multiply in arithmetic, we use the distributive law.	To multiply in algebra, we use the distributive law.
$3 \times 27 = 3(20 + 7)$ $\quad\quad = 3(20) + 3(7)$ $\quad\quad = 60 + 21$ $\quad\quad = 81$	$2x(x + 4) = 2x(x) + 2x(4)$ $\quad\quad\quad = 2x^2 + 8x$

When we multiply a polynomial by a monomial using the distributive law, we say we are *expanding* the product. The following examples show how we expand the product of a monomial and a polynomial.

Example 1

Expand. $8x(x - 3)$

Solution

$8x(x - 3) = 8x(x) + 8x(-3)$ ——————— | Applying the distributive law |
$ = 8x^2 - 24x$

We apply the same method when the polynomial has more than two terms. Since some polynomials cannot be represented with algebra tiles, sometimes we have to use the distributive law.

Example 2

Expand. $(-5a)(a^2 - 4a - 7)$

Solution

$(-5a)(a^2 - 4a - 7) = (-5a)(a^2) + (-5a)(-4a) + (-5a)(-7)$
$ = -5a^3 + 20a^2 + 35a$ ——————— | Applying the distributive law |

DISCUSSING *the* IDEAS

1. Explain your answer to each question.

   a) Can the polynomial in *Example 1* be expanded using algebra tiles?

   b) Can the polynomial in *Example 2* be expanded using algebra tiles?

2. Use algebra tiles to explain why $2x(x + 4)$ can be written as $(x + 4)2x$.

A   1. What product does each diagram represent?

a)

b)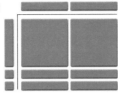

c)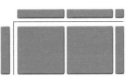

d)

e)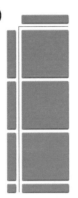

f)

2. Use algebra tiles to expand each expression.

    a) $x(x + 1)$ b) $x(3x + 2)$ c) $2(x^2 + x + 3)$ d) $2x(x + 2)$

3. Expand.

    a) $5(x - 3)$ b) $7(a + 1)$ c) $(-3)(2 + n)$ d) $(-4)(-x - 2)$

    e) $(-1)(2x - 5)$ f) $3(6x - 4)$ g) $5(x^2 - 6x + 3)$ h) $(-2)(-3 + 5n - 3n^2)$

4. Match each product with the appropriate set of algebra tiles.

    a) $2x(x + 1)$ b) $2x(2x + 3)$ c) $2x(x + 5)$

    d) $3x(x + 1)$ e) $x(x + 3)$ f) $x(2x + 2)$

A

B

C

D

E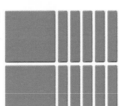

F

5. Expand.

a) $x(3x + 2)$ **b)** $a(5a - 1)$ **c)** $n(3 - 7n)$ **d)** $(-x)(x - 2)$

e) $y(5 - y)$ **f)** $x(4x - 1)$ **g)** $(-x)(7 - 2x + x^2)$ **h)** $n(5n^2 - n + 4)$

6. Expand.

a) $x(x + 3)$ **b)** $(-5)(a - 3)$ **c)** $b(2b^2 - 3b + 1)$ **d)** $p(4 - 3p - p^2)$

e) $7(-6a^2 - 7)$ **f)** $(-12)(-3t^2 + 2t)$ **g)** $(-k)(k^2 - 5k + 1)$ **h)** $(-3)(7 - 2m + 3m^2)$

7. Expand. Before you begin, decide for which expressions you could use algebra tiles.

a) $x(5x^2 - 6)$ **b)** $2(x + 3x^2)$ **c)** $(-3b)(b^3 - b^2)$

d) $2a(3a + 1)$ **e)** $(-4m)(m^2 - m)$ **f)** $x^2(1 - x^3)$

8. Expand.

a) $5x(2x + 3)$ **b)** $2a(3a - 4)$ **c)** $3c(5 - 2c)$ **d)** $(-4n)(2n - 1)$

e) $(-7y)(2y^2 - 5y + 2)$ **f)** $6k(3 - k + 2k^2)$ **g)** $5s(3s^2 - 2s - 7)$ **h)** $(-3p^2)(2 - 3p - p^2)$

9. a) Use the distributive law to multiply 7×236.

b) Use the distributive law to expand $7(2x^2 + 3x + 6)$. Evaluate this polynomial for $x = 10$.

c) Compare your answers in parts a and b. Explain any relationship you discover.

10. The height of any television screen is about $\frac{3}{4}$ of its width.

a) Write an expression for the height of a television screen that is x units wide.

b) Write an expression for the height of a television screen that is 4 units wider than the screen in part a.

c) Write an expression for the area of the television screen in part b.

d) Write an expression for the difference in the areas of the screens in parts a and b.

e) Suppose the difference in areas of the screens in part a and part b is 120 square units. What is the area of each screen?

11. The dimensions of a cereal box, in centimetres, are $5x - 1$, $3x$, and x.

a) Determine an expression for each quantity.

  i) the volume, V, of the box

  ii) the surface area, A, of the box

b) Determine the volume and surface area of the box when $x = 7$ cm.

Two-Variable Algebra Tiles

12. Some algebra tile sets have two different variable tiles, of different lengths. We can call them *x*-tiles and *y*-tiles.

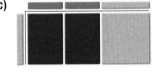 *x*-tile   *y*-tile

Use grid paper, or cut out several paper strips and squares. Show how you can represent 1-tiles, *x*-tiles, *y*-tiles, x^2-tiles, y^2-tiles, and *xy*-tiles.

13. Use grid paper or the paper strips and squares you cut out in exercise 12.

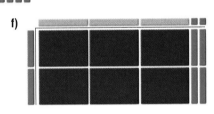

a) Complete this area model of the multiplication expression $2x(3y)$.

b) Write the product as a monomial.

14. What product does each diagram represent?

a) 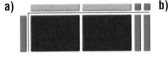   **b)**    **c)**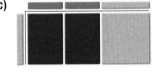

d)    **e)**    **f)**

15. Use grid paper or the paper strips and squares you cut out in exercise 12. Complete an area model for each product. Record your results algebraically.

a) $3x(2y + 1)$ **b)** $5(2x + y + 2)$ **c)** $2y(y + 3x + 1)$ **d)** $3x(2x + y + 4)$

COMMUNICATING the IDEAS

Algebra tiles, polynomials, and sketches are used to solve problems. In your journal, draw a rectangle, length $2x$ units, width $(x + 3)$ units. Write the area as a product. Use the distributive law to write the area as a sum of the areas of two smaller rectangles. Divide the large rectangle into two smaller rectangles. Show their lengths and widths.

7.6 Factoring Polynomials

In Section 7.5, we knew the length and width of a rectangle, and we had to decide which tiles completed the rectangle.

In this section, we'll reverse the procedure.

INVESTIGATION

Using Algebra Tiles to Factor

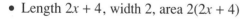

1. Use 3 x-tiles and 6 1-tiles. What polynomial do they represent?

2. Arrange these tiles to form a rectangle.

   a) Write the length of the rectangle as a polynomial.

   b) Write the width of the rectangle as a polynomial.

   c) Write the area of the rectangle as a product of its length and width.

3. Check the rectangles of other students. Did all of you arrange the tiles the same way?

4. Repeat exercises 2 and 3 for these algebra tiles: 4 x-tiles and 8 1-tiles.

5. Explain how the rectangles from the two sets of tiles are different.

In the *Investigation*, you may have found these 3 different rectangles for the algebra tiles that represent $4x + 8$:

- Length $4x + 8$, width 1, area $1(4x + 8)$

- Length $2x + 4$, width 2, area $2(2x + 4)$

- Length $x + 2$, width 4, area $4(x + 2)$

We say that 1 and $4x + 8$ are *factors* of $4x + 8$.
Similarly, 2 and $2x + 4$ are factors of $4x + 8$, and 4 and $x + 2$ are factors of $4x + 8$.

There are three ways to factor $4x + 8$, shown above.
The first two ways: 1, $4x + 8$ and 2, $2x + 4$ are incomplete because the second
factor in each case: $4x + 8$ and $2x + 4$, can be factored again.
The third way is complete. We say that $4x + 8$ is factored *fully* when we write
$4x + 8 = 4(x + 2)$.

This chart compares factoring and expanding in arithmetic and algebra:

In Arithmetic	**In Algebra**
We *multiply* factors to form a product.	We *expand* an expression to form a product.
$(3)(5) = 15$	$4(x + 2) = 4x + 8$
(factor)(factor) = product	(factor)(factor) = product
We *factor* a number by expressing it as a product of factors.	We *factor* a polynomial by expressing it as a product of factors.
For the number 15, the factors are 3 and 5.	For the polynomial $4x + 8$, the factors are 4 and $x + 2$.
$15 = (3)(5)$	$4x + 8 = 4(x + 2)$

The operations of expanding and factoring are inverses; that is, each operation
reverses the other.

Boggle your MIND

On average, the human eye blinks once every 5 s. At this rate, about how many blinks
would there be in your classroom during one math class?

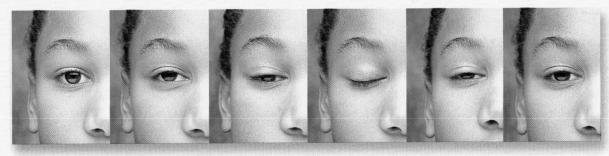

Example 1

Factor fully. $2x^2 + 6x$

Solution

Use 2 x^2-tiles and 6 x-tiles to represent $2x^2 + 6x$. Arrange the tiles to form a rectangle.

The width and length of this rectangle are x and $2x + 6$. But $2x + 6$ can be factored again.
Arrange the tiles in a different rectangle.

The length and width are $2x$ and $x + 3$. From the diagram, $2x^2 + 6x = 2x(x + 3)$

As before, some polynomials cannot be represented with algebra tiles.
They have to be factored algebraically.

Example 2

Factor fully. $2x^3 + 4x^2$

Solution

Factor each term of the polynomial.
$2x^3 = 2 \cdot x \cdot x \cdot x$
$4x^2 = 2 \cdot 2 \cdot x \cdot x$

Identify the factors that are common to each term. Each term has the factors
2 and x and x in common. $2x^2$ is the *greatest common factor*.

Write each term as a product of the greatest common factor and another monomial.
$2x^3 + 4x^2 = 2x^2(x) + 2x^2(2)$
Use the distributive law to write the sum as a product: $2x^3 + 4x^2 = 2x^2(x + 2)$

We use the same method to factor a polynomial with more than two terms, and more than one variable.

Example 3

Factor fully. $-6x^2y + 3xy^2 - 3x^2y^3$

Solution

$6x^2y = 2 \cdot 3 \cdot x \cdot x \cdot y$
$3xy^2 = 3 \cdot x \cdot y \cdot y$
$3x^2y^3 = 3 \cdot x \cdot x \cdot y \cdot y \cdot y$

Each term has the factors 3, x, and y in common.
$3xy$ is the greatest common factor.
$$-6x^2y + 3xy^2 - 3x^2y^3 = 3xy(-2x) + 3xy(y) + 3xy(-xy^2)$$
$$= 3xy(-2x + y - xy^2)$$

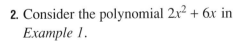

DISCUSSING the IDEAS

1. On page 335, the polynomial $4x + 8$ was expressed in factored form in three different ways. This polynomial has the form $ax + b$. Can all polynomials of the form $ax + b$ be expressed in factored form in three different ways? Use some examples to explain your answer.

2. Consider the polynomial $2x^2 + 6x$ in *Example 1*.

   a) Write as many ways to express this polynomial in factored form as you can.

   b) Explain how each way can be represented with algebra tiles.

3. Explain why the polynomials in *Example 2* and *Example 3* cannot be represented with algebra tiles.

4. For this polynomial: $3x^2 + 9x$

   a) How many different rectangles could you form using algebra tiles?

   b) How many different ways could you factor the polynomial?

   c) How do you identify the greatest common factor?

   d) Write the fully factored polynomial.

A 1. Factor each set of monomials. State the greatest common factor.

a) $3x$, x^2　　　　b) $3b^3$, $3b$　　　　c) $-5y$, $25y^2$

d) $-3x$, $6x^3$, $9x^2$　　e) $2x^2$, $6x^3$, $-8x$　　f) $2y^2$, $4xy$, $-8y^3$

2. State the greatest common factor of each pair of numbers. Each number is written in factored form.

a) $\;9 = 3 \cdot 3$
$\;\;15 = 3 \cdot 5$

b) $18 = 2 \cdot 3 \cdot 3$
$\;\;12 = 2 \cdot 2 \cdot 3$

c) $50 = 2 \cdot 5 \cdot 5$
$\;\;75 = 3 \cdot 5 \cdot 5$

d) $16 = 2 \cdot 2 \cdot 2 \cdot 2$
$\;\;28 = 2 \cdot 2 \cdot 7$

e) $60 = 2 \cdot 2 \cdot 3 \cdot 5$
$\;\;24 = 2 \cdot 2 \cdot 2 \cdot 3$

f) $36 = 2 \cdot 2 \cdot 3 \cdot 3$
$\;\;54 = 2 \cdot 3 \cdot 3 \cdot 3$

g) $490 = 2 \cdot 5 \cdot 7 \cdot 7$
$\;\;140 = 2 \cdot 2 \cdot 5 \cdot 7$

h) $\;495 = 3 \cdot 3 \cdot 5 \cdot 11$
$\;\;1650 = 2 \cdot 3 \cdot 5 \cdot 5 \cdot 11$

i) $540 = 2^2 \cdot 3^3 \cdot 5$
$\;\;450 = 2 \cdot 3^2 \cdot 5^2$

3. Find the greatest common factor.

a) xy, x^2y　　　　b) $3x^2y^2, 6xy$　　　c) $ab, -a^2b^2$

d) $-4xy, 16$　　　e) $-5xy^3, -10x^2y^2$　　f) $6p^2q, -12pq^3$

g) $2m^2n, -4mn^4, 8$　　h) $3x^2y^4, 9x^2y^3, 12xy^2$　　i) $12ab^2, 18a^2bc^2, 24a^3bc$

4. Factor each binomial.

a) $2x + 2$　　b) $3x + 9$　　c) $4x + 10$　　d) $3x + 15$

e) $3k + 12$　　f) $4m + 8$　　g) $4n + 6$　　h) $5w + 15$

5. Factor each binomial. Draw a diagram to illustrate each factored binomial.

a) $x^2 + 2x$　　b) $2x^2 + 4x$　　c) $3x^2 + 9$　　d) $4x^2 + 8x$　　e) $4m^2 + 6$

f) $3k^2 + 18k$　　g) $k^2 + k$　　h) $2z^2 + 4z$　　i) $4x^2 + 2x$　　j) $2y^2 + 8$

6. Factor each binomial.

a) $5y - 10$　　b) $12a + 18$　　c) $3x^2 + 6x$　　d) $2a^2 - 10a$　　e) $4w + 3w^2$

f) $8y^3 - 4y^2$　　g) $6s + 2s^2$　　h) $7k^3 + 35k^4$　　i) $6m^2 - 36m^3$　　j) $8y^4 - 2y^3$

7. Factor. Check by expanding.

a) $14x^2 + 35x$　　b) $25a + 30a^2$　　c) $20n^2 + 80$　　d) $-5x + 10x^2$　　e) $9c^3 + 15c$

f) $-x^3 - x$　　g) $-6y^2 - 3y^3$　　h) $4x + 12x^3$　　i) $\;16m^2 - 4m^3$　　j) $-8d - 8d^3$

8. Factor.

a) $xy + x^2y$　　　b) $-3x^2y^2 + 6xy$　　c) $ab - a^2b^2$　　d) $-4xy - 16$

e) $5xy^2 + 10x^2y^2$　　f) $6p^2q - 12pq^2$　　g) $2m^2n - 4mn$　　h) $3x^2y^2 + 9x^2y^3$

9. Simplify each expression by combining like terms, then factor.

a) $5x^2 - 3x + 2 - x^2 + 11x + 10$

b) $5x^2 - 2x + 2x^2 - 19x + 7$

c) $4a^2 - 3 + 12a^2 - 13 - 24a$

d) $6t^2 - 5t - 2 + 9t + 2$

e) $m^2 - 2m + 3 - m^2 + 6m - 7$

f) $k^3 - k^2 + 2k - 7k^3 - 5k^2 - 12k$

g) $6x^2 + 2 - 3x + 4x^2 - 2x + 3$

h) $9 - 5x + x^2 + 5 + 6x^2 + 12x$

10. Factor each polynomial. Make a diagram to illustrate each factored polynomial, where possible.

a) $16x + 40$

b) $15n - 24$

c) $-2a^2 - 6a$

d) $18n^2 - 12n$

e) $a^3 + 9a^2 + 3a$

f) $3x^2 + 9x$

11. Factor each polynomial. Show all steps.

a) $10x + 15$

b) $6x - 9$

c) $15x + 25$

d) $2x^2 - 4x$

e) $4x^2 - 16x$

f) $3y^3 + 9y^2$

g) $2x^2 + 4x + 8$

h) $12x^3 - 9x^2 + 6x$

12. Factor.

a) $a^3 - 9a^2 + 3a$

b) $-27x^2 - 9x + 3$

c) $5x^3 + 3x^2 - x$

d) $9a^3 + 7a^2 + 18a$

e) $-8d - 24d^2 - 8d^3$

f) $17k - 85k^2 - 51k^3$

13. Factor. Expand to check your work.

a) $3xy^2 + 6x^2y - 9xy$

b) $-2a^2b + 6ab^2 - 4ab$

c) $5m^2n^2 - 10m^3n^2 + 25m^2n$

d) $-28x^2y^2 + 14x^3y^3 - 7x^2y^3$

14. Factor.

a) $a(a + 6) + 7(a + 6)$

b) $x(x - 9) - 2(x - 9)$

c) $8(1 + y) + 2y(1 + y)$

d) $5(2 - x) + x(2 - x)$

e) $2x(x + 3) + 4(x + 3)$

f) $(-3a)(2a - 1) + 6(2a - 1)$

15. Use algebra tiles to attempt to factor each polynomial. Interpret those that do factor in terms of area.

a) $2x - 6$

b) $2x^2 - 6x + 4$

c) $2x^2 + 6$

d) $2x^2 - 6$

COMMUNICATING the IDEAS

In your journal, explain how factoring and multiplying are related. Use examples to illustrate your explanation.

1. Use algebra tiles to represent each polynomial.

   a) $2x^2 + 5x + 3$ b) $x^2 - 3x + 2$ c) $4x^2 - 2x - 3$ d) $-3x^2 - 4x$

2. Write a polynomial to represent the perimeter and a polynomial to represent the area of each rectangle.

   a)
   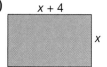
   $x + 4$
   x

   b)
   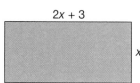
   $2x + 3$
   $x + 1$

   c)

   $x + 5$
   $2x + 1$

3. Which expressions are polynomials?

   a) $x^2 + 4$ b) $5xy$ c) $\frac{5x}{y}$ d) $7 - \frac{2y}{5} + 3x^2$

4. Classify each polynomial in exercise 3 as a monomial, a binomial, or a trinomial.

5. State the coefficient in each term.

   a) $5x$ b) $-2z^3$ c) y^2 d) $\frac{1}{3}x^2y^4$

6. State the constant term in each polynomial.

   a) $4 - 2x$ b) $a^2 + 2a + 3$ c) $4y^2 - 1 + 3y$ d) $5x^2 + 2x$

7. Simplify.

   a) $(5x^2 - 3y^2) + (x^2 + 4y^2)$ b) $(-2x - 7) - (-14x - 6)$
   c) $(8a^2 + 2a - 3) - (-6a^2 + 4a + 7)$ d) $(3x - 2) - (x - 1) + (4x - 3)$
   e) $(4x^2 - 3x) - (x^2 + 2x) + (3x^2 - x)$ f) $(3x^2 + 5x + 7) - (2x^2 - 4x + 9)$

8. Simplify. Determine the value of each polynomial when $x = 2$ and $x = -3$.

   a) $(5 - 2x) - (3 - x) + (7x - 2)$
   b) $(5x^2 - 5x + 7) - (2x^2 - 3x - 5)$

9. Simplify.

   a) $(-25n^2)(8n^2)$ b) $(-35c^3)(-4c^2)$ c) $(17x^2)(5x^3)$ d) $(-28n)(5n^3)$

10. Simplify.

   a) $\frac{-45y^6}{-5y^4}$ b) $\frac{3n^6}{5n^4}$ c) $\frac{25x^4}{-5x^4}$
   d) $\frac{36c^5}{24c^2}$ e) $18x^4 \div 3x$ f) $(-52y^6) \div 13y^5$

11. **Academic Focus** Recall the *x*-tiles and *y*-tiles you cut out on page 333. What product does each diagram represent?

a)

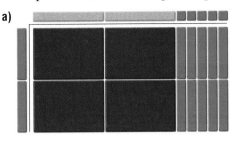

b)

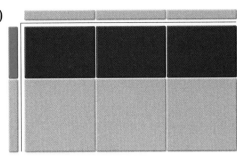

12. Expand.

   a) $4(y - 2)$ b) $8(a - 3)$ c) $(-4)(x + 2)$ d) $3x(5 - x)$

   e) $2y(y - 6)$ f) $(-5x)(3 - x)$ g) $5y(7 - 2y + 3y^2)$ h) $(-6x)(3x^2 + 5x - 12)$

13. Expand.

   a) $3c(5 - 2c)$ b) $(-4n)(2n - 1)$ c) $(-7y)(2y^2 - 5)$

   d) $6k(3 - k + k^2)$ e) $5s(3s^2 - 2s - 7)$ f) $3p^2(2 - 3p - p^2)$

14. **Academic Focus** Factor each polynomial.

   a) $5y - 10$ b) $12a + 18$ c) $-3x^2 + 6x - 12$

   d) $2a^2 - 10a + 2$ e) $4w + 3w^2 - 7w^3$ f) $8y^3 - 4y^2 + 2y$

15. **Academic Focus** Factor. Check by expanding.

   a) $6y + 18y^2$ b) $-3a + 12a^4$ c) $5a^2 - 25a^3$

   d) $3a^3 + 4a^2 + 7a$ e) $3m - 9m^2 + 15m^3$ f) $12k^2 - 48k^4 - 18k^6$

16. **Academic Focus** Simplify, then factor.

   a) $4x^2 - 2x - 3 + 37x + 10x^2 - 4$ b) $5 + 5x - 5x^2 + 5 - 30x + 35x^2$

17. **Mathematical Modelling** In the movie *Honey, I Shrunk the Kids*, an inventor shrinks his children and puts them in the garden. They have many adventures, including being attacked by an ant. In *Gulliver's Travels*, the hero also sailed to the land of Lilliput, where the people were about one-twelfth the height of Gulliver.

   a) How would a miniature person's ratio of volume to surface area compare with this ratio for normal people? Explain.

   b) Choose one biological system from exercise 6, page 326. What health problems might the miniature person have?

CHAPTER 8

Revisiting the Line

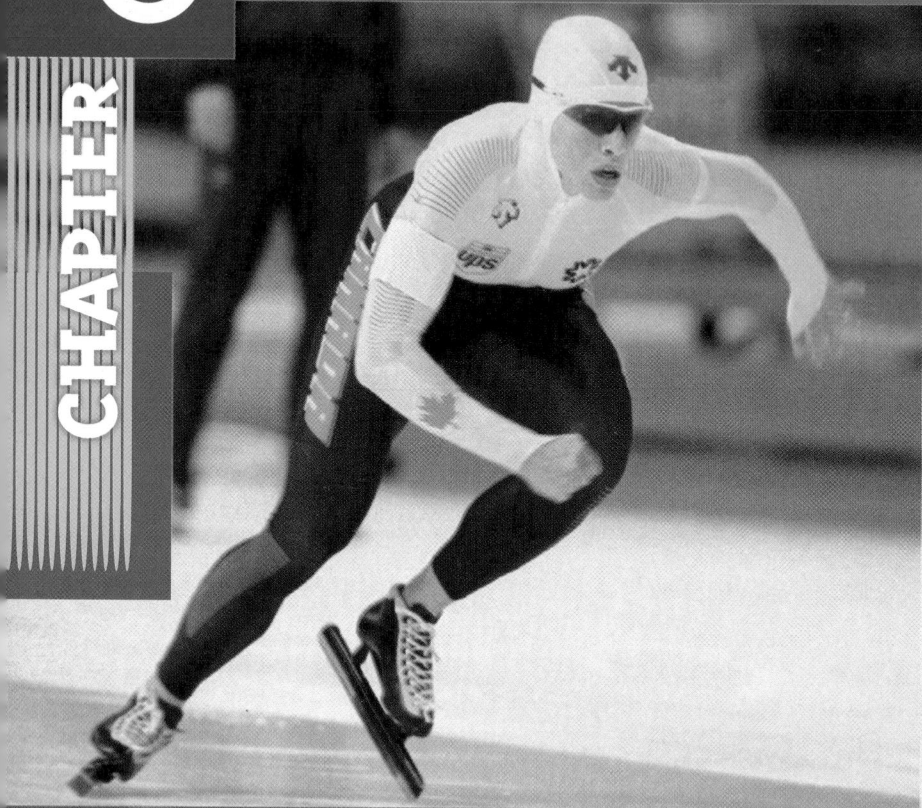

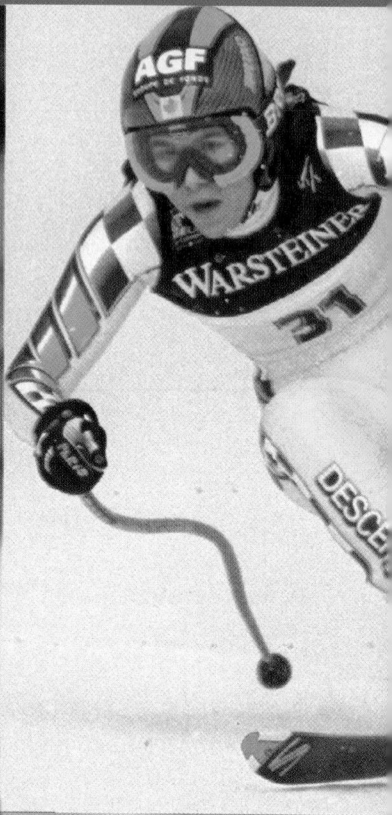

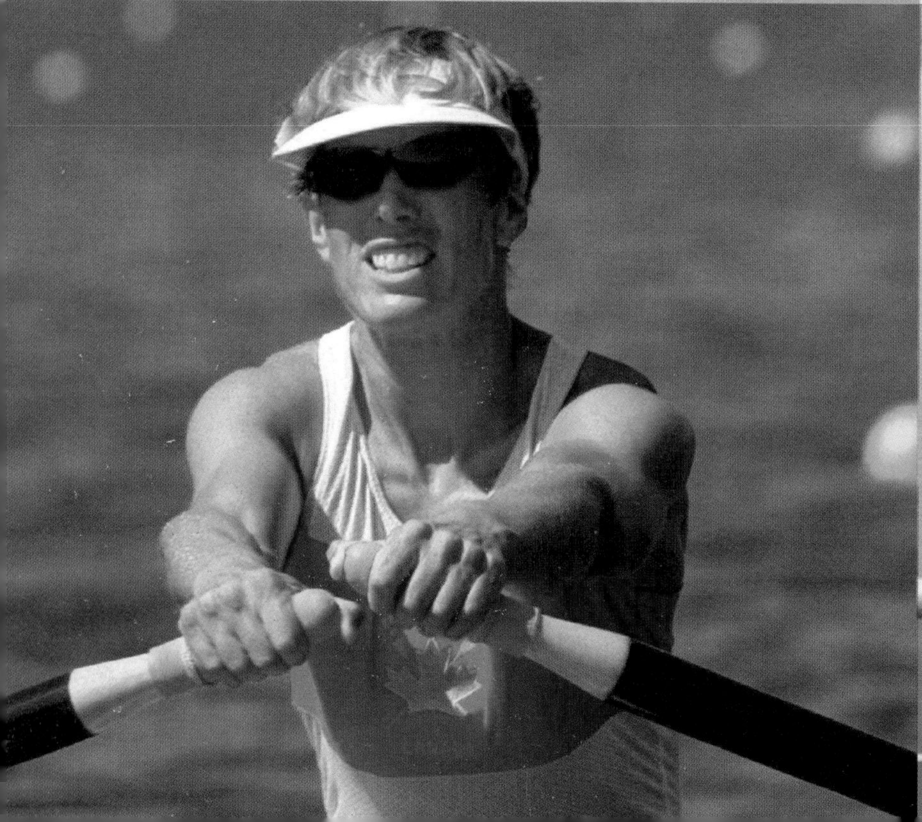

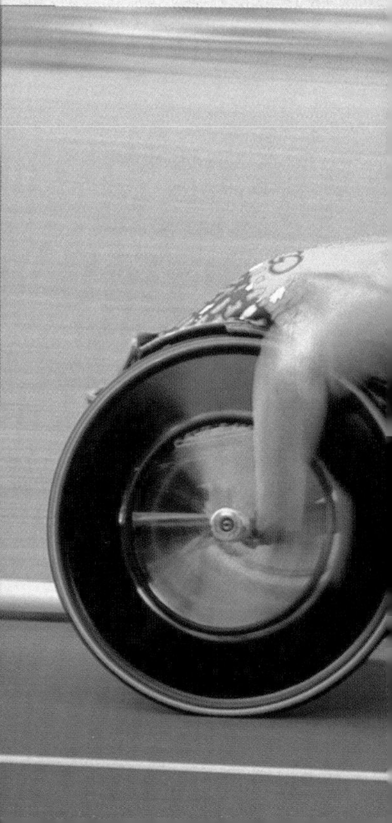

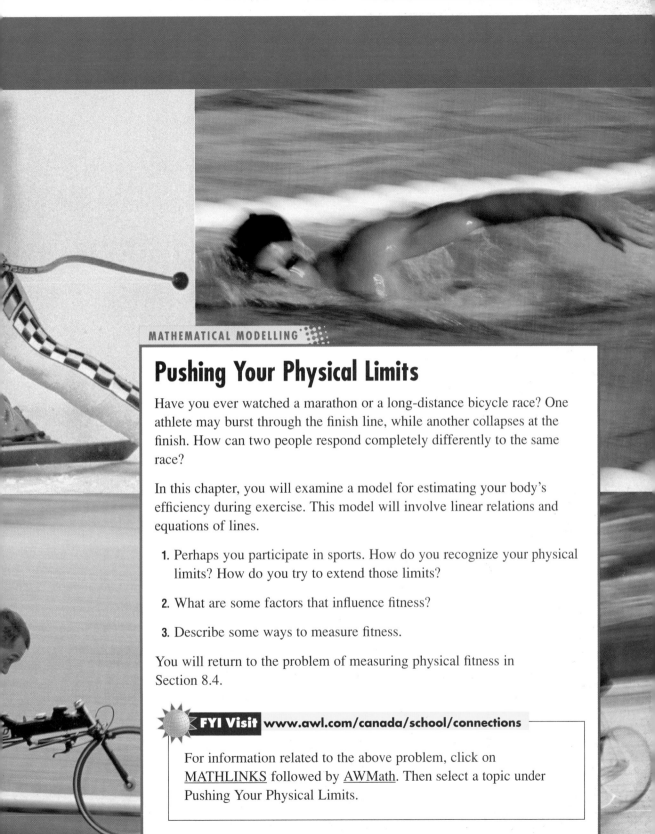

Pushing Your Physical Limits

Have you ever watched a marathon or a long-distance bicycle race? One athlete may burst through the finish line, while another collapses at the finish. How can two people respond completely differently to the same race?

In this chapter, you will examine a model for estimating your body's efficiency during exercise. This model will involve linear relations and equations of lines.

1. Perhaps you participate in sports. How do you recognize your physical limits? How do you try to extend those limits?

2. What are some factors that influence fitness?

3. Describe some ways to measure fitness.

You will return to the problem of measuring physical fitness in Section 8.4.

FYI Visit www.awl.com/canada/school/connections

For information related to the above problem, click on <u>MATHLINKS</u> followed by <u>AWMath</u>. Then select a topic under Pushing Your Physical Limits.

This section reviews these skills and concepts:
- Linear relations
- Slope
- Multiplying rational numbers
- Equation of a straight line

Framing pictures

Sandra runs a business framing pictures. To make a frame for a picture, she must know how much framing material is needed. This depends on the dimensions of the picture and the size of the frame.

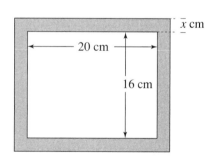

1. One customer has a picture measuring 20 cm by 16 cm. Sandra has framing material with different widths. Let x centimetres represent the width of the framing material. Let L centimetres represent the length of framing material required to frame the picture.

   a) Write an equation for the relation between L and x.

   b) Graph the relation. Should the points be connected? Explain.

   c) Determine the slope and L-intercept of the graph.

   d) What does the L-intercept represent?

   e) What does the slope represent?

2. In exercise 1, describe how the graph would change in each situation. Explain.

   a) Another customer brings in a smaller picture.

   b) A third customer brings in a larger picture.

3. Evaluate each product.

a) $3 \times \frac{1}{4}$ **b)** $3 \times \frac{3}{4}$ **c)** $(-3) \times \frac{3}{4}$ **d)** $3 \times \left(-\frac{3}{4}\right)$

4. One formula for determining slope is slope $= \frac{\text{rise}}{\text{run}}$.

  a) Draw a diagram. Explain how this formula produces large numbers for steep lines and small numbers for lines that are nearly flat.

  b) Draw a diagram to show a line segment with each slope.

    i) 0   **ii)** 1

  c) Draw a diagram to show the difference between a positive slope and a negative slope. Explain how the formula can produce negative slopes.

  d) A line segment has endpoints A(2, 3) and B(6, 8). Explain how you calculate rise and run for this segment.

5. On a grid, draw a line with each slope.

  a) 2   **b)** -2 **c)** $-\frac{1}{2}$ **d)** $\frac{1}{2}$

6. State the slope and y-intercept of the line represented by each equation. Then graph the line.

  a) $y = 2x + 1$ **b)** $y = -2x + 1$

  c) $y = -\frac{1}{2}x + 1$ **d)** $y = \frac{1}{2}x + 1$

7. State the slope and y-intercept of each line. Then write the equation of the line.

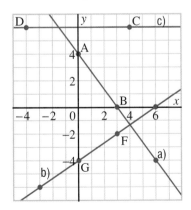

8. Graph the line represented by each equation.

  a) $y = 2$ **b)** $y = 1$ **c)** $y = 0$ **d)** $y = -1$

9. Graph the line represented by each equation.

  a) $x = -1$ **b)** $x = 0$ **c)** $x = 1$ **d)** $x = 2$

Recall from Chapter 4 that the equation $y = mx + b$ represents a straight line with slope m and y-intercept b. We can use this equation to write the equation of a line if we know its slope and its y-intercept. For example, the line shown has slope $\frac{1}{2}$ and y-intercept 1. Its equation is $y = \frac{1}{2}x + 1$.

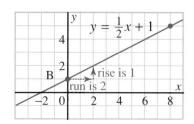

Since the slope of the line is $\frac{1}{2}$, we can start at B(0, 1) and move 2 units right and 1 unit up to obtain other points on the line. We can also move 2 units left and 1 unit down.

Recall that the coordinates of all the points on the line satisfy its equation. For example, the point (8, 5) lies on the line. Substitute $x = 8$ and $y = 5$ into the equation $y = \frac{1}{2}x + 1$ to obtain:

Left side = 5   Right side = $\frac{1}{2}(8) + 1$
$$= 4 + 1$$
$$= 5$$

Since left side = right side, the coordinates (8, 5) satisfy the equation of the line.

Sometimes we have other information about a line, instead of the slope and the y-intercept. As long as there is enough information to graph the line, we can still use $y = mx + b$ to determine its equation.

Given the slope and a point on the line

With a given slope, there is only one line that passes through a given point. The examples below show two ways to determine its equation.

Example 1

a) Graph the line with slope $-\frac{1}{2}$ that passes through the point A(4, 1).

b) Determine the equation of the line.

c) Check that the coordinates of A satisfy the equation of the line.

Solution

a) Draw xy axes. From A(4, 1), move
2 units right and 1 unit down. Repeat.
From A, move 2 units left and 1 unit up.
Repeat.

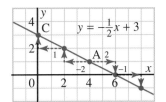

b) Let the equation of the line be $y = mx + b$.
Since the slope is $-\frac{1}{2}$, then $m = -\frac{1}{2}$.
From the graph, the point C(0, 3) is on
the line. Hence, the y-intercept is 3. The
equation of the line is $y = -\frac{1}{2}x + 3$.

c) Substitute $x = 4$ and $y = 1$ into the equation.

Left side = 1   Right side = $-\frac{1}{2}(4) + 3$
$$= -2 + 3$$
$$= 1$$

Since left side = right side, the coordinates of A satisfy the equation of the line.

In *Example 1*, we determined the y-intercept of the line from the graph. We can
also calculate the y-intercept. This method is illustrated in *Example 2*.

Example 2

a) Graph the line with slope $\frac{2}{3}$ that passes through the point A(−1, 3).

b) Determine the equation of the line.

Solution

a) Draw xy axes. From A(−1, 3), move
3 units right and 2 units up. Repeat.
From A, move 3 units left and 2 units down.
Repeat.

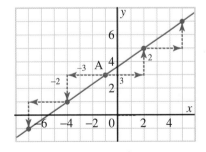

b)

> ### *Think …*
>
> We know two facts about the line:
>
> Fact 1: The slope is $\frac{2}{3}$.
>
> Fact 2: The line passes through (−1, 3).
>
> We use both facts to determine m and b.

Let the equation of the line
be $y = mx + b$.

Using Fact 1:
Since the slope is $\frac{2}{3}$, then $m = \frac{2}{3}$.
Hence, the equation of the line is $y = \frac{2}{3}x + b$.

Using Fact 2:
Since the point A(−1, 3) lies on the line, its coordinates
satisfy the equation.
Substitute −1 for x and 3 for y:

$$y = \frac{2}{3}x + b$$
$$3 = \frac{2}{3}(-1) + b$$
$$3 = -\frac{2}{3} + b$$
$$b = 3 + \frac{2}{3}$$
$$= \frac{9}{3} + \frac{2}{3}$$
$$= \frac{11}{3}$$

Hence, the equation of the line is $y = \frac{2}{3}x + \frac{11}{3}$.

Given two points on the line

There is only one line passing through two given points. If the coordinates of two
points are given, we can determine the equation of the line passing through them.

Example 3

Determine the equation of the line that passes through the points R(1, 4) and S(4, −2).

Solution

Think …

We can determine the slope of the line
from the graph. Then we can use the
method of *Example 2*.

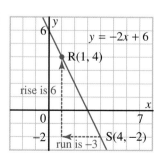

Graph the line.
Let the equation of the line be $y = mx + b$.

Slope of RS $= \dfrac{\text{rise}}{\text{run}}$

$\qquad\quad = \dfrac{4 - (-2)}{1 - 4}$

$\qquad\quad = \dfrac{6}{-3}$

$\qquad\quad = -2$

Since the slope is –2, then $m = -2$.

Hence, the equation of the line is $y = -2x + b$.

Since the point R(1, 4) lies on the line, its coordinates satisfy the equation.

Substitute 1 for x and 4 for y: $\quad y = -2x + b$

$\qquad\qquad\qquad\qquad\qquad\quad 4 = -2(1) + b$

$\qquad\qquad\qquad\qquad\qquad\quad 4 = -2 + b$

$\qquad\qquad\qquad\qquad\qquad\quad b = 6$

Hence, the equation of the line is $y = -2x + 6$.

DISCUSSING *the* IDEAS

1. Explain your answer to each question. If your answer is yes, use the method to determine the equation of the line.

   a) Could you have used the method of *Example 2* to determine the equation of the line in *Example 1*? Explain.

   b) Could you have used the method of *Example 1* to determine the equation of the line in *Example 2*? Explain.

2. How could you check that the equation of the line in *Example 2* is correct?

3. What other ways could you determine the equation of the line in *Example 3*? Discuss your ideas with a partner.

Boggle your MIND

Moniika Vega was the first woman to travel all the way around the world alone on a motorcycle. She left Milan, Italy, on March 7, 1990, and returned to Italy on May 24, 1991. During this time, she travelled 83 500 km. How many days did her trip last? What was the mean distance she travelled each day?

A 1. For each line shown, a point A is marked on a line.

   a) Write the coordinates of A.

   b) Determine the slope of the line from the graph.

   c) Determine the y-intercept from the graph.

   d) Write the equation of the line.

   e) Check that the coordinates of A satisfy the equation of the line.

   i) 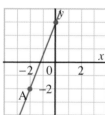   **ii)** 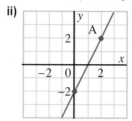   **iii)**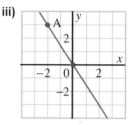

2. Determine the equation of each line.

   a) 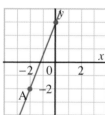   **b)** 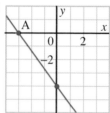   **c)**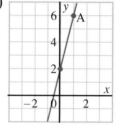

3. For each line shown, two points A and B are marked.

   a) Write the coordinates of A and B.

   b) Determine the slope of AB.

   c) Determine the y-intercept from the graph.

   d) Write the equation of the line.

   e) Check that the coordinates of A and B satisfy the equation of the line.

   i) 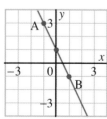   **ii)** 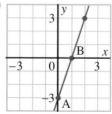   **iii)**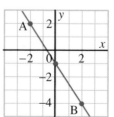

4. Determine the equation of each line.

a)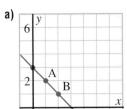

b)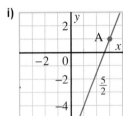

c)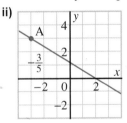

5. Which of the given points lie on the line with equation $y = \frac{3}{2}x + 6$?

a) A(3, −2) **b)** B(−4, 0) **c)** C(0, −6) **d)** D(0, 6)

e) E(2, 9) **f)** F(−2, 3) **g)** G(4, 12) **h)** H(3, 10)

6. a) The equations of lines are given. Which lines pass through the point (−4, 2)?

i) $y = -x$ **ii)** $y = x + 6$ **iii)** $y = 3x + 14$

iv) $y = -\frac{1}{2}x$ **v)** $y = \frac{1}{2}x - 4$ **vi)** $y = -\frac{2}{5}x + \frac{2}{5}$

b) Choose one equation from part a. Write to explain how you determined whether the line passed through the point.

B **7.** For each line shown, a point A is marked on a line with a given slope.

a) Use the equation $y = mx + b$ to calculate the y-intercept of the line.

b) Write the equation of the line.

c) Check that the coordinates of A satisfy the equation of the line.

i) 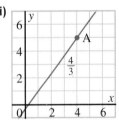 **ii)** **iii)**

8. a) The coordinates of a point and the slope of a line are given. Graph the line through the point with the given slope. Determine the equation of the line.

i) A(2, 5), 3 **ii)** R(−4, 2), 7 **iii)** K(6, −8), −4

iv) M(−10, 3), $-\frac{3}{5}$ **v)** B(5, −2), $\frac{2}{3}$ **vi)** W(−3, 7), $-\frac{7}{2}$

b) Choose one line from part a. Write to explain how you determined the equation of the line.

9. Investigation: Lines Through a Given Point on the x-Axis with Different Slopes The equation $y = mx + b$ represents a line with slope m and y-intercept b; that is, passing through (0, b). In this investigation, you will explore the equations of lines with slope m and passing through other points.

a) Graph the line through (5, 0) with each slope.

    i) 3   **ii)** 2   **iii)** 1   **iv)** 0

    v) −1   **vi)** −2   **vii)** −3

b) Write the *y*-intercept of each line in part a.

c) Write the equation of each line in part a. When you see a pattern develop, use the pattern to write the equations of the other lines.

d) Write the equation of a line through (6, 0) with slope *m*.

e) Write the equation of a line through (*a*, 0) with slope *m*.

10. For each line shown, two points A and B are marked.

    a) Determine the slope of AB.

    b) Use the equation $y = mx + b$ to calculate the *y*-intercept of the line.

    c) Write the equation of the line.

    d) Check that the coordinates of A and B satisfy the equation of the line.

    i) 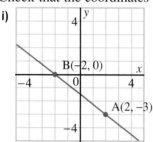   **ii)** 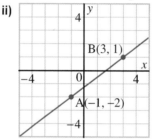   **iii)**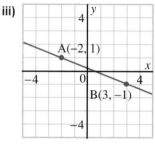

11. a) The coordinates of two points are given. Draw the line through each pair of points. Determine the equation of the line. Check that the coordinates of the points satisfy the equation.

    i) A(2, 2), B(4, 3)   **ii)** R(3, 4), S(−3, 0)   **iii)** F(−1, 5), G(2, −1)

    iv) M(3, −3), N(−6, 0)   **v)** C(0, 2), D(4, 1)   **vi)** W(−4, 7), V(3, 5)

    b) Choose one line from part a. Write to explain how you determined the equation of the line.

12. Mathematical Modelling: Relating Animal and Human Lifetimes: Part III

In Section 2.7, you considered a model for relating the lifetimes of cats or dogs to human lifetimes. The graph from that section is reproduced at the right.

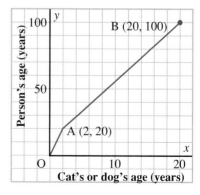

    a) What do the coordinates of A represent? What do the coordinates of B represent?

    b) Determine the equation of the line through A and B.

    c) Explain what the slope of the line represents.

    d) Communicating the Ideas Explain what the equation in part b represents. Use an example to illustrate your explanation.

13. Investigation: Lines Through a Given Point on the *x*-Axis and
Different Points on the *y*-Axis

a) Graph the line through (6, 0) and also through each point on the *y*-axis.
  i) (0, 3)   **ii)** (0, 2)   **iii)** (0, 1)   **iv)** (0, 0)
  v) (0, −1)   **vi)** (0, −2)   **vii)** (0, −3)

b) Write the slope of each line in part a (do not express the fraction in lowest terms).

c) Write the equation of each line in part a. When you see a pattern develop, use the pattern to write the equations of the other lines.

d) Write the equation of a line through (6, 0) and (0, *b*).

e) Write the equation of a line through (*a*, 0) and (0, *b*)

C **14.** A square has vertices A(0, 4), B(−6, 0), C(−2, −6), and D(4, −2). Draw the square on a grid.

a) Determine the equations of the lines containing the four sides.

b) Determine the equations of the lines containing the two diagonals.

15. a) Draw this design on a grid, as shown. Start with the black square with vertices (1, 1), B(1, 2), (2, 2), and D(2, 1).

b) Determine the equation of each line: AB, CD, EF, and GH. What do the lines have in common?

c) Determine the equation of each line: AI, CJ, KL, and MN. Show that they all pass through the same point. What are the coordinates of that point?

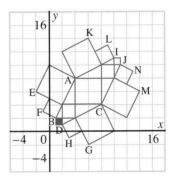

To determine the equation of a line, you need to know two facts about it. For example, two facts that determine a line are the slope and *y*-intercept. In your journal, list as many pairs of facts as you can that determine a line. Refer to the examples and exercises in this chapter for ideas.

8.2 The Equation of a Line: Part II

In Section 8.1, we wrote the equation of a line in the form $y = mx + b$. For example, in *Example 1*, page 347, the equation of the line was $y = -\frac{1}{2}x + 3$. Since this is an equation, we can use the rules for solving equations to write the equation in a different form.

$$y = -\frac{1}{2}x + 3$$

Multiply each side by 2.

$$2y = -x + 6$$

Add x to each side.

$$x + 2y = 6$$

Subtract 6 from each side.

$$x + 2y - 6 = 0$$

The coordinates of points that satisfy the equation $y = -\frac{1}{2}x + 3$ also satisfy the equation $x + 2y - 6 = 0$. In *Example 1*, page 347, we showed that the coordinates of A(4, 1) satisfy the equation $y = -\frac{1}{2}x + 3$. We can check that these coordinates also satisfy the equation $x + 2y - 6 = 0$. Substitute $x = 4$ and $y = 1$ into the equation:

Left side $= 4 + 2(1) - 6$ Right side $= 0$
$ = 0$

Hence, the coordinates of A satisfy the equation $x + 2y - 6 = 0$.

> When one equation can be changed into another equation using the rules for solving equations, the new equation will always produce the same points as the original equation.

When the equation $y = -\frac{1}{2}x + 3$ was changed to $x + 2y - 6 = 0$, all the terms were collected on the left side of the equation. The equation has the form $Ax + By + C = 0$. This is the *standard form* of the equation of a line.

Example 1

Graph the equation $3x + 2y - 12 = 0$.

Solution
Method 1

> ### Think...
> Determine pairs of values of x and y that satisfy the equation. Then plot the corresponding points.

Determine pairs of values for x and y that satisfy the equation.
Choose $x = 0$. Substitute $x = 0$ in $3x + 2y - 12 = 0$, then solve for y.

$$3(0) + 2y - 12 = 0$$
$$2y - 12 = 0$$
$$2y = 12$$
$$y = 6$$

One point on the line has coordinates $(0, 6)$.
Choose $y = 0$. Substitute $y = 0$ in $3x + 2y - 12 = 0$, then solve for x.

$$3x + 2(0) - 12 = 0$$
$$3x = 12$$
$$x = 4$$

Another point on the line is $(4, 0)$.
Plot these points on a grid, then draw a line through them.

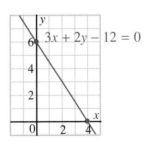

Method 2

> ### Think...
> Write the equation in the form $y = mx + b$ to determine the slope and y-intercept.
> Use the slope and y-intercept to graph the line.

Solve $3x + 2y - 12 = 0$ for y.
$$3x + 2y - 12 = 0$$
Subtract $3x$ from each side. $2y - 12 = -3x$
Add 12 to each side. $2y = -3x + 12$

Divide each side by 2. $\dfrac{2y}{2} = \dfrac{-3x + 12}{2}$

$$y = -\frac{3}{2}x + 6$$

The slope of the line is $-\frac{3}{2}$, and the y-intercept is 6.

Plot the point $(0, 6)$. Use run, 2 and rise, -3 to plot other points on the line. Draw a line through the points.

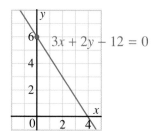

$3x + 2y - 12 = 0$

In the solution of *Example 1*, Method 2, we determined the value of y when $x = 0$ and the value of x when $y = 0$. These values are called *intercepts*.

The y-intercept of a line is the y-coordinate of the point where the line intersects the x-axis. Similarly, the x-intercept is the x-coordinate of the point where the line intersects the x-axis.

Example 2

A line has slope $\frac{3}{5}$ and x-intercept 6.

a) Graph the line.

b) Determine the equation of the line in slope y-intercept form.

c) Determine the equation of the line in standard form.

Solution

a) Draw xy axes. Since the x-intercept is 6, the line passes through A(6, 0).

Start at A(6, 0). Since the slope of the line is $\frac{3}{5}$, use the run, 5, and the rise, 3, to plot other points on the line. Draw a line through the points.

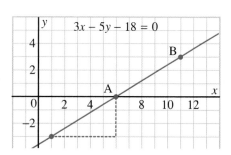

$3x - 5y - 18 = 0$

b)

> ***Think ...***
>
> We know the slope and a point on the line. Use the method of finding the equation of a line with a given slope and through a given point.

Calculate the y-intercept.

Let the equation of the required line be $y = \frac{3}{5}x + b$.

Since A(6, 0) lies on the line, its coordinates satisfy the equation.

Substitute $x = 6$ and $y = 0$.

$0 = \frac{3}{5}(6) + b$

$b = -\frac{18}{5}$

In slope y-intercept form, the equation of the line is $y = \frac{3}{5}x - \frac{18}{5}$.

c) Multiply each side of the equation by 5.

$5y = 3x - 18$

Subtract $5y$ from each side.

$0 = 3x - 5y - 18$

In standard form, the equation of the line is $3x - 5y - 18 = 0$.

DISCUSSING the IDEAS

1. In *Example 1*, Method 1, we graphed a line by determining its intercepts from the equation. Are there any disadvantages to this method of graphing a line? Explain.

2. Suppose the graph of a line is given. Explain how to find the y-intercept and the x-intercept of the line.

3. Suppose the equation of a line is given.

    a) To determine the y-intercept, why do we substitute 0 for x and not for y?

    b) To determine the x-intercept, why do we substitute 0 for y and not for x?

4. In *Examples 1* and 2, how could we check that each graph is correct?

8.2 EXERCISES

A 1. For each line, state the x-intercept, the y-intercept, and the slope.

a)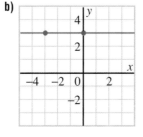

b)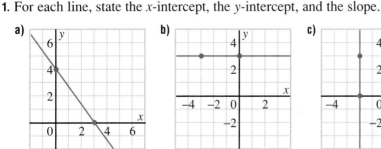

c)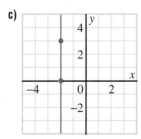

2. The equations of six lines are given. Determine each x- and y-intercept.

   a) $x + 2y - 3 = 0$ b) $2x + y - 3 = 0$ c) $x + y + 2 = 0$

   d) $x - y + 2 = 0$ e) $3x + 2y - 12 = 0$ f) $3x - 2y + 12 = 0$

3. Write each equation in standard form.

   a) $y = -2x + 3$ b) $y = 3x - 2$ c) $y = \frac{1}{2}x + 1$

   d) $y = \frac{2}{3}x - 2$ e) $y = -\frac{3}{2}x + 4$ f) $y = 4x - \frac{5}{2}$

4. Solve each equation for y to write the equation in slope y-intercept form.

   a) $x + y - 4 = 0$ b) $2x + y + 6 = 0$ c) $2x - y - 10 = 0$

   $y = -x + 4$

   d) $x + 2y - 8 = 0$ e) $x - 3y + 9 = 0$ f) $2x + 3y - 6 = 0$

   g) $3x - 2y + 9 = 0$ h) $4x + 3y - 12 = 0$ i) $5x - 2y + 10 = 0$

B   5. The equations of six lines are given. Graph the lines by determining the x- and y-intercepts.

   a) $x + y - 6 = 0$ b) $2x + y - 6 = 0$ c) $x + 2y - 6 = 0$

   d) $3x + 2y + 6 = 0$ e) $3x - 2y + 6 = 0$ f) $2x - 3y - 6 = 0$

6. The equations of six lines are given. Graph the lines by determining the slope and the y-intercept.

   a) $x - y + 4 = 0$ b) $2x - y + 4 = 0$ c) $x - 2y + 4 = 0$

   d) $3x - 2y + 12 = 0$ e) $3x + 2y - 12 = 0$ f) $2x + 3y - 12 = 0$

7. **Investigation: Patterns in $Ax + By + C = 0$**

   a) Identify the patterns in the values of A, B, and C in each list of equations.

      i) $x + y - 9 = 0$ ii) $9x + 2y - 6 = 0$ iii) $4x + 5y + 6 = 0$
         $x + y - 6 = 0$ $6x + 2y - 6 = 0$ $3x + 4y + 5 = 0$
         $x + y - 3 = 0$ $3x + 2y - 6 = 0$ $2x + 3y + 4 = 0$
         $x + y + 0 = 0$ $0x + 2y - 6 = 0$ $1x + 2y + 3 = 0$
         $x + y + 3 = 0$ $-3x + 2y - 6 = 0$ $0x + 1y + 2 = 0$
         $x + y + 6 = 0$ $-6x + 2y - 6 = 0$ $-1x + 0y + 1 = 0$
         $x + y + 9 = 0$ $-9x + 2y - 6 = 0$ $-2x - 1y + 0 = 0$

   b) Plot the graphs of the equations in each list on the same grid. Describe what you see.

   c) Explain how the patterns in the equations account for the patterns in the graphs.

8. The two patterns on page 359 were produced on a graphing calculator. The equation of one line in one pattern is $x + y = 4$.

   a)   i) Which pattern contains a line with this equation?
       ii) What are the equations of the other lines in this pattern?

b) What are the equation of the lines in the other pattern?

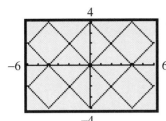

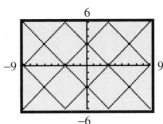

9. The equations of six lines are given below. Suppose you graphed these lines on the graph at the right.

L_1 $2x - 3y + 9 = 0$ $\qquad$ L_2 $2x + 3y + 6 = 0$

L_3 $2x + 3y - 6 = 0$ $\qquad$ L_4 $3x - 2y + 9 = 0$

L_5 $4x - 6y - 9 = 0$ $\qquad$ L_6 $2x - y + 4 = 0$

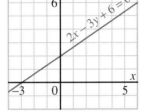

a) Which lines have the same x-intercept as the one on the graph?

b) Which lines have the same y-intercept?

c) Which lines have the same slope?

10. a) Determine the equation of each line.

i) slope 3, through M(2, 1) $\qquad$ **ii)** slope $-\frac{2}{5}$, through R(−1, 4)

iii) slope 2, x-intercept 3 $\qquad$ **iv)** x-intercept 3, y-intercept 4

v) slope $\frac{3}{4}$, through F(4, 0) $\qquad$ **vi)** slope −2, through N(0, 5)

vii) x-intercept $-\frac{2}{3}$, slope $\frac{5}{6}$ $\qquad$ **viii)** x-intercept −5, y-intercept 2

b) Choose one equation from part a. Write to explain how you determined it.

C **11.** This graph shows four lines containing the sides of a rhombus. The equation of one line is $2x + 3y - 12 = 0$.

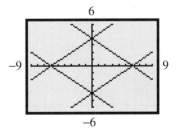

a) Determine the equations of the other three lines.

b) Calculate the area and the perimeter of the rhombus.

COMMUNICATING *the* **IDEAS**

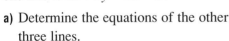

Suppose you know the equation of a line in the form $Ax + By + C = 0$. In your journal, explain how to determine the y-intercept, the x-intercept, and the slope of the line. Illustrate your explanation with an example.

8.3 Intersection of Lines

Where Do They Meet?

The Nguyen family lives in Thunder Bay. The Berg family lives in Kenora. At 12 noon the Nguyens leave by car on a trip to Kenora. They drive at an average speed of 70 km/h. At the same time, the Bergs leave by car on a trip to Thunder Bay. They drive at an average speed of 80 km/h. It is approximately 510 km from Kenora to Thunder Bay. Where are the two cars when they meet?

1. a) Copy and complete the table to show how far the Nguyen family is from Thunder Bay after each hour of the trip.

Time (h)	0	1	2	3	4	5	6	7	8
Distance from Thunder Bay (km)	0								

   b) Draw a graph of distance from Thunder Bay against time for the Nguyen family.

2. a) Copy and complete the table to show how far the Berg family is from Thunder Bay after each hour of the trip.

Time (h)	0	1	2	3	4	5	6	7	8
Distance from Thunder Bay (km)	510								

   b) Use the same grid as in exercise 1b. Draw a graph of distance from Thunder Bay against time for the Berg family.

3. The two lines you drew in exercises 1 and 2 should intersect. What are the coordinates of the point where the lines intersect? What do these coordinates tell you about the locations of the two cars?

4. Use the map to determine the approximate location of the two cars when they meet.

The point where two lines meet is their *point of intersection*. You can determine the coordinates of the point of intersection of two lines from their graphs.

Which Is the Better Plan?

Salespeople at a sporting goods store have a choice of two methods of being paid.

Plan A
A straight 5.5% commission on all sales

Plan B
A monthly salary of $225 plus a 1.9% commission on all sales

You will determine which is the better plan.
Let *x* dollars represent the monthly sales.
Let *y* dollars represent the monthly pay.

Plan A
The monthly pay is $y = 0.055x$.

Plan B
The monthly pay is $y = 225 + 0.019x$.

You will use a TI-83 calculator to graph these equations to determine their point of intersection.

Setup

- Press $\boxed{Y=}$. Use $\boxed{\text{CLEAR}}$ and the scroll buttons to clear all equations and plots.
- Press $\boxed{\text{WINDOW}}$. Insert Xmin = 0, Xmax = 9400, Xscl = 1000, Ymin = 0, Ymax = 500, Yscl = 100.
- Press $\boxed{\text{ZOOM}}$ $\boxed{\blacktriangleright}$ **4** to choose SetFactors. Insert 10 beside both Xfact and Yfact, and press $\boxed{\text{ENTER}}$. This will set the zoom factors to 10 to simplify zooming in.

1. Enter the equations $y = 0.055x$ and $y = 225 + 0.019x$ as follows.
   Press $\boxed{Y=}$ 0.055 $\boxed{X,T,\theta,n}$.
   Move the cursor next to Y2, then press 225 $\boxed{+}$ 0.019 $\boxed{X,T,\theta,n}$.

2. Press $\boxed{\text{GRAPH}}$. Identify each graph on the screen. Sketch the graphs on plain paper. Label each graph with its equation.

3. Press $\boxed{\text{TRACE}}$. Use the arrow keys to move the flashing cursor as close to the point of intersection as you can. Estimate the coordinates of the point of intersection.

4. For a more accurate estimate, press $\boxed{\text{ZOOM}}$ **2** $\boxed{\text{ENTER}}$ to zoom in. Press $\boxed{\text{TRACE}}$ and use the arrow keys again. Read the approximate coordinates of the point of intersection from the screen. Label the intersection point on your graph.

5. What does the horizontal coordinate of the intersection point represent? What does the vertical coordinate represent?

6. Is one of the plans better than the other? Explain.

The problems in Investigations 1 and 2 are examples of problems that are solved by finding the point where two lines intersect on a graph. The coordinates of the point of intersection satisfy the equation of each line.

Example

The equations of two lines are given. Determine the coordinates of the point of intersection. Check the result.

$$3x + y - 11 = 0$$
$$x - 2y - 6 = 0$$

Solution

> ### Think ...
>
> We can graph the equations on the same axes and
> determine the coordinates of the point of intersection. To
> graph the equations, solve each equation for y to
> determine the slope and the y-intercept.

Label the equations ① and ②.

$$3x + y - 11 = 0 \qquad ①$$
$$x - 2y - 6 = 0 \qquad ②$$

Solve each equation for y to express it in the form $y = mx + b$.

Equation ①: $3x + y - 11 = 0$
$$y = -3x + 11$$
The line has slope -3 and y-intercept 11.

Equation ②: $x - 2y - 6 = 0$
$$x - 6 = 2y$$
$$y = \tfrac{1}{2}x - \tfrac{6}{2}$$
$$y = \tfrac{1}{2}x - 3$$
The line has slope $\tfrac{1}{2}$ and y-intercept -3.

Using a graphing calculator

Choose appropriate window settings.
Enter these equations in the Y= list:
$$y = -3x + 11$$
$$y = 0.5x - 3$$
Press TRACE and trace near the point of
intersection. Zoom in for more accurate
results.

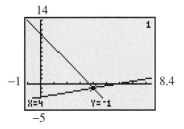

The point of intersection has coordinates
$(4, -1)$.

Using grid paper

Use the y-intercept and the slope to graph
each line on the same grid.

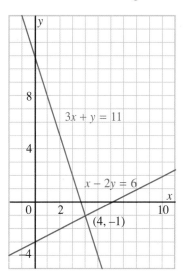

Check:

The values $x = 4$ and $y = -1$ should satisfy both equations.

Substitute $x = 4$ and $y = -1$ in equations ① and ②.

Equation ①: $3x + y - 11 = 0$

Left side $= 3x + y - 11$

$= 3(4) + (-1) - 11$

$= 12 - 1 - 11$

$= 0$

$=$ Right side

Equation ②: $x - 2y - 6 = 0$

Left side $= x - 2y - 6$

$= 4 - 2(-1) - 6$

$= 4 + 2 - 6$

$= 0$

$=$ Right side

The solution $(4, -1)$ is correct.

Each pair of equations in *Investigation 2* and in the *Example* is a *linear system*.
To *solve* a linear system means to determine the ordered pair(s) (x, y) that
satisfies both equations.

DISCUSSING the IDEAS

1. In the *Example*, the equations were graphed by solving for y, then identifying the slope
   and y-intercept. What other method(s) could you use to graph these equations?

2. Do you think it is possible for two lines to appear to intersect on grid lines when they
   do not? How would this affect a solution obtained on grid paper?

3. Explain your answer to each question.
   a) Do you think it is possible for a linear system to have no solution?
   b) Do you think it is possible for a linear system to have more than one solution?

Suppose you have only a 5-L container and an 8-L container.
How can you use them to obtain exactly 4 L of sand?

B 1. Six pairs of lines are defined by the tables of values below.

a) For two of these pairs, you can determine the coordinates of the points of intersection from the tables. Which pairs are these? What are the coordinates of the points of intersection?

b) Graph the other pairs of lines. Determine the coordinates of the points of intersection as accurately as you can from the graphs.

i)

x	y
0	2
1	3
2	4
3	5

x	y
0	5
1	3
2	1
3	−1

ii)

x	y
0	5
1	3
2	1
3	−1

x	y
0	0
1	1
2	2
3	3

iii)

x	y
−2	3
0	−1
2	−5
3	−7

x	y
−1	−5
1	−3
2	−2
5	1

iv)

x	y
−5	6
−3	3
−1	0
1	−3

x	y
−5	0
1	3
3	4
5	5

v)

x	y
−4	3
0	1
2	0
6	−2

x	y
−1	−6
2	0
3	2
5	6

vi)

x	y
−4	1
−1	2
5	4
8	5

x	y
1	−4
2	−1
4	5
5	8

Use your graph from *Investigation 1* to complete exercises 2 and 3.

2. Suppose the Bergs leave Kenora at 1 P.M. instead of 12 noon. About how far would they be from Thunder Bay when their car meets the Nguyens' car?

3. Suppose the Nguyens average only 45 km/h. About how far would they be from Thunder Bay when their car meets the Bergs' car?

4. Refer to *Investigation 2*. Suppose Plan B is changed to a monthly salary of $117.50 plus a 5.6% commission on all sales. Determine when each plan is better.

5. Solve each linear system. Write each coordinate to 2 decimal places.

a) $y = 3x − 2$
$y = −0.5x + 4$

b) $y = 0.35x + 3$
$y = 0.65x + 1$

c) $y = 0.5x − 3$
$y = 2.5x − 1$

d) $2x + y = 7$
$3x - 2y = 6$

e) $x + y = 5$
$x - y = 3$

f) $2x - y = 2$
$3x - y = 4$

6. a) Solve each linear system.

i) $x + y = 5$
$3x + y = 3$

ii) $x - y = -2$
$4x + 2y = 16$

iii) $x + y = 7$
$3x + 4y = 24$

iv) $x - y = 2$
$3x + y = -14$

v) $x - y = 4$
$2x + y = -4$

vi) $5x + 4y = 40$
$5x + 6y = 50$

b) Choose one system from part a. Write to explain how you solved it.

7. Use a map of Ontario. Find two towns on the map and the distance between them. Make up a question similar to that in *Investigation 1*. Answer your question. Exchange questions with a classmate. Answer your classmate's question. Compare answers to both questions.

8. Write a system of two equations. Describe a situation that each equation could represent. Solve the system. Explain the meaning of the solution.

9. One side of a rectangle is 3 cm long. Let x centimetres represent the length of an adjacent side.

a) Write an equation for the perimeter, P, of the rectangle.

b) Write an equation for the area, A, of the rectangle.

c) Graph perimeter against x and area against x.

d) For what values of x is the perimeter:
   i) numerically equal to the area?   **ii)** numerically greater than the area?
   iii) numerically less than the area?

10. In exercise 9, one side of the rectangle was 3 cm long. Use a graph to explain your answer to each question.

a) Suppose one side of the rectangle was 2 cm long. Would it still be possible for the perimeter to be numerically equal to the area?

b) For what lengths of the given side could the perimeter be numerically equal to the area?

COMMUNICATING the IDEAS

Your friend missed today's mathematics class and telephones you about it. How would you explain to her, over the telephone, what a linear system is and what it means to solve a linear system? Write your ideas in your journal.

8.4 Pushing Your Physical Limits

On page 343, you described some ways to measure fitness. In this section, you will examine one measure of fitness.

Your muscles use more oxygen during exercise than they do at rest. One measure of fitness is the maximum volume of oxygen (VO_2 max) that your body can transfer from the bloodstream to its muscle cells during exercise. In general, the higher your VO_2 max, the higher your level of fitness.

Physiologists can measure VO_2 max using a treadmill and specialized measuring equipment. Suppose a 50-kg swimmer is tested. The equipment determines that the maximum amount of oxygen her body can transfer from her bloodstream to her muscle cells is 2500 mL each minute. Since $\frac{2500}{50} = 50$, this means that 1 kg of her body mass transfers 50 mL of oxygen each minute. We say that her VO_2 max is 50 mL/kg/min.

The recovery heart rate model

Since it can be costly and time consuming to measure VO_2 max, mathematical models have been developed to estimate it. One model involves the "step test." In this test, a person repeats a four-step cycle (up-up-down-down) on stairs. Women complete 22 cycles per minute and men complete 24 cycles per minute. Time is regulated by a metronome.

After stepping like this for three minutes, subjects remain standing and take their pulse rate about 15 s into recovery (called the "recovery heart rate"). When the step test was conducted with large numbers of college students, researchers obtained the equations below. In these equations, v represents the VO_2 max (in millilitres per kilogram per minute) and r represents the recovery heart rate (beats/min).

Men:
$v = 113.33 - 0.42r$

Women:
$v = 65.81 - 0.18r$

These equations provide a model for predicting VO_2 max based on recovery heart rate. You can graph to explore the model.

Use a graphing calculator if you have one.

1. **a)** Graph the two equations on the same grid. Plot *VO$_2$ max* on the vertical axis and *Recovery heart rate* on the horizontal axis. Make your axes long enough to graph v up to 120 mL/kg/min and r up to 200 beats/min.

   b) What do you think would be reasonable values of r? What does this tell you about possible values of v?

2. Canadian rower Silken Laumann estimates that her recovery heart rate, after maximum energy output, is 130 beats/min.

   a) Use the graph to estimate Laumann's VO$_2$ max.

   b) The step test was designed to reflect moderate exercise but Laumann was exercising vigorously. Would her actual VO$_2$ max be greater than or less than the estimate in part a? Explain.

3. Spanish cyclist Miguel Indurain registered a VO$_2$ max of 88 mL/kg/min in the season when he won his fifth consecutive Tour de France.

   a) Use the graph to estimate Indurain's recovery heart rate at the time.

   b) Would Indurain's actual recovery heart rate be greater than or less than the estimate in part a? Explain.

4. The graph indicates significantly different results for men and women. Explain why this is so.

5. Where do you fit in? To find out, conduct the step test. Have someone time 3 min of stepping, then 15 s before pulse rates are taken. Take your pulse for 15 s, then multiply by 4 to determine the number of beats per minute. Work with your classmates to construct a class graph to display your results.

6. Your body uses only a percent of the oxygen available. That percent reflects how close you are to your physical limit. Someone on the point of exhaustion is using a very high percent of the available oxygen. How does this explain why some athletes finish a race without being winded, whereas another athlete may be near collapse?

COMMUNICATING the IDEAS

In your journal, write to explain the meaning of VO$_2$ max and why it is used as a measure of physical fitness. Explain why VO$_2$ max depends on both body mass and time, and why a person with a high VO$_2$ max is likely more fit than a person with a lower VO$_2$ max.

Recall that lines in the same plane that do not intersect are *parallel lines.*
Identify pairs of parallel line segments in this picture.

Recall that two lines that intersect at right angles (90°) are *perpendicular lines.*

Identify pairs of perpendicular line segments in the picture above.

Parallel Line Segments

You will need grid paper, a plastic or cardboard rectangle, and a ruler.

1. Draw *xy* axes on a grid. Place the rectangle on the grid. Draw a line
segment along each of two parallel sides of the rectangle.
Remove the rectangle. Label the segments AB and DE.
Determine the slopes of AB and DE.

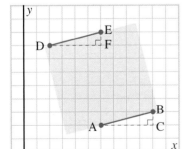

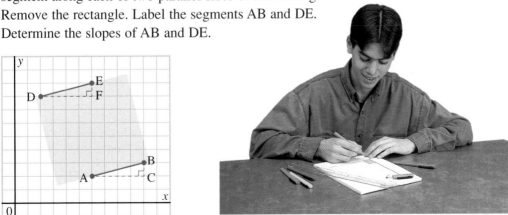

2. Repeat exercise 1 for each of 5 different positions of the rectangle. Include the positions where the parallel sides are vertical, and where the parallel sides are horizontal.

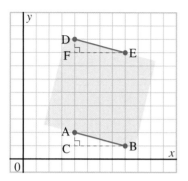

3. a) How are segments AB and DE related? Explain how you know.

   b) How does the rise from A to B compare with the rise from D to E?

   c) How does the run from A to B compare with the run from D to E?

   d) How are the slopes of AB and DE related? Explain.

4. Write a statement about the slopes of parallel line segments.

In this diagram, line segments AB and CD are parallel.

Slope of AB $= \frac{5-3}{6-2}$ Slope of CD $= \frac{6-4}{3-(-1)}$

$\qquad = \frac{2}{4}$ $\qquad\qquad\qquad\qquad = \frac{2}{4}$

$\qquad = \frac{1}{2}$ $\qquad\qquad\qquad\qquad = \frac{1}{2}$

This example illustrates a fundamental property of slope.

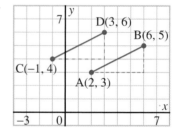

If the slopes of two line segments are equal, the segments are parallel.

If two non-vertical line segments are parallel, their slopes are equal.

Perpendicular Line Segments

You will need grid paper, a plastic or cardboard rectangle, and a ruler.

1. Draw *xy* axes on a grid. Place the rectangle on the grid. Draw a line segment along each of two perpendicular sides of the rectangle. Remove the rectangle. Label the segments AB and GH. Determine the slopes of AB and GH.

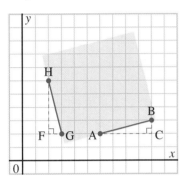

2. Repeat exercise 1 for each of 5 different positions of the rectangle. Include the position where the perpendicular sides are vertical and horizontal.

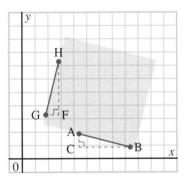

3. a) How are line segments AB and GH related? Explain how you know.

   b) How does the rise from A to B compare with the run from G to H?

   c) How does the run from A to B compare with the rise from G to H?

   d) How are the slopes of AB and GH related? Explain.

4. Write a statement about the slopes of perpendicular line segments.

Here is another way to illustrate the relationship between the slopes of perpendicular line segments.

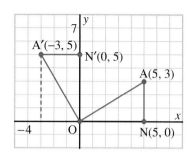

Right △ONA is rotated 90° counterclockwise about O(0, 0) to △ON'A'.

The coordinates of A are (5, 3).
The coordinates of A' are (−3, 5).
OA is perpendicular to OA'.

Slope of OA $= \frac{3-0}{5-0}$ Slope of OA' $= \frac{5-0}{-3-0}$

$\qquad = \frac{3}{5}$ $\qquad\qquad\qquad\qquad = -\frac{5}{3}$

The numbers $\frac{3}{5}$ and $-\frac{5}{3}$ are *negative reciprocals*. The product of negative reciprocals is − 1. This example suggests the relation between slopes of perpendicular line segments.

If the slopes of two line segments are negative reciprocals, the segments are perpendicular.

If two line segments are perpendicular (and neither one is vertical), their slopes are negative reciprocals.

Example 1

Determine whether the quadrilateral with vertices A(0, − 6), B(2, − 1), C(− 1, 5), and D(− 3, 0) is a parallelogram.

Solution

Draw the quadrilateral on a grid.

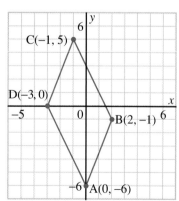

Slope of AB $= \frac{-1-(-6)}{2-0}$ Slope of DC $= \frac{5-0}{-1-(-3)}$

$\qquad = \frac{5}{2}$ $\qquad\qquad\qquad\qquad = \frac{5}{2}$

Slopes of AB and DC are equal, therefore AB ∥ DC.

Slope of AD $= \frac{0-(-6)}{-3-0}$ Slope of BC $= \frac{5-(-1)}{-1-2}$

$\qquad = \frac{6}{-3}$ $\qquad\qquad\qquad\qquad = \frac{6}{-3}$

$\qquad = -2$ $\qquad\qquad\qquad\qquad = -2$

Slopes of AD and BC are equal; therefore AD ∥ BC.

Since both pairs of opposite sides are parallel, ABCD is a parallelogram.

Example 2

A triangle has vertices A(−2, 3), B(8, −2), and C(4, 6). Determine whether it is a right triangle.

Solution

Graph the triangle.

From the graph, ∠C appears to be a right angle.

Calculate the slopes of AC and BC.

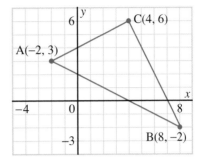

Slope of AC $= \frac{6-3}{4-(-2)}$ Slope of BC $= \frac{6-(-2)}{4-8}$

$\qquad\qquad = \frac{3}{6}$ $\qquad\qquad\qquad\quad = \frac{8}{-4}$

$\qquad\qquad = \frac{1}{2}$ $\qquad\qquad\qquad\quad = -2$

Since $\left(\frac{1}{2}\right)(-2) = -1$, AC is perpendicular to BC, and △ABC is a right triangle.

DISCUSSING the IDEAS

1. Look at the last sentence on page 370. Explain why the word "non-vertical" is included.

2. Look at the second sentence in the display on page 372. Explain why the words "and neither one is vertical" are included.

3. In *Example 1*, do you have to check that both pairs of opposite sides are parallel? Would it be sufficient to check that only one pair is parallel? Explain.

4. In *Example 2*, what are the advantages of drawing the triangle?

Boggle your MIND

The surface area of all the windows at the National Gallery of Canada, in Ottawa, is 28 680 m². It is estimated that a 10-m² window can be cleaned in 2 min. At this rate, how many hours would it take to clean all the windows in the gallery?

8.5 EXERCISES

A **1.** Which pairs of line segments are parallel? Explain how you know.

a)
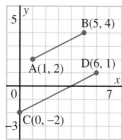

b)
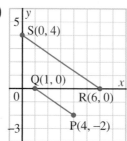

c)
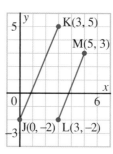

2. Which pairs of line segments are perpendicular? Explain how you know.

a)
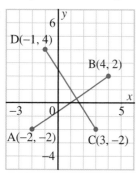

b)
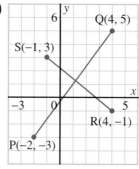

c)
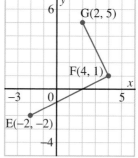

3. Determine the slope of a line segment perpendicular to a segment with each given slope.

a) $\frac{2}{3}$ b) $\frac{5}{8}$ c) $-\frac{3}{4}$ d) $-\frac{1}{2}$ e) $-\frac{1}{3}$

4. Which pairs of numbers are slopes of perpendicular line segments?

a) $\frac{3}{4}, -\frac{4}{3}$ b) $\frac{2}{3}, \frac{3}{2}$ c) $\frac{4}{5}, -\frac{4}{5}$ d) $-4, \frac{1}{4}$ e) $3, \frac{1}{3}$

B **5.** The coordinates of the endpoints of pairs of line segments are given. Graph each pair of line segments. Determine their slopes. Which line segments are parallel?

a) A(−2, −1), B(1, 5) and C(2, −1), D(4, 3)

b) E(−3, 2), F(5, 5) and O(0, 0), H(5, 2)

c) R(−1, 4), S(7, −2) and T(3, 4), U(9, 0)

6. The coordinates of the endpoints of pairs of line segments are given. Graph each line segment. Determine its slope. Which line segments are perpendicular?

a) O(0, 0), B(6, 4) and C(5, −1), D(1, 5)

b) H(−3, 1), I(6, 4) and J(2, 0), K(0, 6)

c) L(5, −3), M(1, 4) and N(1, −1), P(6, 2)

7. Choose one part of exercise 6. Write to explain how you determined whether the line segments were perpendicular.

8. The coordinates of the vertices of quadrilaterals are given. Draw each quadrilateral on a grid. Determine whether it is a parallelogram.

   a) A(5, 3), B(−3, −3), C(−2, −8), D(6, −2)

   b) P(−6, 1), Q(−2, −6), R(10, 2), S(7, 9)

   c) J(−4, 5), K(−2, −1), L(6, −4), M(4, 2)

9. Choose one part of exercise 8. Write to explain how you determined whether the quadrilateral was a parallelogram.

10. The coordinates of the vertices of triangles are given. Draw each triangle on a grid. Determine whether it is a right triangle.

   a) D(−2, 2), E(−6, 2), F(−6, −1)   **b)** A(3, 0), B(−4, 4), C(−1, −2)

   c) P(−3, 1), Q(3, −3), R(7, 3)   **d)** K(3, 2), L(−5, −1), M(−2, −8)

11. a) Graph the points A(1, −2), B(3, 1), and C(6, −1). Draw line segments to form a triangle. Determine the slope of each side of the triangle.

   b) What type of triangle is it? Explain.

   c) Determine the coordinates of a fourth point, D, that would form a rectangle with points A, B, and C.

12. a) Graph the points A(1, −2), B(3, 1), C(4, −1), and D(6, 2). Join the points to form a quadrilateral.

   b) Determine the slope of each side of the quadrilateral.

   c) What is the name of this quadrilateral? Explain.

13. a) Graph four points that form a parallelogram.

   b) Determine the slope of each side of the parallelogram.

   c) Use slope to explain why the figure is a parallelogram.

14. The coordinates of the vertices of quadrilaterals are given. Draw each quadrilateral on a grid. Determine whether it is a rectangle.

   a) A(5, 4), B(−4, −2), C(−2, −5), D(7, 1)

   b) J(−3, 2), K(−2, −3), L(6, −2), M(5, 3)

   c) P(5, 1), Q(−4, 4), R(−6, −2), S(3, −5)

15. The coordinates of the endpoints of line segments are given. Graph each segment. Determine the coordinates of a point C so that AC is perpendicular to AB.

   a) A(3, 2), B(6, 8)   **b)** A(0, 5), B(5, 3)   **c)** A(1, 3), B(1, −2)

16. Choose one part of exercise 15. Write to explain how you determined the coordinates of C.

17. Points A, B, and C are three vertices of a rectangle. Plot the points on a grid. Determine the coordinates of the fourth vertex.

    a) A(2, −1), B(5, −3), C(7, 0)   **b)** A(1, 8), B(−3, −2), C(6, 6)

    c) A(−4, 7), B(−6, 4), C(3, −2)   **d)** A(2, 4), B(−2, 2), C(1, −4)

18. Choose one part of exercise 17. Write to explain how you determined the coordinates of the vertex.

19. a) The coordinates of the endpoints of a line segment are given. For each line segment, write the coordinates of the endpoints of a parallel line segment.

    i) A(7, 6), B(−6, 3)   **ii)** C(−3, 7), D(1, −5)

    iii) E(2, 3), F(−2, −7)   **iv)** G(−4, 2), H(6, −4)

  b) Compare your answers for part a with those of a classmate. Write to explain any differences.

20. a) Use the line segments in exercise 19. For each line segment, write the coordinates of the endpoints of a perpendicular line segment.

  b) Compare your answers for part a with those of a classmate. Write to explain any differences.

C **21.** The points A(−2, 0), B(6, 4), and C(−3, 4) are given. Determine the coordinates of a point D on the *y*-axis so that line segment CD is parallel to AB.

22. The points A(6, 3), B(2, 9), and C(2, 3) are given. Determine the coordinates of a point D so that CD is parallel to AB when D is on the *y*-axis.

23. A line segment has endpoints C(6, 2) and D(8, 5). Point P is such that PC is perpendicular to CD. Determine the coordinates of P if P is on:

    a) the *x*-axis   **b)** the *y*-axis

24. The line segment joining R(8, 6) and S(4, 8) is the shortest side of a right △RST. Point T is on the *x*-axis. Determine the possible coordinates of T.

COMMUNICATING *the* IDEAS

Suppose your friend asks you for help with tonight's homework. How would you explain how to tell if two line segments are perpendicular? Use examples to illustrate your explanation. Record your answer in your journal.

8.6 The Equation of a Line: Part III

In Section 8.5, you learned that if two line segments are parallel, then their slopes are equal. Also, if two line segments are perpendicular, then their slopes are negative reciprocals. Similarly, if two lines are parallel, then their slopes are equal. Also, if two lines are perpendicular, then their slopes are negative reciprocals.

We will now investigate the equations of parallel lines and the equations of perpendicular lines.

If you have a graphing calculator, complete Investigation 1. If you do not have a graphing calculator, complete Investigation 2.

INVESTIGATION 1

Parallel and Perpendicular Lines Using a Graphing Calculator

Setup
Press [WINDOW]. Insert Xmin = –9, Xmax = 9, Xscl = 1, Ymin = –6, Ymax = 6, Yscl = 1.

1. a) Press [Y=] 3 [X,T,θ,n] [+] 2 to input $y = 3x + 2$.

   b) Press [GRAPH] to display the graph of this equation.

Parallel lines

2. a) Write the slope of the line you graphed in exercise 1.

   b) Write the equations of 3 other lines that have the slope you wrote in part a. Insert each equation in the Y= list. Press [GRAPH].

   c) Were your equations correct? How do you know?

   d) Compare your equations with those of a classmate. What do you notice? Explain.

3. a) Write the equation of the line that is parallel to the line represented by $y = 3x + 2$ and has y-intercept -1.

b) Input this equation, then press ⌈GRAPH⌋ to check.

Clear all equations except $y = 3x + 2$ from the Y= list.

Perpendicular lines

4. a) Write the slope of any line that is perpendicular to the line represented by $y = 3x + 2$.

b) Write the equations of 3 other lines that have the slope you wrote in part a. Insert each equation in the Y= list. Press ⌈GRAPH⌋.

c) Were your equations correct? How do you know?

d) Compare your equations with those of a classmate. What do you notice? Explain.

5. a) Write the equation of the line that is perpendicular to the line represented by $y = 3x + 2$ and has y-intercept -1.

b) Input this equation, then press ⌈GRAPH⌋ to check.

6. Suppose you have a list of equations of lines. Without graphing:

a) How can you tell which lines are parallel?

b) How can you tell which lines are perpendicular?

INVESTIGATION 2

Parallel and Perpendicular Lines Using Grid Paper

1. The equation $y = 3x + 2$ represents a line.

a) What is the slope of this line? What is the y-intercept?

b) Graph the line on grid paper.

Parallel lines

2. a) On the same axes, graph 3 lines that are parallel to the line in exercise 1.

b) Determine the y-intercept of each line.

c) Write the equation of each line. Compare your equations with those of a classmate. What do you notice? Explain.

3. a) Write the equation of the line that is parallel to the line represented by $y = 3x + 2$ and has y-intercept -1.

b) Graph this equation.

Perpendicular lines

4. a) Write the slope of any line that is perpendicular to the line in exercise 1.

b) On the same axes, graph 3 lines that are perpendicular to the line in exercise 1.

c) Determine the *y*-intercept of each line.

d) Write the equation of each line. Compare your equations with those of a classmate. What do you notice? Explain.

5. a) Write the equation of the line that is perpendicular to the line represented by $y = 3x + 2$ and has *y*-intercept -1.

b) Graph this equation.

6. Suppose you have a list of equations of lines. Without graphing:

a) How can you tell which lines are parallel?

b) How can you tell which lines are perpendicular?

From the *Investigations*, you should have learned these facts about parallel and perpendicular lines:

- Lines are parallel when their equations in the form $y = mx + b$ have the same value of *m*. For example, $y = 2x + 3$ and $y = 2x - 4$ represent parallel lines.

- Lines are perpendicular when their equations in the form $y = mx + b$ have values of *m* that are negative reciprocals. For example, $y = 2x + 3$ and $y = -\frac{1}{2}x - 5$ represent perpendicular lines.

Example 1

Determine the equation of the line that passes through A(3, 1) and is parallel to the line shown.

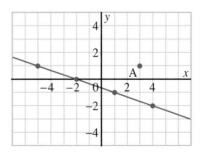

Solution

> *Think ...*
>
> We need to determine the slope of the given line. Then we determine the equation of the line through A with this slope.

For the given line,

slope $= \frac{\text{rise}}{\text{run}}$

$= \frac{-1}{3}$

$= -\frac{1}{3}$

The required line is parallel to the given line.

So, the required line through A has slope $-\frac{1}{3}$.

From A, move 3 units right and 1 unit down.

Mark a point B. Draw the line through A and B.

The y-intercept of this line is 2. This line has

equation $y = mx + b$, where $m = -\frac{1}{3}$ and $b = 2$.

The equation is $y = -\frac{1}{3}x + 2$.

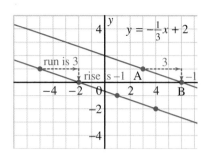

Example 2

Determine the equation of the
line that passes through A(3, 1)
and is perpendicular to the given line.

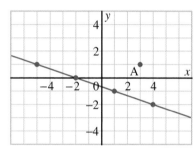

Solution

> ### Think ...
>
> We need to determine the slope of the given
> line. Then we determine the slope of any line
> perpendicular to it. Then we determine the
> equation of the line through A with this slope.

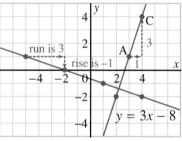

From *Example 1*, the slope of the given line is $-\frac{1}{3}$.
The slope of any line perpendicular to the given line is 3. From A, move
1 unit right and 3 units up. Mark a point C. Draw the line through A and C.

> ### Think ...
>
> We need to know the y-intercept of the required line. This line does not intersect the
> y-axis on the grid as it is drawn. We can either extend the grid and the line to obtain the
> y-intercept from the graph, or we can calculate the y-intercept.

Calculate the *y*-intercept.

Let the equation of the required line be $y = 3x + b$.

Since A(3, 1) lies on this line, its coordinates satisfy the equation.

Substitute $x = 3$ and $y = 1$.

$1 = 3(3) + b$

$-8 = b$

The equation is $y = 3x - 8$.

DISCUSSING the IDEAS

1. When you know the slope of a line, how can you determine the slope of a perpendicular line?

2. Look at the Solutions of *Examples 1* and *2*.

   a) Could you complete *Example 1* by using the method of *Example 2*? Explain.

   b) Could you complete *Example 2* by using the method of *Example 1*? Explain.

8.6 EXERCISES

1. Which pairs of lines are parallel? Explain how you know.

a)
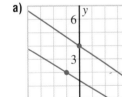

b)

c)

2. Which pairs of lines are perpendicular? Explain how you know.

a)
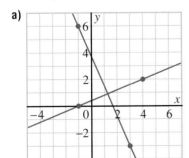

b)
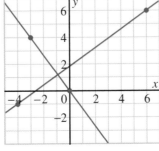

c)
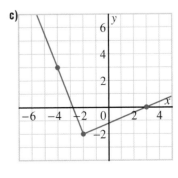

3. a) Which equations represent parallel lines? Explain.

b) Which equations represent perpendicular lines? Explain.

$$y = 0.5x + 5 \quad y = 0.5x \qquad y = 2x - 3 \qquad y = -2x$$

$$y = \tfrac{2}{3}x + 5 \quad y = -\tfrac{2}{3}x \qquad y = -\tfrac{3}{2}x + 3 \quad y = \tfrac{3}{2}x - \tfrac{1}{2} \qquad y = -\tfrac{3}{2}x - 4$$

B **4. a)** On a grid, draw a line through A(0, −3) with slope $\tfrac{2}{3}$.

b) On the same grid, draw two lines through B(1, 2): one parallel to the line in part a, the other perpendicular to the line in part a.

c) The three lines you have drawn contain three sides of a square. In how many ways can you draw a fourth line to complete the square? Draw these lines.

5. a) Graph the line with equation $y = x + 4$.

b) i) What is the slope of the line in part a?
ii) What is the slope of a line that is parallel to the line in part a?

c) Graph the line parallel to the line in part a, with y-intercept −2.

d) Write the equation of the line in part c.

6. a) Graph the line with equation $y = 2x - 1$.

b) i) What is the slope of the line in part a?
ii) What is the slope of a line that is perpendicular to the line in part a?

c) Graph the line perpendicular to the line in part a, with y-intercept 5.

d) Write the equation of the line in part c.

7. Draw this line on grid paper.

a) i) Draw a line through A(4, 5) that is parallel to the given line.
ii) Determine the equation of this line.

b) i) Draw a line through A(4, 5) that is perpendicular to the given line.
ii) Determine the equation of this line.

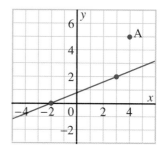

8. a) Graph the line defined by $y = \tfrac{3}{2}x + 3$.

b) i) On the same axes, graph the line parallel to the line in part a, with y-intercept 1.
ii) Determine the equation of this line.

c) i) On the same axes, graph the line perpendicular to the line in part a, passing through B(2, −1).
ii) Determine the equation of this line.

9. Determine the equation of the line that passes through A(2, 3) and is parallel to the line defined by $3x - 2y + 12 = 0$.

10. Determine the equation of the line that passes through B(3, −1) and is perpendicular to the line defined by $2x + y − 9 = 0$.

11. Determine the equation of each line that is parallel to the line with equation $y = 2x + 6$ and that passes through each point in each list. When you see a pattern in the equations, use the pattern to write the remaining equations.

a) (1, 6)   **b)** (1, 6)   **c)** (1, 6)
    (2, 6)   (1, 5)   (2, 5)
    (3, 6)   (1, 4)   (3, 4)
    (4, 6)   (1, 3)   (4, 3)
    (5, 6)   (1, 2)   (5, 2)
    (6, 6)   (1, 1)   (6, 1)

12. a) Graph the line that is parallel to the *x*-axis and passes through A(3, 5). Determine its equation.

    b) Graph the line that is perpendicular to the *x*-axis and passes through A(3, 5). Determine its equation.

    c) Graph the line that is parallel to the *y*-axis and passes through B(−1, 4). Determine its equation.

    d) Graph the line that is perpendicular to the *y*-axis and passes through B(−1, 4). Write its equation.

13. Graph the line L_1 with equation $y = −2x + 5$. Determine, if possible, the equation of each line below. If there is no such line, explain why. If there is more than one such line, explain why.

    a) the line parallel to L_1, with *y*-intercept 1

    b) the line parallel to L_1, with slope −2

    c) the line perpendicular to L_1, passing through A(−2, 5)

    d) the line perpendicular to L_1, with *x*-intercept 2 and *y*-intercept 3.

COMMUNICATING *the* IDEAS

Recall this paragraph from page 346: "Sometimes we have other information about a line, instead of the slope and the *y*-intercept. As long as there is enough information to graph the line, we can still use $y = mx + b$ to determine its equation." In your journal, write to explain a strategy that you can always use to determine the equation of a line when enough information to graph the line is given. Use examples to illustrate your explanation.

8   Consolidating Your Skills

1. **Investigation: Lines Through Different Points on the x-Axis with the Same Slope**

   a) Graph the line with slope 2 through each point.

      i) $(5, 0)$ **ii)** $(3, 0)$ **iii)** $(1, 0)$
      iv) $(-1, 0)$ **v)** $(-3, 0)$ **vi)** $(-5, 0)$

   b) Write the y-intercept of each line in part a.

   c) Write the equation of each line in part a. When you see a pattern develop, use the pattern to write the equations of the other lines.

   d) Write the equation of a line through $(6, 0)$ with slope m.

   e) Write the equation of a line through $(a, 0)$ with slope m.

2. **Investigation: Lines Through a Given Point on the y-Axis and Different Points on the x-Axis**

   a) Graph the line through $(0, 6)$ and also through each point on the x-axis.

      i) $(3, 0)$ **ii)** $(2, 0)$ **iii)** $(1, 0)$
      iv) $(-1, 0)$ **v)** $(-2, 0)$ **vi)** $(-3, 0)$

   b) Write the slope of each line in part a (do not express the fractions in lowest terms).

   c) Write the equation of each line in part a. When you see a pattern develop, use the pattern to write the equations of the other lines.

   d) Write the equation of a line through $(0, 6)$ and $(a, 0)$.

   e) Write the equation of a line through $(0, b)$ and $(a, 0)$.

3. A quadrilateral has vertices A$(-1, 4)$, B$(-3, -2)$, C$(3, -1)$, and D$(4, 5)$. Determine whether the quadrilateral is a parallelogram.

4. A triangle has vertices P$(-4, -2)$, Q$(6, 4)$, and R$(-7, 3)$. Show that $\angle$QPR is a right angle. Write to explain how you completed the exercise.

5. A quadrilateral has vertices A$(-2, 2)$, B$(-1, 3)$, C$(5, -2)$, and D$(4, 3)$. Determine whether it is a parallelogram or a rectangle. Write to explain how you identified the quadrilateral.

6. The points P$(1, 4)$, Q$(-1, -2)$ and R$(4, -3)$ are given. Determine the coordinates of a point S so that RS is parallel to PQ and S is on:

   a) the x-axis   **b)** the y-axis

7. Use the points in exercise 6. Determine the coordinates of a point S so that RS is perpendicular to PQ and point S is on:

   a) the x-axis   **b)** the y-axis

8. a) On a grid, draw a line with slope $\frac{2}{5}$ through A(–3, 2).

b) Draw a line through C(–2, –1) that is parallel to the line in part a.

c) Draw a line through C(–2, –1) that is perpendicular to the line in part a.

9. a) On the same axes, draw a line through P(5, 2) with each slope.

   i) $\frac{2}{3}$ **ii)** $-\frac{1}{4}$ **iii)** $-\frac{5}{7}$ **iv)** 0
   v) not defined by a real number

b) Choose one slope from part a. Write to explain how you drew the line.

10. Which of these points lie on the line $y = \frac{2}{5}x + \frac{4}{5}$?

   a) C(3, 2)   **b)** D(7, 4)   **c)** E(–5, 1)   **d)** F(8, 4)   **e)** G($\frac{1}{2}$, 1)

11. Determine the equation of the line that passes through each pair of points.

   a) A(3, 5) and B(–5, –3)   **b)** C(–4, 7) and D(5, –4)

12. Academic Focus Determine the equation of the line that passes through
J(5, 5) and is:

   a) parallel to the line $y = -\frac{3}{4}x - 4$
   b) perpendicular to the line $y = -\frac{5}{2}x + 5$

13. Academic Focus Graph each line without making a table of values.

   a) $2x - 3y + 12 = 0$ **b)** $3x + 5y = 0$ **c)** $5x + 2y - 15 = 0$

14. Academic Focus Solve each linear system.

   a) $x + y = -8$ **b)** $x + 2y = 6$
       $x - 2y = 7$ $2x - 3y = 5$

15. Mathematical Modelling Refer to the equations on page 367 relating
VO_2 max, v, and recovery heart rate, r, for the people who took the step test.

   a) A female skier took the step test and had a recovery heart rate of
   145 beats/min. Estimate her VO_2 max.

   b) A male cyclist has a VO_2 max of about 55 mL/kg/min. Estimate his
   recovery heart rate after a step test.

16. Mathematical Modelling Suppose two women take the step test and
have different recovery heart rates.

   a) Which woman would be more fit — the one with the higher
   recovery heart rate or the one with the lower recovery heart rate?

   b) Explain your answer to part a in each case.
       i) Using the equation relating v and r
       ii) Using the graph relating v and r
       iii) Using the meaning of VO_2 max

1. List in order from least to greatest.

a) $\frac{1}{3}$, $-\frac{2}{3}$, $\frac{4}{3}$, 0.33, 0.45, $-\frac{1}{2}$
b) -1.6, 0, $-\frac{8}{3}$, 1.2, $\frac{9}{8}$, $-\frac{8}{7}$

c) -0.12, 0.29, $\frac{1}{9}$, $-\frac{1}{8}$, $-\frac{1}{9}$, $\frac{1}{4}$

2. Determine each percent.

a) 40% of 250
b) $29\frac{1}{2}$% of 800
c) 1.25% of 3700

3. Mayumi had 9 hits in 20 at-bats. Assume she continues to hit at the same rate.

a) How many at-bats would Mayumi need to get 63 hits?

b) How many hits would she have after 180 at-bats?

c) Approximately how many at-bats would she need to get 50 hits?

4. a) Graph these relations on the same grid.

Rule 1: Double the number and add 3 to the result.
Rule 2: Add 3 to the number and double the result.
Rule 3: $y = 2x - 3$
Rule 4: $y = 2(x - 3)$

b) How are the graphs alike? How are they different? Write to explain the similarities and the differences in the graphs.

5. Simplify.

a) $(7^5 \times 7^3)^2$
b) $(3^2 \times 3^6)^2$
c) $(11^{-6} \times 11^4)^{-3}$
d) $(7^6 \div 7^2)^5$
e) $(5^{11} \div 5^8)^{-3}$
f) $(10^5 \div 10^{-1})^{-2}$

6. The volume of Earth is about 1.1×10^{12} km^3.

a) The volume of the sun is about 1.3×10^6 times as great as the volume of Earth. Calculate the volume of the sun.

b) The volume of Earth is about 49 times the volume of the moon. Calculate the volume of the moon.

7. Write examples of two rational numbers between the numbers in each pair.

a) 3.65, 3.69
b) -1.476, -1.47

c) $0.3\overline{97}$, 0.4
d) $-5.3\overline{76}$, $-5.3\overline{7}$

e) $\frac{8}{9}$, $\frac{9}{10}$
f) 2.236 067..., 2.236 071 23...

8. Solve each equation.

a) $2x - 5 = 13$
b) $3x + 4 = 5x - 10$

c) $7 - 6x = -11$
d) $1 - 2x = 5x - 6$

9. Solve each equation. Round the answer to 2 decimal places.

   a) $3.6x - 2.5 = 8.9 + 1.7x$ **b)** $3.1(4x - 2) = 19.3x$

   c) $5.9(8x + 1) = -2(3.8x - 6)$ **d)** $0.2(4 - 3.1x) = 4.5x - 6.3$

10. John has \$3.80 in nickels and quarters. There are 32 coins in all. How many nickels and how many quarters are there?

11. Raji's car has an average rate of fuel consumption of 8 L/100 km. The gas tank holds 60 L. When Raji buys gas, she fills the tank. Raji can calculate the volume of gas left in her car's tank using the equation $F = 60 - 8d$, where F is the volume of fuel, in litres, and d is the distance driven since the last fill-up, in hundreds of kilometres.

   a) Raji has travelled 200 km since her last fill-up. What is the value of d? Use the equation to determine how much gas Raji has left.

   b) Raji has travelled 550 km since her last fill-up. What is the value of d? Use the equation to determine how much gas Raji has left.

   c) To determine how far Raji can travel on one tank of gas, substitute 0 for F in the equation then solve for d.

12. Simplify.

   a) $(2a^2 - 5a + 1) + (3a^2 + 2a - 8)$ **b)** $(5 - 2x) - (3 + 6x) + (1 - x)$

   c) $(-2a^4)(9a^3)$ **d)** $\frac{28x^4}{-4x}$

   e) $50b^5 \div 4b^2$ **f)** $(-2)(3a^2 - 4a + 3)$

13. Expand.

   a) $3x(3x^3 - 4x) + 2x^4$ **b)** $(-2m^3)(m - 4m^3)$

   c) $7a(2a^2 - 3a)$ **d)** $(-3p)(2p - 4p^2 + 5)$

14. Academic Focus Factor each polynomial.

   a) $9a^2 + 3a$ **b)** $8x^2y + 16xy^2 - 24xy$

15. The coordinates of the endpoints of line segments are given. Determine the slope of a line segment parallel and perpendicular to each line segment.

   a) A(0, 4), B(2, 0)   **b)** C(−1, 1), D(3, 3)

   c) E(4, −2), F(−1, 3)   **d)** G(0, 1), H(−5, −1)

   e) J(2, 3), K(−1, 3)   **f)** K(3, 5), M(3, −2)

16. Academic Focus Graph the line defined by $2x - 3y + 12 = 0$. On the same axes, graph each line. Determine the equation of each line.

   a) the line parallel to $2x - 3y + 12 = 0$, with y-intercept 2

   b) the line perpendicular to $2x - 3y + 12 = 0$, passing through C(3, 5)

CHAPTER 9 Line of Best Fit

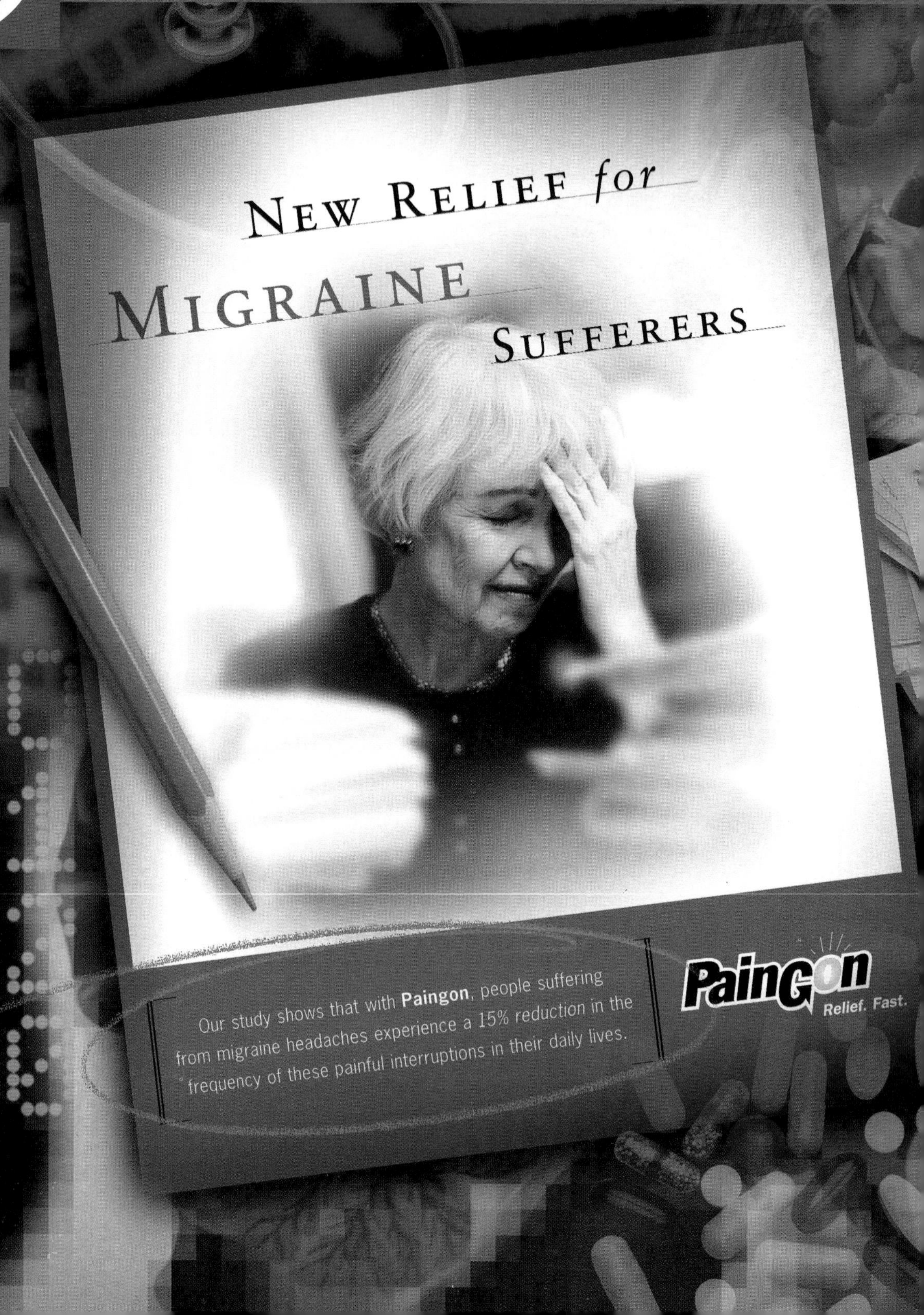

NEW RELIEF for
MIGRAINE
SUFFERERS
Our study shows that with Paingon, people suffering from migraine headaches experience a 15% reduction in the frequency of these painful interruptions in their daily lives.
PainGon
Relief. Fast.

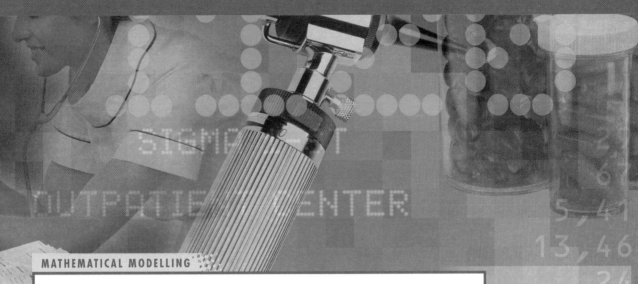

Good News for Migraine Sufferers

We see an advertisement like this in newspapers, on billboards, and on television. What does it mean? Can we believe the claims made?

A company making such a claim must have strong supporting evidence. What is this evidence? What safeguards ensure that the claim can be supported? When scientists conduct these kinds of studies, what issues must they deal with before writing their reports? As a consumer and possible "sufferer", are you aware of what such a claim might mean?

1. What data would a researcher need to gather, to be able to make a claim like the one in the advertisement?

2. Must every user of the medication experience the same reduction in frequency for the claim to be true? Explain.

3. How does the researcher know that it is the medication that is causing any reduction in frequency, and not some other factor?

You will return to these questions in Sections 9.2 and 9.7.

FYI Visit www.awl.com/canada/school/connections

For information related to the above problem, click on
<u>MATHLINKS</u> followed by <u>AWMath</u>. Then select a topic under
Good News for Migraine Sufferers.

This section reviews these concepts:

- Sampling
- Collecting and plotting data
- Determining the equation of a straight line

1. Work with a partner.

   a) Roll a single die twice. Record the numbers that appear on the upper and lower faces.

   b) Let the upper number be represented by x, and the lower number by y. Draw axes, then plot each outcome as a point.

   c) Join the points with a straight line. Determine the equation of the line.

   d) Roll the die two more times. Plot the results on the graph in part c.

   e) Explain the results of this experiment.

2. The student council in a school wants to sell sweatshirts to raise money.It is to conduct a survey to help decide which colour of sweatshirts to sell. Which of the following methods is likely to give an accurate reflection of the opinions of the students in the school? Explain your choice.

   – Question all the spectators at a school basketball game.

   – Question every student who buys a plate of french fries for lunch.

   – Question every third girl in grade 10.

   – Question every fifth student who walks into the main office during the day.

   – Question every tenth student entering the auditorium for an assembly.

3. Determine the equation of each line.

   a) the line with slope 3 and y-intercept 6

   b) the line with slope -2 that passes through the point $(2, 3)$

   c) the line with y-intercept 4 that is parallel to the line $y = 3x + 6$

   d) the line with x-intercept -2 and y-intercept 3

   e) the line through points $(1, 2)$ and $(3, 5)$

A table of random numbers like this one is of great interest to mathematicians simply because it has no patterns.

```
0 4 0 9 0 3 6 1 2 7 3 1 1 7 5 7 6 6 2 1 7 0 3 5 5 4 0 8 3 9 1 4 9
2 4 5 1 5 1 1 5 6 5 7 2 5 0 9 5 5 1 5 1 7 4 0 9 4 9 1 6 9 2 2 7 5
0 4 9 7 1 6 9 6 3 6 6 8 4 0 8 9 3 3 4 7 1 8 0 0 3 7 2 2 5 5 9 5 4
6 5 7 5 3 3 5 5 3 3 2 5 1 5 5 6 3 2 7 6 8 2 6 5 8 4 5 2 9 9 6 5 0
7 6 8 4 9 7 1 6 9 4 8 9 9 2 4 3 1 9 0 5 3 3 0 0 6 6 2 3 6 0 5 9 2
4 6 8 5 6 5 9 9 9 4 9 5 4 8 1 2 1 3 2 2 5 7 6 6 8 3 5 0 3 2 7 2 2 3
2 8 6 0 5 3 4 9 9 8 7 9 8 8 6 0 8 4 3 3 3 3 1 5 7 3 4 7 3 3 2 4 6
4 6 2 8 3 8 9 0 1 8 8 4 2 2 4 4 4 2 1 6 6 0 2 1 6 9 0 9 1 0 0 7 1
5 9 1 2 6 5 8 2 3 3 9 3 9 6 2 0 7 9 1 3 3 5 2 3 2 8 4 4 8 3 4 0 0
3 8 5 7 7 2 7 3 9 7 4 0 0 4 5 7 3 1 0 1 5 9 0 5 6 2 1 0 7 0 7 9 5
0 6 6 7 6 6 9 8 2 3 1 0 9 9 2 3 6 6 8 3 2 1 9 3 6 1 3 8 9 5 3 1 7
4 7 5 3 5 3 5 6 7 0 0 4 6 1 7 6 9 1 2 7 4 1 7 7 4 8 8 3 0 2 0 8 1
9 6 4 5 9 9 1 4 9 7 6 6 5 6 8 0 1 4 9 4 3 5 5 1 8 5 2 6 6 7 9 8 4
1 8 3 1 7 3 2 5 5 8 7 7 1 8 6 1 3 3 0 3 7 7 4 0 5 3 3 9 7 4 0 7 6
3 2 5 3 0 1 6 1 1 9 9 0 8 0 8 3 9 9 5 5 9 2 5 3 3 3 4 7 8 3 0 1 6
```

Statisticians often use tables like this in situations where they do not want any patterns to occur. Here is one of those situations.

Matilda the Psychic claims to be able to read people's minds. Harry Houdini does not believe her. He has designed a test to check her claims.

Each card in a deck is marked with one of these symbols: ♥, ♣, ♠, ♀, ✳.
Harry draws one card and stares at it, making sure that Matilda cannot see it.
Matilda writes down what she thinks the card is. Houdini does this 6 times,
being careful to return each card and shuffle the deck before drawing the next
card. Here is a typical result.

Houdini's card	♣	✳	♀	♥	♥	♣
Matilda's guess	♀	♥	♀	♣	♥	✳

Matilda was right two times. Did this happen by chance, or does she have some
special perception? If Matilda was simply guessing, is it likely that she would
guess two correctly?

Numbers with Neither Rhyme nor Reason

You can answer the questions on page 391 by using the table of random numbers.

Start anywhere in the table of random numbers. Record the next 6 numbers along any row, column, or diagonal. Refer to the results below. In the first row, match each number you found with the corresponding card in the second row.

Number	0 or 1	2 or 3	4 or 5	6 or 7	8 or 9
Matilda's guess	♠	♣	♥	♀	✳

For example, starting at the 3rd number in the 5th row, 6 consecutive numbers are: 4 9 7 1 6 9

This corresponds to guessing: ♥ ✳ ♀ ♠ ♀ ✳

There are two matches with Houdini's cards, the first ✳ and the first ♀. This time, Matilda had two correct guesses.

Work with a partner.

1. Use the table of random numbers. Guess 6 cards at random. Count the number of matches with Houdini's cards. Do this 30 times. Record the number of matches each time.

2. How often did you get two or more matches?

3. Do you think it is likely that Matilda can read minds? Explain.

Follow these steps to do the experiment using a TI-83 calculator.

- Press MATH ▶ ▶ ▶ 5 to display randInt(.

- Press 1 , 5) ENTER to display a random number from 1 to 5.

- If you continue to press ENTER, you will get as many random numbers as you want. The screen shows six random numbers. Your screen will probably be different.

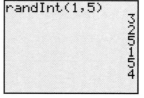

```
randInt(1,5)
            3
            5
            2
            1
            5
            4
```

- Press CLEAR to delete the information.

4. a) Use the six numbers on the screen. How often did you get two or more matches?

b) Repeat exercises 1 and 2 using a calculator.

5. a) After intensive testing, Harry found that Matilda guessed two correct cards consistently. Can this be explained as chance? Explain.

b) In your experiments, how many times did you get 3 matches?

c) If you were conducting this experiment, what would you do differently?

When we have a large amount of data, it is often useful to study only a portion of it to gain insight into the complete set of information. All the things or people being considered is the *population*. The portion studied is a *sample*.

- When you sip a spoonful of soup to test how hot a bowl of soup is, you are sampling. Based on the temperature of the soup in your spoon, you decide if it is too hot to eat. In this case, the spoonful of soup is the sample and the bowl of soup is the population.

- Quality control workers will check light bulbs by selecting a small sample of the production run, to see how long they will work before burning out. Obviously, the workers would not want to test every bulb.

Various companies use sampling to survey the Canadian population. These companies usually obtain reliable results because they use statistically sound sampling methods. Constructing the sample carefully increases the likelihood of obtaining valid predictions.

- Gallup is a company that publishes monthly opinion surveys to identify trends in Canada. For a national survey, Gallup interviews 1000 people in Canada. This sample represents the population of about 26 000 000 Canadians who are 15 years and older.

- A. C. Nielsen is a company that monitors the TV viewing habits of Canadians. The company has monitoring devices on TV sets in 1500 Canadian households. This sample represents the population of nearly 10 500 000 TV viewing households in Canada.

- The Society of Composers, Authors, and Music Publishers of Canada (SOCAN) is an organization that samples, in one year, about two weeks of air time on every Canadian radio station. SOCAN uses these data to decide how much royalty should be paid to each recording artist whose songs are played on the radio.

If a sample is to represent a population, we must be sure that:

- The sample accurately reflects the population. This means that all parts of the population are fairly represented.

- All members of the population have an equal chance of being selected.

Suppose a survey is conducted to determine the favourite TV program of students in your school. Only students in your class are surveyed. Since students in other classes have not been asked, the sample is not a random sample. All students in your school are not represented.

If the sample is selected at random, then it accurately reflects the population, and conclusions about the population are likely to be true.

Example 1

A Sudbury company is hired by a sports magazine to find out how Canadians think Canadian athletes will perform in the next Olympic Winter Games. To collect the data, the company considers sampling Canadians in one of the following ways.

a) Conduct phone-in surveys on radio talk shows.

b) Put an advertisement in all major newspapers asking people to tell their preferences.

c) Send questionnaires to 500 major businesses to be completed by anyone selected at random.

Describe a weakness of each method.

Solution

a) Only people who are listening to the radio would be polled. The sample is not random.

b) Only sports fans would respond to this advertisement. The sample is not random.

c) This sample tends to exclude groups such as students, farmers, homemakers, senior citizens, and self-employed people. Therefore, it is not a random sample.

Example 2

These are the surnames of the 36 students in a mathematics class. Use a random sample of 6 surnames. Estimate the mean, median, and mode for the number of letters in a surname in the population.

Balfour	Forsyth	Kennedy	Majic	Richardson	Thompson
Barnett	Francesconi	Keyes	Ng	Rucker	Triantafylido
Borshay	Gianelia	Kilbank	Norris	Sarraude	Veerman
Burt	Gillis	King	Peressini	Sinclair	Walker
Dunlop	Hood	Lee	Perkins	Stelzer	Willoughby
Durocher	Karpenko	MacPherson	Reardon	Tabori	Zimnicki

Solution

Method 1 Using dice

The names are in 6 rows and 6 columns. Roll a pair of dice with different colours. The first die represents the row number. The second die represents the column number. For example, (2, 5) represents the name Rucker. Repeat this experiment until 6 names have been recorded. Using this method, the following sample was obtained:

Thompson   Rucker   Sarraude   Gillis   Dunlop   Willoughby

The numbers of letters in these names are: 8, 6, 8, 6, 6, 10

The mean is $\dfrac{8+6+8+6+6+10}{6} = \dfrac{44}{66}$
$$\doteq 7.3$$

For the medium, arrange the numbers in order: 6, 6, 6, 8, 8, 10. The median is the middle number. But there is no middle number. So, the median is the mean of the two middle numbers: $\dfrac{6+8}{2} = 7$

The mode is the number that occurs most often: 6

Method 2 Using a table of random numbers

Number the surnames as follows.

01	Balfour	10	Gillis	19	Majic	28	Sinclair
02	Barnett	11	Hood	20	Ng	29	Stelzer
03	Borshay	12	Karpenko	21	Norris	30	Tabori
04	Burt	13	Kennedy	22	Peressini	31	Thompson
05	Dunlop	14	Keyes	23	Perkins	32	Triantafylido
06	Durocher	15	Kilbank	24	Reardon	33	Veerman
07	Forsyth	16	King	25	Richardson	34	Walker
08	Francesconi	17	Lee	26	Rucker	35	Willoughby
09	Gianelia	18	MacPherson	27	Sarraude	36	Zimnicki

Start anywhere in the table of random numbers on page 391. Record 2-digit numbers up to 36 systematically. Numbers may be recorded horizontally or vertically, forwards or backwards. For example, starting at the beginning of the second row, these numbers were obtained:

24   15   11   25   09   17

This gives the following sample:

Reardon   Kilbank   Hood   Richardson   Gianelia   Lee

The numbers of letters in these names are: 7, 7, 4, 10, 8, 3
For this sample: the mean is 6.5; the median is 7; the mode is 7.

Method 3 Using a graphing calculator

Use the numbered surnames in Method 2. Use a TI-83 calculator to generate numbers randomly from 1 to 36.

- Press [MATH] [▶] [▶] [▶] **5** to display randInt(.

- Press 1 [,] 36 [ )] [ENTER] to display a random number from 1 to 36.

- Continue pressing [ENTER] until 6 different numbers are displayed.

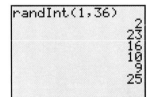

The screen shows this sample:

Barnett   Perkins   King   Gillis   Gianelia   Richardson

The numbers of letters in these names are: 7, 7, 4, 6, 8, 10
For this sample: the mean is 7.0; the median is 7; the mode is 7.

The results of *Example 2* are only estimates of the actual mean, median, and mode of the population of 36 names. Compare the estimates with the actual values: the mean is 7.1; the median is 7; and the mode is 7.

As this example indicates, when a sample is chosen randomly, the mean, median, and mode of the sample will usually be close to the mean, median, and mode of the population. But this will not always happen. In the above example, the sample chosen could have contained the six shortest names or the six longest names. The chance that this will happen is about one in a million. The mean, median, and mode for these samples will be very different from those above.

DISCUSSING the IDEAS

1. In *Example 1*, explain another weakness of each survey method.

2. In *Example 2*, Method 2, explain how each two-digit number was determined from the table of random numbers.

3. Following *Example 2*, values for the mean, median, and mode are given. Explain how each value was determined.

4. Explain the advantages and disadvantages of each method of generating a random sample.

   a) dice   b) table of random numbers   c) graphing calculator

9.1 EXERCISES

1. Explain why each sample may not provide accurate information about its population.

   a) A survey of your classmates is used to estimate the average age of students in your school.

   b) A survey of senior citizens is used to determine the music that is best liked by Canadians.

   c) To determine the ratio of domestic cars to foreign cars purchased by Canadians, a person records the numbers of domestic cars and foreign cars in the parking lot of the General Motors Assembly Plant in Oshawa, Ontario.

   d) To determine which movie is best liked by teenagers, 12 of your closest friends are interviewed.

e) To estimate how many Canadians want the legal drinking age raised, a radio station runs an open-line talk show titled "Should we lower the drinking age?" and tallies the number of callers who are in favour and against.

2. Which of the following methods will give a representative sample? Explain your thinking.

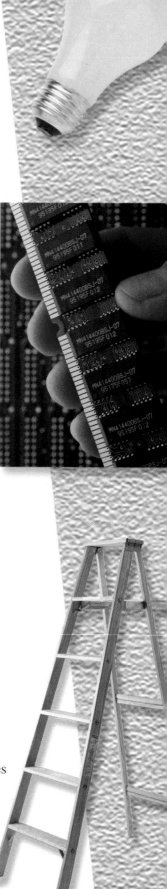

a) The editors of a health food magazine wanted to know if organic foods make people feel better. They asked readers to write in with their experiences.

b) A polling company wants to know how much support there is for the government's tax reduction plans. It plans to survey every third person who walks into the City Stock Exchange.

c) A second polling company also wants to know how much support there is for the government's tax reduction plans. It decides to phone people in their homes at 8:00 P.M. The company selects the numbers from the city phone book by selecting the 100th name on each page.

d) A light bulb manufacturer wants to test to find out how long its light bulbs will burn before failure. It selects the first 100 bulbs manufactured on Monday morning.

e) A computer manufacturer wishes to check a shipment of 10 000 RAM chips from a supplier. The production manager selects one carton at random, then selects five chips at random from that carton.

3. For each situation, identify what you think the population is. Explain why data are collected from a sample and not the population.

a) The quality of flash bulbs

b) The number of Canadian families who eat at least one meal together as a family per week

c) The purity of processed food

d) The strength of aluminum extension ladders

e) The cost of ski equipment

f) The percent of the population with each blood type

4. In each situation, why would data be collected from a sample and not from the population?

a) To find the average age of drivers when they get their drivers' licences

b) To find the number of hours a high-efficiency light bulb will burn

c) To find the average volume of milk in a 4-L bag

5. Refer to *Example 2*.

a) Use a random sample of 6 surnames. Estimate the mean, median, and mode for the number of letters in a surname in the population.

b) Suppose your sample had consisted of the 6 shortest surnames. What are the mean, median, and mode for this sample?

c) Suppose your sample had consisted of the 6 longest surnames. What are the mean, median, and mode for this sample?

B **6. Investigation: What is the average surname length in your class?**
Obtain a list of surnames for the students in your class. Investigate the average surname length.

a) Decide how large a sample you need.

b) Decide how you will ensure that the sample is random.

c) Obtain your sample.

d) Estimate the mean, median, and mode for the population.

7. Investigation: What is the average hand span? Have everyone in the class measure her or his hand span to the nearest half-centimetre. Your hand span is the greatest possible distance between the tips of your thumb and your 5th finger. Record each hand span measurement and the student's name. Investigate the average hand span for your class by repeating exercise 6a to d.

8. Investigation: What is the average pulse? Have everyone in the class measure her or his pulse. To measure your pulse, press a finger on your wrist just below your thumb. Count the number of beats in 15 s, then multiply by 4. Investigate the average pulse for your class by repeating exercise 6a to d.

9. Choose one of the investigations below. Work in a group of 3 or 4 students to collect the data.

a) Describe the population.

b) Decide how large a sample you need.

c) Decide how you will ensure that the sample is random.

d) Estimate the mean, median, and mode for the population.

The average age and height of the students in your school	The average amount spent on lunch in the cafeteria
The average time spent waiting in line in the cafeteria	The average number of letters in English words

10. For each study described, answer these questions.

    i) What is the population about which the information is sought?

    ii) How is the sample chosen?

    iii) Is it a random sample?

a) You decide to purchase a new CD because you like the title song.

b) Researchers are investigating the percent of farms that have started growing canola instead of wheat. They purchase mailing lists from farm equipment supply companies, and mail a survey form to every 50th name on each list.

c) Researchers are trying to determine the percent of popular support in Ontario for extending the school year to 12 months. They telephone people selected randomly from the Toronto telephone directory.

d) To determine the spending habits of Canada's teenagers, researchers interviewed young shoppers at a downtown mall.

e) To determine whether Canadian voters support Canada's peacekeeping role abroad, researchers telephoned 5 residences in each political riding.

11. How would you collect data to find the following information? Give reasons for your answers.

a) The popularity of a TV program

b) The most popular breakfast cereal

c) The average number of compact discs owned by high-school students

d) The average number of people in one car in rush hour

e) The most popular recording artist or group

f) The average weekly fast-food budget for a teenager

C **12.** This table of numbers is called a Latin Square.

a) Compare this table with the table on page 391. Are the numbers in this table random? Explain.

b) Describe an experiment in which it might be appropriate to use the numbers in a Latin Square.

```
0 2 4 3 7 5 9 1 8 6
1 3 8 0 2 7 4 6 9 5
8 0 5 2 1 9 6 3 4 7
7 1 0 5 4 3 2 8 6 9
4 5 2 1 3 6 0 9 7 8
5 8 1 6 9 0 7 4 3 2
6 7 3 9 0 8 5 2 1 4
2 6 9 7 8 4 1 5 0 3
9 4 7 8 6 2 3 0 5 1
3 9 6 4 5 1 8 7 2 0
```

COMMUNICATING the IDEAS

In your journal, write to explain the advantages of using a sample to collect data from a population. Include some of the things you must keep in mind when choosing a sample.

9.2   Good News for Migraine Sufferers: Part I

On page 389, you considered how a pharmaceutical company can justify a claim made in its advertisement about the effectiveness of a medication.

A research team conducted a study with 72 men and 72 women, all of whom are migraine sufferers. For six months, each person recorded the number of migraine headaches he or she experienced. During the same 6-month period the following year, the people took a pill regularly and recorded the number of migraine headaches they experienced. Unknown to them, half the pills contained the medication being tested, while the other half contained no medication. These pills are called "placebos", and have no effect.

The research team prepared the data below. There is an ordered pair for every person in the study. This example shows the meaning of the ordered pairs.

(16, 15)

| Number of migraine headaches reported during the first 6-month period | Number of migraine headaches reported by the same person during the second 6-month period one year later |

| People who received the medication | |
Men	Women
(18, 16) (24, 20) (15, 14) (23, 20) (24, 22) (15, 14)	(21, 17) (23, 21) (18, 17) (18, 15) (23, 21) (22, 19)
(25, 24) (15, 14) (15, 13) (15, 14) (19, 17) (15, 13)	(17, 14) (21, 18) (19, 17) (18, 16) (25, 23) (18, 16)
(25, 23) (21, 18) (19, 16) (21, 18) (17, 15) (25, 21)	(23, 21) (17, 15) (21, 17) (24, 19) (27, 22) (20, 19)
(24, 22) (19, 17) (25, 22) (16, 14) (15, 13) (25, 22)	(19, 17) (27, 25) (23, 18) (17, 14) (24, 21) (24, 22)
(23, 21) (25, 22) (25, 23) (15, 14) (23, 20) (18, 16)	(22, 19) (20, 18) (20, 18) (23, 22) (24, 22) (27, 22)
(17, 16) (21, 19) (19, 17) (22, 19) (25, 22) (21, 19)	(23, 19) (19, 17) (26, 21) (17, 16) (24, 21) (22, 19)

People who received the placebo	
Men	**Women**
(17, 18) (21, 19) (21, 20) (21, 22) (13, 12) (12, 12)	(16, 15) (22, 24) (15, 16) (12, 12) (21, 23) (13, 14)
(18, 20) (13, 12) (22, 23) (17, 17) (15, 14) (21, 21)	(13, 12) (17, 19) (22, 22) (17, 16) (15, 16) (15, 15)
(13, 13) (16, 16) (13, 13) (14, 13) (14, 14) (20, 19)	(16, 16) (20, 22) (14, 13) (21, 23) (18, 19) (20, 19)
(22, 22) (19, 20) (20, 21) (21, 20) (18, 19) (14, 13)	(22, 23) (12, 11) (17, 15) (12, 12) (20, 19) (19, 21)
(22, 20) (15, 14) (16, 15) (19, 17) (20, 21) (14, 15)	(20, 19) (12, 13) (12, 13) (17, 18) (12, 11) (21, 20)
(18, 17) (16, 16) (13, 14) (21, 20) (19, 20) (22, 20)	(12, 12) (13, 13) (12, 13) (19, 18) (19, 19) (18, 19)

Graphing the results for samples of people who received the medication

1. Create a random sample of the people who received the medication. The size of your sample should be approximately 20% of these people. To ensure randomness, use either of the following methods to get an ordered pair.

Using a coin and a die
Flip a coin to select a man or a woman. Then use a die to select an individual: roll the die once to select a row and again to select a column. For example, if you get heads, choose a woman. If you get a 5 and a 3 on the die, choose the ordered pair in the 5th row and the 3rd column of the data for women. This ordered pair is (20, 18).

Using a graphing calculator
- Press [MATH] [▶] [▶] [▶] **5** to display randInt(.
- Press 1 [,] 6 [,] 3 [ )] [ENTER] to display 3 random numbers from 1 to 6. For example, the first screen below shows the numbers 2, 5, 3. Since the first number is even, choose a man. (If the first number was odd, choose a woman). The other numbers are 5 and 3. Choose the ordered pair in the 5th row and the 3rd column of the data for men.

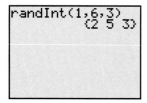
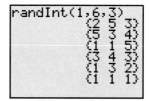

- To repeat, continue pressing [ENTER]. The second screen above shows the information for choosing six ordered pairs.
- Press [CLEAR] to delete the information.

2. Graph the ordered pairs from your sample. Label the axes as shown.

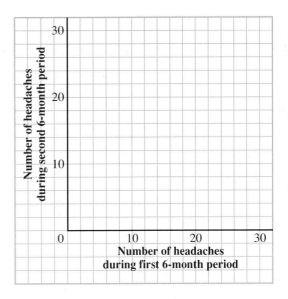

Graphing the results for samples of people who received the placebo

3. a) Repeat exercises 1 and 2 for the people who received the placebo. Use a different graph.

b) Consider whether it would be more effective to use one graph instead of two. Explain.

4. Does there appear to be any relation between taking the medication and having fewer headaches? Explain.

5. Discuss these questions with a partner.

a) Do you think your sample size is large enough? Explain.

b) What other methods are there to select your random samples?

c) Why is it important to ensure that the samples are selected at random?

d) Do you think you would get the same results if you were to use different samples? Explain.

Save your samples and graphs for use in Section 9.7.

COMMUNICATING *the* **IDEAS**

In your journal, write a report to describe your results. Include your graphs as part of your report. Be sure to explain the purpose of a placebo.

Arm Span and Height Relationships

Work with a partner. You will need a tape measure or metre ruler.

1. How do you think arm span and height are related?

2. Measure and record your arm spans, with your arms stretched out as much as possible. Measure and record your heights.

3. Combine your data with those of other students in your group or class. Record the data in a table.

Student's name	Arm span (cm)	Height (cm)

4. Plot the data on a grid. Represent *Arm span* on the horizontal axis and *Height* on the vertical axis. This graph is a *scatter plot*. A scatter plot is any graph consisting of a set of points.

5. Describe any trends in the data. What appears to be the relationship between arm span and height? How does this relationship compare with you prediction in exercise 1?

6. Place a ruler so that it passes as close as possible to all the plotted points (use a transparent ruler, if possible). Draw a straight line along the ruler. This line is a *line of best fit*.

7. Use the line of best fit.
   a) Predict the height of someone whose arm span is 1.4 m.
   b) Predict the arm span of someone whose height is 1.6 m.

Save your data for use in 9.3 Exercises and Consolidating Your Skills.

In *Investigation 1*, you drew a line of best fit for the data. Lines of best fit are useful for predicting unknown values. In this section you will graph lines of best fit and make predictions from the graphs. You will also determine the equation of a line of best fit and use the equation to make predictions.

Olympic Discus Records

The table shows the winning distances for the discus event at the Olympic Summer Games since 1948.

Year	Men's distance (m)	Women's distance (m)
1948	52.78	41.92
1952	55.03	51.42
1956	56.36	53.69
1960	59.18	55.10
1964	61.00	57.27
1968	64.78	58.28
1972	64.40	66.62
1976	67.50	69.00
1980	66.64	69.96
1984	66.60	65.36
1988	68.82	72.30
1992	65.12	70.06
1996	69.39	69.65

You will look for trends in the data. If there is a trend, you can use it to predict the winning distances in future Olympics, such as the 2012 Olympic Games.

1. Make a scatter plot for the men's distances. Plot *Years* on the horizontal axis and *Winning distances* on the vertical axis.

2. Use a ruler to draw a line of best fit.

3. Use the line of best fit. Estimate the winning distance for the men's discus event in the 2012 Olympic Games. Compare your estimate with other students' estimates.

In the *Investigations*, you drew lines of best fit for given data. Drawing a line of best fit is a useful method for predicting and estimating.

Example 1

a) Draw a line of best fit for the women's data on page 405.

b) Use the line to predict the winning distance for the women's discus in 2012.

Solution

a)

Women's Olympic Discus Results

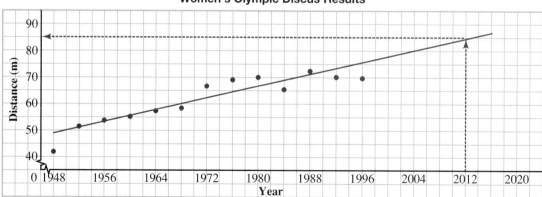

b) Start with 2012 on the horizontal axis. Draw a vertical line to the line of best fit, then draw a horizontal line to the vertical axis. The distance is 85 m. In 2012, the winning distance for the women's discus might be about 85 m.

When data points lie close to a line of best fit, we can use the line to predict data at points for which measurements were not taken. However, the more widely scattered the data points are around a line of best fit, the less reliable the predictions.

Example 2

a) Determine the equation of the line of best fit in *Example 1*.

b) Use the equation to predict the winning distance for the women's discus in 2012.

Solution

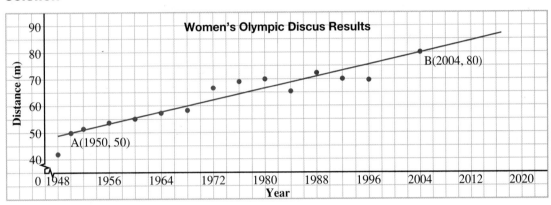

a) Mark two points on the line of best fit whose coordinates are easy to read. For example, the points could be A(1950, 50) and B(2004, 80).

Slope of AB $= \dfrac{80 - 50}{2004 - 1950}$

$= \dfrac{30}{54}$

$\doteq 0.5556$

Let the equation of the line be $y = mx + b$.

The slope of the line is approximately 0.5556. Substitute 0.5556 for m.

$y \doteq 0.5556x + b$

Since A(1950, 50) lies on the line, its coordinates satisfy the equation. Substitute 1950 for x and 50 for y, then solve for b.

$50 \doteq 0.5556(1950) + b$

$\doteq 1083.42 + b$

$b \doteq 50 - 1083.42$

$\doteq -1033.42$

Therefore, the vertical intercept of the line is about -1033.42.

The equation of the line of best fit is approximately $y = 0.5556x - 1033.42$.

b) Substitute 2012 for *x* in the equation.

$$y \doteq (0.5556)(2012) - 1033.42$$
$$\doteq 84.45$$

The winning distance for the women's discus in 2012 might be about 84 m.

1. In *Investigation 1*, you graphed arm spans horizontally and heights vertically.

   a) Suppose you had graphed heights horizontally and arm spans vertically. How would your graph be different from the one you drew in *Investigation 1*?

   b) Does it matter which measurement is graphed horizontally and which is graphed vertically? Explain.

2. In *Investigation 1*, what factors affected the outcome of the experiment? Suppose you were to repeat the experiment. What would you do differently to account for these factors?

3. Explain the zigzag marks near the origin in the graphs in *Examples 1* and *2*. What do they represent?

4. In *Example 1* and *Example 2*, the winning time was predicted for the women's discus in 2012.

   a) Do you think the women's gold medallist will achieve this distance? Explain your thinking. What assumptions are you making?

   b) Is it possible for the women's gold medallist in 2012 to throw less than 70 m? Is it likely? Explain your thinking.

   c) Would you be surprised by a winning throw of 90 m in 2012? Explain.

5. Refer to the solution of *Example 2*.

   a) The points A and B were used to determine the equation. Suppose other points had been used. Would the equation be the same? Would the predicted distance in 2012 be the same? Explain.

   b) The fact that A lies on the line was used to determine the vertical intercept, *b*. Would the result have been the same if B had been used instead of A? Explain.

   c) Look at the graph in *Example 2*. Explain how you could show that the vertical intercept is approximately -1033.

6. Describe how a line of best fit can be used to give an estimated range for a predicted event.

A **1.** Examine this scatter plot.

  a) Would it be appropriate to draw a line of best fit?

  b) Should a line of best fit pass through the origin? Explain.

  c) Should we always construct a line of best fit by connecting the first and last points? Explain.

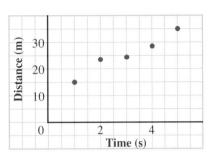

2. Would it be appropriate to construct a line of best fit for the data in this scatter plot? Explain.

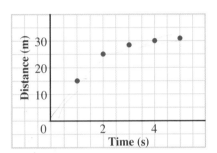

3. For these scatter plots, which line of best fit do you think would provide the most reliable predictions? Explain your choice.

a)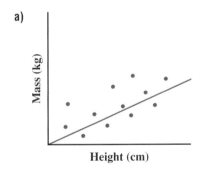

Height (cm)

b)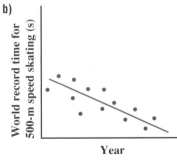

Year

c)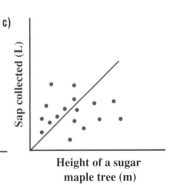

Height of a sugar maple tree (m)

B **4.** **Investigation: Foot length and height relationships** Work with a partner. Measure and record your foot lengths. Combine your data with those of other students in your group or class. Use the heights from *Investigation 1*.

  a) How do you think foot length and height are related?

  b) Record the data in a table.

Student's name	Foot length (cm)	Height (cm)

c) Create a scatter plot of the data. Decide which measurements are graphed horizontally and which are graphed vertically.

d) Draw a line of best fit for the data.

e) Describe any trends in the data. What appears to be the relationship between foot length and height? How does this relationship compare with your prediction in part a?

f) Use the line of best fit.
  i) Predict the foot length of someone whose height is 1.6 m.
  ii) Predict the height of someone whose foot length is 20 cm.

5. a) Use the line of best fit you drew in *Investigation 2*. Determine the equation of the line of best fit.

b) Use the equation. Predict the winning distance for the men's discus in 2012.

c) Compare the answer to part b with the estimate in exercise 3, page 405.

6. Investigation: Foot length and arm span relationships
Work with a partner. Use the foot length data from exercise 4 and the arm spans from *Investigation 1*.

a) How do you think foot length and arm span are related?

b) Record the data in a table.

Student's name	Foot length (cm)	Arm span (cm)

c) Create a scatter plot of the data.

d) Draw a line of best fit for the data.

e) Describe any trends in the data. What appears to be the relationship between foot length and arm span? How does the relationship compare with your prediction in part a?

f) Use the line of best fit.
  i) Predict the foot length of someone whose arm span is 1.4 m.
  ii) Predict the arm span of someone whose foot length is 22 cm.

g) Use the line of best fit in part d. Determine the equation of the line of best fit.

h) Use the equation.
  i) Predict the foot length of someone whose arm span is 1.4 m.
  ii) Predict the arm span of someone whose foot length is 22 cm.

i) Compare your answers to parts f and h.

Height and Radius Length

An anthropologist investigated the changes in human body size and shape over time. She concluded that 19th century pioneer men were roughly the same height as men today, but pioneer women were shorter than women today.

To reach this conclusion, the anthropologist used established relationships about men's and women's heights, and the lengths of the radius bone in the lower arm.

Conduct an investigation to determine relationships between height and the length of the radius. Recall the radius bone, from page 281.

It's impossible to measure the radius exactly, because you are not a skeleton. But, if you use a consistent method for measuring the lower arm, you can minimize measurement errors.

To measure the lower arm: place your hand flat against a surface, while a partner measures from the surface to the tip of your elbow. All your measurements will be consistently greater than the radius length.

- Work with a partner. Measure and record each person's height, and your estimate for the length of the radius. Indicate F for female and M for male.

- Enter your data in a class chart that separates female and male data.

7. a) How do you think height and radius length are related?

   b) Construct a scatter plot of the female data, and another scatter plot of the male data.

   c) Draw a line of best fit for each scatter plot.

   d) Describe any similarities between the relationships for females and for males. Describe any differences you notice.

   e) Describe any trends in the data. What appears to be the relationship between height and radius length? How does this relationship compare with your prediction in part a?

   f) The anthropologist's research was based on relationships for adult males and females. In what ways might this affect the validity of your results?

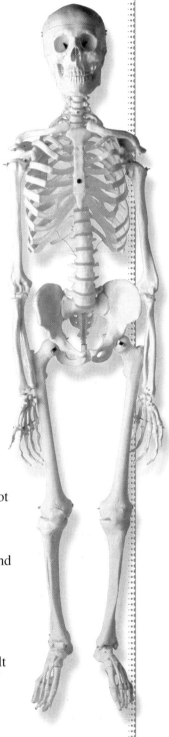

8. The table shows the winning times for the 800-m race at the Olympic Summer Games.

Year	Men's time (seconds)	Women's time (seconds)
1960	106.30	124.30
1964	105.10	121.10
1968	104.30	120.90
1972	105.90	118.55
1976	103.50	114.94
1980	105.40	113.42
1984	103.00	117.60
1988	103.45	116.10
1992	103.66	115.54
1996	102.58	117.73

a) Construct a line of best fit for each set of data. Predict the winning times in the year 2024.

b) In approximately what year would the men's and women's winning times be about the same?

9. Open the *Olympic Summer Games* database. Find the winning times for the men's 100-m freestyle event from 1956 to 1988.

a) Graph the winning times and years, then construct a line of best fit.

b) How many of the winning times are within 1 s of the line of best fit? Do you think the line is a good representation of the winning times?

c) Use the line of best fit to estimate the result for the 1992 Olympics. Find the result on the Internet or in an almanac. How close was your estimate?

d) Determine the equation of the line of best fit.

e) Use the equation to estimate the result for the 1992 Olympics.

f) How do your estimates from parts c and e compare with the actual time?

COMMUNICATING the IDEAS

In your journal, write to describe how to construct a line of best fit and how to use it to make predictions. Explain also how you can decide how reasonable are the predictions you obtain from a line of best fit.

In Section 9.3, you graphed lines of best fit. In earlier chapters, you used a graphing calculator to graph data in a table, and also to graph an equation. You can combine these skills to graph a line of best fit on a graphing calculator using estimation.

INVESTIGATION

Length of a Line of Coins

You will need 15 pennies and a ruler.

1. **a)** Put some pennies in a line and measure its length in millimetres.

   b) Repeat with other numbers of pennies until you have four sets of results. Record the results in a table (the data shown below are for a different coin).

Number of coins	Length (mm)
14	297
11	233
9	190
6	127

2. Use a graphing calculator to graph the data. Follow these steps.

   Step 1. Enter the data.

   - Press [STAT] **1**. Clear lists L1 and L2 if necessary.
   - Enter the numbers of pennies in list L1 and the lengths in list L2.

   Step 2. Set up the scatter plot.

   - Press [2nd] [Y=] **1** to select Plot 1. Press [ENTER].
   - Select the first plot type, and make sure that L1 and L2 are beside Xlist and Ylist.

   Step 3. Set up the window.

   - Press [WINDOW]. Enter appropriate values.

   Step 4. Graph the data.

   - Press [GRAPH].

The graph for the data above is shown. Your graph should look similar to this. The graph suggests that there is a linear relationship between the length of the line of coins and the number of coins. If a line of best fit were drawn, it would pass through the origin. Recall that the equation of a line passing through the origin has the form $y = mx$, where m represents the slope of the line.

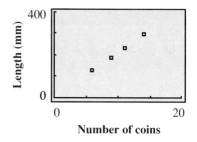

If you graph equations of the form $y = mx$ for different values of x, you can find one that appears to pass through the points on the graph. For the first screen below, the value of m was too small. For the second screen, it was just right.

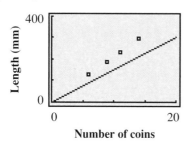

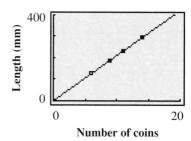

3. **Mental Math and Estimation**

   a) Press ⟨ Y= ⟩, and clear any equations. Move the cursor beside Y1=.

   b) Press ⟨___⟩ ⟨X,T,θ,n⟩ ⟨ENTER⟩ ⟨GRAPH⟩, where ⟨___⟩ represents a number that you think is close to the slope of the line. Repeat using other numbers until your line passes through the plotted points.

   c) What is the equation of the line of best fit?

   d) Explain what the slope of the line represents.

4. You can use your line of best fit to estimate the lengths of lines formed by other numbers of pennies not plotted on the screen. Use each method below to estimate the lengths of two other lines of pennies.

   a) *Using trace*

   With the graph on the screen, press ⟨TRACE⟩. Press ⟨▼⟩ to move the cursor to the line, and not the plotted points. To estimate the length for other numbers of pennies, enter the number you want then press ⟨ENTER⟩.

b) *Using a table*

Press ⎡2nd⎤ ⎡WINDOW⎤ to select TBLSET. Make sure that your screen looks like the one below left. Then press ⎡2nd⎤ ⎡GRAPH⎤ to select TABLE. You will get a table of values like the one shown below right. You can scroll down the table to see as many values as you want.

 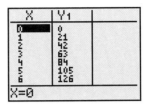

5. **Mental Math and Estimation** Compare your graph in exercise 3 with the graphs on page 414. What coin do you think was used to create these graphs? Explain.

In exercise 3 in the *Investigation*, you estimated the equation of the line of best fit. You will encounter similar situations in the exercises, but the data may not fit the line as closely as they did in the *Investigation*.

DISCUSSING the IDEAS

1. In the *Investigation*, how do we know that the line of best fit passes through the origin?

Boggle your MIND

The chart lists the national debts of eight different countries in 1988. For ease of comparison, each number is given in U.S. dollars. Use the *Land Use* or *World Health and Education* database from the data disk to determine the population of each country. Based on this population, calculate the national debt per capita in each country in that year. Investigate to find out how these national debts compare with national debts today.

Country	National Debt (U.S. $)
Argentina	12 290 000 000
Australia	48 740 000 000
Canada	231 990 000 000
Italy	775 050 000 000
Malawi	1 250 000 000
Malaysia	32 790 000 000
United States	2 097 000 000 000
Uruguay	1 930 000 000

B **1.** The table shows the heights of several seedlings after various growing times.

Time (days)	1	3	2	3	3	2	1	2
Height (mm)	6	13	11	14	15	10	4	7

a) What relationship would you expect between growing time and height?

b) Enter the data into a graphing calculator. Enter the times in list L1 and the heights in list L2.

c) Use a calculator to create a scatter plot.

d) Describe any trends in the data. What appears to be the relationship between growing time and height? How does this relationship compare with your prediction in part a?

e) Use a calculator to estimate the equation of the line of best fit. Display the line of best fit on the scatter plot.

f) Sketch the graph you obtained. Show the plotted points, the line of best fit, and its equation.

g) What does the slope of the line of best fit represent? Explain.

2. Investigation: Your Pulse

a) Count the number of pulse beats in each time:
7 s, 17 s, 38 s, 52 s
Record the results in a table.

Time (s)	Number of beats
7	
17	
38	
52	

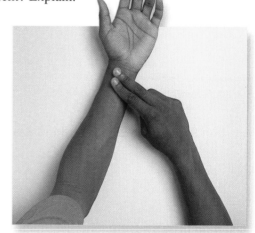

b) Enter the data into a graphing calculator. Enter the times in list L1 and the number of beats in list L2.

c) Use a calculator to create a scatter plot.

d) Use a calculator to estimate the equation of the line of best fit. Display the line of best fit on the scatter plot.

e) Sketch the graph you obtained. Show the plotted points, the line of best fit, and its equation.

f) What does the slope of the line of best fit represent? Explain.

3. **Investigation: The Extension of an Elastic Band** Refer to your results for the experiment in exercise 12, page 79. Subtract each stretched length from the length of the elastic band with the empty bag attached. This is the *extension* of the elastic band. Record your results in a table.

Object	Mass (g)	Extension (cm)

a) How do you think mass and extension are related?

b) Enter the data into a graphing calculator. Enter the masses in list L1 and the extensions in list L2.

c) Use a calculator to create a scatter plot.

d) Describe any trends in the data. What appears to be the relationship between mass and extension? How does this relationship compare with your prediction in part a?

e) Use a calculator to estimate the equation of the line of best fit. Display the line of best fit on the scatter plot.

f) Use the equation to predict the extension for a mass that is different from any of the known masses.

g) Sketch the graph you obtained. Show the plotted points, the line of best fit, and your result for part f. Record the equation of the line of best fit.

h) Is the line of best fit a reasonable model for the data? Explain.

i) What does the slope of the line of best fit represent? Explain.

4. **Investigation: Lengths of Shadows**
Work in a group or with a partner. You will need a table or other horizontal surface in sunshine. You will also need some objects with different heights and a ruler.

a) Place one object vertically on the table so that its shadow is cast on the table. Measure the height of the object and the length of its shadow.

b) Repeat part a for the other objects.

c) Enter the data into a graphing calculator. Enter the heights in list L1 and the shadow lengths in list L2.

d) Use a calculator to create a scatter plot.

e) Use a calculator to estimate the equation of the line of best fit, and display the line of best fit on the scatter plot.

f) Use the equation to predict the height of your shadow at the time the other measurements were made.

g) Sketch the graph you obtained. Show the plotted points, the line of best fit, and your result for part f. Record the equation of the line of best fit.

h) Is the line of best fit a reasonable model for the data? Explain.

i) What factors affected the outcome of this investigation? Suppose you were to repeat the investigation. What would you do differently to account for these factors?

5. The standard measure for tree size is the diameter at breast height (DBH). The table shows the DBH of 16 red pine trees at various ages. Red pine is a coniferous tree found throughout Eastern Canada.

Age (years)	DBH (cm)	Age (years)	DBH (cm)
9	8	27	30
20	12	5	5
11	6	16	9
4	1	22	12
16	20	3	4
18	9	29	19
12	9	23	19
23	14	21	13

a) Use a graphing calculator to create a scatter plot.

b) Estimate the equation of the line of best fit.

c) Suggest some reasons why a line does not fit the data points closely.

6. The table shows the DBH of two species of spruce trees at various ages. The measures are typical for these trees.

Age (years)	White Pine DBH (cm)	Black Spruce DBH (cm)
13	6.0	3.8
20	12.5	7.1
28	17.8	9.7
42	22.3	14.3
54	29.6	17.5
63	39.5	18.6
83	44.3	24.1
88	46.8	26.4
99	50.0	27.8
104	53.6	29.4
120	57.1	33.5
130	60.9	36.5

a) Use a graphing calculator to create two scatter plots.

b) Estimate the equation of the line of best fit for each species.

c) What do the slopes of the lines of best fit represent? Explain.

d) Which tree grew faster? About how many times as fast did this tree grow than the other tree? Explain.

e) What diameter would a tree of each species have when its age is 50 years?

f) Estimate the age of a tree of each species when it has a DBH of 30 cm.

COMMUNICATING the IDEAS

Your friend missed today's mathematics class and telephones you to ask about it. How would you explain to her, over the telephone, how to use a graphing calculator to estimate the equation of a line of best fit for some given data? In your journal, write down what you would say.

9.5 Equation of the Line of Best Fit

In previous sections, you worked with lines of best fit. You used grid paper or a graphing calculator to estimate the position of a line that comes closest to some plotted points. A major disadvantage of this method is that different people will come up with different lines using the same data. There is a need for a method that always gives the same line.

Height to Arm Span Relations for Gorillas

On page 404, you investigated the relation between height and arm span for students in your class. This table gives similar data for gorillas, obtained from several North American zoos.

Name	Arm span (cm)	Height (cm)
Pete	234	164.0
Kiki	243	165.0
King Tut	275	165.0
Hatari	245	162.5
Mahari	180	117.5
Katherine	188	125.0
Timbo	215	135.0
Sara	260	169.0
Kakinga	250	156.0
Tuffy	265	170.0

1. Use a graphing calculator. Follow these steps.

   Step 1. Enter the data.
   • Press [STAT] **1**. Clear lists L1 and L2 if necessary.
   • Enter the arm spans in list L1 and the heights in list L2.

   Step 2. Set up the scatter plot.
   • Press [2nd] [Y=] to select STAT PLOT. Press **1** to select Plot 1.
   • Make sure that the first plot type is selected, and that L1 and L2 are beside Xlist and Ylist.

Step 3. Set up the window.
- Press WINDOW. Enter appropriate values.

Step 4. Graph the data.
- Press GRAPH.

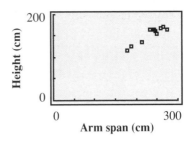

Arm span (cm)

Your graph should be the same as this one, except possibly for the window settings. The graph suggests that there is a linear relationship between the height and arm span of gorillas.

2. To graph the equation of the line of best fit, follow these steps.

Step 5. Calculate the equation.
- Press STAT ▶ to obtain the stat calc menu below left.
- Press **4** to select LinReg(ax + b).
- Press ENTER. The screen below right will appear. The equation of the line of best fit has the form $y = ax + b$, with the values of a and b shown. These numbers are the slope and the y-intercept of the line of best fit.

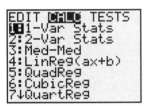

LinReg
y=ax+b
a=.5733340622
b=17.87982835

Step 6. Graph the equation.
- Write down the equation, using rounded values for the slope and the y-intercept. To 3 decimal places, the slope a is approximately 0.573. The y-intercept b is approximately 17.880.
- Press Y=, and enter the equation $y = 0.573x + 17.880$.
- Press GRAPH.

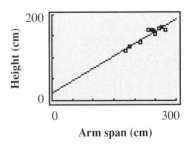

Arm span (cm)

3. The plotted points are crowded together on the right half of the screen.

a) Press ZOOM **9**. The calculator automatically resets the window so that the plotted points are spread across the window.

b) Press TRACE. Use ▶ and ◀ to move the cursor among the points. Compare the coordinates on the screen with the table on page 420.

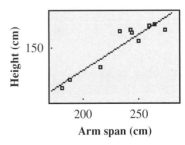

Arm span (cm)

c) Press ▼ to move the cursor to the line. Use ▶ and ◀ to move along the line.

d) In the table on page 420, the arm span of Kiki is 243 cm. Press 243 ENTER. The cursor will jump to the point on the line where $x = 243$.
   i) What is the predicted height for an arm span of 243 cm?
   ii) How does the predicted height compare with Kiki's height?

e) Repeat part d for some other gorillas in the table. Which gorilla's height is closest to the height predicted by the equation?

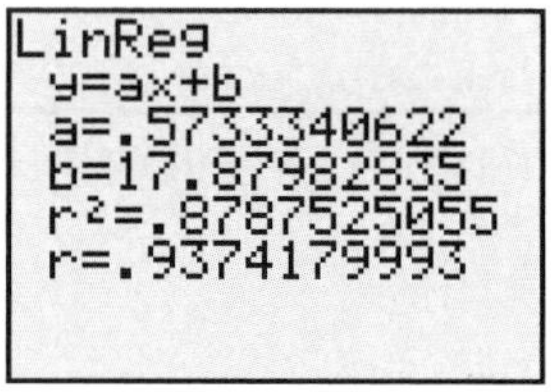

In the *Investigation*, you used a graphing calculator to calculate the equation of the line of best fit. You can also "measure" how well a line fits the set of data. Your calculator may have displayed additional lines on the LinReg screen containing a value of r.
If not, press 2nd 0 to obtain CATALOG.
Scroll down many lines until you come to the line "DiagnosticOn". Press ENTER ENTER.

```
LinReg
 y=ax+b
 a=.5733340622
 b=17.87982835
 r²=.8787525055
 r=.9374179993
```

With this setting, you will get a screen like the one shown above when you calculate the equation of a line of best fit. The number r is a measure of how well the line fits the data. When $r = 1$, the fit is perfect. This means that all the points lie on the line. The closer r is to 1, the closer the line fits the data. In this case, $r \doteq 0.937$; since this is fairly close to 1, the fit is reasonable.

DISCUSSING the IDEAS

1. Why is it important to use a calculator to determine the equation of the line of best fit?

2. When entering data in lists L1 and L2, does the order in which the points are entered make a difference to the result? Explain.

3. In the *Investigation*, suppose we had entered heights in list L1 and arm spans in list L2.
   a) Would the graph that results be the same as the one on page 421? Explain.
   b) Would the equation of the line of best fit be the same as the equation on page 421? Explain.

4. Refer to the screen in exercise 3, page 421. Notice the tick marks at the bottom and the left side of the screen. How do we know that these represent 200 and 250 on the horizontal axis and 150 on the vertical axis?

9.5 EXERCISES

A 1. What is the least number of points you need to determine a line of best fit? Explain.

2. A student calculated the circumferences of three circles, with these results.

Radius (cm)	1.0	2.0	2.5
Circumference (cm)	3.1	6.2	7.9

She entered the data into a TI-83 calculator, and obtained these results.

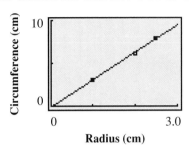 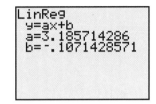

a) What is the equation of the line of best fit for these data?

b) Is this a suitable model for the data? Explain.

c) Enter the data and follow the steps on pages 420–421 to determine the equation of the line of best fit. You should get the results above.

3. A student calculated the areas of three circles, with these results.

Radius (cm)	1.0	2.0	2.5
Area (cm²)	0.8	3.1	4.9

He entered the data into a TI-83 calculator, and obtained these results.

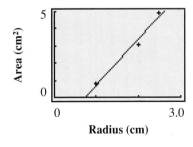 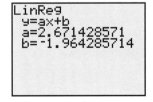

a) What is the equation of the line of best fit for these data?

b) Is this a suitable model for the data? Explain.

c) Enter the data and follow the steps on pages 420–421 to determine the equation of the line of best fit. You should get the results above.

B **4.** Refer to the *Investigation, page 420.*

   a) Repeat the investigation, with one change. Enter the heights in list L1 and the arm spans in list L2.

   b) Compare the graph you obtained with the graph on page 421. In what ways are they similar? In what ways are they different?

   c) Compare the equation of the line of best fit you obtained with the equation on page 421. Are there any similarities?

5. Refer to *Investigation 2, page 405.*

   a) Enter the data for women into a graphing calculator.

   b) Determine the equation of the line of best fit.

   c) Compare the equation in part b with the equation in *Example 2, page 407.*

6. Investigation: Length of a Burning Candle
   You will need a small birthday candle 6 to 8 cm high, plasticine, a clock or watch, and a ruler.

   a) Set the candle firmly in plasticine so that it is vertical. Before you light it, measure the length of the candle from the edge of the plasticine to the end of the wax. Mark the candle in centimetres from the edge of the plasticine.

   b) Carefully light the candle and start timing. Try not to disturb the flame. Every 2 minutes, measure and record the height of the candle to the nearest half centimetre. After 10 minutes, blow out the candle and measure its height. Do not let the candle burn down completely.

   c) Enter the data into a graphing calculator. Enter the times in list L1 and the heights in list L2.

   d) Graph the data.

   e) Use a graphing calculator to determine the equation of the line of best fit, and display the line of best fit on the graph.

   f) Use your equation to predict how long it would take to burn the candle down to the plasticine.

   g) Sketch the graph you obtained. Show the plotted points, the line of best fit, and your result for part f.

   h) What factors affected the results of this investigation? Suppose you were to repeat the investigation. What would you do differently to account for these factors?

7. a) Draw this diagram on grid paper.

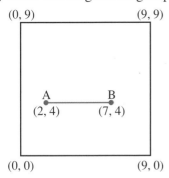

(0, 9)   (9, 9)

A ———— B
(2, 4)   (7, 4)

(0, 0)   (9, 0)

b) Use a graphing calculator to create random numbers or the table of random numbers on page 391. Create 6 points at random inside the square. Label these points C, D, E, F, G, H. Join A and B to each of these points to form 6 triangles.

c) Calculate the length of the altitude and the area of each △ABC, ABD, and so on.

d) Graph the data in part c.

e) Use a graphing calculator to determine the equation of the line of best fit. Explain the result.

8. In Ontario, a driver who has more than 0.08 mL of alcohol per 100 mL of blood is legally impaired. The amount of alcohol in a person's blood (called the blood-alcohol level) is found using a breathalyser.

Researchers conducted a test to determine how the amount of alcohol in a person's bloodstream was reduced over time. These data were collected.

Time (h)	0.0	0.5	1.0	1.5
Blood-alcohol level (mL per 100 mL)	0.094	0.090	0.085	0.080

One evening, a driver was stopped on a highway and the breathalyser indicated a reading of 0.06. Legally, he was not impaired, but when he informed the police officer that he had been driving for 2.5 h, the officer considered charging him.

a) Graph the data. Determine the equation of the line of best fit.

b) Use the model in part a. Determine what the driver's blood-alcohol level was when he started driving.

c) What assumptions are you making in part b? Explain.

9. Mathematicians have found that the *mean data point* always lies on the line of best fit. The *x*- and *y*-coordinates of the mean data point are the means of all the *x*-coordinates and of all the *y*-coordinates of the original data.

a) Choose one of exercises 4 to 8. Calculate the coordinates of the mean data point.

b) Verify that the mean data point lies on the line of best fit.

10. **Investigation: Bouncing Ball Experiment**

This screen was obtained using a reasonably bouncy ball and a CBR attached to a TI-83 calculator. The CBR was held with its sensor facing straight down. The ball was dropped directly below the CBR and bounced a few times before coming to rest.

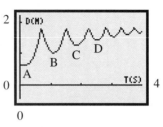

a) Discuss with a partner how the motion of the ball relates to the graph. Consider these questions:
   i) When is the ball falling (moving away from the CBR)?
   ii) When is the ball rising (moving toward the CBR)?

b) Perform the experiment, and create a graph similar to the graph shown.

c) Trace to find the coordinates of points A, B, C, and D. Record these coordinates.

d) Use the coordinates of the points in part c. Calculate the heights of the ball above the floor at the peaks of its path. Record these heights in a table. For time, use the x-coordinates of the points.

Time, x				
Height of ball, y				

e) Graph the data and determine the equation of the line of best fit.

f) In part e, you assumed that the points on the graph lie along a straight line. Is this a reasonable assumption? Explain.

g) Use your equation to answer each question.
   i) For what value of x will y become 0? What is significant about this in terms of the ball?
   ii) Assume the mathematical model can be used to make predictions about the past as well as the future. When was the ball at a height of 2 m?

11. The table shows the approximate price index in 1981 dollars of cigarettes, and the approximate annual cigarette consumption per capita for 15- to 19-year-olds across Canada from 1980 to 1989. The price is not in real dollars because the purchasing power of a dollar changes over the years. Instead, the table shows a price index that relates the price to 1980 dollars.

Year	1980	1981	1982	1983	1984	1985	1986	1987	1988	1989
Price Index	100	102	105	115	122	140	158	161	173	200
Number per capita	3250	3200	3000	2600	2250	2000	1800	1600	1500	1300

a) Plot the data on two separate graphs, with *Time* along the horizontal axis. Compare the graphs and discuss their relationships with a classmate.

b) Determine the equation of the line of best fit for the price index data. Use your equation to predict when the price index might reach 400.

c) Determine the equation of the line of best fit for the number per capita data. Use your equation to predict when the number per capita will be zero.

d) Discuss these data and your predictions with a classmate.

12. We have to be careful when using mathematical models to make predictions. Often, there are social or political changes that affect the model. The data below were taken from the Ontario Government report *Youth and Tobacco, 1997: A Cause for Concern*. It shows the percent of high school girls who smoked more than one cigarette during the previous year.

Year	1981	1983	1985	1987	1989	1991	1993	1995	1997
Percent	35.1	30.1	26.4	25.1	24.5	21.9	25.2	27.5	28.7

a) Consider the years 1981 to 1991 only.
   i) Graph the data.
   ii) Determine the equation of the line of best fit.
   iii) Use your equation to predict the percent of high school girls who smoke more than one cigarette in 1993, 1995, and 1997.

b) Consider the years 1991 to 1997 only.
   i) Graph the data.
   ii) Determine the equation of the line of best fit.
   iii) Use your equation to predict the percent of high school girls who smoke more than one cigarette in 1999.

c) Suggest some reasons why the percent changed so dramatically after 1991.

COMMUNICATING *the* IDEAS

In your journal, write to explain some advantages of using technology to determine the equation of the line of best fit for given data. If you can think of any disadvantages, include them in your explanation.

9.6 Who Is the World's Fastest Human?: Part II

On page 139, you used line-segment models to help you decide whether Donovan Bailey or Michael Johnson was faster at the 1996 Summer Olympics. In this section, you will develop another model.

The Line-of-Best-Fit Model

Use the data on page 157 and a TI-83 calculator.

1. a) Enter the data for Bailey into lists L1 and L2.

b) Use the calculator to determine an equation for the line of best fit.

c) Record your equation, and compare it with those of your classmates.

d) Let *t* seconds represent the time since the start of the race.
Let *d* metres represent the distance raced up to this time.
Write an equation to represent Bailey's distance, *d*, in terms of his time *t*.

2. Your equation is a mathematical model for Bailey's run.

a) Use your model to estimate each distance. Explain any differences.
  i) the distance run in 9.84 s
  ii) the distance run in 5.6 s

b) What distance does your model predict for 0 s? Explain.

c) According to your model, what was Bailey's average speed?

d) Compare your answer to part c with your answer to exercise 2b, page 139. Explain why these are different.

3. Repeat exercise 1 using the data for Johnson.

4. Your equation is a mathematical model for Johnson's run.

a) Use your model to estimate each distance. Explain any differences.
  i) the distance run in 19.32 s
  ii) the distance run in 10.12 s

b) What distance does your model predict for 0 s? Explain.

c) According to your model, what was Johnson's average speed?

d) Compare your answer to part c with your answer to exercise 3b, page 139. Explain why these are different.

5. a) According to your models, which runner was faster? Explain.

b) Can you think of any reasons to doubt this model? Discuss with a partner.

The 150-m Model

After many arguments, the question about whether Bailey or Johnson was faster remained unsettled. Nationalistic pride on either side of the border prompted the Ottawa-based Magellan Group to organize a race between Bailey and Johnson. The date was set: they agreed to race 150 m at Toronto's Skydome on June 1, 1997, for one million dollars. A series of articles in the *Ottawa Citizen* explored the mathematics and physics behind the race in order to predict a winner.

6. a) Use your equations from exercises 1 and 3 to predict a winner for the 150-m race.

  b) Based on this information, what would you expect the winning and losing times for this race to be?

  c) Is there any reason to doubt your predictions? Explain.

7. Bailey's best time in a 200-m race before the Olympics was 20.76 s. Johnson's best time in a 100-m race before the Olympics was 10.09 s. How might this information be used to adjust your model?

8. These data are from the 150-m race.

Bailey's time (s)	0	5.74	10.24	14.99
Johnson's time (s)	0	5.83	10.63	
Distance (m)	0	50	100	150

  a) Was there anything about Bailey's times that surprised you (that is, did not match your model)? Explain.

  b) How do we know there was something wrong with Johnson's leg before the 100-m mark?

Suppose you were wealthy enough to be able to donate a prize of one million dollars to be awarded once every 10 years to the world's fastest human. This would give you the power to make up the rules to decide who would win the prize. In your journal, write to describe your rules, and explain your reasons.

Refer to the data on pages 401–402. The graphs in this section were obtained using data from all the people in the study, not just samples.

1. The screens below show the results for everyone who received the placebo.

   a) Write the equation of the line of best fit.

   b) Suppose the placebo had no effect. What would you expect the equation of the line of best fit to be? Explain.

   c) Decide if the equation of the line of best fit is reasonable.

People who received the placebo

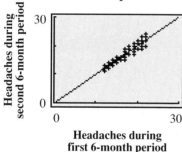

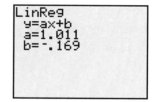

2. The screens below show the results for everyone who received the medication.

   a) Write the equation of the line of best fit.

   b) Consider your answer to part a. What does the line of best fit for those patients who received the medication indicate about the medication's effectiveness?

People who received the medication

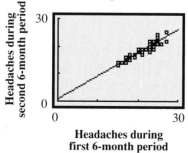

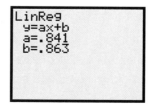

3. Use your samples from pages 402–403.

   a) Determine the equation of the line of best fit for each sample.

   b) Are the results for your samples consistent with the results on page 403 for all the people who participated in the study? Explain.

COMMUNICATING *the* **IDEAS**

Can the company reasonably claim a 15% reduction in the number of headaches? In your journal, write to explain how you reached your conclusion, starting with the advertisement on page 388.

Number of hours of television watched each week

Teens	Males	Females
17 h 01 min	23 h 37 min	26 h 25 min

Children
(ages 2 to 11)
18 h 42 min

All people over
the age of 2
23 h 24 min

Boggle your MIND

The art shows some statistics about the number of hours of television watched by Canadians every week. Over the next few weeks, keep track of your television viewing times. Ask your family or a few friends to do the same. Calculate the mean number of hours of television viewed for each person and for the group. How do the numbers compare with the statistics given here?

1. **Investigation:** **Wrist size and neck size relationships** Work with a partner. You will need a tape measure.

   a) How do you think wrist size and neck size are related?

   b) Measure and record your wrist sizes. Measure and record your neck sizes.

   c) Combine your data with those of other students in your class. Record the data in a table.

Wrist size (cm)	Neck size (cm)

   d) Create a scatter plot of the data on grid paper. Represent *Wrist size* on the horizontal axis and *Neck size* on the vertical axis.

   e) Draw a line of best fit.

   f) Describe any trends in the data. What appears to be the relationship between wrist size and neck size? How does this relationship compare with your predictions in part a?

   g) Determine the equation of the line of best fit.

   h) Use the graph and the equation of the line of best fit. Predict the neck size of a person with a wrist size of 12 cm.

   i) Explain any differences in the answers to part h.

2. In exercise 1, what factors affected the results of this investigation? Suppose you were to repeat the investigation. What would you do differently to account for these factors?

3. Describe a suitable sample to obtain valid information about each issue.

   a) To determine the music that is best liked by teenagers

   b) To estimate how many Canadians want the legal drinking age raised

   c) To determine the television show most watched by Canadians

   d) To estimate the average amount of time spent in outdoor activities every week by teenagers

   e) To determine the percent of the population with blood type A+

4. Suppose you have to choose a random sample of 6 students from your class. List as many different ways as you can to choose 6 students at random.

5. Refer to *Investigation 1*, page 404.

   a) Enter the data into a graphing calculator. Use the calculator to create a scatter plot.

   b) Use the calculator to estimate the equation of the line of best fit, and display the line of best fit on the scatter plot.

   c) Use the calculator to determine the equation of the line of best fit.

   d) Explain any differences in the answers to parts b and c.

   e) What does the slope of the line of best fit represent? Explain.

   f) Use the equation of the line of best fit from part c.
      i) Predict the arm span of someone whose height is 1.5 m.
      ii) Predict the height of someone whose arm span is 1.0 m.

6. Refer to the graph you drew for the men's discus events, and the graph on page 406 for the women's discus events.

   a) Estimate the winning distances for men and women in the 2000 Olympic Games. Find the results for that year on the Internet, in an almanac, or in a database. How do they compare to your estimates?

   b) According to the graphs, in which Olympic Games did the women first surpass the men? Look at the results. When did the women first surpass the men in the discus event?

7. Mathematical Modelling In Section 9.3, you saw several examples of winning times or distances in the Olympic Summer Games. In every example, a graph suggests that there is a linear relationship between the winning time or distance and the year. You used the graph to determine a line of best fit. This line is a mathematical model that shows how the winning time or distance has changed over the years.

   a) Do you think the results predicted by the model are accurate? Explain.

   b) Do you think the linear model would continue to apply for a long time in the future? Explain.

   c) What might happen to the model as new times or distances in these events become known?

8. Mathematical Modelling Use the data on pages 401–402.

   a) Create a random sample of men who received the medication. Graph the data from your sample and determine the equation of the line of best fit.

   b) Repeat part a for men who received the placebo.

   c) Are the results for your samples consistent with the results on page 430 for all the people who participated in the study? Explain.

9. Mathematical Modelling Repeat exercise 8 for women.

Lori Bowden-#1 Canadian Women's Triathlete 1998

Designing a Cooler

Mathematics can be used to make a system or object as efficient as possible. This is called *optimization.*

Your task in this chapter is to determine the best shape and dimensions for a portable cooler. This cooler must maintain the temperature of its contents for as long as possible. It must also appeal to consumers by having a low cost and functional design. To design the cooler:

- You will develop and use formulas for the surface areas and volumes of different geometric solids.
- You will determine how the dimensions of a solid are related when it contains a given volume and has a minimum surface area.
- You will determine the dimensions that produce the minimum surface area.
- You will discover relationships between surface area and volume.

Until you develop your models, here are some questions to consider:

1. What factors contribute to the rate at which a hot liquid cools in a closed vacuum flask?

2. What factors contribute to the rate at which the ice melts in a closed cooler?

3. What does it mean to say that a system or object is efficient?

You will return to these questions in Sections 10.4, 10.8, and 10.12.

 FYI Visit www.awl.com/canada/school/connections

For information related to the above problem, click on <u>MATHLINKS</u> followed by <u>AWMath</u>. Then select a topic under Designing a Cooler.

This section reviews these skills and concepts:

- Surface area and volume of a rectangular prism
- Formulas for length, area, and volume

Surface Area and Volume of a Rectangular Prism

You will need grid paper, a pencil, a ruler, scissors, and tape. A net for a cube is shown below right.

1. On grid paper, create a net for a rectangular prism that is not a cube. Ensure you leave at least 2 squares between the net and the edge of the paper for tabs.

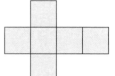

2. Check that the opposite sides of each face of the prism are equal.

3. Draw a narrow strip along two edges of the net. These strips are tabs.

4. Label the edges l, w, and h for the length, width, and height of the prism, respectively.

5. Use the fact that pairs of faces have equal areas. Write a formula for the surface area, A, of a prism with dimensions l, w, and h.

6. Measure the net. Use the formula to determine the surface area of the prism whose net you have drawn.

7. Cut, fold, and tape the net to form a prism, with the grid on the outside surface.

8. Assume 1 grid square represents 1 face of a smaller cube. Write a formula to determine the number of smaller cubes, n, that would fit inside your prism.

9. Use the formula to determine the volume of your prism.

10. Look at the formulas in exercise 11. Identify the formulas for the surface area and volume of a rectangular prism.

11. In previous grades, you learned several measurement formulas. Some of these are listed below.

a) Identify each figure and solid above.

b) Explain what each formula represents.

c) Match each formula with a solid or the figure above.

d) Summarize the formulas in a systematic way. Use diagrams to illustrate what the formulas represent.

$A = lw$ $\qquad A = s^2$ $\qquad V = lwh$ $\qquad P = 2(l + w)$

$C = 2\pi r$ $\qquad A = 6x^2$ $\qquad P = 4s$ $\qquad A = \dfrac{h(a + b)}{2}$

$A = \pi r^2$ $\qquad V = x^3$ $\qquad C = \pi d$ $\qquad A = \dfrac{1}{2}bh$

$A = 2(lw + lh + hw)$

10.1   Areas of Composite Figures

Many figures are combinations or composites of geometric figures.

Figures in a Tangram

Recall the tangram you used in earlier grades.

Copy this diagram on grid paper.
Draw a 20-cm square.
Draw one diagonal.
Draw part of the second diagonal, as shown in the diagram.
Complete the construction, using the fact that all indicated segments are equal.

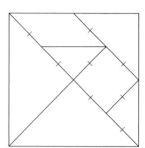

1. Identify each figure in the tangram.

2. Determine the area of each figure in the tangram.

3. Describe the relationships among the areas of the figures in exercise 2.

4. Determine the area of the tangram in two ways. Are the areas equal?

The front view of a house is a composite of a rectangle and a triangle. A window could be a composite of a semicircle and a rectangle.

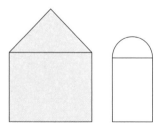

We can use the formulas we reviewed on page 437 to solve problems involving the perimeter and area of composite figures.

Example 1

Determine the approximate length of frame
needed to create a wooden frame for this
Roman window.

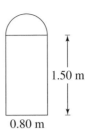

1.50 m

0.80 m

Solution

The window is a rectangle and a semicircle.
The perimeter, P, of a rectangle is given by $P = 2(l + w)$, where l and w are
the length and width, respectively.

Substitute $l = 1.50$ and $w = 0.80$.
$P = 2(1.50 + 0.80)$
  $= 2(2.30)$
  $= 4.60$

The circumference, C, of a circle is given by $C = 2\pi r$, where r is the radius.
The circumference of a semicircle is $S = \frac{2\pi r}{2}$, or $S = \pi r$.
The radius is one-half the width of the rectangle; so, $r = 0.40$ m.

Substitute $r = 0.40$.
$S = \pi(0.40)$
  $\doteq 1.2566$
  $\doteq 1.26$

To the nearest centimetre, the length of frame needed is
4.60 m + 1.26 m = 5.86 m.

Example 2

A contractor hired to tile the lobby of an office
building needs to determine the area of the
lobby as accurately as possible to purchase the
correct amount of tiles. Measurements were
taken and this diagram was drawn.

Determine the area of the lobby to the
nearest tenth of a square metre.

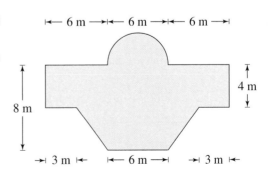

Solution

The lobby comprises a semicircle, a rectangle, and a trapezoid.

The area, A, of a circle is given by $A = \pi r^2$, where r is the radius.

The area, A_s, of a semicircle is given by $A_s = \frac{\pi r^2}{2}$.

From the diagram, the diameter of the semicircle is 6 m.

So, the radius, $r = 3$ m

Substitute $r = 3$.

$A_s = \frac{\pi(3)^2}{2}$

$\doteq 14.137$

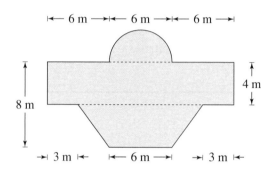

The area, A_r, of the rectangle is $A = lw$, where $l = 6$ m + 6 m + 6 m, or 18 m, and $w = 4$ m.

Substitute for l and w.

$A_r = 18 \times 4$

$= 72$

The area, A_t, of a trapezoid is given by $A_t = \frac{h(a + b)}{2}$, where a and b are the lengths of the parallel sides, and h is the distance between them.

From the diagram, $a = 6\,\text{m}$

$b = 18\,\text{m} - 3\,\text{m} - 3\,\text{m}$

$= 12\,\text{m}$

$h = 8\,\text{m} - 4\,\text{m}$

$= 4\,\text{m}$

Substitute for a, b, and h.

$A_t = \frac{4(12 + 6)}{2}$

$= 36$

The area of the lobby is the sum of the three areas:

$14.137 + 72 + 36 = 122.137$

The area of the lobby is approximately 122.1 m^2.

1. In *Example 1*, why can we only determine the approximate length of the frame?

2. In *Example 1*, explain why a length of 5.86 m is correct to the nearest centimetre.

3. What is the greatest exponent you could expect to see in an area formula? Explain.

10.1 EXERCISES

A 1. Calculate the perimeter of each figure.

a)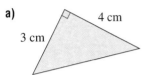

3 cm, 4 cm

b)

10 cm, 3 cm, 4 cm
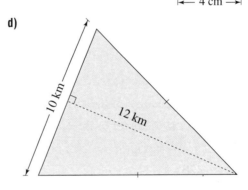

c)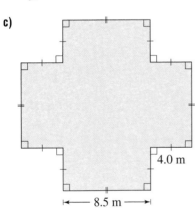

4.0 m, 8.5 m

d)

10 km, 12 km

2. Calculate the area of each figure in exercise 1.

3. Determine the shaded area of each figure.

a)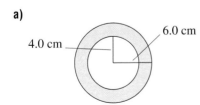

4.0 cm, 6.0 cm

b)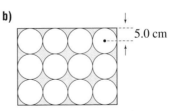

5.0 cm

c)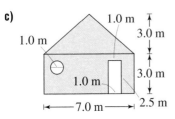

1.0 m, 1.0 m, 3.0 m, 3.0 m, 1.0 m, 7.0 m, 2.5 m

d)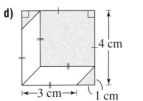

4 cm, 3 cm, 1 cm

4. Determine the numbers of rectangles and triangles in this figure.

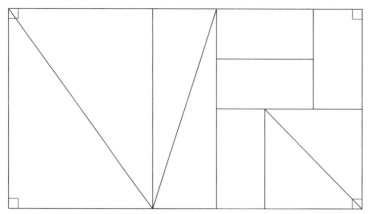

5. Describe the figure suggested by each area formula.

    a) $A = \pi(5.2)^2 - \pi(4.8)^2$ **b)** $A = 4 \times 3 + \frac{1}{2}\pi(1.5)^2$

B **6.** The circumference of a circle is 14.5 cm.

    a) Calculate the diameter of the circle.

    b) Calculate the radius of the circle.

    c) Calculate the area of the circle.

7. The area of a circle is 63.6 m².

    a) Calculate the radius of the circle.

    b) Calculate the diameter of the circle.

    c) Calculate the circumference of the circle.

8. A Roman window comprises a rectangle and a semicircle (below left). The dimensions of the rectangle are 60 cm by 100 cm. Determine the perimeter of this window.

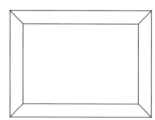

9. A picture frame measures 30.0 cm by 20.0 cm (above right). The four trapezoids that comprise this frame are cut from one piece of wood 2.0 cm wide. Each cut removes 0.3 cm from the piece of wood.

    a) Determine the area of a picture that fills this frame.

    b) Determine the minimum length of wood needed to make the frame.

    c) How would your answer to part b change if the framing material was wider? Explain.

10. The field inside a 400-m running track is to be seeded. Each straight portion of the track is 100 m. Each curved part of the track is a semicircle. One 1.5-kg bag of grass seed will seed an area of 80 m^2.

a) What is the length of each curved part of the track?

b) Determine the width of the field.

c) Determine the area of the field to the nearest 10 m^2.

d) Determine the number of bags of seed required.

e) One 1.5-kg bag of grass seed costs $12.64. How much does it cost to seed the field?

PROBLEM SOLVING FOCUS

An Underground Sprinkler System

The planning and use of an underground sprinkler system for a lawn involve measurement in different ways. For each question on page 444, decide whether it involves length, area, or volume, then answer the question.

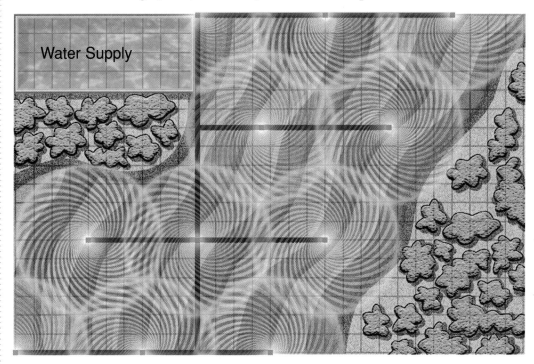

Scale: The side of 1 square = 0.25 m

11. How many square metres of lawn must be watered?

12. Approximately how many square metres of lawn are watered by each sprinkler?

13. Approximately how much water would be needed to cover the entire lawn with 2 cm of water?

14. Suppose you were installing this sprinkler system. How much pipe would you need to connect the sprinklers to each other and to the water supply?

15. Grain elevators are common on the prairies. The front of this grain elevator is to be painted. One can of paint covers an area of 4 m². Determine how many cans of paint need to be purchased.

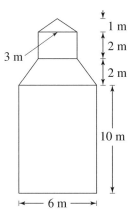

16. A dog is tied to a 2-m leash at ground level on the side of a building. The leash is attached 1 m from the corner of the building.

  a) Copy this diagram. Sketch the region within the dog's reach.

  b) Determine the area of this region, to the nearest square metre.

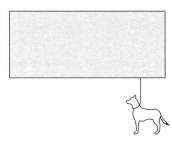

C **17.** The area of the small square is 8 cm². Determine the perimeter of the large square.

COMMUNICATING the IDEAS

Your friend missed today's mathematics lesson and telephones you about it. How would you explain, over the telephone, what a composite figure is and how its area can be determined? Write your ideas in your journal.

APPLIED
FOCUS

Area for a Given Perimeter

You will need grid paper.

Suppose you have 40 m of fencing. You want to make a rectangular dog pen. What is the maximum area you can provide for a dog?

We will model this problem using 1 cm to represent 1 m.

1. On grid paper, draw a rectangle with perimeter 40 cm.

   a) What is the length of the rectangle?

   b) What is the width?

   c) What is the area?

2. Repeat exercise 1. Draw as many different rectangles as you can that have perimeter 40 cm. Copy and complete this table.

Length (cm)	Width (cm)	Area (cm²)	Perimeter (cm)

3. Look at the table.

   a) What is the greatest area?

   b) What are the dimensions of the rectangle with the greatest area?

By using grid paper, you were probably only able to draw rectangles with dimensions that are whole numbers. We can use a spreadsheet to calculate areas of rectangles with dimensions that are rational numbers.

4. Set up this spreadsheet. Enter the text and formulas shown.

	A	B	C
1	Maximum area with perimeter 40		
2			
3	Width	Length	Area
4	0.1	=20-A4	=A4*B4
5	=A4+0.1		

a) Explain what the formula in each cell does.

   i) Cell A5   **ii)** Cell B4   **iii)** Cell C4

b) Highlight cell A5. Fill Down. Highlight cells B4 and C4. Fill Down. What is the maximum area of the rectangle?

c) What are the dimensions of the rectangle with the maximum area?

5. Compare your answers to exercises 3b and 4c. What do you notice?

Designing an Enclosure

Workers at a resort set up a rectangular area to store outdoor equipment and furniture. They use metal stands. They have 26 stands, each 3 m long. The storage enclosure they set up could have different shapes.

The length could be much longer than the width.

The length and width could be almost equal.

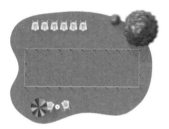
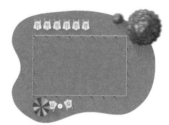

1. Suppose 3 metal stands are used for the width.

   a) How many stands could be used for the length?

   b) What are the dimensions of this enclosure, in metres?

   c) What is the area enclosed?

2. Repeat exercise 1 for each condition given.

   a) The workers use 4 stands for the width.

   b) They use 5 stands for the width.

3. a) Record your results from exercises 1 and 2 in a table.

Number of stands along the width	Number of stands along the length	Width of enclosure (m)	Length of enclosure (m)	Area enclosed (m²)
3				
4				
5				

b) Extend your table to show the results for greater widths.

c) How many stands should be used for the width and length to make the largest possible enclosure? What are the dimensions of this enclosure?

DISCUSSING the IDEAS

1. For a given perimeter, describe the rectangle that has the greatest area.

2. In *Investigation 2*, suppose the workers found two more metal stands. Explain where these metal stands should be placed to maximize the area of the enclosure.

10.2 EXERCISES

1. A city zoo rents strollers and wagons. Zoo workers are building a rectangular enclosure to contain the strollers and wagons. They have 30 metal stands, identical to the ones described in *Investigation 2*.

a) What are the dimensions of the largest rectangular area of the enclosure?

b) Can they make an enclosure with an area of 50 m²? If so, what are its dimensions?

2. Melanie has 36 patio tiles, each 0.6 m square.

a) Suppose she uses the patio tiles to form a path. What are the dimensions of the narrowest rectangular path she can make?

b) Suppose she uses the patio tiles to form a square patio. What are the dimensions of the patio?

3. Campbell has 10 railroad ties, each 1.8 m long. He uses the ties to enclose a rectangular garden.

a) What are the possible dimensions of the different rectangles he could form?

b) What is the area of each rectangle in part a?

B 4. Steve wants to fence a rectangular garden. The fencing material comes in 1-m long units that cannot be cut. Suppose Steve has 20 m of fencing. What are the dimensions of the largest garden he can make? Explain your answer.

5. If a spreadsheet program is available, use it to complete this exercise. A lifeguard has 400 m of rope to enclose a rectangular swimming area at a beach. The diagrams show different ways she can do this.

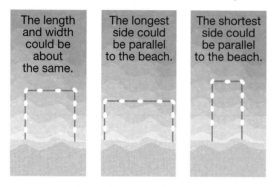

| The length and width could be about the same. | The longest side could be parallel to the beach. | The shortest side could be parallel to the beach. |

a) Do you think the area of the enclosed region depends on the way the rope is arranged? Explain.

b) Suppose the side parallel to the beach measures 300 m. How long is the other side of the rectangle? Calculate the area of water enclosed by the rope.

c) Repeat part b if the side parallel to the beach measures:
   i) 250 m   ii) 200 m   iii) 150 m   iv) 100 m

d) Record your results in a table.

Length of side parallel to beach (m)	Length of side perpendicular to beach (m)	Total length of rope (m)	Area enclosed (m²)
300			
250			

e) What are the dimensions of the largest possible rectangular swimming area? How are these dimensions related?

6. A store owner wants to create a rectangular area for a store display. He has 6 m of rope. What are the dimensions of the largest area he can enclose in each situation? Explain your answers.

a) The rope encloses the entire area.

b) There is a wall on one side.

c) There are walls on 2 sides.

7. For every rectangle, a perimeter and an area can be calculated. The perimeter and the area form an ordered pair (P, A) that can be plotted on a grid. If many points are plotted, you can investigate how areas and perimeters of rectangles are related. The instructions below assume that a program called RCTNGLES has been transferred to your calculator.

When you run the program, you can choose whether you want to plot ordered pairs (P, A) or (A, P). The results will be graphed on screens with the scales shown.

After you make your choice, the calculator asks how many points you want to plot. You should choose a few hundred.

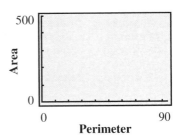

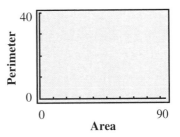

The calculator generates dimensions of rectangles at random and calculates their perimeters and areas. It then plots the points on a screen. When you have finished with the graph, press ENTER to quit the program.

a) Use the program to create a graph to show the relationship between the areas and the perimeters of rectangles.

b) Copy the graph into your notebook. Describe the graph.

c) If you plotted enough points, you should see a curve on the screen. What kind of rectangle do you think corresponds to points that lie on the curve? Explain.

8. Refer to *Investigation 2*. Determine the dimensions of the largest enclosure the resort workers can make for each situation.

a) Use metal stands for 3 sides of the enclosure, with a wall on the remaining side.

b) Use metal stands for 2 sides of the enclosure, with walls on two adjacent sides.

9. The resort workers in *Investigation 2* decide to separate the outdoor equipment from the furniture. They set up two storage enclosures of equal area, with a common side. The diagram shows one way to do this, using 26 metal stands.

a) Calculate the combined area of the two storage enclosures.

b) Find some other ways to arrange the metal stands to make the two storage areas. Calculate the combined area for each. Record your results in a table.

Number of stands along each of the 3 sides	Number of stands along each of the other 2 sides	Overall width (m)	Overall length (m)	Combined area (m²)
6	4			

c) How should the stands be arranged to make the largest possible enclosure? What are the dimensions and the area of this enclosure?

10. You will need some string and a sheet of 1-cm grid paper. Cut a piece of string and tie the ends together to form a loop.

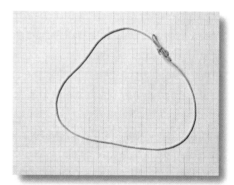

a) Describe the shape of the largest region on the graph paper you can enclose with the string. Experiment, using different shapes.

b) What is the area of the largest region?

c) Suppose the string is 42.5 cm long. What are the dimensions of the largest region?

C 11. The opposite corners of a checkerboard are removed, as shown. Suppose you have a supply of dominoes, each of which covers two squares of the checkerboard. What is the maximum number of dominoes you can place on the checkerboard, without overlapping?

Suppose you have several rectangles that have the same area. In your journal, explain how you could tell, just by looking, which one has the least perimeter. Illustrate your answer with some examples.

From compact disc cases to refrigerators, many items that we see and use everyday are rectangular prisms. A die is a special rectangular prism in which all edges have the same length; this prism is a cube.

From your work in *Reviewing Your Skills*, you should have developed these formulas.

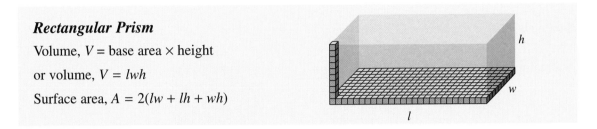

Rectangular Prism

Volume, V = base area × height

or volume, $V = lwh$

Surface area, $A = 2(lw + lh + wh)$

Two triangular prisms are formed by cutting a rectangular prism in half along a diagonal of a base.

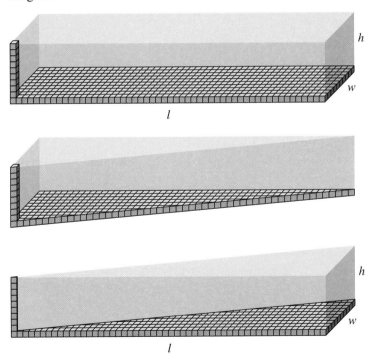

Therefore, the volume of a triangular prism is one-half the volume of the corresponding rectangular prism.

To calculate the volume of a triangular prism, we use the general formula for the volume of a prism.

The surface area of a triangular prism is the sum of the areas of its five faces.

Triangular Prism

Volume, V = base area × height

Surface area, A = the sum of the areas of the faces

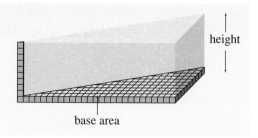

height

base area

Example 1

Determine the surface area of this carton.

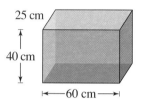

25 cm

40 cm

|← 60 cm →|

Solution

Use the formula $A = 2(lw + lh + wh)$. Substitute $l = 60$, $w = 40$, and $h = 25$.

$A = 2[(60)(40) + (60)(25) + (40)(25)]$
$ = 2[2400 + 1500 + 1000]$
$ = 9800$

The surface area of the carton is 9800 cm^2.

Example 2

A railway car approximates a rectangular prism. It has a volume of 82.5 m^3.
The car is 3 m wide and 11 m long. Determine the height of the railway car.

Solution

Use the formula $V = lwh$.
Substitute $V = 82.5$, $l = 11$, and $w = 3$.

$82.5 = 11 \times 3 \times h$
$82.5 = 33h$
$\dfrac{82.5}{33} = h$
$h = 2.5$

The height of the railway car is 2.5 m.

Example 3

A large Toblerone® bar has the dimensions shown.

6.0 cm

6.0 cm

6.0 cm

6.0 cm

30.5 cm

Determine the volume and surface area of this prism.

Solution

Volume, V = base area × height
The base of the prism is the triangular face.
The height of the prism is the length of the bar.

The area of the triangular face = $\frac{1}{2}bh$

Use the Pythagorean Theorem to determine h.

$h^2 = 6.0^2 - 3.0^2$

$\quad = 27$

$h = \sqrt{27}$

$\quad \doteq 5.196$

The area of the triangle $\doteq \frac{1}{2}(6.0)(5.196)$

$\qquad\qquad\qquad \doteq 15.588$

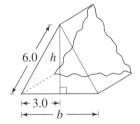

6.0 h

3.0

b

So, $V \doteq 15.588 \times 30.5$

$\quad \doteq 475.434$

The volume of the prism is approximately 475 cm^3.
The surface area of the prism = sum of the areas of the faces.
There are 2 triangular faces, each with area 15.588.
There are 3 rectangular faces, each with area 6.0 × 30.5 = 183.
The surface area of the prism $\doteq 2(15.588) + 3(183)$

$\qquad\qquad\qquad\qquad\quad \doteq 580.176$

The surface area of the prism is approximately 580 cm^2.

1. Look at the formula for the volume of a rectangular prism. How does the volume of a rectangular prism change in each case?

   a) The length is doubled.

   b) Both the length and width are doubled.

   c) All the length, width, and height are doubled.

2. Look at the formula for the surface area of a rectangular prism. How does the surface area change in each case?

   a) The length is doubled.

   b) Both the length and width are doubled.

   c) All the length, width, and height are doubled.

3. **a)** In *Example 3*, what other way is there to calculate the volume of the triangular prism?

   b) Could you use your method in part a to determine the volume of any triangular prism? Explain.

   c) Explain why the volume of the prism in *Example 3* is not equal to the volume of the chocolate it contains.

10.3 EXERCISES

  1. Calculate the surface area and volume of each prism.

a)

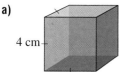

4 cm

b)

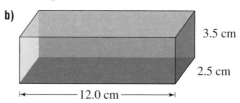

3.5 cm

2.5 cm

12.0 cm

c)

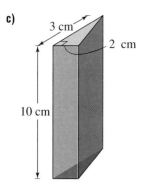

3 cm

2 cm

10 cm

d)

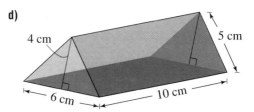

4 cm

5 cm

6 cm

10 cm

2. For each prism, several measurements are given. Calculate each unknown measurement.

a)

$V = 180 \text{ cm}^3$

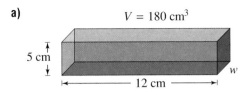

5 cm

12 cm

w

b)

$A = 138 \text{ cm}^2$

3 cm

3 cm

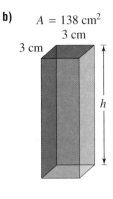

h

c)

$V = 280 \text{ cm}^3$

5 cm

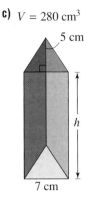

h

7 cm

3. Describe and draw the solid whose surface area is represented by this expression:

$A = 2(10 \times 6) + 2(4 \times 10) + 2(4 \times 6)$

4. A student correctly determined the surface area of a box. She used this expression:

$A = 2(3 \times 4) + 2(4 \times 5) + 1(3 \times 5)$. Describe the box.

B **5.** Calculate the surface area and volume of each solid.

a)

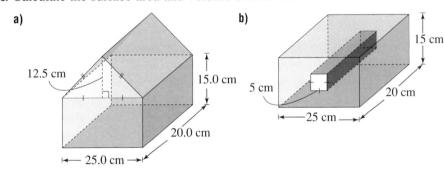

12.5 cm

15.0 cm

20.0 cm

25.0 cm

b)

15 cm

5 cm

20 cm

25 cm

c)

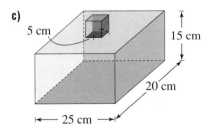

5 cm

15 cm

20 cm

25 cm

d)

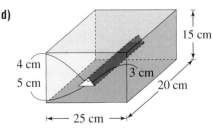

4 cm

5 cm

3 cm

15 cm

20 cm

25 cm

6. The box of a dump truck has dimensions 1 m by 2 m by 4 m. Explain how this truck was able to carry 9 m³ of soil.

7. Appliances such as refrigerators, freezers, and microwave ovens have volumes measured in cubic feet (cu. ft., or ft³). A fridge has a volume of 24 cu. ft. Determine at least 6 sets of possible dimensions for the inside of this fridge. Which dimensions are the most likely?

8. **Academic Focus** Use the diagram on page 451 for the triangular prism. It has length h and a base that is a right triangle with legs w and l.

a) Derive a formula for the volume, V, of this prism.

b) Derive a formula for the surface area, A, of this prism.

9. Determine the minimum amount of packaging needed to completely cover a Toblerone® bar with these dimensions: length 20.7 cm; triangular face has edges 3.5 cm and height 3.0 cm. Express the surface area to the nearest square centimetre.

10. Volumes of fluids are measured in capacity units of millilitres or litres. One millilitre equals 1 cm^3. There are 1000 mL in 1 L. A 2-L carton of milk approximates a rectangular prism. Determine 3 sets of possible dimensions for a 2-L carton of milk. Which set of dimensions is most likely? Measure the dimensions of a 2-L carton of milk to check.

11. A manufacturer of coolers lists the capacity of one cooler as 50 L. The internal dimensions are 31 cm by 32 cm by 50 cm. Was the manufacturer's information correct? Explain.

12. A cooler has a 60-L capacity. Its internal length is 60 cm and its internal width is 40 cm. Determine the internal height and the internal surface area of the cooler.

13. a) How many cubic centimetres fit 1 m^3? Explain.

b) What percent of the space in one cubic metre would 250 000 cm^3 fill?

14. A packing crate is a rectangular prism. Its surface area is 24 m^2.

a) Determine some possible dimensions for this crate.

b) What is the volume of this crate?

c) Suppose each dimension of the crate was reduced by 50%. How much material would be saved?

d) What would the new volume be?

15. A storage container is a rectangular prism. Its volume is 48 m^3. The width of the prism is one-third its length. Its height is two-thirds its length. Determine the dimensions of the container.

COMMUNICATING the IDEAS

In your journal, describe how you calculate the surface area of a rectangular prism that has 3 different edge lengths.

10.4 Designing a Cooler: Part I

On page 435, you considered the problem of determining the best shape and dimensions for a portable cooler. We will assume the cooler has a certain capacity. This means that its volume is known. Let us assume this volume is 50 L, or 50 000 cm³.

The cooler must maintain the temperature of its contents for as long as possible. Since heat from outside enters the cooler through its top, sides, and bottom, we would like its total surface area to be a minimum. Hence, we have this problem to solve:

How can we design a solid to contain a volume of 50 000 cm³ and have a minimum surface area?

In this section, we will assume the cooler has the shape of a rectangular prism. This is a model for its design. You will consider other models in Sections 10.8 and 10.12.

To begin, we will use smaller volumes than 50 000 cm³ because they are easier to manage. The same principles can be applied to any given volume.

The Square-Based Prism Model

Although other rectangular prisms can be used, we will assume the prism has a square base. You will begin by making some models, then you will use technology to analyze the models.

Part A Using a Physical Model

You will need 3 sheets of grid paper, a ruler, scissors, and tape or glue. You will construct three rectangular prisms each with a volume of 125 cm³.

1. **a)** Choose any measurement between 3.5 cm and 8.0 cm as the side length for the square base.

   b) Calculate the area of the base.

   c) Divide the volume by the base area to determine the height of the prism.

2. **a)** Draw the net of your prism on grid paper. Add tabs where necessary. If there is no room for the top, the top can be omitted.

   b) Use the net to determine the surface area of the prism.

   c) Cut out the net and tape or glue it together to form the prism.

3. Repeat exercises 1 and 2 (using different side lengths in exercise 1a) to create three prisms.

4. Each of your prisms should have a square base and a volume of 125 cm³.

    a) Compare the surface areas of the three prisms.

    b) Compare the heights of the prisms with the side lengths of their bases.

    c) Choose the prism that has the least surface area. How does its height compare with the base side length?

In exercises 1 and 2, you used three different side lengths for the base. Although one of your prisms had a surface area smaller than the others, other prisms could have still smaller surface areas. Visualize changing the shape of the prism, but keeping its volume as 125 cm³.

A short, wide design has top and bottom faces with large areas.

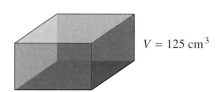

$V = 125 \text{ cm}^3$

A tall, narrow design has side faces with large areas.

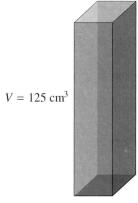

$V = 125 \text{ cm}^3$

You can use technology to calculate the surface areas for many side lengths. Then you can determine the dimensions that produce the minimum surface area more accurately. Whether you use a spreadsheet or a graphing calculator, the first step is the same. You must set up the spreadsheet or the graphing calculator to complete the same calculations as for exercises 1 and 2.

If you are using a spreadsheet, complete Part B and Part D.
If you are using a TI-83 calculator, complete Part C and Part D.

Part B Using a Spreadsheet

Recall what you did in exercises 1 and 2:
- You started with a side length for the square base.

- You calculated the area of the square base.
- You divided 125 by the area to calculate the height.
- You constructed a net and used it to calculate the surface area.

5. Set up a spreadsheet similar to the one below. Copy the formulas in cells B3, C3, and D3 into row 4. Then Fill Down the formulas in row 4 until the areas in column D begin to increase.

	A	B	C	D
1	Minimizing the Surface Area of a Rectangular Prism			
2	Side Length	Base Area	Height	Surface Area
3	3.5	=A3^2	=125/B3	=2*B3+4*(A3*C3)
4	=A3+0.5			

  a) Explain how the formulas in row 3 represent the steps in exercises 1 and 2.

  b) What is the minimum surface area? For what height does it occur?

6. Consider the prism that has the minimum surface area.

  a) How does its height compare with the side length of its base?

  b) What kind of prism is it?

  c) How is its edge length related to its volume?

  d) Graph surface area against height. How does the graph confirm your result in exercise 5b?

7. Up to now, you have been using a prism with a volume of 125 cm^3. Suppose the volume were different.

  a) Predict the shape of the prism that has the minimum surface area.

  b) Choose a volume that is much larger or much smaller than 125 cm^3. Make the appropriate change to the formula in cell C3. Fill Down the new formula in column C. You may need to change the number in cell A3 so that the minimum surface area will appear in column D.

  c) Do the results confirm your prediction? Explain.

Go to Part D.

Part C Using a Graphing Calculator

To use a graphing calculator, you need to visualize the graph you want. It will have *Side length of the base* along the horizontal axis and *Surface area* along the vertical axis. In the Y= list, you enter a formula to calculate the areas. This formula will depend only on the base side length, *x* centimetres.

8. To determine the formula, recall what you did in exercises 1 and 2.

  a) First, you started with a base side length and calculated the area of the base. Suppose the side length is *x* centimetres. Write an expression for the area.

b) Then, you divided 125 by the area to determine the height. Write an expression for the height.

c) Next, you constructed a net and used it to calculate the surface area. Draw a net and label the side length x and the height h. Use your net to write an equation for the surface area of the prism, A, in terms of x.

You can use a graphing calculator to graph surface area against base side length. Then you can trace to determine the minimum area.

Setup

Clear any plots. Clear any equations in the Y= list. To set up the graphing window, use the base lengths and surface areas from exercises 1 and 2 to help you decide appropriate values for Xmin, Xmax, Ymin, and Ymax. Press MODE, and set the display to show values to 2 decimal places.

9. a) In exercise 8c, you should have found that the formula for surface area is $A = 2x^2 + \frac{500}{x}$. Enter the equation $y = 2x^2 + \frac{500}{x}$ in the Y= list.

b) Press TRACE, and trace along the curve until the value of y is as small as possible. Record the values of x and y.

The value of y represents the minimum surface area of the prism. The value of x represents the length of the base of the prism that has the minimum surface area. Now you can calculate the height of this prism.

10. Consider the prism that has the minimum surface area.

a) Use your results from exercise 8 to calculate the height of this prism.

b) How does its height compare with the side length of its base?

c) What kind of prism is it?

d) How is its edge length related to its volume?

11. Up to now, you have been using a prism with a volume of 125 cm³. Suppose the volume were different.

a) Predict the shape of the prism that has the minimum surface area.

b) Choose a volume that is much larger or much smaller than 125 cm³. Make the appropriate change to the equation in the Y= list and repeat exercises 8 to 10.

c) Do the results confirm your prediction?

Part D Looking Back

12. You should have found that the height of the prism that has the minimum surface area is approximately equal to the side length of the base.

a) Suggest a possible reason why the height you obtained is not equal to the side length of the base.

b) Describe how you could determine the dimensions more accurately.

13. In general, suppose a rectangular prism has a given volume. Suppose also that it has the minimum possible surface area.

a) Describe the prism.

b) Describe how the edge length is related to the volume.

14. You have determined the dimensions of the rectangular prism with volume 125 cm³ and minimum surface area. This is the *optimal* prism.

a) Construct a net of the optimal prism on grid paper. Add tabs.

b) Cut out the net and tape or glue it together to form the optimal prism.

c) Compare this prism with the ones you constructed in exercises 1 to 3.

Whether you used a graphing calculator or a spreadsheet, you should have discovered the following result. The result is true for all rectangular prisms, not just square-based prisms.

These rectangular prisms have the same volume and different surface areas. The prism that has the minimum surface area is a cube.

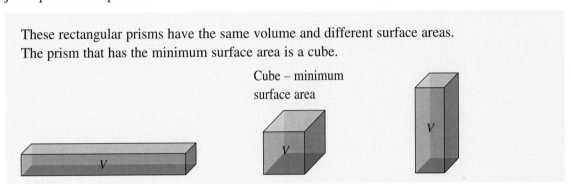

Cube – minimum surface area

Consider again the question posed on page 457 (for a rectangular prism). We now know that the optimal rectangular prism containing a volume of 50 000 cm³ is a cube. We can calculate its edge length and the surface area.

Let x centimetres represent the edge length of the cube.
Since the volume is 50 000 cm³, then
$$x^3 = 50\ 000$$

To solve this equation, we write
$$x = \sqrt[3]{50\ 000}$$

This number is called the *cube root* of 50 000. Here are some possible methods for determining this number.

- You can use a scientific calculator. Key in: 50000 [2nd] [y^x] 3 [=] to display 36.84031498.

- You can use a graphing calculator. On the TI-83, press [MATH] **4** 50000 [ )] [ENTER] to display the screen shown.

- You could use a graphing calculator to graph the equation $y = x^3$, and trace to the point where y is close to 50 000.

The result is $x \doteq 36.84$. Hence, the optimal cube has edges about 36.84 cm long.

15. a) Calculate the surface area of the optimal prism.

  b) Check that the volume of the optimal prism is 50 000 cm^3.

COMMUNICATING *the* IDEAS

Write a report to describe your design for the 50-L cooler. Assume it has the shape of a rectangular prism. Include in your report:

- a description of your design, with a labelled diagram
- an explanation about why your design maintains the temperature of the contents for as long as possible
- an explanation of how the design could be modified for larger or smaller coolers
- your opinion about whether people would accept your design, and how you might change it if they do not

Boggle your MIND

Trace the isosceles triangle on the right. Glue your tracing onto a piece of cardboard. Cut out the tracing along the white lines. You now have five pieces. Use all five pieces to form each of the figures shown below. What other figures can you form using all five pieces?

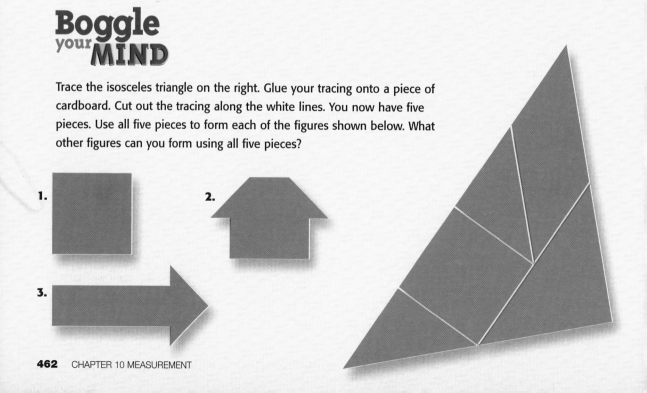

1.

2.

3.

Minimum Surface Area for a Rectangular Prism

The Acme Box Company designs and manufactures boxes, cans, and other containers. It has been hired to design a box to hold 1000 cm^3 of popcorn kernels. The box could have different shapes.

The length, width, and height of the box could be different.

The length, width, and height could be about the same.

1. Suppose the base is 20 cm long and 5 cm wide.

   a) What is the area of the base?

   b) What height is needed so that the volume is 1000 cm^3?

   c) Calculate the surface area of this box.

2. Repeat exercise 1 for each base described below.

   a) 25 cm long and 4 cm wide

   b) 25 cm long and 8 cm wide

3. a) Record your results from exercises 1 and 2 in a table.

Length (cm)	Width (cm)	Height (cm)	Volume (cm^3)	Surface area (cm^2)
20	5			
25	4			
25	8			

b) Which of these three sizes requires the least amount of cardboard to make?

c) Find another size of box that requires less cardboard than the one in part b. Include it in your table.

d) Describe the shape of the box that requires the minimum amount of cardboard.

DISCUSSING the IDEAS

1. In the *Investigation*, suppose Acme needs to design a larger box to hold 2000 cm³ of popcorn kernels. It is to be made with the minimum amount of cardboard. Would the dimensions of this box be double the dimensions of the box in exercise 3c of the *Investigation*? Explain.

10.5 EXERCISES

A

1. a) List several possible sets of dimensions for a rectangular prism with volume 24 cm³. Each dimension should be a whole number.

b) Which prism has the least surface area?

2. a) List several possible sets of whole-number dimensions for a rectangular prism with volume 32 cm³.

b) Which prism has the least surface area?

3. a) List several possible sets of whole-number dimensions for a rectangular prism with volume 100 cm³.

b) Which prism has the least surface area?

B

4. If a spreadsheet program is available, use it to complete this exercise. The Acme Box Company has been hired to design boxes to hold 4000 cm³ of popcorn for movie theatres. The boxes have an open top and a square base.

a) Suppose the base is 10 cm long and 10 cm wide. What is the height for a volume of 4000 cm³? Calculate the surface area of this box.

b) Repeat part a for each base described.
  i) 12 cm by 12 cm   **ii)** 14 cm by 14 cm

c) Record your results from parts a and b in a table.

Length (cm)	Width (cm)	Height (cm)	Volume (cm³)	Surface area (cm²)
10	10			
12	12			
14	14			

d) Determine the dimensions of the box that requires the minimum amount of cardboard. Describe the box. Do you think it would be a good idea for movie theatres to use this shape? Explain.

Square-Based Prisms with a Fixed Volume

You will need 36 1-cm cubes.

5. Use all the cubes to make a rectangular prism with a square base. Copy and complete this table for the prism you constructed.

Length (cm)	Width (cm)	Height (cm)	Surface area (cm²)	Volume (cm³)

6. Repeat exercise 5 several times until you have constructed all possible square-based prisms. How many prisms did you construct?

7. Look at the table.

a) What is the minimum surface area?

b) What are the dimensions of the prism with the minimum surface area?

Suppose you were able to use millimetre cubes instead of centimetre cubes. Could you construct a square-based prism with a smaller surface area? You can use a spreadsheet to find out.

8. Set up a spreadsheet document. Enter the information shown.

	A	B	C	D
1	Surface area of a square-based prism			
2				
3	Length/width	Height	Area of base	Surface area
4	0.1	=36/A4^2	=A4^2	=2*C4+4*A4*B4
5	=A4+0.1			

a) Explain what the formula in each cell does.

    i) Cell B4   **ii)** Cell C4   **iii)** Cell D4   **iv)** Cell A5

b) Highlight cell A5. Fill Down. Highlight cells B4, C4, and D4. Fill Down. What is the minimum surface area of the prism?

c) What are the dimensions of the prism with the minimum surface area?

9. Compare your answers to exercises 7b and 8c. What do you notice?

---

10. Suppose you have an 8-cm cube.

The 8-cm cube can be divided into 4-cm cubes.

These 4-cm cubes can be divided further into 2-cm cubes.

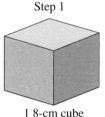

Step 1

1 8-cm cube
$V = 512$ cm^3

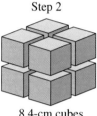

Step 2

8 4-cm cubes
$V = 512$ cm^3

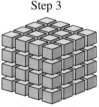

Step 3

64 2-cm cubes
$V = 512$ cm^3

a) Calculate the total surface area of the cubes in each step above.

b) Suppose you divided the 2-cm cubes in a fourth step. Determine the total surface area of the 1-cm cubes.

c) Look for a pattern in the total surface area from step to step. Suppose you know the surface area of the cubes in a step. How could you find the surface area of the cubes in the next step?

d) What is the surface area of the cubes in the tenth step?

11. Sugar cubes come in boxes of 144 cubes. There are 2 layers of cubes. Each layer forms a 12 by 6 rectangle. The company wants to design a box that uses less cardboard and still holds 144 sugar cubes.

a) Calculate the surface area of the box, in square units, that would enclose the cubes shown.

b) Determine three other ways to arrange 144 sugar cubes in a box. Calculate the surface area of each box.

c) How would you arrange 144 sugar cubes to use the least amount of cardboard?

d) Do you think it would be a good idea for sugar cube boxes to be redesigned? Why?

12. Mary bought some caramels at the bulk food store. She wants to pack them in a box. The caramels are 2 cm by 2 cm by 1 cm.

a) Mary found a box measuring 8 cm by 5 cm by 4 cm. What is the maximum number of caramels she can pack in this box? Explain your answers.

b) Mary found another box whose dimensions are double the dimensions of the box in part a. What is the maximum number of caramels she can pack in it?

13. If a spreadsheet program is available, use it to complete this exercise.

a) Measure a juice box. Calculate its total surface area.

b) Determine some dimensions of boxes that contain the same volume of juice, but have a smaller surface area.

c) Do you think it would be a good idea for juice box manufacturers to change the dimensions of their boxes? Explain.

14. If a spreadsheet program is available, use it to complete this exercise. The Acme Box Company makes boxes from pieces of cardboard 28.0 cm long and 21.6 cm wide. Equal squares are cut from each corner and the sides are folded up. Plain copy paper measures approximately 28.0 cm by 21.6 cm. On a piece of paper like this, draw lines 6 cm from each side. Cut a 6-cm square from each corner. Fold up the sides to make an open box.

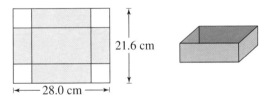

a) Calculate the volume of the box.

b) Suppose you change the size of the cutout square. Predict what will happen to the volume. Will it be the same, greater, or smaller?

c) To check your prediction, copy and complete the table below. Use lengths of the cutout square from 1 cm to 9 cm.
  i) The length of the cutout square increases from 1 cm to 9 cm. What happens to the volume of the box?
  ii) Suppose the length of the cutout square increases beyond 9 cm. What would happen to the volume of the box? What would happen if the length of the cutout square were less than 1 cm?

Length of the cutout square (cm)	Length of the box (cm)	Width of the box (cm)	Height of the box (cm)	Volume of the box (cm³)

d) Draw a graph of the volume of the open box against the length of the cutout square. Use the graph to answer these questions.

 i) What is the volume of the largest box that could be made from this size of cardboard? What size of square should be cut from the corners to make this box?

 ii) Suppose the Acme Box Company wanted to use the cardboard to make a box with a volume of 900 cm³. What size of square should be cut from the corners to make this box?

15. Here are two designs for a building.

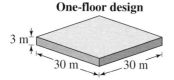

One-floor design

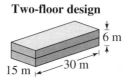

Two-floor design

a) Check that each building has 900 m² of floor space and a volume of 2700 m³.

b) For each design, calculate the total area of the roof and the four outside walls. Which building do you think is cheaper to heat in the winter? Explain.

c) Three other designs for the building are shown below. Check that each has 900 m² of floor space and a volume of 2700 m³.

 i) Two-floor design

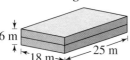

 ii) Three-floor design

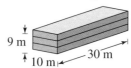

 iii) Four-floor design

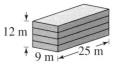

d) For each design, calculate the total area of the roof and the four outside walls. Are any of these likely to be cheaper to heat in the winter than those above? Explain.

e) For each design, calculate the ratio of surface area to volume. Record your results in a table. Is it better to have a high ratio of surface area to volume or a low ratio of surface area to volume? Explain.

Length (cm)	Width (cm)	Height (cm)	Volume (cm³)	Outside surface area (cm²)	Ratio of surface area to volume

16. For every rectangular prism, a surface area and a volume can be calculated. The surface area and the volume form an ordered pair (A, V) that can be plotted on a grid. If many points are plotted, you can investigate how surface areas and volumes of prisms are related. The instructions below assume that a program called SOLIDS has been transferred to your calculator.

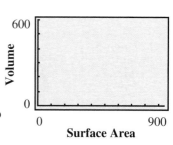

When you run the program, you must choose prisms or cylinders. Choose prisms. Then you must choose whether you want to plot ordered pairs (A, V) or (V, A). Choose either of these. The results will be graphed on screens with the scales shown.

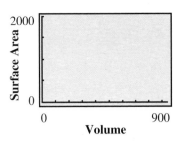

The calculator generates dimensions of rectangular prisms at random and calculates their surface areas and volumes. It then plots the points on a screen. When you have finished with the graph, press ENTER to quit the program.

a) Use the program to create a graph to show the relationship between the surface areas and volumes of rectangular prisms.

b) Copy the graph into your notebook. Describe the graph.

c) If you plotted enough points, you should see a curve on the screen. What kind of rectangular prism do you think corresponds to points that lie on the curve? Explain.

C 17. Refer to exercise 11. Sugar cubes measure 1.5 cm along each edge.

a) Calculate the surface area of the box for exercise 11a, in square centimetres.

b) Calculate the surface area of the box that uses the minimum amount of cardboard.

18. Refer to exercise 12.

a) Mary found a smaller box measuring 5 cm by 5 cm by 3 cm. What is the maximum number of caramels she can pack in this box? Explain.

b) Mary found another box whose dimensions are double the dimensions of the box in part a. What is the maximum number of caramels she can pack in it?

COMMUNICATING the IDEAS

Suppose you have several rectangular prisms, all with the same volume. In your journal explain how you could tell, just by looking, which one has the least surface area. Illustrate your answer with some examples.

Total Surface Area

You will need some tin cans with labels attached, a sharp knife, and a millimetre ruler.

Choose one can. What do you think *total surface area* means?
Devise a plan to calculate the total surface area of this can. Then use your plan to calculate the total surface area.

1. **a)** What did you notice about the shape of the label?

   b) How did you calculate the area of the label? What does this tell you about the area of the curved surface of the can?

2. How did you calculate the area of the bottom of the can?

3. What is the total surface area of the can?

4. Suppose a cylinder has radius, *r*, and height, *h*. Based on what you have discovered using the can, describe how to calculate the total surface area of the cylinder.

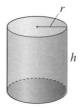

5. Write a formula for the total surface area, *A*, in terms of *r* and *h*. Compare your formula with other students' formulas.

Look at the cylinder, below left. Imagine there is a paper label on the cylinder. When you unroll the label, it forms a rectangle with length equal to the circumference of the cylinder. The width of the rectangle is equal to the height of the cylinder. The area of the curved surface of the cylinder is equal to the area of the rectangle. The total surface area includes the two circles at the ends.

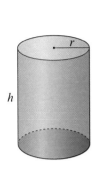

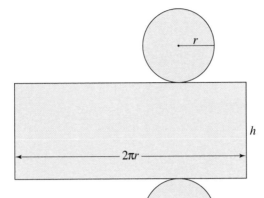

A cylinder has radius r and height h.
The area of the curved surface is:
A_{curved} = circumference × height
       = $2\pi rh$
The area of each end is:
$A_{base} = \pi r^2$
The total surface area is given by the formula:

$$A = A_{curved} + 2 \times A_{base}$$
or $A = 2\pi rh + 2\pi r^2$

Total Surface Area of a Cylinder

For a cylinder radius, r, height, h, the total suface area, $A = 2\pi rh + 2\pi r^2$

Boggle
your MIND

A 30-g drink box holds the same amount of beverage as a 400-g glass bottle. What if drink boxes replaced all glass containers? Do you think this would be a good idea? Why?

Example 1

A can of baked beans has the dimensions shown. Calculate its surface area.

Solution

Use the formula $A = 2\pi rh + 2\pi r^2$.
Substitute $r = 3.7$ and $h = 11.0$.

$A = 2\pi(3.7)(11.0) + 2\pi(3.7)^2$
$\doteq 341.742$

The surface area is approximately 341.7 cm^2.

3.7 cm

11.0 cm

HEINZ
Deep-Browned
BEANS
with
pork & tomato sauce

Example 2

A 60-cm cardboard tube is open at both ends. Its surface area is 950 cm^2.
Determine its radius to the nearest centimetre.

Solution

Since the cylinder is open at both ends, use
the formula for the curved surface area.
Use the formula $A = 2\pi rh$.
Substitute $A = 950$ and $h = 60$.

$\qquad 950 = 2\pi r(60)$
$\qquad 950 = 120\pi r$
$\qquad \dfrac{950}{120\pi} = r$ ——————— Key in: 950 ÷ 120 ÷ π to display 2.519953266
$\qquad 2.520 \doteq r$

The radius is approximately 2.5 cm.

DISCUSSING the IDEAS

1. Both *Examples 1* and *2* calculated the surface area of a cylinder. Explain why different formulas were used.

2. Explain how you can remember the formula for the surface area of a cylinder.

3. In *Example 1*, what calculator key strokes were used to calculate the surface area?

4. In *Example 1*, what is the surface area of the can in terms of π?

A **1.** Estimate the area of each circle. Calculate the area of each circle. Give the answers to 1 decimal place.

a)
10 cm

b)
8 cm

c)
6.7 cm

2. A net for a cylinder is shown.

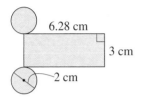
6.28 cm
3 cm
2 cm

a) Calculate the circumference of each circle.

b) Divide the length of the rectangle by 2π.

c) How does the length of the rectangle compare with the circumference of each circle?

d) Determine the total surface area of the cylinder.

3. Estimate the total surface area of each cylinder. Calculate the total surface area. Give the answers to 1 decimal place.

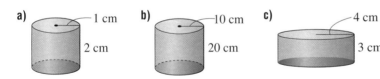

a) 1 cm, 2 cm   b) 10 cm, 20 cm   c) 4 cm, 3 cm   d) 2.2 cm, 12.4 cm

4. A cylinder has a radius of 10 cm and a height of 40 cm.

a) Calculate the surface area in terms of π.

b) Calculate the surface area to 2 decimal places.

5. One cylinder has a base radius of 3 cm and a height of 4 cm. Another cylinder has a base radius of 4 cm and a height of 3 cm. Do you think their total surface areas are equal? If not, which one do you think has the greater total surface area? Explain.

6. a) Check your answer to exercise 5 by calculating the total surface area of each cylinder.

b) What is the ratio of the total surface areas?

7. Estimate, then calculate the total surface area of each cylinder.

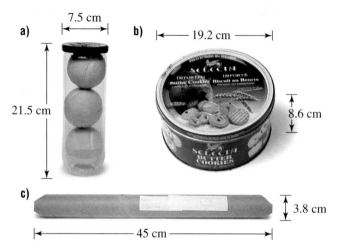

a) 7.5 cm, 21.5 cm

b) 19.2 cm, 8.6 cm

c) 45 cm, 3.8 cm

8. Mathematical Modelling The reticulated python of Southeast Asia is the world's longest snake. Use a cylinder as a model for a snake. Determine the length of a python with a surface area of 25 000 cm² and an average radius of 5 cm.

B **9.** A square piece of cardboard measuring 20 cm on a side is used to form the curved surface of a cylinder. Circles cut from another piece of cardboard are used for the top and the bottom.

20 cm

a) Calculate the radius of the cylinder to 2 decimal places.

b) Calculate the total surface area of the cylinder.

10. A juice can has a cardboard curved surface and two metal ends.

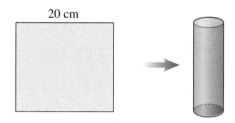

a) What area of cardboard is needed to make the can?

b) What is the area of each metal end?

c) What is the total surface area of the juice can?

6.6 cm

11.6 cm

11. Academic Focus

a) Factor the formula $A = 2\pi rh + 2\pi r^2$.

b) Complete *Example 1* using the factored formula.

c) In which form do you think it is easier to use the formula: factored form or non factored form? Explain.

12. Newsprint is one of Canada's major exports. It is shipped in cylindrical rolls. The rolls shown have a diameter of 102 cm and a length of 137 cm. What is the area of the outer wrapping of the roll?

Total Surface Areas of Cylinders with the Same Radius

Some cylinders have the same radius but different heights. How might their total surface areas be related?

To answer this question, you will need as many different cans as you can find that have the same radius and different heights. Without measuring, how can you be certain that all the cans have the same radius?

13. a) Measure the diameter and height of each can. Then calculate its radius and total surface area. Record these data in a table.

Height, h (cm)	Total surface area, A (cm^2)

b) Graph the data on a grid. Plot *Height* along the horizontal axis. Draw a straight line or smooth curve through the points.

c) Determine the *A*-intercept. What does this represent?

14. a) All the cans have the same radius r. Substitute your value of r into the formula $A = 2\pi rh + 2\pi r^2$. You will obtain an equation relating the total surface area of a can to its height h.

b) Compare your equation with your results in exercises 13b and c. What do you notice?

15. a) On the same screen:

    i) Graph your equation from exercise 14a.

    ii) Graph a scatter plot of the data from your table.

    iii) Graph the line of best fit for the data in your table, and determine its equation.

b) Compare the equation of the line of best fit with your equation from exercise 14a. Suggest some reasons for any discrepancies.

16. Why do you think manufacturers would make cans with the same radius but different heights?

C **17.** Calculate the total surface area of each object. Give the answers to 1 decimal place.

a)
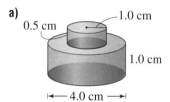

b)
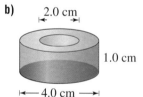

18. Academic Focus What happens to the total surface area of a cylinder in each case?

a) Its radius is not changed, but its height is: doubled; tripled; multiplied by n.

b) Its height is not changed, but its radius is: doubled; tripled; multiplied by n.

c) Both the height and the radius are: doubled; tripled; multiplied by n.

COMMUNICATING the IDEAS

In your journal, describe how you calculate the total surface area of a cylinder if you know its dimensions.

INVESTIGATION

Volume of a Cylinder

Work in a group. You will need an empty tin can, some centimetre cubes, and a millimetre ruler.

1. How many cubes will fit in one layer on the base of the can?

2. a) Describe a way you could use the centimetre cubes to determine the volume of the can.

b) Estimate the number of centimetre cubes you would need.

3. Measure the height and the diameter of the can.

a) How could you use your measurements to calculate the volume of the can?

b) Calculate the volume in cubic centimetres.

c) Compare your result with your previous estimate. If they are different, explain why.

4. Suppose a cylinder has radius, r, and height, h.

a) Write a formula for the volume, V, of the cylinder in terms of r and h.

b) Compare your formula with those of other groups.

Imagine that a cylinder is filled with layers of centimetre cubes. The number of cubes, including part cubes, needed to cover the base is equal to the area of the base. If you multiply this by the number of layers, the result is the total number of cubes that fill the can. This is the volume of the can.

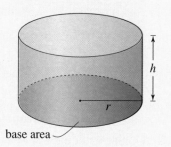

Volume of a Cylinder

The volume, V, of a cylinder with radius, r, and height, h, is given by the formula:

$$V = \text{base area} \times \text{height}$$
$$\text{or} \quad V = \pi r^2 h$$

Example

Depending what a building is used for, it must have a regulation number of air changes per hour. To plan a building's ventilation system to meet these regulations, a mechanical engineer needs to know the volume of space each floor of the building encloses.

The Peachtree Westin Plaza in Atlanta features a cylindrical hotel. The hotel has a base diameter of 60 m. Each floor of the hotel has an interior height of 3.5 m. Calculate the volume of space occupied by each floor of the hotel.

Solution

Use the formula $V = \pi r^2 h$.
The base radius is 30 m. Substitute $r = 30$ and $h = 3.5$.

$V = \pi r^2 h$
$= \pi \times 30^2 \times 3.5$
$\doteq 9896$

The volume of space occupied by each floor of the hotel is about 9900 m³.

DISCUSSING the IDEAS

1. Explain how you can remember the formula for the volume of a cylinder.

2. It is usually easier to measure the diameter of a cylinder instead of the radius. Explain how the formula for the volume of the cylinder would change if the diameter, d, were used instead of the radius, r.

3. **Mathematical Modelling** In the *Example*, give some reasons why the volume of space occupied by each floor of the hotel would be less than 9900 m³.

10.7 EXERCISES

1. Estimate, then calculate the area of each circle. Give the answers to 1 decimal place.

a)
12 cm

b)
0.4 cm

c)
9 cm

d)
6.5 cm

2. Estimate, then calculate the volume of each cylinder. Give the answers to 1 decimal place.

a)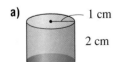
1 cm
2 cm

b)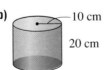
10 cm
20 cm

c)
4 cm
3 cm

d)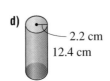
2.2 cm
12.4 cm

3. One litre is often represented by a cube measuring 10 cm along each edge.

   a) Calculate the volume of a cylinder that fits inside the cube.

   b) What percent of the space in the cube is occupied by the cylinder? Give the answers to 1 decimal place.

B **4.** A can of paint is marked 978 mL. It has a base diameter of 10.4 cm and a height of 12.5 cm. Calculate the volume of the can, in cubic centimetres. Does the result confirm that the can's capacity is 978 mL? Explain.

5. Calculate the volume of the cylinder formed if rectangle ABCD is rotated about:

   a) side AB   **b)** side BC

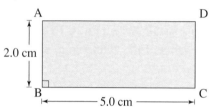

6. Academic Focus

   a) What happens to the volume of a cylinder if its radius is not changed, but its height is doubled? Tripled?

   b) What happens to the volume of a cylinder if its height is not changed, but its radius is doubled? Tripled?

   c) What happens if both the height and the radius are doubled? Tripled?

7. A circular log has a mass of 100 kg.

   a) A second log cut from the same tree has the same radius as this one but is half as long. What is the mass of the second log?

   b) A third log cut from the same tree has the same length as the first log but is one and a half times as thick as this one. What is the mass of the third log?

   c) A fourth log cut from the same tree is half as long and one and a half times as thick as this one. What is the mass of the fourth log?

8. a) Calculate the volume of the newsprint described in exercise 12 on page 475.

   b) Measure a newspaper. Estimate how many newspapers like this one could be printed from one roll of newsprint.

9. A roll of tape has an outside diameter of 58 mm and an inside diameter of 32 mm. The tape is 19 mm wide and 10 m long.

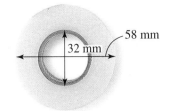

a) Calculate the volume of tape in the roll, in cubic millimetres.

b) Calculate the thickness of the tape.

10. Recall exercise 16, page 468, where you used the SOLIDS program to graph the relationship between the surface areas and volumes of prisms.

a) Use the SOLIDS program to create a graph to show the relationship between the surface areas and volumes of cylinders.

b) Copy the graph into your notebook. Describe the graph.

c) If you plotted enough points, you should see a curve on the screen. What kind of cylinder do you think corresponds to points that lie on the curve? Explain.

PROBLEM SOLVING FOCUS

Which Cylinder Has the Greater Volume?

You will need two congruent pieces of paper. Measure the length and width of the paper.

11. a) Roll one piece of paper to form a cylinder.

b) Roll the other piece of paper to form a different cylinder.

c) Determine the height and the base radius for each cylinder. Then calculate their volumes. Are the volumes the same? If not, which cylinder has the greater volume?

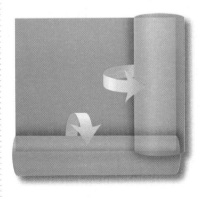

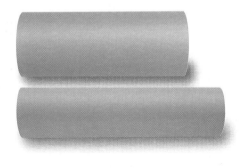

12. What shape would the paper have to be for the volumes to be equal?

13. Refer to the paper in exercise 11.

   a) Suppose another piece of paper had the same width, but was twice as long. How would the volumes of the two cylinders compare?

   b) Suppose another piece of paper had the same length, but was one-half as wide. How would the volumes of the two cylinders compare?

14. Determine the dimensions of a sheet of paper for which the volume of one cylinder is two times the volume of the other cylinder.

15. Determine the volume of each cylinder with the given dimensions. Give each answer to the nearest cubic centimetre.

   a) radius 5.00 cm; height 3.18 cm

   b) radius 7.50 cm; height 1.42 cm

   c) radius 3.99 cm; height 5.00 cm

   d) radius 3.26 cm; height 7.50 cm

   What do you notice about the volumes?

16. Calculate the volume of each object. Give the answers to 1 decimal place.

   a)

   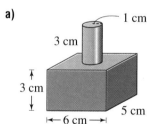

   b)

   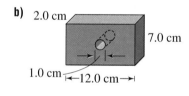

17. A machine bales hay in rolls 1.8 m in diameter and 1.2 m long.

   a) What is the radius of each roll?

   b) What volume of hay is in each roll?

18. **Academic Focus** Recall the activity on page 475, exercises 13 to 16. Conduct a similar investigation to determine how the volumes of cylinders with the same radius are related. Follow these steps:

- Create a table.
- Graph your results.
- From your graph, estimate volumes of cans with different heights.
- Obtain an equation that expresses the volume, *V*, of a can in terms of its height, *h*.
- Enter your data in a graphing calculator. Determine the equation of the line of best fit. Graph this line and your equation for *V* on a scatter plot of the data.

19. A cylindrical hot-water tank has a diameter of 56 cm and a height of 132 cm.

   a) Calculate the volume of the tank to the nearest cubic centimetre. What is the capacity of the tank in litres?

   b) Calculate the surface area of the tank to the nearest square centimetre.

20. Calculate the volume of each object in exercise 17, page 476.

21. A refinery has five cylindrical storage tanks each measuring 12.2 m in diameter and 24.4 m high. The tanks are full.

   a) What is the total storage capacity of the refinery?

   b) Tanker trucks have cylindrical tanks 11 m long and 1.8 m in diameter. How many truck loads would be needed to empty all the tanks of the refinery?

C 22. Get two tin cans with different sizes. Measure the cans. Suppose you were to fill the smaller can with water, then pour the water into the larger can.

   a) Calculate how deep the water would be in the larger can.

   b) Try the activity and measure the depth of the water. How does it compare with your calculations?

23. Two identical jars contain equal quantities of water and milk. Suppose a cup of milk were removed and mixed with the water. Then a cup of the mixture were removed and mixed with the milk. Would there be more milk in the water or more water in the milk? Explain your answer.

COMMUNICATING *the* IDEAS

In your journal, describe how you calculate the volume of a cylinder if you know its dimensions. Include in your account a formula for the volume in terms of the radius, *r*, and height, *h*, and a formula for the volume in terms of the diameter, *d*, and height, *h*.

10.8   Designing a Cooler: Part II

On pages 457 to 462, you designed a portable cooler in the shape of a rectangular prism that has a volume of 50 000 cm³ and a minimum surface area. You found that the optimal prism was a cube with edges about 36.8 cm.

In this section, we will assume that the shape of the cooler is a cylinder. In Section 10.12, we will consider other models, then you can decide upon the best design.

The Cylinder Model

You will begin by making some models, then you will use technology to analyze the models.

Part A Using a Physical Model

You will need some paper, a ruler, scissors, and tape or glue. You will construct three different paper cylinders all with a volume of 125 cm³.

1. a) Choose any measurement between 1.6 cm and 4.0 cm as the radius of the cylinder.

  b) Calculate the area of the base.

  c) Divide the volume by the area to determine the height of the cylinder.

2. a) Use the radius in exercise 1a to calculate the circumference of the base.

  b) Construct a rectangle whose length is equal to the circumference of the base, and whose height is equal to the height you found in exercise 1c.

  c) Calculate the area of the rectangle.

  d) Cut out the rectangle, and tape it to form the curved part of the cylinder.

  e) Visualize the circular base and top of your cylinder. Calculate the total surface area of the cylinder, including the base and the top.

3. Repeat exercises 1 and 2 (using different radii in exercise 1a) to create three cylinders.

4. All your cylinders should have a circular base and a volume of 125 cm³.

  a) Compare the surface areas of the three cylinders.

  b) Calculate the diameters of the bases of the three cylinders.

  c) Compare the heights of the cylinders with the diameters of their bases.

  d) Choose the cylinder that has the least surface area. How does its height compare with the diameter of its base?

In exercises 1 and 2, you used three different radii. Although one of your cylinders had a surface area smaller than the others, other cylinders could have still smaller surface areas. Visualize changing the shape of the cylinder, but keeping its volume as 125 cm^3.

A short, wide design has tops and bottoms with large areas.

A tall, narrow design has a curved surface with a large area.

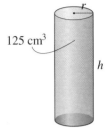

You can use technology to calculate the surface areas for many different radii. Then you can determine the dimensions that produce the minimum surface area more accurately. Whether you use a spreadsheet or a graphing calculator, the first step is the same. You must set up the spreadsheet or the graphing calculator to do the same calculations as for exercises 1 and 2.

If you are using a spreadsheet, complete Part B and Part D.
If you are using a TI-83 calculator, complete Part C and Part D.

Part B Using a Spreadsheet

Recall what you did in exercises 1 and 2:

- You started with a radius for the base.
- You calculated the area of the base.
- You divided 125 by the area to calculate the height.
- You constructed a rectangle and used it to form the cylinder.
- You calculated the area of the rectangle, and the areas of the top and the bottom to determine the total surface area.

5. Set up a spreadsheet similar to the one below. Copy the formulas in cells B3, C3, and D3 into row 4. Then Fill Down the formulas in row 4 until the areas in column D begin to increase.

	A	B	C	D
1	Minimizing the Surface Area of a Cylinder			
2	Base Radius	Base Area	Height	Surface Area
3	1.6	= PI( )*A3^2	=125/B3	=2*B3+2*PI( )*A3*C3
4	=A3+0.5			

a) Explain how the formulas in row 3 represent the steps in exercises 1 and 2.

b) What is the minimum surface area? For what radius does it occur?

6. Consider the cylinder that has the minimum surface area.

 a) What is the base diameter of this cylinder?

 b) How does its height compare with its base diameter?

 c) Graph surface area against height. How does the graph confirm your result in exercise 5b?

7. Up to now, you have been using a cylinder with a volume of 125 cm³. Suppose the volume were different.

 a) Predict how the height of the cylinder with minimum surface area would be related to the base diameter.

 b) Choose a volume that is much larger or much smaller than 125 cm³. Make the appropriate change to the formula in cell C3. Fill Down the new formula in column C.

 c) Do the results confirm your prediction? Explain.

Go to Part D.

Part C Using a Graphing Calculator

You will create a graph with *Base radius* along the horizontal axis and *Surface area* along the vertical axis. In the Y= list, enter a formula to calculate the areas. This formula will depend only on the base radius, *r* centimetres.

8. To determine the formula, recall what you did in exercises 1 and 2.

 a) First, you started with a base radius and calculated the area of the base. Suppose the base radius is *r* centimetres. Write an expression for the area.

 b) Then, you divided 125 by the area to determine the height. Write an expression for the height.

 c) Next, you used the base radius and height to calculate the surface area. Write a formula for the surface area, *A*, of the cylinder in terms of *r*.

You can use a graphing calculator to graph surface area against base radius. Then you can trace to determine the minimum area.

Setup

Clear any plots. Clear any equations in the Y= list. To set up the graphing window, use the base radii and surface areas from exercises 1 and 2 to help you decide appropriate values for Xmin, Xmax, Ymin, and Ymax. Press $\boxed{\text{MODE}}$, and set the display to show values to 2 decimal places.

9. a) In exercise 8c, you should have found that the formula for surface area is $A = 2\pi r^2 + \frac{250}{r}$. Enter the equation $y = 2\pi x^2 + \frac{250}{x}$ in the Y= list.

 b) Press $\boxed{\text{TRACE}}$, and trace along the curve until the value of *y* is as small as possible. Record the values of *x* and *y*.

The value of y represents the minimum surface area of the cylinder. The value of x represents the base radius of the cylinder that has the minimum surface area. Now you can calculate the height of this cylinder.

10. Consider the cylinder that has the minimum surface area.

  a) Use your results from exercise 8 to calculate the height of this cylinder.

  b) What is the base diameter of this cylinder?

  c) How does its height compare with its base diameter?

11. Up to now, you have been using a cylinder with a volume of 125 cm^3. Suppose the volume were different.

  a) Predict how the height of the cylinder with minimum surface area would be related to the base diameter.

  b) Choose a volume that is much larger or much smaller than 125 cm^3. Make the appropriate change to the equation in the Y= list and repeat exercises 8 to 10.

  c) Do the results confirm your prediction?

Part D Looking Back

12. You should have found that the height of the cylinder that has the minimum surface area is approximately equal to the base diameter.

  a) Suggest a possible reason why the height you obtained is not equal to the base diameter.

  b) Describe how you could determine the dimensions more accurately.

13. In general, suppose a cylinder has a given volume. Suppose also that it minimum possible surface area.

  a) Describe the cylinder.

  b) Describe how the diameter and the height are related to the volume.

14. You have determined the dimensions of the cylinder with volume 125 cm^3 and minimum surface area. This is the *optimal* cylinder.

  a) Construct the rectangle whose length is equal to the circumference of the optimal cylinder and whose width is equal to the height of the optimal cylinder.

  b) Cut out the rectangle and tape or glue it together to form the curved part of the optimal cylinder.

  c) Compare this cylinder with the ones you constructed in exercises 1 to 3.

Whether you used a graphing calculator or a spreadsheet, you should have discovered the following result. The result is true for all cylinders.

These cylinders have the same volume and different surface areas. For the minimum surface area, the height of the cylinder equals its base diameter.

Minimum surface area
height = diameter

Consider again the question posed on page 457 (for a cylinder). We now know that the optimal cylinder containing a volume of 50 000 cm^3 has equal height and diameter. We can calculate these values and the surface area.

Let r centimetres represent the radius of the cylinder. Hence, both the diameter and the height are represented by $2r$ centimetres. Since the volume is 50 000 cm^3, then

$$\pi r^2 \times 2r = 50\ 000$$
$$2\pi r^3 = 50\ 000$$

This equation can be solved in different ways. Here are some possible methods:

- Use systematic trial to find a value of r that makes the left side approximately 50 000.
- Solve the equation algebraically for r and use a calculator to determine its value.
- Use a graphing calculator to graph the equation $y = 2\pi r^3$, and trace to the point where y is approximately 50 000.

15. a) Solve the equation $2\pi r^3 = 50\ 000$ to determine the radius of the optimal cylinder.

b) Determine the diameter and the height of the optimal cylinder.

c) Calculate the surface area of the optimal cylinder.

d) Check that the volume of the optimal cylinder is 50 000 cm^3.

COMMUNICATING the IDEAS

Write a report to describe your design for the 50-L cooler, assuming that it has the shape of a cylinder. Refer to *Communicating the Ideas* on page 462. Compare the cylindrical cooler with the cubical cooler.

Triangular pyramid

Pentagonal pyramid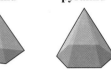

Rectangular pyramid

Hexagonal pyramid

A *pyramid* is a solid with a base that is a polygon. The other faces are triangles with a common vertex.

INVESTIGATION 1

Surface Area of a Pyramid

1. Here is a net for a pyramid.

  a) Identify the base and the triangular faces.

  b) Predict the type of pyramid you would form if you fold the net.

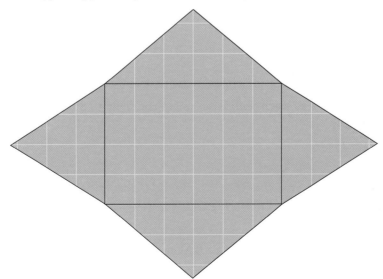

You will need 1-cm grid paper, scissors, and a millimetre ruler.

2. Draw the net on page 489 on 1-cm grid paper. Cut out the net.

3. Fold the net to make the pyramid. Identify the type of pyramid.

4. Explain how you could determine the surface area of the pyramid you have constructed.

   a) How many faces does the pyramid have?

   b) Are any faces congruent? Identify congruent faces.

   c) Determine the area of each face.

   d) Determine the surface area of the pyramid.

5. How could you find the surface area of a square pyramid?

6. How could you find the surface area of a triangular pyramid?

To calculate the surface area of a pyramid, calculate the total area of its faces.

Example 1

The Great Pyramid in Egypt was originally constructed with a smooth limestone surface. Over the ages, this limestone was removed and used on other buildings. Each face of the Great Pyramid is a triangle with base 229 m and height 185 m. Calculate the total area of the four triangular faces of the pyramid.

Solution

There are four triangular faces, each with base 229 m and height 185 m. The area of each face is

$$\frac{\text{base} \times \text{height}}{2} = \frac{229 \text{ m} \times 185 \text{ m}}{2}$$

$$= 21\ 182.5 \text{ m}^2$$

The total area of all four faces is
$4 \times 21\ 182.5 \text{ m}^2 = 84\ 730 \text{ m}^2$

To the nearest 1000 m², the surface area is 85 000 m².

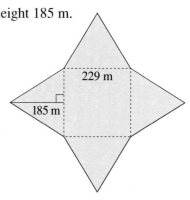

Surface Area of a Cone

You will need paper, a millimetre ruler, a protractor, compasses, scissors, and tape.

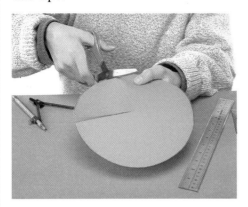

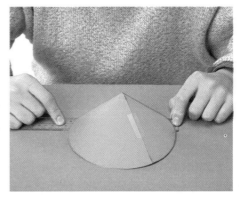

Step 1 Construct a circle with any convenient radius. Draw a radius, and draw another radius perpendicular to it. Cut out the larger part of the circle. What fraction of the circle is this part?

Step 2 Tape your part circle to form a cone. Measure the height, *h*, of the cone What shape is the base of the cone? What is the radius, *r*, of the base? Record your values of *h* and *r*. Use these values to complete the calculations in *Steps 3* and *4*.

Step 3 *h* and *r* are the measures of two sides of a right triangle. Use the Pythagorean Theorem to calculate the length of the third side. How is the length of this side related to the part circle you cut out in *Step 1*?

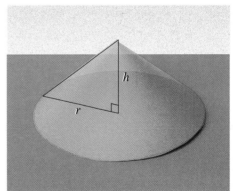

Step 4 Calculate the circumference of the base of the cone. How does this compare with the circumference of the circle in *Step 1*?

1. How does the surface area of the cone compare with the area of the circle in *Step 1*?

2. Calculate the area of the curved surface of the cone.

Suppose a cone has base radius, *r*, and height, *h*. There is a formula for the area of the curved surface, but it is not as simple as the other formulas in this chapter. Instead of using a formula, it is better to calculate the area as follows.

The area of the curved surface is equal to the area of part of a circle. Calculate the radius of the part circle using the Pythagorean Theorem.

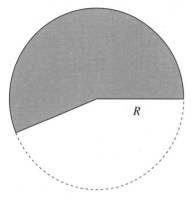
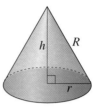

Then calculate the area of the curved surface of the cone using this equation:

$$\frac{\text{Area of cone}}{\text{Area of circle}} = \frac{\text{Circumference of cone}}{\text{Circumference of circle}}$$

The total surface area of a cone is the sum of the area of the curved surface and the area of the base.

Boggle
your MIND

The Banff Springs Hotel in Banff, Alberta uses about 87 000 rolls of toilet paper every year. What is the volume of toilet paper used at the hotel in one year? About how far would the paper reach if it were unrolled and put in a line?

Example 2

Hands Fireworks manufactures 6 different conical fireworks.
One of these, the Volcano, has a base radius of 3.3 cm and
a height of 18 cm. What area of paper is needed to cover
the curved surface of this firework?

Solution

Visualize cutting the curved surface and flattening it.
The paper will form part of a circle. The area of the curved
surface of the cone is equal to the area of the part of the circle.

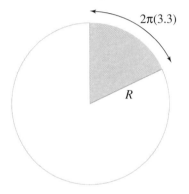

Calculate the radius, R, of the part circle using the
Pythagorean Theorem.

$$R^2 = 3.3^2 + 18^2$$
$$= 334.89$$
$$R = \sqrt{334.89}$$

Calculate the area of the curved surface of the cone using
this equation:

$$\frac{\text{Area of cone}}{\text{Area of circle}} = \frac{\text{Circumference of cone}}{\text{Circumference of circle}}$$

$$\frac{\text{Area of cone}}{\pi \times (\sqrt{334.89})^2} = \frac{2\pi \times 3.3}{2\pi \times \sqrt{334.89}}$$

$$\frac{\text{Area of cone}}{334.89\pi} = \frac{3.3}{\sqrt{334.89}}$$

$$\text{Area of cone} = \frac{334.89\pi \times 3.3}{\sqrt{334.89}}$$

$$\doteq 189.72$$

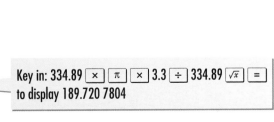

Key in: 334.89 $\boxed{\times}$ $\boxed{\pi}$ $\boxed{\times}$ 3.3 $\boxed{\div}$ 334.89 $\boxed{\sqrt{x}}$ $\boxed{=}$
to display 189.720 7804

The area of paper needed to cover the curved surface of the firework is
approximately 190 cm^2.

1. The method to find the surface area of a cone on page 492 applies only to a *right circular cone*.

   a) What information on the diagram on page 492 suggests why the cone is called a right circular cone?

   b) Visualize a cone that is not a right circular cone. Describe how it is different from the cone on page 492.

   c) Explain why the method used in this section cannot be used to determine the surface area of the cone you described in part b.

2. In *Example 2*, the height of the cone is 18 cm and the base radius is 3.3 cm. Suppose the height remains the same but the base radius changes.

   a) Describe what happens to the shape of the cone when the base radius becomes larger and larger, and when it becomes smaller and smaller.

   b) Describe what happens to the area of the curved surface of the cone when the base radius becomes larger and larger, and when it becomes smaller and smaller.

3. In *Example 2*, suppose the base radius remains the same but the height changes.

   a) Describe what happens to the shape of the cone when the height becomes larger and larger, and when it becomes smaller and smaller.

   b) Describe what happens to the area of the curved surface of the cone when the height becomes larger and larger, and when it becomes smaller and smaller.

10.9 EXERCISES

1. In *Example 1*, we did not include the areas of all the faces of the pyramid. How can you tell whether to include the areas of all the faces or just some of them?

2. **a)** How does the area of the faces in the pyramid in *Example 1* compare with the area of the walls in your classroom?

   b) How many classrooms like yours would you need to have walls with the same total area as the walls in the pyramid?

3. In *Example 1*, the square pyramid has four congruent triangular faces.

   a) How many congruent faces are there in a triangular pyramid? Explain.

   b) How many congruent faces are there in a hexagonal pyramid? Explain.

4. One cone has a base radius of 4 cm and a height of 3 cm. Another cone has a base radius of 3 cm and a height of 4 cm. Do you think their total surface areas are the same? If not, which one do you think has the greater total surface area? Give a reason for your answer.

5. a) Check your answer to exercise 4 by calculating the total surface area of each cone.

b) What is the ratio of the total surface areas?

6. Which net folds to make a pyramid? Explain how you know.

a)

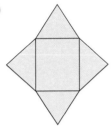

b)

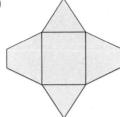

7. Determine the surface area of each pyramid. Give the answer to 1 decimal place.

a)

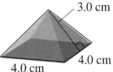

3.0 cm
4.0 cm
4.0 cm

b)

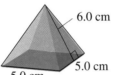

6.0 cm
5.0 cm
5.0 cm

c)

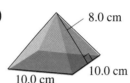

8.0 cm
10.0 cm
10.0 cm

8. Determine the area of the curved surface of each cone. Give the answer to 1 decimal place where necessary.

a)

12 cm
5 cm

b)

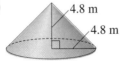

4.8 m
4.8 m

c)

40 cm
50 cm

9. Determine the surface area of each tetrahedron to 1 decimal place.

a)

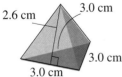

2.6 cm
3.0 cm
3.0 cm
3.0 cm

b)

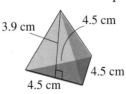

3.9 cm
4.5 cm
4.5 cm
4.5 cm

10. Determine the total surface area of each cone. Give the answer to 1 decimal place where necessary.

a)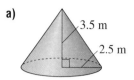
3.5 m
2.5 m

b)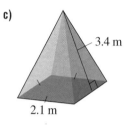
55 cm
15 cm

c)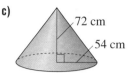
72 cm
54 cm

11. Determine the surface area of each pyramid.

a)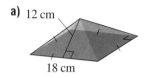
12 cm
18 cm

b)
33 cm
34 cm
18 cm
25 cm

c)
3.4 m
2.1 m

 12. Draw a net for each described pyramid. Determine its surface area to 1 decimal place.

a) a square base with side length 5.5 cm, triangular faces with height 8.4 cm

b) a rectangular base 12.00 cm by 7.50 cm, the triangular face on the longer side has height 14.25 cm, the triangular face on the shorter side has height 15.00 cm

c) each face an equilateral triangle with side lengths 4.1 cm

 13. Set up a spreadsheet document.

a) Design a spreadsheet that will calculate the area of the four faces of a square pyramid. Use the solution to *Example 1*, page 490 to help you. Use the dimensions in *Example 1* to check your spreadsheet.

b) Change the spreadsheet so that it will calculate the total surface area of a pyramid. Use the pyramids in exercise 11 to check your spreadsheet.

14. The Louvre is a famous art gallery in Paris, France. It is housed in a historic palace and was opened in 1793. In 1989, it was expanded. One addition is a large glass square pyramid that covers the main entrance. Each wall of this pyramid is a triangle with base 35.4 m and height 27.9 m. Calculate the surface area of the glass in the pyramid.

15. A carpenter is building two playhouses for a day-care centre. The roof of each playhouse is a pyramid. One roof has a square base with length 3.8 m. The height of each triangular face is 4.2 m. The other roof has a rectangular base 1.9 m by 2.6 m. The heights of the triangular faces are 2.4 m and 2.2 m, respectively. For each playhouse, the roof sits on walls 1 m high.

    a) How much wood is needed for each playhouse?

    b) Which playhouse needs more wood?

    c) Suppose wood costs $15.25/m². How much would it cost to build each playhouse?

16. The square base of a pyramid has side lengths of 6 cm. Each triangular face has a height of 10 cm.

    a) Determine the surface area of the pyramid.

    b) Determine the surface area of the pyramid if the side lengths and height are doubled.

    c) Determine the surface area of the pyramid if the side lengths and height are tripled.

    d) Compare your answers for parts a, b, and c. What do you notice?

17. For Halloween, a clown's hat is made by stapling together the straight edges of a quarter of a circle with radius 30.0 cm.

    a) What is the radius of the base of the hat?

    b) How high is the hat?

    c) What is the area of the material used to make the hat?

18. A cone has base radius, r, and height, h. Determine a formula in terms of r and h for:

    a) the area of the curved surface, C

    b) the total surface area, A

19. A cone just fits inside a cubical box. The box has edges of length x centimetres.

    a) Determine a formula for the total surface area, A, of the cone in terms of x.

    b) Predict what the graph of A against x would look like.

    c) Use a graphing calculator to check your prediction in part b.

In your journal, describe how you calculate the surface area of a cone and a pyramid if you know their dimensions. Illustrate your description with some examples.

ACADEMIC FOCUS

Comparing a Pyramid and a Cone

You will create a pyramid that has the same base and the same height as a cube. You will determine the relationship between the volume of the pyramid and the volume of the cube.

Volume of a Pyramid

1. Create a cube by assembling an enlargement of this net.

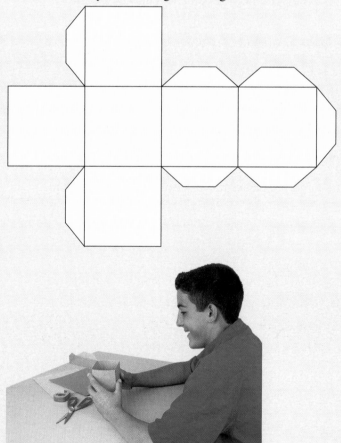

2. Create a pyramid by assembling an enlargement of this net.

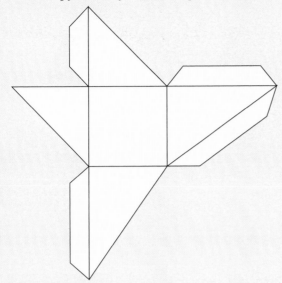

3. Estimation Estimate how the volume of the pyramid compares with the volume of the cube.

4. Create two more pyramids like the first one.

5. Arrange your three pyramids to form a cube. Tape the pyramids together.

6. How is the volume of one pyramid related to the volume of the cube?

A pyramid with a square base is only one of many types of pyramids. Whether a pyramid has a triangular base, a rectangular base, or any other base, its volume is always one-third the volume of the corresponding prism.

Volume of each pyramid = $\frac{1}{3}$ × volume of corresponding prism

7. Suppose the bases of the pyramids above were regular polygons. Suppose also that the number of sides increases as shown on page 500.

a) Describe what happens to the pyramids.

b) Describe what happens to the corresponding prisms.

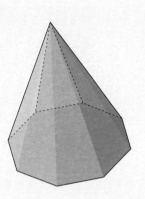
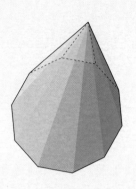
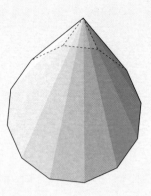

8. Visualize a cone that fits inside a cylinder. How is the volume of the cone related to the volume of the cylinder?

When a rectangular pyramid just fits inside a rectangular prism, you can fill the pyramid three times and pour its contents into the prism. Then the prism will be full.

This is because the volume of a prism is exactly three times the volume of a rectangular pyramid with the same base and the same height. That is, the volume of the pyramid is one-third the volume of the prism.

Volume of a Rectangular Pyramid

The volume of a rectangular pyramid with base dimensions l and w, and height h is given by the formula:

$$V = \frac{1}{3} \times \text{base area} \times \text{height}$$

or $\quad V = \frac{1}{3}lwh$

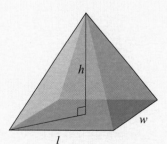

When a cone just fits inside a cylindrical can, you can fill the cone three times and pour its contents into the can. Then the can will be full.

These three volumes taken together …

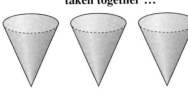

… are equal to this volume.

This is because the volume of a cylinder is exactly three times the volume of a cone with the same height and the same base radius. That is, the volume of the cone is one-third the volume of the cylinder.

Volume of a Cone

The volume of a cone with radius, r, and height, h, is given by the formula:

$V = \frac{1}{3} \times$ base area $\times$ height

or $V = \frac{1}{3}\pi r^2 h$

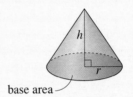

base area

Example 1

Academic Focus Recall the Great Pyramid in Egypt from *Example 1*, page 490. It has a square base about 229 m long and a height of about 147 m. Calculate the volume of stone used to create this pyramid.

Solution

Use the formula $V = \frac{1}{3} \times$ base area $\times$ height.
The base area is 229^2 m². The height is 147 m.
Substitute these values in the formula.

$V = \frac{1}{3} \times 229^2 \times 147$
  $= 2\,569\,609$

To the nearest 1000 m³, the volume is 2 570 000 m³.

Example 2

Coke is one by-product of Suncor's crude oil plant in Fort McMurray, Alberta. This fuel is used to produce electricity and steam for other parts of Suncor's operations. The coke is stored in large, conical piles. When Suncor's engineers have to assess how much coke is in a pile, they survey it to measure the height and the diameter of the base. They input this information in a computer which then calculates the volume of the pile. Suppose a coke pile has a base diameter of 20 m and a height of 8 m. Calculate the volume of coke in the pile.

Solution

The base radius is 10 m.
Substitute $r = 10$ and $h = 8$.
Use the formula $V = \frac{1}{3}\pi r^2 h$.
$V = \frac{1}{3} \times \pi \times 10^2 \times 8$
$\doteq 838$
The volume of the pile is about 840 m^3.

DISCUSSING the IDEAS

1. **Academic Focus** Recall the pyramids you constructed in the *Investigation*.

   a) Explain how these pyramids are different from others you may have seen.

   b) What is a pyramid?

2. **Academic Focus: Mathematical Modelling** Refer to *Example 1*.

   a) What assumptions are being made about the Great Pyramid?

   b) Do you think these assumptions are reasonable? Explain.

   c) Was the volume of stone used to create the pyramid more or less than the volume in *Example 1*, or do you need more information to answer this question? Explain.

3. **Mathematical Modelling** In *Example 2*, give some reasons why the volume of coke is probably less than 838 m^3.

A **1. Academic Focus** How does the formula for the volume of a rectangular pyramid compare with the formula for the volume of a cone?

2. Academic Focus The diagrams show three views of the same rectangular prism. How do the volumes of the three pyramids compare? Explain your answer.

3. Academic Focus Determine the volume of each pyramid.

a)

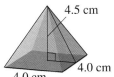

4.5 cm

4.0 cm
4.0 cm

b)

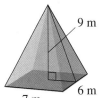

9 m

7 m
6 m

c)

12.2 m

9.5 m
9.5 m

4. A cylinder has volume 96 cm³. What is the volume of a cone that just fits inside the cylinder?

5. A cone has volume 54 cm³. What is the volume of a cylinder that just holds the cone?

6. One litre is often represented by a cube measuring 10 cm along each edge.

a) Calculate the volumes of a cylinder and a cone that fit inside the cube.

b) What percent of the space in the cube is occupied by the cylinder? By the cone? Give the answers to 1 decimal place.

7. A cone and a cylinder have the same base. Suppose they also have the same volume. How are their heights related? Explain.

8. Determine the volume of each cone.

a)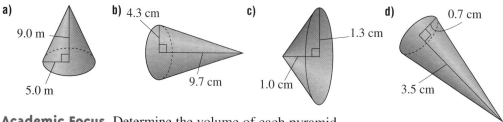
9.0 m
5.0 m

b) 4.3 cm
9.7 cm

c) 1.3 cm
1.0 cm

d) 0.7 cm
3.5 cm

B **9. Academic Focus** Determine the volume of each pyramid.

    a) base 12 m by 12 m, height 4 m   **b)** base 24 m by 12 m, height 4 m

    c) base 12 m by 12 m, height 8 m   **d)** base 12 m by 12 m, height 16 m

10. Academic Focus A cube is divided into six congruent pyramids. The base of each pyramid is a face of the cube. The edges of the cube are 30 cm long. What is the volume of each pyramid?

11. Academic Focus What happens to the volume of a rectangular pyramid if:

    a) its base is not changed, but its height is doubled? Tripled?

    b) its height and base width are not changed, but its base length is doubled? Tripled?

    c) its height is not changed, but both its base length and width are doubled? Tripled?

    d) all three of its dimensions are doubled? Tripled?

12. Academic Focus The Louvre is a famous art gallery in Paris, France. See exercise 14, page 496 for information about the Louvre. Calculate the volume of the pyramid over the main entrance to the Louvre.

13. Academic Focus The Muttart Conservatory in Edmonton consists of two large and two small pyramids. Each small pyramid has a square base of side length 19.5 m and a height of 18.0 m. The dimensions of each large pyramid are about 1.3 times as great as these.

    a) How many times as great as the volume of a small pyramid is the volume of a large pyramid?

    b) Compare the method you used to solve part a with the method used by other students. Explain any differences.

14. Determine the volume of each cone, to 2 decimal places.

    a) base radius 1.6 cm, height 3.5 cm   **b)** base radius 0.35 m, height 1.8 m

    c) height 27 cm, base radius 8 cm   **d)** height 57 cm, base radius 42 cm

15. A cone-shaped funnel has radius 5.7 cm and height 4.3 cm. How much can the funnel hold? Express your answer to 1 decimal place.

16. A farmer stores feed in a cone-shaped storage unit. The storage unit has base diameter 14.3 m and height 27.4 m. How much feed can this unit store?

17. An engineer is designing a cone-shaped storage unit to hold 5000 m³ of sand. The unit has base radius 15 m. What is its height, to 1 decimal place?

18. Cone A has base radius 25 cm and height 10 m. Cone B has height 25 cm and base radius 10 m. Which cone has the greater volume? Explain.

C 19. A cone has volume 47 cm³. It has a height of 5 cm. Determine the length of the radius of the base, to 1 decimal place.

20. A cone has volume 376 m³. The diameter of its base is 12 m. Determine the height of the cone, to 1 decimal place.

21. Calculate the volume of the cone formed if right △ABC is rotated about:

    a) side AB   **b)** side BC

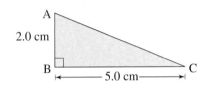

22. Construct the three figures shown. Make a cone from each figure by joining the straight edges and securing them with tape.

    i) 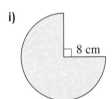   **ii)**   **iii)**

    a) Without measuring, determine the base radius, the height, and the volume of each cone to the nearest tenth of a unit.

    b) Measure to confirm your answers for the radius and the height.

    c) **Academic Focus** Determine the area of the curved surface of each cone to the nearest tenth of a square centimetre.

COMMUNICATING *the* **IDEAS**

In your journal, describe how you calculate the volume of a cone. Include in your account:

- an explanation of how the volumes of cones are related to the volumes of cylinders with the same base and the same height
- a description of the information you need about a cone before you can calculate its volume

This photograph of Mars shows spectacular features of its surface. Mars approximates a sphere.

A sphere is like a ball. All the points on the sphere are the same distance from the *centre*. A line segment joining the centre to any point on the sphere is called its *radius, r*. The *diameter, d,* of a sphere is twice as long as its radius.

Surface Area of a Sphere

You will need an orange that is nearly spherical, a millimetre ruler, and some 1-cm grid paper.

Step 1
Measure the diameter of the orange as accurately as you can.

Step 2
Peel the orange and arrange the pieces on the grid paper. Press them down to make them as flat as possible, and trace around them.

Step 3

By counting full squares and part squares, estimate the area of the orange peel in square centimetres.

Step 4

Divide the area by the square of the diameter of the orange. Record the result.

1. Repeat *Steps 1* to *4* with a different orange. Determine the mean of the results in *Step 4*.

2. How does the area of the peel in *Step 3* compare with the surface area of the orange?

3. What probable conclusion can you make about the ratio of the surface area of a sphere to the square of its diameter?

4. Suppose a sphere has diameter, *d*. Write a formula for its surface area, *A*.

INVESTIGATION 2

Volume of a Sphere

You will need an empty 355-mL frozen orange juice can, a millimetre ruler, an old tennis ball, a sharp knife, masking tape, some water, and an overflow container.

Step 1

Measure the diameter of the tennis ball. Carefully cut the can so that its inside height is equal to the diameter of the ball.

Step 2

Place the can in the overflow container. Fill the can to the top with water, but do not allow it to overflow. Make sure there is no water in the overflow container.

Step 3

Soak the ball with water. Then slowly place it in the can, allowing the water to overflow into the container. Push the ball right down to the bottom of the can.

Step 4

Take the can out of the overflow container, remove the ball, and empty the can. Then pour the water from the overflow container into the can. Measure the depth of the water.

1. How do you think the volume of the water in the can at the end of *Step 4* compares with the volume of the ball? Discuss your answer with other students.

2. At the end of *Step 4*, what fraction of the can is filled with water?

3. In this *Investigation*, the diameter of the cylinder is equal to its height. The sphere has the same diameter as the cylinder. What probable conclusion can you make about the volume of the sphere compared with the volume of the cylinder?

4. Suppose both the cylinder and the sphere have radius r. Write formulas for the volumes, V_C and V_S, of the cylinder and the sphere.

In *Investigation 1*, you probably discovered that the surface area of a sphere is approximately 3 times the square of its diameter. Using more advanced mathematics, it can be shown that the surface area, A, of a sphere with diameter, d, is exactly πd^2.

Since $d = 2r$,

we write: $A = \pi(2r)^2$

$\qquad\quad = 4\pi r^2$

The surface area of a sphere with radius, r, is $A = 4\pi r^2$.

In *Investigation 2*, you probably discovered that the volume of a sphere is approximately $\frac{2}{3}$ the volume of the cylinder into which it just fits. Using more advanced mathematics, it can be shown that the volume of the sphere is exactly $\frac{2}{3}$ the volume of the cylinder. If the sphere has radius r, then the cylinder has base radius r and height $2r$. Hence, the volume of the sphere is:

$V = \frac{2}{3} \times$ volume of cylinder

$\quad = \frac{2}{3} \times \pi r^2 h$

$\quad = \frac{2}{3} \times \pi r^2 \times 2r$

$\quad = \frac{4}{3}\pi r^3$

The volume of a sphere with radius, r, is $V = \frac{4}{3}\pi r^3$.

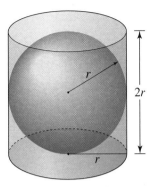

Sphere

Surface area, $A = 4\pi r^2$

Volume, $V = \frac{4}{3}\pi r^3$

Example

The mean radius of Earth is approximately 6365 km. Calculate the surface area and the volume of Earth.

Solution

Visualize Earth as a sphere. Substitute 6365 for r in the formulas for the surface area and volume of a sphere.

$A = 4\pi r^2$ $V = \frac{4}{3}\pi r^3$

$\quad = 4 \times \pi \times 6365^2$ $\quad = \frac{4}{3} \times \pi \times 6365^3$

$\quad \doteq 5.1 \times 10^8$ $\quad \doteq 1.1 \times 10^{12}$

The surface area of Earth is approximately 5.1×10^8 km^2. Its volume is approximately 1.1×10^{12} km^3.

1. In the *Example*, suppose you use the decimal approximation for π, 3.14, instead of the $\boxed{\pi}$ key on a calculator. How would this affect the final answers?

2. Explain why the formula for the surface area of a sphere contains r^2 while the formula for the volume contains r^3.

3. **Mathematical Modelling** Earth is not spherical. It is flattened at the poles. Its polar radius is 8 km less than its mean radius, while its equatorial radius is 13 km more than its mean radius.

   a) Calculate Earth's volume using the polar radius and the equatorial radius.

   b) Would the actual volume be closer to the volume obtained using the polar radius or the volume obtained using the equatorial radius? Explain.

10.11 EXERCISES

1. Calculate the surface area and volume of each sphere. Give the volumes to the nearest whole unit. The radius is given.

a)

10 cm

b)

5 cm

c)

15.2 cm

2. Calculate the surface area and the volume of each ball.

Sport	Diameter of ball (cm)
a) Baseball	7.4
b) Golf	4.3
c) Table tennis	3.7
d) Volleyball	20.9

3. In this self-portrait, the Dutch artist, M.C. Escher, is holding a reflecting sphere.

   a) Estimate the diameter of the sphere in this picture.

   b) Use your estimate. Calculate the surface area and the volume of the sphere.

4. The radius of Uranus is almost 4 times as great as the radius of Earth. The radius of the moon is approximately $\frac{1}{4}$ that of Earth. Use the information in the *Example*. Determine the surface area and volume of:

a) Uranus   **b)** the moon

5. Which has the greater volume, a sphere with a radius r, or a cube with edges of length r? Explain.

6. The mean radius of the moon is approximately 1740 km. Determine the surface area and volume of the moon.

B **7.** A spherical balloon is blown up from a diameter of 20 cm to one of 60 cm. By how many time has its:

a) surface area increased?   **b)** volume increased?

8. What happens to the surface area and the volume of a sphere if its radius is doubled? Tripled?

9. If we did not know that the moon is spherical, we might think that it was a circle. How does the surface area of the part of the moon we see when the moon is full compare with the area of the circle that it appears to be?

10. Calculate the radius of the sphere with each volume.

a) 45.7 m^3 **b)** 23.8 cm^3 **c)** 1356 mm^3

11. A sphere just fits inside a cube with edges of length 10.0 cm. Calculate the surface area and the volume of the sphere.

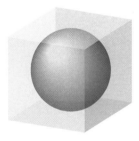

12. Academic Focus Repeat exercise 11 for a cube with edges of length x centimetres.

13. A basketball has a circumference of 75 cm. Determine:

a) its radius   **b)** its surface area   **c)** its volume

14. Use an astronomy book or the *Moon and Planets* database from the data disk. Determine the mean radius of each planet in our solar system. Use this information to calculate the surface area and volume of each planet.

15. Academic Focus Determine formulas for the surface area and the volume of a sphere with:

a) diameter, d **b)** circumference, C

How Do Sled Dogs Keep Warm?

In cold, windy Antarctic conditions, shelter is essential to human survival. Yet, sled dogs sleep outside, curled up, and covered by drifting snow.

Scientists know that a mammal produces heat in proportion to its body size and loses heat in proportion to its surface area. How do sled dogs maintain their body heat in extremely cold and windy conditions?

16. a) What does "produce heat in proportion to its body size" mean?

   b) What does "lose heat in proportion to its surface area" mean?

   c) Which animals do you think would be better adapted to cold climates—those with small values of the ratio $\frac{\text{surface area}}{\text{volume}}$ or those with large values of this ratio? Explain.

17. a) Consider a dog lying stretched out as a cylinder. Choose reasonable estimates for the radius and the length of the cylinder representing the dog. Calculate the ratio $\frac{\text{surface area}}{\text{volume}}$ for this sleeping position.

   b) Consider a dog lying curled up as a sphere. Choose a reasonable estimate for the radius of the sphere representing the dog. Calculate the ratio $\frac{\text{surface area}}{\text{volume}}$ for this sleeping position.

18. a) How do the results of exercise 17 explain why sled dogs curl up to sleep?

   b) Sled dogs allow a layer of snow to cover them as they sleep. What effect do you think this has on the dog's temperature?

   c) What attributes do sled dogs have that would help them keep warm?

   d) Animals in the cold regions of the world have smaller appendages (limbs, ears, and tails) than animals in tropical areas. This principle is called *Allen's rule*. How can Allen's rule be explained mathematically?

19. a) Graph the equation $A = 4\pi r^2$ for the surface area of a sphere against its radius.

b) Use the trace key. Determine the surface area of a sphere with radius 5 cm.

c) Use the trace key. Estimate the radius of a sphere with surface area 100 cm².

d) Trace to check your answers for surface area in exercise 2.

20. a) Graph the equation $V = \frac{4}{3}\pi r^3$ for the volume of a sphere against its radius.

b) Use the trace key. Determine the volume of a sphere with radius 5 cm.

c) Use the trace key. Estimate the radius of a sphere with volume 100 cm³.

d) Trace to check your answers for volume in exercise 2.

21. A squash ball has a radius of 2.0 cm. It fits in a box in the shape of a cube. Visualize a sphere in a cube.

a) Calculate the surface area of the ball and the surface area of the box. What assumptions are you making about the dimensions of the box?

b) Calculate the ratio of the surface area of the ball to the surface area of the box.

c) Calculate the volume of the ball and the volume of the box.

d) Calculate the ratio of the volume of the ball to the volume of the box. Compare the result with part b. What do you notice?

22. It's been said that packing a ball in a box into which it just fits leaves about half the space in the box empty. Does this seem reasonable? To test this theory, set up the following spreadsheet on the computer.

	A	B	C	D	E
1	Volume of a ball and a box				
2					
3	Radius	Side length of box	Volume of box	Volume of ball	Empty space
4		=2*A4	=(2*A4)^3	=4/3*PI()*A4^3	

a) Explain each formula in cells B4, C4, and D4.

b) Enter a formula in cell E4 to calculate the amount of empty space in the box.

c) Enter several different values for the radius in cell A4. Is the statement about half the space in the box reasonble? Does the length of the radius affect your answer? Explain.

COMMUNICATING *the* IDEAS

In this chapter, formulas are given for the surface areas and volumes of several objects.

a) In your journal, summarize the formulas in a systematic way.

b) How can you tell, just by looking at formula, whether it is a formula for surface area or a formula for volume?

10.12   Designing a Cooler: Part III

On pages 457 and 482, you designed portable coolers. They have the shape of a rectangular prism and a cylinder that contain a volume of 50 000 cm³, and have a minimum surface area. You should have obtained the results below. The optimal prism is a cube. The optimal cylinder is as close to a cube as it can be.

Rectangular Prism Model

The optimal prism is a cube with edges about 36.8 cm.

$V = 50\,000\,\text{cm}^3$

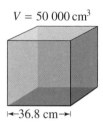

◄—36.8 cm—►

Cylinder Model

The optimal cylinder has both height and diameter about 39.9 cm.

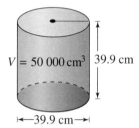

$V = 50\,000\,\text{cm}^3$ | 39.9 cm

◄—39.9 cm—►

1. Verify that the volumes of the optimal prism and the optimal cylinder are each approximately 50 000 cm³.

2. a) Calculate the surface area of the optimal prism and the optimal cylinder.

   b) Which model is more efficient? Explain.

   c) Calculate the difference in the surface areas of the two models.

The Sphere Model

Suppose the portable cooler has the shape of a sphere. Recall that the formula for the volume of a sphere is $V = \frac{4}{3}\pi r^3$. If we substitute 50 000 for V, we obtain the equation $\frac{4}{3}\pi r^3 = 50\,000$.

3. a) Solve the equation $\frac{4}{3}\pi r^3 = 50\,000$ using any method that works. The result is the radius of a sphere that has a volume of 50 000 cm³.

   b) Calculate the surface area of the sphere.

4. Compare the surface area of the sphere with the surface areas of the optimal prism and the optimal cylinder. Which model is most efficient? Explain.

A sphere has the smallest surface area for any given volume. This is the reason why it is the most efficient shape for a cooler. The most efficient rectangular prism is a cube because a cube is as close to a sphere as a rectangular prism can be. Similarly, the most efficient cylinder is one whose height equals its diameter, because this is as close to a sphere as a cylinder can be.

5. Why might the spherical model not be the best choice for a portable cooler?

Combination Models

A cooler might be designed as a combination of a sphere and a cylinder whose height equals its diameter. Here are two possible models.

Cylinder with hemisphere at each end

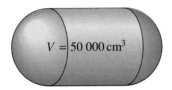

$V = 50\,000\,\text{cm}^3$

Cylinder with hemisphere on top

$V = 50\,000\,\text{cm}^3$

Choose one of the two models above. Use it to complete exercises 6 and 7.

6. Let r centimetres represent the base radius of the cylinder.

  a) Write an expression for the volume of the model.

  b) Since you know that the volume is $50\,000\,\text{cm}^3$, use your expression in part a to write an equation in r.

  c) Solve the equation using any method.

7. a) Write an expression for the surface area of the model.

  b) Use your answer to exercise 6c to calculate the surface area of the model.

  c) How does the surface area of your model compare with the surface areas of the previous models?

COMMUNICATING the IDEAS

In your journal, write a report to describe your design for the 50-L cooler, which has the shape of one of the combination models. Include in your report:

- a description of your design, with a labelled diagram
- an explanation of why your model is better than any of the other models
- suggested modifications for making the model more "user friendly"

What Shapes Make Cardboard Cylinders?

1. a) Suppose you were to cut open a spiral can and unroll the cardboard. What shape do you think it would have?

b) Check your prediction in part a. You will need a frozen orange juice can, a sharp knife, and a lift-type can opener. Carefully remove the bottom of the can with the can opener. Then cut the cardboard along the seam and flatten it. Was your prediction correct?

c) Calculate the surface area of the can.

2. a) Construct two copies of this parallelogram, and cut them out.

b) Tape the edges of the parallelogram in two different ways to form two cylinders, with no overlap.

c) Calculate the base diameter and the height of each cylinder. Give the answers to the nearest millimetre. Check by measuring.

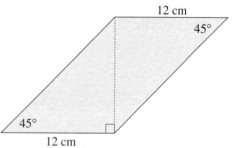

3. Every parallelogram can be used to construct two cylinders in this way. Draw an example of a parallelogram for which the two cylinders would be identical.

4. A child's toy consists of interlocking pieces of 1-cm thick foam. Each piece is 15 cm square. There is 1 piece for each letter of the alphabet and each number from 0 to 9. The pieces can be joined to form cubes and prisms.

6 pieces used   **10 pieces used**

a) What is the maximum number of cubes that can be made at one time?

b) What are the surface area and volume of each cube in part a?

c) What are the volume and surface area of the largest prism that can be made?

5. Calculate the volume of each solid to the nearest cubic unit.

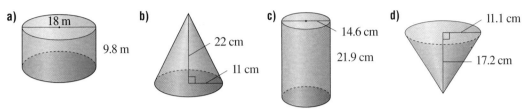

a) 18 m, 9.8 m

b) 22 cm, 11 cm

c) 14.6 cm, 21.9 cm

d) 11.1 cm, 17.2 cm

6. Calculate the surface area of each cylinder in exercise 5.

7. **Academic Focus** Calculate the surface area of each cone in exercise 5.

8. Two rectangular pieces of cardboard each measuring 30 cm by 50 cm are used to form the curved surfaces of two different cylinders. Circles cut from another piece of cardboard are used for the tops and the bottoms.

a) Calculate the radius of each cylinder to 2 decimal places.

b) Calculate the total surface area of each cylinder.

c) Calculate the volume of each cylinder.

9. What is the volume of sawdust in a conical pile that is 3.2 m in diameter and 2.8 m in height?

10. Determine the surface area and the volume of each ball listed below.

Sport	Diameter of ball
Baseball	24 cm
Table tennis	4.0 cm
Tennis	6.5 cm

11. The mean radius of the sun is approximately 694 000 km. Determine the surface area and the volume of the sun.

12. A sphere just fits inside a cylinder with base radius 12 cm and height 24 cm. Calculate the surface area and volume of the cylinder and of the sphere to the nearest whole number.

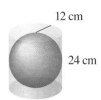

12 cm

24 cm

13. A cylindrical silo has a height of 12.5 m and a base diameter of 6.4 m. Its top is half a sphere with the same diameter. Calculate the total volume of the silo to the nearest cubic metre.

14. Tennis balls are packed in cans 8.4 cm in diameter and 25.5 cm high. Three dozen of these cans are packed in a box 51 cm by 51 cm by 26 cm. What is the total volume of wasted space?

15. Academic Focus Calculate the volume of each pyramid to the nearest cubic unit.

a)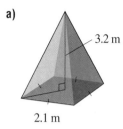

3.2 m

2.1 m

b)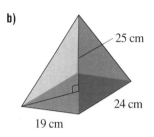

25 cm

24 cm

19 cm

c)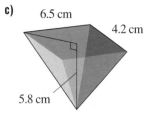

6.5 cm

4.2 cm

5.8 cm

16. Academic Focus A square-based pyramid is 24 cm wide and 52 cm high. It is cut, as shown, to create a pyramid 39 cm high with base 18 cm square. The other piece is discarded. What is the volume of the discarded portion, to the nearest cubic unit?

17. A 14-m railway car is used for transporting fluids. The car is cylindrical with hemispherical ends. The radius of the cylinder is 2 m. Calculate the volume of the car to the nearest cubic metre.

18. A cone and a sphere have the same volume. The radius of the sphere and the base of the cone are 1 cm. Determine the height of the cone.

19. A crate has the shape of a rectangular prism with volume 500 L.

a) Calculate the dimensions for the crate to have minimum surface area.

b) Calculate the minimum surface area.

20. A cylindrical drum has volume 500 L.

a) Calculate the dimensions for the cylinder to have minimum surface area.

b) Calculate the minimum surface area.

21. Determine the radius and surface area of a sphere with volume 500 L.

22. Compare the answers to exercises 19, 20, and 21. List the solids in order from least to greatest surface area.

23. Academic Focus: Volumes of Cylinders with the Same Height Recall the activities from pages 475 and 483. Conduct similar investigations using cylinders that have the same height but different radii.

a) How are the total surface areas and radii of the cylinders related?

b) How are the volumes and radii of the cylinders related?

24. **Mathematical Modelling** In Section 10.12, neither cones nor pyramids were considered as possible shapes for a cooler.

a) Why do you think this is?

b) To investigate the optimal pyramid with a spreadsheet, set up a spreadsheet similar to the one below. Copy the formulas in cells B3, C3, D3, and E3 into row 4. Then Fill Down the formulas in row 4 far enough until the areas in column E begin to increase.

	A	B	C	D	E
1	Minimize the Surface Area of a Square-Based Pyramid				
2	Base Length	Base Area	Height	Face Height	Surface Area
3	46.0	=A3^2	150000/B3	=SQRT(C3^2+B3/4)	=B3+2*A3*D3
4	=A3+0.1				

i) What is the minimum surface area?

ii) What are the base length and the height of the optimal pyramid?

iii) Compare the surface area of the optimal pyramid with the surface areas of the optimal prism, the optimal cylinder, and the sphere (see page 514, exercise 4).

iv) Explain the formulas in cells C3, D3, and E3.

c) To investigate the optimal pyramid with a graphing calculator, set the graphing window to Xmin = 0, Xmax = 94, Xscl = 10, Ymin = 0, Ymax = 20000, Yscl = 5000. In the Y= list, enter the equation shown in the screen at the right. This equation expresses the surface area of a square-based pyramid, y square centimetres, in terms of the base length, x centimetres.

i) Press [GRAPH] to show the relationship between surface area and base length.

ii) Press [TRACE] and use the arrow keys to estimate the minimum surface area. Zoom in for a more accurate estimate.

iii) What are the base length and the height of the optimal pyramid?

iv) Compare the surface area of the optimal pyramid with the surface areas of the optimal prism, the optimal cylinder, and the sphere (see page 514, exercise 4).

CHAPTER

11 Geometry

Satire on False Perspective

Paradise Garden

The Annunciation

Representing 3-Dimensional Objects in 2 Dimensions

In word processors, you can create 3-D letters. The letters are on a flat surface but they appear to have depth.

Hundreds of years ago, artists did not give depth to their pictures. Objects and figures often looked distorted, and those in the background were frequently too large. Geometry was used to produce a 3-dimensional effect. Artists then achieved the appearance of reality in their paintings. We say these paintings have "perspective." A painting has perspective when you can see lines that appear to meet at one or more distant points.

1. Which painting on these pages has perspective? In this painting, find some examples of lines that would meet if they were extended.

An artist sometimes intentionally violates the laws of perspective to create an amusing scene or an object that cannot exist.

2. Examine the engraving *Satire on False Perspective*. Find as many examples as you can of things that are wrong with this engraving.

After exploring properties of geometric figures using *The Geometer's Sketchpad*, you will extend your skills to construct 2-dimensional representations of 3-dimensional objects. Your sketches will use the rules of perspective drawing known by artists, but they will also be "dynamic." Using the power of computer software, you will manipulate and explore your designs under changing conditions. You will revisit this topic in Section 11.12.

 FYI Visit www.awl.com/canada/school/connections

For information related to the above problem, click on <u>MATHLINKS</u> followed by <u>AWMath</u>. Then select a topic under Representing 3-Dimensional Objects in 2 Dimensions.

This section reviews these concepts:

- Geometry terms
- Angles

Throughout history, people have used geometric ideas such as symmetry, parallelism, and perpendicularity in designs. Oriental carpets, tile floors, early Canadian quilts, Indian beadwork patterns, and modern wallpaper borders are examples of geometry in the art around us.

Look at the photograph above. Use it to complete exercises 1 to 3.

1. In the photograph:

   a) Identify as many different types of geometric figures as you can.

   b) Identify pairs of parallel lines and pairs of perpendicular lines.

2. Look for pairs of equal angles in the photograph. Explain how you know they are equal.

3. In the photograph, find examples of:

   a) an acute angle   **b)** an obtuse angle

   c) supplementary angles   **d)** complementary angles

4. Identify the geometric figures in each picture.

a)

b)

c)

d)

5. a) Describe the property of angles formed by two intersecting lines, below left.

b) Find the measure of ∠ABC.

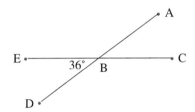

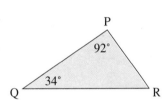

6. What is the measure of ∠PRQ, above right? Explain the property of triangles you used.

7. Find the value of each variable. Explain how you know.

a)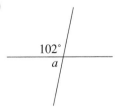

b)

c)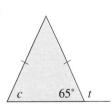

d)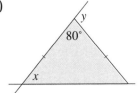

e)

f)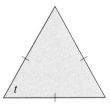

8. In exercise 7, identify:

a) two complementary angles

b) two supplementary angles

Dynamic software, such as *The Geometer's Sketchpad*, allows us to explore geometry in a new way. We can investigate theorems or explore new ideas by observing how measurements and relationships change as a diagram is manipulated.

This introduction will help you become familiar with the software before attempting the Investigations in the following sections.

INVESTIGATION 1

The Toolbox

From the File menu, choose New Sketch.

1. On the left of the screen is a column called the Toolbox. Before you work with *The Geometer's Sketchpad*, you must select one of these tools.

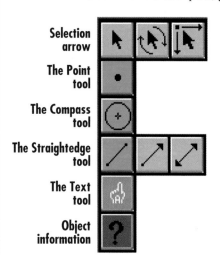

Selection arrow

The Point tool

The Compass tool

The Straightedge tool

The Text tool

Object information

There are 3 Selection arrows. Click on the Selection arrow, hold down the mouse button and drag to the right. Beside the Translation arrow is a Rotation arrow and a Dilatation arrow. To choose either of these, drag to highlight the tool you want, then release the mouse button.

There are 3 Straightedge tools. To see them, click on the Straightedge tool, hold down the mouse button and drag to the right. Beside the Segment tool, there is a Ray tool and a Line tool.

2. Follow the instructions below to explore some features of the Toolbox.

Click on this tool ...   *... and do this:*

a) Draw 4 points by clicking anywhere on the screen. Notice that a point has a black outline when first drawn. The outline disappears when the second point is drawn.

b) Click on one point. Hold down the mouse button and drag to an adjacent point. Click on this point. Hold down the mouse button and drag to the next point. Repeat until a quadrilateral is drawn. Notice the little black squares on each segment as it is completed. These show when a segment is *selected*.

c) Click on one vertex. Notice that the black outline reappears. This shows that the point is selected. Hold down the mouse button and drag the figure. By dragging different vertices, you can make the figure a square, a parallelogram, or even a straight line.

d) As you move closer to a point or line, the hand turns black. Click, and the object will be labelled. Click again and the label disappears.

e) Labels can be changed to other letters or even words. Use the Text tool to double-click on the label, not on the object. A dialog box appears and a new label can be typed.

f) Use the Compass tool to draw a circle. Hold down the mouse button anywhere on the screen. Move the mouse. A circle is drawn. Notice the four little black squares. These appear when the circle is selected.

g) The circle has a point on it called the *control point*. Drag this point to make the circle larger or smaller.

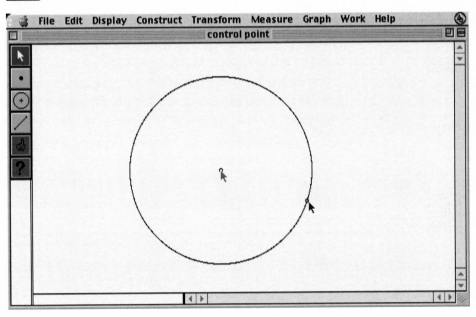

Sketchpad Tip

When a segment or a circle has black squares on it, or when a point is outlined in black, the object is selected. You may not be able to carry out a procedure if the wrong objects are selected. To *deselect* an object, click on the Selection tool, then click anywhere on the screen.

The Measure Menu

From the File menu, choose New Sketch.

There are eight menus at the top of the screen. Click on each menu to display its contents.

Many of the options are grey. They cannot be chosen unless the correct objects have been selected.

In this investigation, you will explore the Measure menu and learn some special geometry features of *The Geometer's Sketchpad.*

Measuring Circles

Click on this tool ...   ... and do this:

a) Draw a circle. Go to the Measure menu. Several items are now black. Choose Radius. The radius will be measured and the measure displayed on the screen. (If the measurement is not in centimetres, you can change it. From the Display menu, choose Preferences. Under Distance Unit, select cm, then click OK.)

b) Check that the circle is still selected. From the Measure menu, choose Area. The area measure is displayed. From the Measure menu, choose Circumference. Its measure is displayed.

c) Drag the control point of the circle. Observe how the measurements change.

d) To move a measurement, click on it, hold down the mouse button, then drag the measurement to a new location.

Measuring Length

Click on this tool ...   ... and do this:

a) Draw a segment. Two black squares show that the segment is selected.

b) From the Measure menu, choose Length. The length of the segment will appear on the screen.

c) Click on an endpoint of the segment. Drag by holding down the mouse button. Notice that the measurement changes.

Measuring Area and Perimeter

Click on this tool ...   *... and do this:*

Draw five points on the screen. Do not connect them. We will use a different technique to complete a pentagon.

a) Hold down the shift key, then click on each point. From the Construct menu, choose Segment. A pentagon is constructed.

b) Click anywhere on the screen to deselect everything.

c) Hold down the shift key, then click on each side of the pentagon. Go to the Measure menu. Notice that it is not possible to select Perimeter and Area because they are grey.

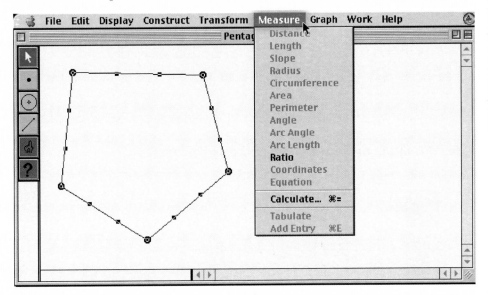

d) Click anywhere on the screen to deselect everything.

e) Hold down the shift key, then click on each vertex of the pentagon.

f) From the Construct menu, choose Polygon Interior. The pentagon interior is now striped. This shows that it is selected.

g) From the Measure menu, choose Area.

h) Drag a vertex of the pentagon. Watch the area measurement change as the figure changes.

i) Select the pentagon interior. From the Display menu, choose Color, then pick your favourite colour. Click anywhere on the screen.

The Transform Menu

In earlier grades you investigated flips, slides, and turns. We will explore a few transformations by reflecting a pentagon and constructing an equilateral triangle.

Reflecting a pentagon

Use the pentagon from *Investigation 2*, or construct a new pentagon. Colour it red.

Click on this tool ...   *... and do this:*

a) Draw a line segment beside the pentagon.

b) Click on the segment. From the Transform menu, choose Mark Mirror. The little black squares flash to show the segment is now a mirror.

c) Click on the pentagon to select it.

d) From the Transform menu, choose Reflect. The image pentagon is striped. Change its colour to blue.

e) Drag a vertex of the red pentagon. Watch the effect on the image.

Using a rotation to construct an equilateral triangle

Click on this tool ...   *... and do this:*

a) Draw a line segment.

b) Click on one endpoint of the segment. From the Transform menu, choose Mark Center. A flash appears to indicate that the point is now a centre of rotation.

c) Click on the segment and on each endpoint. Remember to hold down the shift key.

d) From the Transform menu, choose Rotate. When the dialog box appears, type 60 and click OK. Why did you type 60?

e) Draw the third side of the triangle.

f) Drag a vertex of the triangle. Explain how you know the triangle is still equilateral.

g) Save this sketch.

Explore More

In this investigation, you will learn to use some commands in the Construct menu and the Graph menu.

From the File menu, choose New Sketch.

Constructing Parallel Lines

1. Draw a line segment and a point above the segment.

2. Select the segment and the point. From the Construct menu, choose Parallel Line.

3. Drag an endpoint of your original segment. Note: If you *draw* two lines that look parallel, dragging one line will not affect the other line. If you *construct* two parallel lines, dragging one line will cause the other line to move.

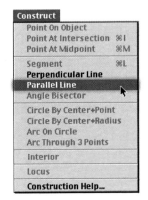

Constructing a Perpendicular Line

1. Draw a line segment.

2. Select the segment. From the Construct menu, choose Point on Object.

3. Select the segment and the point. From the Construct menu, choose Perpendicular Line.

4. Drag an endpoint of your original segment. What do you notice?

5. To replace the perpendicular line with a segment:
   - Select the perpendicular line.
   - From the Construct menu, choose Point on Object.
   - Deselect all objects.
   - Select the perpendicular line again. From the Display menu, choose Hide Line.
   - Select the two constructed points. From the Construct menu, choose Segment.

Constructing with Coordinate Geometry

Sometimes it is helpful to have a coordinate grid for sketches.

1. Draw a triangle on the screen.

2. From the Graph menu, choose Show Grid.

3. Select a vertex of the triangle. From the Measure menu, choose Coordinates.

4. Select a side of the triangle. From the Measure menu, choose Slope.

5. Use the Line tool, which is one of the Straightedge tools, to draw a line with slope 2.

6. Select the line. From the Measure menu, choose Equation.

Animation

1. Use the Compass tool to draw a circle.

2. Use the Segment tool to draw a segment with one endpoint on the circle. (Do not connect the segment to the circle's control point.)

3. Deselect all objects.

4. Select the endpoint of the segment on the circle, then select the circle. From the Display menu, choose Animate. A dialog box will appear. Click OK (or Animate).

Scripts

The Geometer's Sketchpad remembers your steps and can create a routine called a script.

1. Follow the instructions in *Investigation 3* to construct an equilateral triangle.

2. Choose the Selection arrow. Draw a box around the triangle by holding down the mouse button and dragging.

3. From the Work menu, choose Make Script. A window with the script appears.

4. Delete the equilateral triangle.

5. To play the script, provide the objects listed under Given. For a triangle, the script requires two points. Draw the two points, then press either Play or Fast in the Script window.

6. Save the script. Use it to draw an equilateral triangle whenever you need to.

B 1. Open a New Sketch.

   a) Draw 4 points and label them clockwise as P, Q, R, and S.

   b) Use the Segment tool to join the points. This is quadrilateral PQRS.

   c) Use the Compass tool to draw a circle that just touches the inside of the quadrilateral. You may need to drag P, Q, R, and S. Are all the sides of the quadrilateral equal? What lengths do appear to be equal?

2. **a)** Check that the triangle in *Investigation 3* is equilateral by measuring the lengths of its sides.

   b) Label the vertices of the equilateral triangle A, B, and C. Measure the angles in the triangle. Angle ABC is measured by selecting A, then B, then C (remember to hold down the shift key). From the Measure menu, choose Angle.

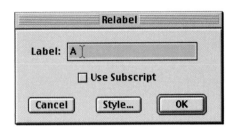

3. **a)** Use rotation to construct a square.

   b) How could a square be constructed by using a reflection? Try it.

4. Some capital letters, such as M and V, have vertical lines of symmetry. Construct M and V by reflection. If you delete the mirror line, the reflected half of the letter will also disappear. Instead, hide the mirror line by selecting it, then from the Display menu, choose Hide Segment.

5. Construct 5 parallel lines. Create a grid by constructing 5 more parallel lines perpendicular to the first 5 parallel lines.

6. Construct a triangle. Use a grid to determine the coordinates of the vertices and to measure the slopes of the sides.

7. Use the Hide command. Find a way to construct a parallelogram with sides that are line segments.

8. Refer to *Investigation 4*, Constructing with Coordinate Geometry. *The Geometer's Sketchpad* will not find the equation of a line segment, only of a line. Explain how you could find the equations of the sides of the triangle.

COMMUNICATING
the IDEAS

In your journal, list some advantages and disadvantages of using computer software, such as *The Geometer's Sketchpad*, when working with geometric figures.

Cars driving in opposite directions on a highway are often separated by a median. This is a concrete barrier or a strip of land that divides the road in half.

In the triangle at the right, line segment AM is a median.

In the diagram, M is the midpoint of side BC.
The line segment AM is a median of △ABC.

A *median* of a triangle is the line segment
that joins a vertex to the midpoint of the opposite side.

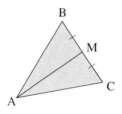

Use *The Geometer's Sketchpad*.

SETUP

From the File menu, choose New Sketch.

1. To construct △ABC:

Click on this tool ...   *... and do this:*

a) Draw 3 points.

b) Click on each point to display its label. To change a label, double-click and type a new letter. Make sure the labels are A, B, and C.

c) Hold down the shift key and click on each point. This selects the points. When a point is outlined in black, it is selected.

d) From the Construct menu, choose Segment.

e) Click anywhere on the screen to deselect segments and points.

2. To construct the midpoint of AB:

Click on this tool ...   *... and do this:*

a) Click on side AB to select it. The two black squares on the line segment show that it has been selected.

b) From the Construct menu, choose Point At Midpoint.

c) Click on the midpoint to display its label, D. Double-click on D, then change it to M.

3. To construct the median CM:

Click on this tool ...   *... and do this:*

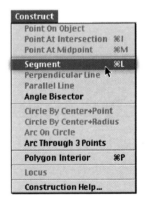

a) Hold down the shift key and click on points C and M.

b) From the Construct menu, choose Segment.

Sketchpad Tips

- To construct: always use the Construct menu.
- To select multiple objects: hold down the shift key while clicking on each object.
- To construct segment AB: select A and B, then from the Construct menu choose Segment.
- To label: choose the Text tool. Click on the object to display its label. To change a label: double-click on the label and type a new letter.
- To hide an object: click on the object, then from the Display menu choose Hide.
- If you make a mistake and want to delete a construction, click on it, then from the Edit menu, select Undo.
- After labelling, ensure you click on the Selection arrow before the next construction.
- Ensure you know what is selected before you choose from the Construct menu.
- Ensure you deselect after each construction.

In *Investigations 1* to *3*, you will observe the properties of the medians in a triangle. These properties will be used in Section 11.3.

Medians and Area

1. Construct △ABC and median CM as in *Setup*.

2. Select points A, C, and M. From the Construct menu, choose Polygon Interior. From the Display menu (or by clicking the correct mouse button), choose Color and pick red. Click anywhere on the screen to deselect △ACM.

3. Select points B, C, and M. Construct the interior as in exercise 2. Colour it blue.

4. Click on the red triangle to select it. (It is striped when it is selected.) From the Measure menu, choose Area. Record the area measurement. Click anywhere on the screen to deselect the red triangle.

5. Repeat exercise 4 for the blue triangle.

6. Click on any vertex and drag it across the screen. Observe the area measurements. What do you notice? Record your observations.

7. Write a statement about a median of a triangle and its area.

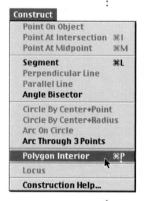

Three Medians

1. Construct △ABC and median CM as in *Setup*.

2. Select segment AC. From the Construct menu, choose Point At Midpoint. Label the midpoint N.

3. Select B and N. Construct segment BN.

4. Construct the midpoint of side BC. Label it P. Construct the median AP.

5. What do you notice about the medians?

6. Drag a vertex of the triangle to see if what you noticed is true for other triangles.

7. Write a statement about this property of medians in a triangle.

8. Select two medians. From the Construct menu, choose Point At Intersection. Label this point, O. The point O is the *centroid* of a triangle.

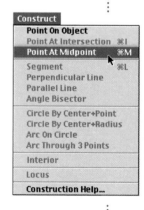

A Property of the Centroid

1. Construct △ABC, medians AP, BN, and CM, and centroid O, as in *Investigation 2*.

2. Select the three medians AP, CM, and BN. From the Display menu, choose Hide Segments. You should see △ABC, and points M, N, P, and O.

3. Construct segments AO and OP. From the Measure menu, choose Length.

4. Select AO and OP. From the Measure menu, choose Ratio.

5. Drag a vertex of △ABC. Observe the measurements of AO and OP, and their ratio. What do you conclude?

6. Construct BO and ON. Find the ratio of their lengths.

7. Construct CO and OM. Find the ratio of their lengths.

8. Drag a vertex of △ABC. Observe the measurements and the ratios. Record your observations.

9. Write a statement to describe how the centroid divides a median in a triangle.

COMMUNICATING the IDEAS

Now that you have worked further with *The Geometer's Sketchpad*, list more advantages and disadvantages of using computer software when working with geometric figures.

Boggle your MIND

Get 6 toothpicks and some Plasticine or tape to hold them together. Use the 6 toothpicks to make 4 equilateral triangles.

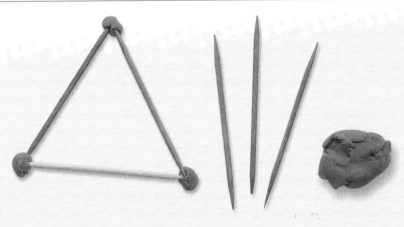

A *median* of a triangle is the line segment that joins a vertex to the midpoint of the opposite side. If you completed Section 11.2, you have already worked with the medians of a triangle. The properties you observed are summarized.

Median Properties

1. A median divides the area of a triangle in half.

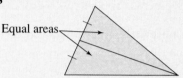

Equal areas

2. The three medians of a triangle meet at one point. This point is the *centroid*.

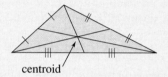

centroid

3. On each median, the centroid is twice as far from the vertex as it is from the midpoint of the opposite side.

$$AO = 2OM$$

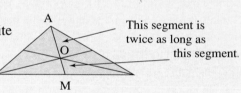

This segment is twice as long as this segment.

These properties can be used to solve problems.

Example 1

The area of △PQM is 56 cm². Calculate the area of △PQR.

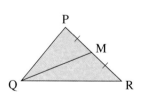

Solution

From the diagram, PM = MR
Thus, QM is a median.
From Median Property 1, area △PQR = 2(area △PQM)
$$= 2(56)$$
$$= 112$$
The area of △PQR is 112 cm².

Example 2

In $\triangle PQR$, O is the centroid; OM = 14 cm.
Calculate the length of QM.

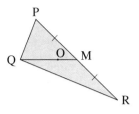

Solution

From Median Property 3, QO = 2OM

Thus, QM = 3OM

$\qquad$ QM = 3(14)

$\qquad\qquad$ = 42

The length of QM is 42 cm.

DISCUSSING *the* IDEAS

1. Explain what the medians of a triangle are. Explain why the word "median" is appropriate.

2. In *Example 1*, explain why the area of $\triangle PQR$ is twice the area of $\triangle PQM$.

3. In *Example 2*, explain why QM = 3OM.

11.3 EXERCISES

1. The area of $\triangle PQR$ is 72 cm². Calculate the area of $\triangle PQS$.

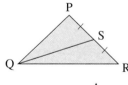

2. In $\triangle ABC$, N is the centroid; BN = 12 cm. Calculate the length of NQ.

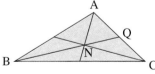

3. Point O is the centroid of $\triangle PQR$; PS = 30 cm. Calculate the length of PO.

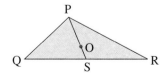

4. In *Investigation 1*, page 534, you found that a median divides the area of a triangle in half. Cut out a scalene triangle. Draw a median. Cut along the median to divide the triangle into two parts.

a) Do the two parts have the same shape? Explain.

b) Do the two parts have the same area? Explain.

c) Draw a triangle so that when you cut along a median, the two parts are congruent.

d) Can you draw a triangle so that when you cut along a median, the two parts are isosceles triangles? Explain.

5. Draw a triangle on cardboard. Cut out the triangle. Construct one median.

a) Try to balance the triangle on the thin edge of a ruler aligned with the median. Explain why the triangle should balance on the ruler.

b) The centroid is sometimes called the *point of balance* of a triangle. Find the centroid of your cardboard triangle. Try to balance the triangle on a pencil point at the centroid.

6. Construct equilateral △ABC with sides 10 cm. Construct the medians AP, BN, and CM.

a) Measure and record all angles and sides of the six small triangles formed by the medians. What do you notice?

b) Make a conjecture about a property of medians in equilateral triangles.

c) Check your conjecture in part b by repeating the construction using *The Geometer's Sketchpad*.

7. A student is designing a triangular sunroof for a patio table. The sunroof will be supported by a single pole. A chalk line marks one median. The length of the median is 1.5 m. At what distance from the vertex should the hole for the support be drilled?

8. On grid paper or using *The Geometer's Sketchpad*, plot △ABC with vertices A(1, 7), B(3, 1), and C(11, 7). (See page 529.)

a) Find the midpoints of AB, BC, and AC.

b) Find the coordinates of the centroid of △ABC.

9. The area of △QNS is 24 cm². What is the area of △QRS? Explain how you know.

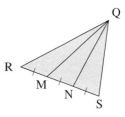

10. Academic Focus From the File menu, choose New Sketch.

a) Construct △ABC, medians AP, BN, CM, and centroid O.

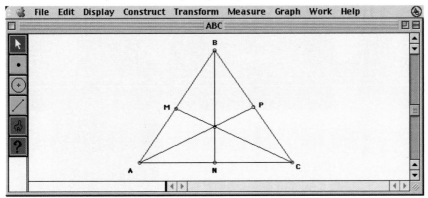

b) Construct the interior of each of the six triangles formed by the medians.

c) Measure the area of each triangle. What do you notice?

d) Drag a vertex of △ABC and observe your measurements.

e) Write a statement about the medians in a triangle.

f) Use the fact that the centroid divides the median in the ratio 2 : 1. Explain the statement you wrote in part e.

11. Plot △ABC with vertices A(0, 3), B(8, 5), and C(4, 1).

a) Draw the medians. Find the coordinates of the centroid.

b) Find the equations of the three medians of the triangle.

12. Two triangles lie between parallel lines *m* and *l*; with AC = 5 cm and BD = 10 cm. What is the ratio of the area of △BCD to the area of △ABC? Explain.

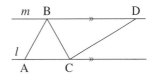

13. All the medians in equilateral △ABC are 15 cm long. Calculate the lengths of the sides of the triangle to the nearest tenth of a centimetre.

COMMUNICATING *the* **IDEAS**

The word *median* is also used in statistics to describe a property of data. How are this use of median and the use of median in this section similar? Write about it in your journal.

The altimeter in an airplane is an instrument that measures the height of the plane above sea level. Jets, such as the B-747, fly at altitudes between 30 000 feet and 40 000 feet. The height of a triangle is also called the altitude.

In the diagram, line segment AD is an altitude of △ABC.

An *altitude* of a triangle is the line segment drawn from a vertex perpendicular to the opposite side.

Use *The Geometer's Sketchpad*.

SETUP

From the File menu, choose New Sketch.

1. To construct △PQR:

Click on this tool …   *… and do this:*

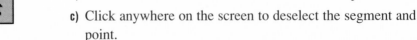

a) Draw a horizontal line segment by clicking on the screen, then drag. The segment is selected.

b) From the Construct menu, choose Point on Object.

c) Click anywhere on the screen to deselect the segment and point.

d) Click on the segment again to construct a second point.

e) Construct a point on one side of the segment.

f) Click on the point on one side of the segment. Double-click on the label and change it to R.

g) Repeat this procedure to label the points P and Q you constructed on the segment.

h) Click on P and R. From the Construct menu, choose Segment.

i) Click on Q and R, then construct segment QR.

j) Drag a vertex of △PQR until all the angles are acute.

2. To construct the altitude from R:

Click on this tool …   *… and do this:*

a) Hold down the shift key, and select segment PQ and vertex R.

b) From the Construct menu, choose Perpendicular Line.

c) Hold down the shift key and select segment PQ and the perpendicular line. From the Construct menu, choose Point At Intersection.

d) Click on the intersection point. Double-click the label and change it to T.

In *Investigations 1* to *3*, you will observe the properties of the altitudes in a triangle. These properties will be used in Section 11.5.

INVESTIGATION 1

Measuring Angles

1. Construct △PQR and altitude RT as in *Setup*.

2. Drag vertex R of △PQR. Observe the change in the altitude and the position of T.

3. Select P, then R, then Q. From the Measure menu, choose Angle. The measure of ∠PRQ is shown on the screen.

4. Repeat exercise 3 to measure ∠PQR and ∠RPQ. Deselect the vertices.

5. Drag R so that T is between P and Q. Record the measurements of ∠PQR, ∠RPQ, and ∠PRQ. Repeat this for another position of T between P and Q.

6. Drag R so that T is not between P and Q. We say that T is on PQ (or QP) *extended*. For two different positions of T, record the measurements of ∠PQR, ∠RPQ, and ∠PRQ.

7. Write to explain how the type of triangle affects the positions of T.

Determining Area

1. Construct △PQR and altitude RT as in *Setup*.

2. Select P, Q, and R. From the Construct menu, choose Polygon Interior. From the Measure menu, choose Area. The area of △PQR is displayed.

3. Measure PQ by selecting its endpoints. From the Measure menu, choose Distance. Repeat for the measure of RT.

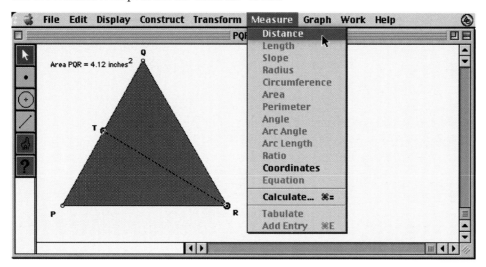

4. Select the measurements of PQ and RT. From the Measure menu, choose Calculate.

5. In the calculator, click on 1 / 2 *. From the Values menu, select Distance (P to Q). Click on *. Then from the Values menu, select Distance (R to T).

6. Your answer will be displayed on the screen. What did you calculate in exercise 5?

7. To find the area of △PQR, we use the formula $A = \frac{1}{2}(\text{base} \times \text{height})$. When PQ is the base, what is the altitude RT?

Constructing Three Altitudes

For this investigation, we construct a triangle using lines instead of
line segments.

1. Use the Point tool to construct 3 points. Label these points A, B, and C.

2. Click on the Straightedge tool and drag to the right. You will see three
   icons: Segment—two endpoints, Ray—one endpoint and one arrow,
   and Line—two arrows. Choose the Line icon.

3. Select A, B, and C. From the Construct menu, choose Line. You now
   have a triangle with extended sides.

4. Change the colour for your construction. From the Display menu,
   select Color and choose red.

5. To construct the altitude from A to BC, select A and line BC. From the
   Construct menu, choose Perpendicular Line.

6. Repeat the method in exercise 5 to construct the altitudes from B and
   from C. What do you notice about the altitudes?

7. The point of intersection of the altitudes is the *orthocentre*. Drag a
   vertex of the triangle. Observe the orthocentre in other triangles.
   Record your observations.

8. Write to explain how the type of triangle affects the position of the
   orthocentre.

In the *Investigations*, you should have discovered that in an obtuse triangle, the
perpendiculars from two vertices do not intersect the opposite sides. In this
case, the opposite sides must be extended so that these altitudes can be drawn.

In a right triangle, two altitudes coincide with the sides of the triangle.

COMMUNICATING the IDEAS

The Geometer's Sketchpad is used to measure angles and lengths. How have you measured
angles and lengths previously? Which method do you believe is more accurate? Explain.

An *altitude* of a triangle is the line segment from a vertex perpendicular to the opposite side. If you completed Section 11.4, you have already worked with the altitudes of a triangle. The properties you observed are summarized.

Altitude Properties

1. The length of an altitude is a height of the triangle. It is used to calculate the area of the triangle.

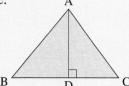

Altitude, AD = 5
Base, BC = 8
Area of $\triangle ABC = \frac{1}{2}(5)(8)$
$= 20$

2. The three altitudes of a triangle meet at the orthocentre, O. When the triangle is obtuse, the orthocentre is outside the triangle.

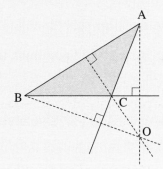

These properties can be used to solve problems.

Example 1

In $\triangle PQR$, the altitude RT = 8 cm and the base PQ = 11 cm. Calculate the area of $\triangle PQR$.

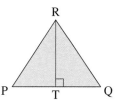

Solution

Use the area formula.
Area $= \frac{1}{2}(\text{base} \times \text{height})$
$= \frac{1}{2}(11)(8)$
$= 44$
The area of $\triangle PQR$ is 44 cm^2.

Example 2

The area of △ABC is 12 cm².
Altitude BD = 4 cm
What is the length of AC?

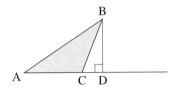

Solution

Use the area formula.
Area = $\frac{1}{2}$(base × height)

Area = $\frac{1}{2}$(AC)(BD)

Substitute the known measurements.
$12 = \frac{1}{2}$(AC)(4)
$12 = 2$AC
AC = 6

The length of AC is 6 cm.

DISCUSSING the IDEAS

1. In *Example 1*, the area was calculated using altitude RT and base PQ. Explain how you would calculate the area using QR as the base instead. Why can a line segment that is not at the bottom of the triangle still be a base?

2. In *Example 2*, the altitude BD is outside the triangle. Where will the orthocentre be?

3. a) Is it possible for the orthocentre of a triangle to coincide with a vertex? Explain, using a diagram.

   b) Is it possible for the orthocentre of a triangle to lie on one side but not at a vertex? Explain, using a diagram.

11.5 EXERCISES

1. Calculate the area of each triangle.

a)

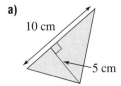

10 cm

5 cm

b)

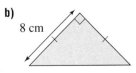

8 cm

c)

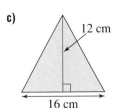

12 cm

16 cm

2. The area of △ABC (below left) is 27 cm² and BC = 9 cm.
Calculate the length of altitude AD.

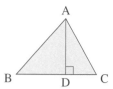 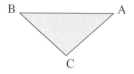

3. For △ABC (above right), explain why it is necessary to extend BC before constructing the altitude from A.

4. a) Draw a large scalene triangle.

- Construct the altitudes of the triangle. Label the orthocentre.
- Use a different colour to construct the medians. Label the centroid.
- Are the centroid and the orthocentre the same point? Explain.

b) Repeat part a using an isosceles triangle. Write to describe the locations of the centroid and the orthocentre.

c) Repeat part a using an equilateral triangle. Write to describe the locations of the centroid and the orthocentre.

d) In an equilateral triangle, the centroid and the orthocentre are the same point. Explain how you could have deduced this from your results in part b.

5. Paula is planning to paint a triangle on a rectangular canvas that is 32 cm by 48 cm. Calculate the area of the largest triangle she can paint.

6. a) Calculate the area of △ABC.

b) Calculate the length of AC.

c) Calculate the length of altitude BD to the nearest tenth of a metre.

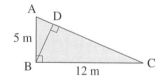

Construction
FOCUS

Estimating Roofing Materials

Use this information to complete exercises 7 to 10.
Denise and Jack are planning to put new shingles on their roof. Before purchasing the materials they must:

- Determine the area of the roof.
- Calculate how many shingles they need.

The *hip roof* on their house has two triangular sections and two trapezoidal sections. Denise and Jack made these measurements.

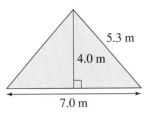

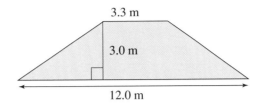

7. Use the formulas for the area of a triangle and the area of a trapezoid. Calculate the area of each section.

8. The roof has 2 triangular sections and 2 trapezoidal sections. What is the area of the roof?

9. To allow for waste, 10% of the area must be added to the area.

   a) Calculate 10% of the area of the roof.

   b) What is the area, including the allowance for waste?

10. Shingles are sold in bundles. One bundle covers 3 m² (this includes allowances for overlap). Use the area from exercise 9b. How many bundles are needed?

11. Drew and Natalie own a large bungalow. They calculate the area of their roof is 320 m².

    a) They must allow 10% for waste. What area of shingles do they require?

    b) Calculate the number of bundles needed to cover the roof.

    c) One bundle costs $15.50. What is the total cost of the shingles?

12. Use the same method as Denise and Jack. Calculate the number of bundles of shingles required for a house with this roof.

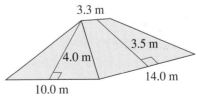

13. Draw the triangle with vertices A(3, 1), B(5, 7), and C(8, 1). Draw the altitude from B to meet AC at D.

    a) State the coordinates of point D.

    b) Determine the equation of the altitude.

14. The side PQ of △PQR has slope 3. Find the slope of the altitude from R to PQ.

Investigating the Altitude to the Hypotenuse

When an altitude is drawn to the hypotenuse of a right triangle, two smaller right triangles are created. In these exercises, you will explore the relationship among these triangles.

You will need:
• two sheets of paper
• scissors
• a protractor and a ruler

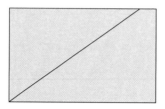

15. To construct a right triangle, draw a line from one corner of your paper to the opposite side. Construct and cut out two identical right triangles. Label each as △ABC, with ∠A the right angle.

16. One way to construct an altitude is by folding. To construct the altitude through vertex A, fold the triangle so that the line through B and C folds onto itself and point A is on the crease. On one triangle, construct the altitude AD to the hypotenuse.

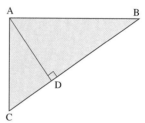

17. There are now three triangles. Measure the angles in all the triangles. What do you notice? Triangles with this property are *similar* triangles.

18. Cut along AD to make △ABD and △ACD. Label the vertices.

19. Place the small triangles on top of the large triangle so that one set of equal angles coincide.

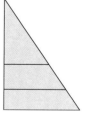

a) What do you notice about the sides opposite this equal angle?

b) Measure and compare the lengths of the corresponding sides.

c) Write a statement about the ratios of corresponding sides in similar triangles.

In your journal, explain what the altitude in a triangle is, and how it can be used in different types of problems. Use examples to illustrate your explanation.

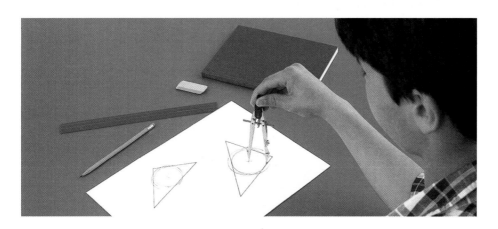

11.6 Using *The Geometer's Sketchpad*: Angle Bisectors of Triangles

Have you ever tried to draw a circle that fits perfectly inside a triangle? Try it! It isn't easy because you don't know where the centre of the circle is. Studying the angle bisectors of a triangle will help you solve this problem.

In the diagram, line segment CD is an angle bisector of △ABC because it bisects ∠C.

An *angle bisector* is a line that divides an angle into two equal angles.

In *Investigations 1* to *4*, you will observe the properties of the angle bisectors in a triangle. These properties will be used in Section 11.7.

Use *The Geometer's Sketchpad*.

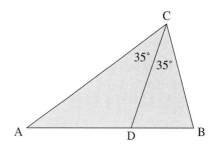

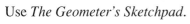

INVESTIGATION 1

Constructing an Angle Bisector

From the File menu, choose New Sketch.

1. Construct △ABC, as described in *Setup*, page 532.

2. Hold down the shift key. Select point A, then B, then C. From the Construct menu, choose Angle Bisector. This produces a ray from B that cuts ∠ABC in half.

3. Construct the point of intersection of the bisector and side AC. Label this point D.

4. Select the angle bisector. From the Display menu, choose Hide Ray. The angle bisector is hidden.

5. Construct segment BD.

Angle Bisectors and Distance

1. Construct △ABC and BD, the bisector of ∠B, as in *Investigation 1*.

2. Select BD. From the Construct menu, choose Point on Object. Move the point so that it is easily visible. Label this point P.

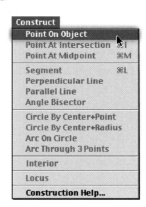

3. Measure the distance from P to BA:

- Select P and BA. From the Construct menu, choose Perpendicular Line.
- Select the perpendicular line and side BA. From the Construct menu, choose Point At Intersection. Label this point Q.
- Hide the perpendicular line. Construct segment PQ.
- Measure the length of PQ.

4. Measure the distance from P to BC:

- Construct a line through P perpendicular to BC.
- Construct the Point At Intersection of the perpendicular and side BC. Label this point R.
- Hide the perpendicular line. Construct segment PR.
- Measure the length of PR.

5. What do you notice about the lengths of PQ and PR?

6. Move point P along BD. Observe the measurements.

7. Drag a vertex of △ABC. Observe the measurements.

8. Write a statement about any point on an angle bisector.

Constructing Three Angle Bisectors

1. Construct △ABC and BD, the bisector of ∠B, as in *Investigation 1*.

2. Bisect ∠BAC. Bisect ∠ACB. What do you notice about the angle bisectors?

3. Select two angle bisectors. Construct their intersection point.

4. From the Construct menu, choose Point at Intersection. Label it O.

5. Drag a vertex of △ABC. Observe how the angle bisectors change position as the shape of △ABC changes.

6. Write a statement about the three angle bisectors of a triangle.

Constructing the Incircle

1. Use △ABC from *Investigation 3*.

2. Measure the distance from O to AB:
   - Construct a line through O, perpendicular to AB.
   - Construct the Point At Intersection of the perpendicular and AB. Label it S.
   - Hide the perpendicular line, then construct the segment OS.
   - Measure the length of OS.

3. Construct a circle with centre O and radius OS: select O and OS. From the Construct menu, choose Circle by Center + Radius. What do you notice?

4. Drag a vertex of △ABC to see if the same result holds for other triangles.

5. Write a statement about the intersection point of the angle bisectors in a triangle.

COMMUNICATING the IDEAS

List the tools that are needed to construct an incircle if computer software, such as *The Geometer's Sketchpad*, is not available. Do you believe these tools will become extinct when everyone has access to a computer? Explain.

11.7   Angle Bisectors of Triangles

An *angle bisector* is a line that divides an angle into two equal angles. If you completed Section 11.6, you have already worked with the angle bisectors in a triangle. The properties you observed are summarized.

Angle Bisector Properties

1. Each point on an angle bisector is *equidistant* from the arms of the angle. Since ∠ABD = ∠DBF, then ED = DF

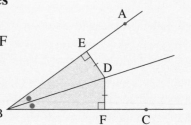

2. The three angle bisectors in a triangle meet at a single point. This intersection point is the *incentre*. It is the centre of the circle that just touches each side of the triangle. This is the *incircle*.

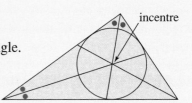

These properties can be used to solve problems, including the problem posed on page 549.

Example 1

A student is creating a design for art class. He wants to draw the largest circle that will fit inside △ABC. Describe what he should do.

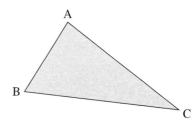

Solution

The largest circle is the incircle.
Draw the bisector of ∠A and the bisector of ∠B.
The centre of the circle is the point where the bisectors intersect. Label this point O.
Draw a line through O, perpendicular to one side of the triangle. Label the point of intersection Q.
Use compasses to draw a circle with centre O and radius OQ.

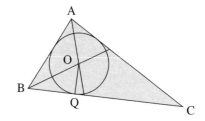

Example 2

The circle, centre O, is the incircle of isosceles $\triangle PQR$.
Determine the measure of $\angle PRO$.

Solution

Since $\triangle PQR$ is isosceles,
$\angle PQR = \angle PRQ$

Since the sum of the angles in the triangle is 180°,

$\angle PQR + \angle PRQ + 40° = 180°$
$\qquad \angle PQR + \angle PRQ = 140°$

Two equal angles have a sum of 140°.

So, each angle is $\dfrac{140°}{2} = 70°$
$\qquad\qquad\qquad \angle PRQ = 70°$

Since O is the incentre, RO is an angle bisector.

Therefore, $\angle PRO = \frac{1}{2}\angle PRQ$
$\qquad\quad \angle PRO = \frac{1}{2}(70°)$
$\qquad\qquad\quad = 35°$

DISCUSSING the IDEAS

1. In *Example 1*, why did the student not need to draw the bisector of $\angle C$?

2. In *Example 1*, explain why the student must draw a perpendicular segment from O to BC.

3. In *Example 2*, how can you tell from the diagram that $\triangle PQR$ is isosceles?

4. In *Example 2*, suppose QO is drawn. What kind of triangle is $\triangle QOR$? Explain how you know.

A 1. Point P is on the bisector of each angle. Determine the value of each variable. Explain your reasoning.

a)

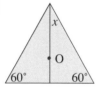

3 cm

b)

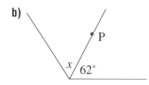

62°

2. Point O is the incentre of each triangle. Determine the value of each variable. Explain your reasoning.

a)

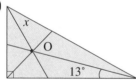

60°   60°

b)

52°
87°

c)

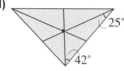

13°

d)

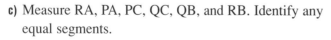

25°

42°

B 3. Point O is the incentre of the triangle. Determine the value of *x*. Explain your reasoning.

50°

4. Draw equilateral △ABC.

   a) Construct the medians. Label the centroid O.

   b) Draw a perpendicular from O to side AB. Label the point of intersection Q.

   c) Draw a circle, centre O and radius OQ.

   d) What can you conclude about the centroid of an equilateral triangle?

5. **a)** Construct △PQR, then construct the angle bisectors.

   b) Draw the incircle of the triangle. Mark points A, B, and C where the circle touches the sides of the triangle.

   c) Measure RA, PA, PC, QC, QB, and RB. Identify any equal segments.

   d) Write to describe relationships among the line segments in part c.

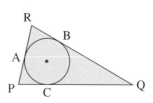

6. Point O is the incentre of equilateral △ABC (below left). Determine the measure of ∠APC and ∠PAC. Explain your reasoning.

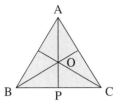
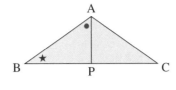

7. Triangle ABC is isosceles with AB = AC (above right). Segment AP is the bisector of ∠BAC. What is the sum of the two marked angles? Explain your reasoning.

The Circumcircle of a Triangle

Cellular phones are an important means of communication. They rely on transmission towers placed throughout the country. A cellular phone company wants to locate a tower to serve three towns. The company will place the tower so that it is the same distance from each town. How does the company know where to locate the tower?

In exercises 8 to 11, you will explore a property to help you solve this problem.

Start a New Sketch in *The Geometer's Sketchpad*.

8. a) Construct line segment AB.

b) Construct the midpoint of AB. Label it J.

c) Construct a line through J, perpendicular to AB. This line is the *perpendicular bisector* of AB.

d) Select the perpendicular line, then construct a point on it. Label the point P.

e) Join AP and BP. Measure their lengths. What do you notice?

f) Move point P along the perpendicular. Observe the measurements.

g) Write a statement about the relationship between a point on the perpendicular bisector of a segment and the endpoints of the segment.

9. a) Construct and label △ABC.

b) Construct the perpendicular bisector of AB:

- Construct the midpoint of AB. Label it J.
- Construct a line through J, perpendicular to AB.

c) Construct the perpendicular bisector of BC.

d) Construct the perpendicular bisector of AC.

e) What do you notice about the three perpendicular bisectors?

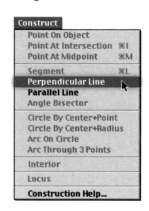

f) Construct the intersection point, P, of the perpendicular bisectors. Remember that you select only two bisectors to do this.

g) Drag a vertex of △ABC. Observe what happens to P.

h) Construct segment AP, then measure its length.

i) Select point P and segment AP. From the Construct menu, choose Circle By Center + Radius. What do you notice?

j) Drag a vertex of △ABC to observe the results in other triangles.

10. Look up the prefix *circum* in a dictionary. Explain why the intersection point of the perpendicular bisectors of the sides of a triangle is called the *circumcentre* of the triangle.

11. Explain how the cellular phone company can use the results of exercises 8 and 9 to identify the best location for the cell tower.

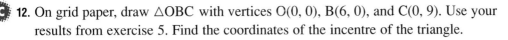

12. On grid paper, draw △OBC with vertices O(0, 0), B(6, 0), and C(0, 9). Use your results from exercise 5. Find the coordinates of the incentre of the triangle.

13. Consider a right triangle, with legs 5 cm and 12 cm.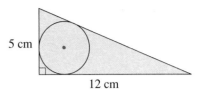

a) Determine the area of the incircle of the triangle.

b) Determine the area of the triangle.

c) Use *The Geometer's Sketchpad*. Experiment to find the dimensions of the right triangle with the smallest area for this incircle.

To make the circle remain while the hypotenuse moves:

- Construct a small square ABCD (see below). Construct a circle with vertex C as the centre, and the side of the square as a radius.

- Extend two sides of the square: Select point A and side CB. Construct a line through A parallel to BC. Then select point A and side DC. Construct a line through A parallel to DC.

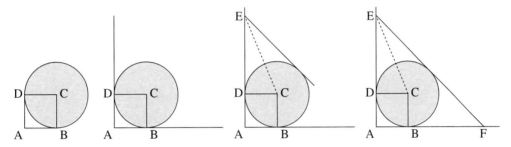

- Construct a point E on the vertical line. Construct segment EC. Double-click on EC to make it a reflection line. Select line AE. From the Transform menu, choose Reflect. This reflects AE in the line EC. Label F, the point of intersection of this line and AB.

- Construct the triangle interior and measure the area. Drag vertex E to observe how the area changes.

d) What are the dimensions of the triangle with the smallest area?

COMMUNICATING the IDEAS

In your journal, explain why the point of intersection of the angle bisectors of a triangle is equidistant from the sides of the triangle.

Using *The Geometer's Sketchpad*: Interior and Exterior Angles

Do you have an argyle sweater, a hat with a diamond border, or a floor with trapezoidal tiles? Designs such as these are created from geometric figures.

Not all figures will cover a surface. For figures to tessellate (that is, to join with no gaps), their angles must fit together. Will any triangle or quadrilateral tessellate? To answer this question, you will investigate some properties of interior and exterior angles in triangles and quadrilaterals. These properties will be used in Section 11.9.

 Use *The Geometer's Sketchpad*.

> **INVESTIGATION 1**

Measuring and Tabulating the Angles in a Triangle

1. Construct ∠ABC as in *Setup*, page 532.

2. Hold down the shift key. Click on point A, then B, then C.

3. From the Measure menu, choose Angle. The measure of ∠ABC is displayed.

4. Follow a procedure similar to exercise 3 to display the measures of ∠BAC and ∠BCA.

5. Hold down the shift key. Click on the three angle measures. From the Measure menu, choose Calculate.

6. Use the calculator to find the sum of the angle measures:
  • From the Values menu, choose one angle, then click on ⬚+⬚.
  • From the Values menu, choose a second angle, then click on ⬚+⬚.
  • From the Values menu, choose the third angle, then click OK.
  The screen displays the sum of the angle measures.

7. Select the four measurements. From the Measure menu, choose Tabulate. The screen displays the measurements in a table.

8. Drag a vertex of the triangle. The angle measurements change, but the table does not. A table gives a permanent record of your measurements.

9. Select the table. From the Measure menu, choose Add Entry. The table will extend to include your new measurements.

The Sum of Interior Angles

1. Construct △ABC and a table of measurements as in *Investigation 1*. Add entries to the table until you have recorded 5 sets of measurements. Write a statement about the sum of the angles in a triangle.

2. Start a New Sketch. Construct quadrilateral ABCD.

3. Measure the angles. Use the calculator to find their sum.

4. Set up a table to record the measurements.

5. Drag a vertex of the quadrilateral. Observe the change in the measurements.

6. What happens when you drag a vertex so the quadrilateral contains an angle greater than 180°?

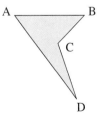

7. Can you explain why the sum of the angles changes? Suppose *The Geometer's Sketchpad* could display measurements of reflex angles. What would the sum be?

8. Drag a vertex so that all the angles are less than 180°. Add entries to the table until you have recorded 5 sets of measurements. Write a statement about the sum of the angles in a quadrilateral.

9. Construct a diagonal of the quadrilateral. What is the sum of the interior angles of the two triangles formed by the diagonal? How does this construction explain the sum of the angles in a quadrilateral?

Constructing and Measuring Exterior Angles

The angle marked with a star is an *exterior* angle of △ABC. This exterior angle is created by extending side BC beyond vertex C. Angle BAF and ∠EBC are two other exterior angles of △ABC.

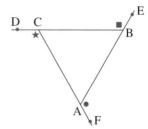

In this investigation, construct triangles using rays instead of segments.

- Construct and label three points A, B, and C. Click on the Segment tool and drag to the right. Select the Ray tool.

- Select the three points. From the Construct menu, choose Ray.

To measure exterior angles:

- Construct a point on each ray outside the triangle. Look at the diagram above. Construct D on the ray from B. Then select D, C, and A to measure the exterior angle at C.

1. Start a New Sketch. Construct △ABC using rays, as instructed above.

2. Construct the exterior points as explained above. Measure ∠ACB and ∠ACD. Use the calculator to find their sum.

3. Drag a vertex of △ABC and observe the results. Explain what you notice. Make a prediction about the measure of an exterior angle of a triangle.

4. Check your prediction by measuring ∠ABC and its exterior angle ∠CBE, then checking their sum.

5. Write a statement about a property of an exterior angle of a triangle.

6. Measure ∠ABC and ∠CAB. Use the calculator to find their sum.

7. Measure ∠ACD. What do you notice?

8. Drag a vertex of △ABC and observe the results.

9. Make a prediction about one of the other exterior angles. Check your prediction. If your prediction was false, reexamine your results and revise your prediction.

10. Write a statement about another property of the exterior angles of a triangle.

The Sum of Exterior Angles

1. Start a New Sketch.

2. Construct △ABC using rays, as instructed above.

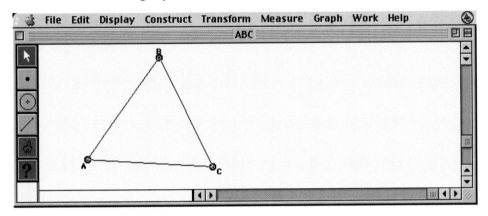

3. Find the sum of the exterior angles and tabulate the measurements. (See the instructions on page 558.)

4. Record 5 sets of measurements in the table. Examine the results. Make a conjecture about the sum of the exterior angles of a triangle.

5. Make the triangle as small as a point by dragging the vertices toward one another. What do you notice? How does this help explain your conjecture?

6. Predict the sum of the exterior angles of a quadrilateral. Construct a quadrilateral using rays. Measure the exterior angles. Was your prediction correct? If not, revise your conjecture. Remember to recalculate if the quadrilateral contains a reflex angle.

7. Make the quadrilateral very small by dragging the vertices toward one another. What do you notice?

8. Write a statement about the exterior angles of a triangle and of a quadrilateral.

COMMUNICATING the IDEAS

You know the sum of the exterior angles of a triangle and a quadrilateral. In your journal, write to explain how you could apply what you know to finding the sum of the exterior angles of a pentagon.

If you completed Section 11.8, you have already worked with the interior and exterior angles in triangles and quadrilaterals. The properties you observed are summarized.

Properties of Interior and Exterior Angles in Triangles and Quadrilaterals

1. The interior angles in a triangle add to 180°.

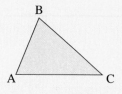

$$\angle A + \angle B + \angle C = 180°$$

2. The interior angles in a quadrilateral add to 360°.

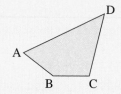

$$\angle A + \angle B + \angle C + \angle D = 360°$$

3. In a triangle and a quadrilateral, an exterior angle is supplementary to the interior adjacent angle.

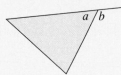
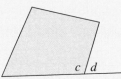

$$a + b = 180° \qquad c + d = 180°$$

4. An exterior angle of a triangle is equal to the sum of the interior opposite angles.

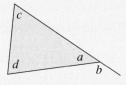

$$b = c + d$$

5. The exterior angles of a triangle and a quadrilateral add to 360°.

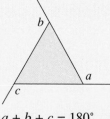
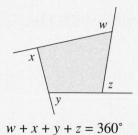

$$a + b + c = 180° \qquad\qquad w + x + y + z = 360°$$

These properties can be used to solve problems.

Example 1

Determine the size of each indicated angle.

a)

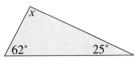

b)

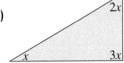

Solution

a) Since the sum of the interior angles of a triangle is $180°$,

$$x + 62° + 25° = 180°$$
$$x = 180° - 62° - 25°$$
$$x = 93°$$

The indicated angle is $93°$.

b) Set up an equation to solve for the variable.

$$x + 2x + 3x = 180°$$
$$6x = 180°$$
$$x = 30°$$

Therefore, $2x = 60°$ and $3x = 90°$
The three angles are $30°$, $60°$ and $90°$.

Example 2

Determine the size of each indicated angle.

a)

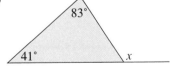

b)

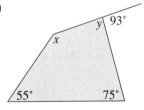

Solution

a) Since the exterior angle is equal to the sum of the interior opposite angles,

$$x = 41° + 83°$$
$$= 124°$$

b) Since an exterior angle is the supplement of the interior adjacent angle,

$$y + 93° = 180°$$
$$y = 180° - 93°$$
$$y = 87°$$

Since the sum of the interior angles of a quadrilateral is 360°,

$$x + y + 55° + 75° = 360°$$
$$x + 87° + 55° + 75° = 360°$$
$$x + 217° = 360°$$
$$x = 143°$$

DISCUSSING the IDEAS

1. In *Example 1a*, what are the measures of the exterior angles of the triangle?

2. *In Example 1b*, the angles in the triangle were represented by x, $2x$, and $3x$.

   a) Why type of triangle is it?

   b) What type of triangle would have angles represented by x, $7x$, and $7x$?

3. In *Example 2a*, explain why the exterior angle is equal to the sum of the interior opposite angles.

4. Is the exterior angle of a quadrilateral equal to the sum of the three interior opposite angles? If it is not, how is the exterior angle related to these interior angles?

11.9 EXERCISES

A **1.** Determine the measure of each angle x. Explain your reasoning.

a)

b)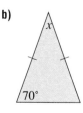

c)

d)

2. Determine the measure of each angle x. Explain your reasoning.

a)

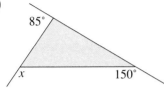

b)

c)

d)

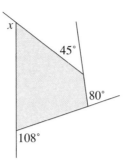

3. Consider the question posed on page 558. Will any triangle or quadrilateral tessellate?

a) Construct a scalene triangle. Make six copies of the triangle on stiff paper or cardboard, then cut them out.

b) Repeat part a for a quadrilateral.

c) Use the triangle. Try to form a pattern by arranging the triangles around a vertex with no gaps and no overlaps.

d) Repeat part c for the quadrilateral.

e) Could the triangles be arranged so their vertices meet at a single point with no gaps or overlaps? Explain.

f) Could the quadrilaterals be arranged so their vertices meet at a single point with no gaps or overlaps? Explain.

g) Measure all the angles at the common vertex. Determine their sum. What do you notice?

h) You experimented with only one triangle and one quadrilateral. Will any triangles or quadrilaterals work? Check the results of classmates who drew different triangles and quadrilaterals. Explain your reasoning.

4. Look in magazines or catalogues for designs that use triangles and quadrilaterals to cover surfaces or fabrics. Collect at least three different designs. Outline the figures, then explain why they tessellate.

5. Determine the measure of each indicated angle. Explain your reasoning.

a)

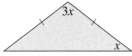

b)

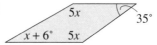

c)

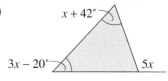

d)

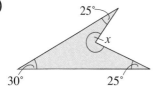

e)

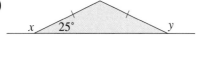

f)

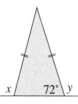

6. a) Determine the values of x and y in each diagram.

i)

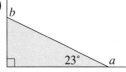

ii)

b) Explain the results in part a. Write a statement about the exterior angles of an isosceles triangle formed by extending the base.

7. a) Determine the values of a, b, and $a + b$ in each diagram.

i)

ii)

b) Explain the results in part a. Write a statement about the exterior angles of a right triangle formed by extending the legs.

8. Determine the measure of each indicated angle. Explain your reasoning.

a)

b)

c)

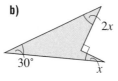
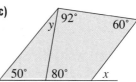

9. Determine the measure of each exterior angle of a regular pentagon.

ACADEMIC FOCUS

Polygons

Have you ever looked closely at a loonie? It approximates a *hendecagon*, a polygon with 11 sides. All the sides of a loonie have the same length and all the angles have the same measure. Therefore, the loonie approximates a *regular* hendecagon.

To draw a loonie, you need to know the size of the angles. In the following exercises, you will investigate the interior angles of a hendecagon and other polygons.

You know the sum of the angles in a triangle is 180° and the sum of the angles in a quadrilateral is 360°. You will calculate or measure the angles in a few other polygons and look for a pattern.

If you have *The Geometer's Sketchpad*, use it to complete exercises 10, 11, and 14.

10. Sketch a pentagon. Draw diagonals from one vertex to divide the pentagon into 3 triangles. What is the sum of the angles in a pentagon? If you have *The Geometer's Sketchpad*, construct a pentagon: draw 5 points, then join adjacent points with segments. Measure the angles and determine their sum.

11. Repeat exercise 10 for a hexagon and a heptagon.

12. Copy this table. Record your results from exercises 10 and 11.

Polygon	Number of sides	Sum of the interior angles
Triangle	3	180°
Quadrilateral	4	360°
Pentagon	6	
Hexagon	7	
Heptagon	5	

13. Look at the completed table for exercise 12. Describe the relationship between the number of sides and the sum of the interior angles in a polygon. Explain the relationship.

14. Predict the sum of the interior angles of a *decagon*, a 10-sided polygon. Check your conjecture using *The Geometer's Sketchpad*, if possible.

15. a) What is the name of a regular triangle?

    b) What is the name of a regular quadrilateral?

    c) Which familiar object has the shape of a regular octagon?

16. What is the sum of the interior angles of a loonie?

17. What is the measure of one angle of a loonie, to 1 decimal place?

18. Write an equation to relate the number of sides, *n*, of a polygon and the sum of its interior angles, *s*.

C 19. In *Example 1b*, the measures of the angles are in the ratio 1 : 2 : 3. Suppose the measures of the angles in a quadrilateral were in the ratio 1 : 2 : 3 : 4. What would the measure of each angle be?

20. Suggest why an exterior angle of a triangle is not defined as the entire exterior angle around the vertex. That is, if one angle is 60°, why is the exterior angle not defined as 300°, instead of 120°?

21. a) Which of these regular polygons will tessellate? Explain your reasoning.

i)   ii)   iii)   iv)   v)

    b) Suppose you want to use regular octagons to make a design that tessellates. What other figure would you need to fill the gaps? Explain.

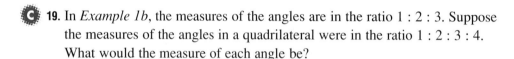
COMMUNICATING the IDEAS

In your journal:
   a) Explain why an exterior angle in a triangle is equal to the sum of the interior opposite angles.

   b) Explain why a quadrilateral cannot have two reflex angles.

Trina Raynes is a carpenter. When she hangs a door, she makes sure the sides of the frame are parallel and the top and sides of the frame are square.

- Trina measures the sides of the doorframe to check they are equal.

- Then Trina uses a square to check that the top and sides of the doorframe form right angles.

Why does Trina not need to measure the angles at the base of the frame?
In this section, we will investigate the geometry property Trina uses in her work.

Use *The Geometer's Sketchpad*.

SETUP

From the File menu, choose New Sketch.

1. To construct AB, CD, and transversal EF:

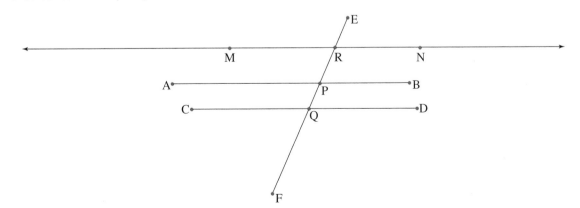

Click on this tool ...	*... and do this:*
	a) Draw two horizontal line segments.
	b) Draw a third line segment that intersects the other two. This segment is a transversal.
	c) Label the three segments AB, CD, and EF as shown.
	d) Select AB and EF. From the Construct menu, choose Point At Intersection.
	e) Select CD and EF. From the Construct menu, choose Point At Intersection.
	f) Click on the intersection point of AB and EF. Label it P.
	g) Click on the intersection point of CD and EF. Label it Q.

2. To construct a line MN parallel to AB:

Click on this tool ...	*... and do this:*
	a) Draw a point above AB and to the left of segment EF.
	b) Click on the point. Label it M.
	c) Select point M and segment AB. From the Construct menu, choose Parallel Line.
	d) Click on the parallel line. From the Construct menu, choose Point On Object.
	e) Drag the new point to the right of EF.
	f) Select the parallel line and segment AB. From the Construct menu, choose Point At Intersection.
	g) Click on the two constructed points. Label the intersection point R and the point on the parallel line N.

In the *Investigation*, you will observe properties of parallel lines.

Angles Formed by a Transversal

In the *Setup*, transversal EF intersects AB, CD, and MN. Four angles are formed at each intersection point.

1. Construct AB, CD, MN, and EF as in *Setup*.

2. Measure the four angles at each of points R, P, and Q. (If necessary, refer to page 541 to review measuring an angle.)

3. Drag point A. If you have constructed the diagram correctly, the line through M and N should move, too. It should remain parallel to AB. If it does not, reconstruct the parallel line.

4. Hold down the mouse button and move each angle measurement until it is visible. Line up the measurements for the four angles at P by clicking on them and dragging. Repeat for the angles at Q and R.

m∠APE =	m∠APF =	m∠BPE =	m∠BPF =
m∠CQE =	m∠CQF=	m∠DQE =	m∠DQF =
m∠MRE=	m∠MRF =	m∠NRE =	m∠NRF =

5. Examine the measures of the four angles at each point. What do you notice?

6. Drag point A.

   a) Describe the effect on the angle measures at Q.

   b) Describe the effect on the angle measures at R.

7. Drag point C until the angles at Q are equal to those at P and at R. What do you notice about CD?

8. Write a statement about the angles formed by a transversal intersecting two non-parallel lines.

9. Write a statement about the angles formed by a transversal intersecting two parallel lines.

COMMUNICATING the IDEAS

A friend of yours has forgotten how to measure an angle using *The Geometer's Sketchpad*. In your journal, write to explain how this is done.

If you completed Section 11.10, you have already worked with angles and parallel lines. The properties you observed are summarized.

Properties of Angles Formed by a Transversal

1. A transversal that intersects two lines creates eight angles.

There are 2 pairs of *alternate angles*.

- c and e
- d and f

There are 4 pairs of *corresponding angles*.

- b and f
- c and g
- a and e
- d and h

There are 2 pairs of *interior angles*.

- c and f
- d and e

2. When a transversal intersects two parallel lines, the angles at each intersection point form patterns.

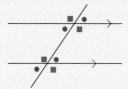

- The two angles in each pair of alternate angles are equal.

- The two angles in each pair of corresponding angles are equal.

- The interior angles are supplementary.

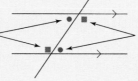

These angles add to 180°.   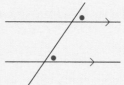   These angles add to 180°.

These properties can be used to solve problems.

Example 1

Determine the angle measure indicated by each small letter.

a)
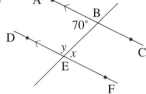

b)
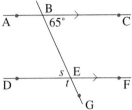

Solution

a) AC is parallel to DF. Since ∠FEB
   and ∠ABE are alternate angles,
   ∠FEB = ∠ABE
   $x = 70°$

   Since ∠DEB and ∠ABE are
   interior angles,
   ∠DEB + ∠ABE = 180°
   $y + 70° = 180°$
   $y = 110°$

b) AC is parallel to DF. Since ∠CBE
   and ∠DEB are alternate angles,
   ∠CBE = ∠DEB
   $s = 65°$

   Since ∠GEB is a straight angle,
   $s + t = 180°$
   $65° + t = 180°$
   $t = 115°$

Example 2

Determine the angle measure indicated by each small letter.

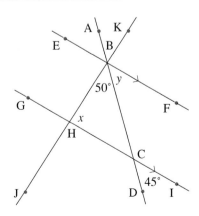

Solution

EF is parallel to GI. Since ∠FBC and ∠ICD are
corresponding angles,
∠FBC = ∠ICD
   $y = 45°$

Since ∠CHB and ∠HBF are interior angles,
∠CHB + ∠HBF = 180°
   $x + (50° + y) = 180°$
   $x + 50° + 45° = 180°$
   $x + 95° = 180°$
   $x = 85°$

1. In *Example 1*, suggest another way to determine the values of x and y.

2. In *Example 2*, explain why $\angle HBF$ is $50° + y$.

11.11 EXERCISES

A 1. Determine the measure of each angle at P, Q, and R.

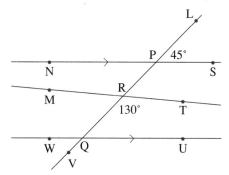

2. Name:

a) a pair of acute alternate angles

b) a pair of obtuse corresponding angles

c) a pair of interior angles

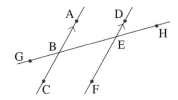

3. Sometimes lines that look parallel are not parallel. Which of the lines l_1, l_2, and l_3 are parallel? Explain your reasoning.

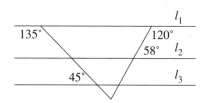

B 4. Determine the measure of each indicated angle. Explain your reasoning.

a)

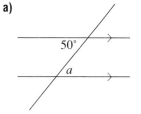

b)

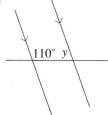

c)

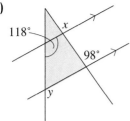

d)

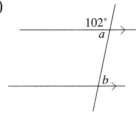

5. Determine the measure of each indicated angle. Explain your reasoning.

a)

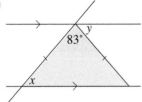

b)

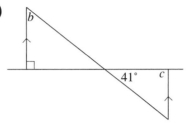

6. Determine the measure of each indicated angle, below left.

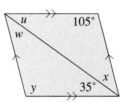

7. Determine the measure of each indicated angle, above right.

8. Can two intersecting lines both be parallel to a third line? Draw a diagram to support your answer.

9. Refer to the question on page 569. Explain why Trina does not need to measure the angles at the base of the frame.

C **10.** Marsha is making a model for art with a supply of coloured straws. She attaches a red straw to a green straw at right angles. She then attaches a blue straw to the green straw at right angles. Are the red and blue straws parallel? Explain.

COMMUNICATING the IDEAS

In your journal, summarize the properties of the angles formed when a transversal intersects two parallel lines. Include sketches with your explanation.

11.12 Representing 3-Dimensional Objects in 2 Dimensions

We know that the two rails in a set of tracks never meet but, when they disappear into the distance, it appears that they do!

To create a realistic painting of railway tracks, an artist must know the rules of perspective drawing. One rule is that parallel lines appear to meet at a single point in the distance.

In this activity, you will examine perspective by constructing a box with one-point perspective.

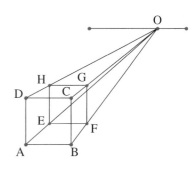

Start a New Sketch in *The Geometer's Sketchpad.*

1. To construct a square:

   • Draw a short horizontal line segment, then label the two endpoints A and B.

   • Double-click on point A. Point A is now a centre of rotation.

   • Select segment AB and point B. From the Transform menu, choose Rotate. When the dialog box appears, type 90 and click OK. There will now be two segments at right angles. Label the new endpoint D.

   • Construct segment BD.

   • Double-click on segment BD. Segment BD is now a line of reflection.

   • Select segments AB and AD. From the Transform menu, choose Reflect.

   • Hide segment BD. Select the new vertex and label it C.

   • Drag point A and observe that the figure remains a square.

2. To construct a point in the distance:

   • Draw a long line segment as far away from the square as possible.

   • Click on the line segment. From the Construct menu, choose Point On Object. Label the point O.

   • Construct segments AO, BO, CO, and DO.

3. To complete the box:
- Click on segment AO. From the Construct menu, choose Point On Object. Label the point E.
- Select point E and segment AB. From the Construct menu, choose Parallel Line.
- Select the new line and segment BO. From the Construct menu, choose Point At Intersection. Label the intersection point F.
- Hide the line through E and F, then construct segment EF.
- Select point F and segment BC. From the Construct menu, choose Parallel Line.
- Select the new line, and segment CO. From the Construct menu, choose Point At Intersection. Label the intersection point G.
- Hide the line through F and G, then construct segment FG.
- Select point G and segment DC. From the Construct menu, choose Parallel Line.
- Select the new line and segment DO. From the Construct menu, choose Point At Intersection. Label the intersection point H. Hide the line through GH, then construct segments GH and EH.
- Drag point O to observe the box from different angles.
- Hide the perspective lines, then join corresponding vertices of the box with segments. Then move point O.

4. From exercises 1 to 3, explain how you know that ABCD is a square.

5. a) What is the relationship between ∠OHG and ∠ODC? Explain.
   b) Find an angle equal to ∠OEF.   c) Find an angle equal to ∠OBA.

6. a) Find an angle equal to ∠DAO.   b) Find an angle equal to ∠BAO.

7. The construction in exercises 1 to 3 introduces perspective. You can use the same ideas to create drawings of other 3-dimensional objects. Try drawing your initials in 3 dimensions.

COMMUNICATING the IDEAS

In your journal, write to explain how you used *The Geometer's Sketchpad* to make a 3-dimensional drawing of a letter.

Many games are played on four-sided fields and courts. Tennis, racquetball, volleyball, basketball, and football use rectangular playing areas. We refer to a baseball field as a diamond, but it is actually a square.

The infield in baseball is 90 feet (about 27.4 m) on each side. The pitcher is 60 feet 6 inches (about 18.4 m) from the batter. Is the pitcher the same distance from all the bases and from home plate? In this section, you will investigate some properties of quadrilaterals that will help you answer this question. These properties will be used in Section 11.14.

Use *The Geometer's Sketchpad*.

SETUP

From the File menu, choose New Sketch.

1. To construct quadrilateral ABCD:

Click on this...	*... and do this:*
	a) Draw 4 points.
	b) Label the points clockwise as A, B, C, and D.
	c) Select all 4 points in order. From the Construct menu, choose Segment.

2. To construct parallelogram PQRS:

Click on this tool …   *… and do this:*

a) Draw a horizontal line segment.

b) Label the endpoints P and S.

c) Draw a point above the segment PS.

d) Label the point Q.

e) Select P and Q. From the Construct menu, choose Segment.

f) Select Q and segment PS. From the Construct menu, choose Parallel Line.

g) Select S and segment PQ. From the Construct menu, choose Parallel Line.

h) Select the two constructed lines. From the Construct menu, choose Point At Intersection.

i) Label the intersection point R.

j) Select lines QR and SR. From the Display menu, choose Hide Lines.

k) Select Q and R. From the Construct menu, choose Segment.

l) Select S and R. From the Construct menu, choose Segment.

3. To construct rectangle KLMN:

Click on this tool …   *… and do this:*

a) Draw a segment.

b) Label the endpoints of the segment K and N.

c) Select K and segment KN. From the Construct menu, choose Perpendicular Line.

d) Select the perpendicular line. From the Construct menu, choose Point On Object.

e) Label the point L.

f) Select the line KL. From the Display menu, choose Hide Line.

g) Select K and L. From the Construct menu, choose Segment.

h) Select L and segment KN. From the Construct menu, choose Parallel Line.

i) Select N and segment KL. From the Construct menu, choose Parallel Line.

j) Select the two constructed lines. From the Construct menu, choose Point At Intersection.

k) Label the intersection point M.

l) Select lines LM and MN. From the Display menu, choose Hide Lines.

m) Select L and M. From the Construct menu, choose Segment.

n) Select M and N. From the Construct menu, choose Segment.

Save your sketches.

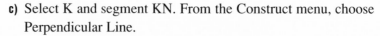
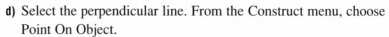

Diagonals and Their Lengths

1. For quadrilateral ABCD:

a) Construct quadrilateral ABCD, as in *Setup*.

b) Construct diagonals AC and BD.

c) Select AC and BD. Construct: Point At Intersection. Label the intersection point E.

d) Measure AE and EC, BE and ED. What do you notice?

e) Drag the vertices until the measures of AE and EC are equal. What do you notice about the shape of ABCD?

f) Drag the vertices until AE, EC, BE, and ED are equal. What do you notice about the shape of ABCD?

g) Write a statement about the diagonals in a quadrilateral.

2. For parallelogram PQRS:

   a) Construct parallelogram PQRS as in *Setup*.

   b) Construct diagonals PR and QS.

   c) Select PR and QS. Construct: Point At Intersection. Label the intersection point T.

   d) Measure PT, TR, QT, and TS. What do you notice?

   e) Drag vertex S to see if your observations are true for other parallelograms.

   f) Measure PQ and QR.

   g) Drag vertex P until the lengths PQ and QR are equal. A parallelogram with equal sides is a *rhombus*. What do you notice about the lengths of PT, TR, QT, and TS in a rhombus?

   h) Write a statement about the diagonals in a parallelogram.

3. For rectangle KLMN:

   a) Construct rectangle KLMN as in *Setup*.

   b) Construct diagonals KM and LN.

   c) Select KM and LN. Construct: Point At Intersection. Label the intersection point O.

   d) Measure KO and OM. What do you notice?

   e) Drag vertex K to see if your observations are true for other rectangles.

   f) Measure LO and ON. What do you notice?

   g) How are your results for the rectangle different from the parallelogram results?

   h) Write a statement about the diagonals in a rectangle.

Diagonals and Angle Measures

1. For quadrilateral ABCD:

   a) Use quadrilateral ABCD from *Investigation 1*.

   b) Measure ∠AEB, ∠CEB, ∠AED, and ∠CED. What do you notice?

   c) Drag vertex B. Name any angles that are always equal. Explain why they are equal.

   d) Drag the vertices until ∠AEB = ∠CEB = ∠AED = ∠CED. What is the measure of these four angles?

e) Measure AB, BC, CD, and DA. What do you notice?

f) Drag the vertices until ∠AEB = ∠CEB = ∠AED = ∠CED, AD = AB, and CB = CD. A quadrilateral with adjacent sides equal is a *kite*.

g) Write a statement about the angles formed by the diagonals in a quadrilateral. Include a statement about the special case of a kite.

2. For parallelogram PQRS:

a) Use parallelogram PQRS from *Investigation 1*.

b) Measure ∠PTQ, ∠RTQ, ∠PTS, and ∠RTS. What do you notice?

c) Drag vertex Q. Name any angles that are always equal. Explain why they are equal.

d) Drag vertex Q until ∠PTQ = ∠RTQ = ∠PTS =∠RTS. What do you notice about the shape of PQRS?

e) Measure PQ and QR. Does this confirm your observation in part d? Explain.

f) Write a statement about the angles formed by the diagonals in a parallelogram. Include a statement about the special case of a rhombus.

3. For rectangle KLMN:

a) Use rectangle KLMN from *Investigation 1*.

b) Measure ∠KOL, ∠MOL, ∠KON, and ∠MON. What do you notice?

c) Drag vertex L to see if your observations are true for other rectangles.

d) Drag vertex L until KL = LM. What is the shape of KLMN?

e) Write a statement about the angles formed by the diagonals in a rectangle. Include a statement about the special case of a square.

INVESTIGATION 3

Trapezoids

A *trapezoid* is a quadrilateral with only one pair of opposite sides parallel.

1. Construct a trapezoid and its diagonals.

2. Measure the diagonals.

3. Measure the angles between the diagonals.

4. Write a statement about the angles formed by the diagonals in a trapezoid.

ACADEMIC FOCUS

Midpoint Construction

1. a) Construct quadrilateral ABCD.

   b) Select AB, BC, CD, and DA. Construct: Point At Midpoint. Label the midpoints M, N, O, and P, respectively.

   c) Select M, N, O, and P. Construct: Segment.

   d) Investigate the properties of quadrilateral MNOP by measuring and recording:
      - lengths of sides
      - measures of angles
      - lengths of diagonals
      - distances from the vertices to the intersection point of the diagonals
      - measures of angles formed by the diagonals

   e) Make a conjecture about quadrilateral MNOP.

   f) Test your conjecture by dragging a vertex of ABCD and observing how the measurements change.

   g) Write a statement about the shape of MNOP. Justify your conclusion.

2. A student wants to make a parallelogram template out of cardboard. Explain how the student could use the results of exercise 1 to create the parallelogram.

3. What properties must ABCD have if MNOP is a rectangle? Explain.

ACADEMIC FOCUS

Diagonals of a Regular Pentagon

1. a) Construct segment AB.

   b) Double-click on point A to make A a centre of rotation.

   c) Select segment AB and point B. From the Transform menu, choose Rotate. In the dialog box, type 108 then click OK. Label the new endpoint E.

d) Double-click on E. Select AE and point A. Rotate AE through 108°. Label the new endpoint D.

e) Double-click on D. Select ED and point E. Rotate ED through 108°. Label the new endpoint C.

f) Construct segment CB.

g) Explain why this construction forms a regular pentagon.

2. a) Construct the diagonals of the pentagon in exercise 1. What do you notice?

b) Drag vertex A to see if your observation is true for other regular pentagons.

c) Construct the intersection points of the diagonals. Label the points P, Q, R, S, and T.

d) Make a conjecture about the shape of PQRST.

e) Check your conjecture about PQRST by measuring its sides and interior angles.

f) Write a statement about the diagonals of a regular pentagon.

3. a) In exercise 2, consider the star formed by joining A, C, E, B, D, A in order. Hide the segments that are not part of the star.

b) Measure the angles in this star.

c) Select the 5 angle measurements at the "points" of the star. From the Measure menu, choose Calculate. Use the calculator to find the sum of the angle measurements.

d) Drag vertex A and observe the angle measurements.

e) Beside your star, draw another 5-pointed star:
   • Draw 5 points with the Point tool.
   • Label the points, clockwise: M, N, O, P, Q.
   • Select the points in the order M, O, Q, N, P. Construct: Segment.

f) Measure the angles in the new star, then use the calculator to find their sum. What do you notice?

g) Drag vertex M to check your observations.

h) Write a statement about the sum of the angles at the points in a 5-pointed star.

4. a) How many diagonals meet at each vertex of a pentagon? What is the total number of diagonals?

b) Sketch a hexagon and its diagonals. How many diagonals meet at each vertex of a hexagon? What is the total number of diagonals?

c) Copy then complete this table.

Polygon	Number of sides	Number of diagonals at each vertex	Total number of diagonals
Triangle	3	0	0
Quadrilateral	4	1	2
Pentagon	5		
Hexagon	6		
Heptagon	7		
Octagon	8		

d) Conjecture an equation for the number of diagonals, d, that meet at each vertex of a polygon with n sides.

e) Conjecture an equation for the total number of diagonals, D, in a polygon with n sides.

f) Use your equations.

  i) How many diagonals meet at each vertex of a 20-sided polygon?

  ii) What is the total number of diagonals in a 20-sided polygon?

5. Why is the sum of the angles at the points of a 5-pointed star always 108°? Use this diagram and your knowledge of sums of angles to explain.

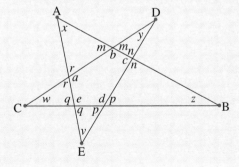

At the end of each *Investigation*, you were asked to write a statement. Did you use pen and paper or a computer? Explain the advantages and disadvantages of each method.

In Section 11.13, you observed many properties of quadrilaterals. These properties are summarized.

Properties of Quadrilaterals

A parallelogram has:

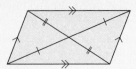

- diagonals that bisect each other

A rectangle has:

- diagonals that bisect each other
- equal diagonals

A rhombus has:

- diagonals that bisect each other
- diagonals that are perpendicular

A square has:

- diagonals that bisect each other
- equal diagonals
- diagonals that are perpendicular

A kite has:

- diagonals that are perpendicular

These properties can be used to solve problems.

Example 1

ABCD is a square. Use the properties of a square to state which angles and segments are equal in ABCD.

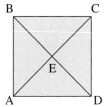

Solution

Both pairs of opposite sides are parallel. Since BC is parallel to AD, with alternate angles equal,

∠BCA = ∠DAC
∠CBD = ∠ADB

Since BA is parallel to CD, with alternate angles equal,
∠DCA = ∠BAC
∠CDB = ∠ABD

Since the diagonals bisect each other,
AE = EC   ①
BE = ED   ②
Since the sides are perpendicular,
∠BAD = ∠ADC = ∠DCB = ∠CBA = 90°
Since the diagonals are equal,
AC = BD   ③
From ①, ②, and ③, since the diagonals bisect
each other and the diagonals are equal,
AE = EC = BE = ED

Since all the sides are equal,
AB = BC = CD = DA

Since the diagonals are perpendicular,
∠AEB = ∠BEC = ∠CED = ∠DEA = 90°

We can use the properties of quadrilaterals to solve problems.

Example 2

A tile has the shape of a quadrilateral. Its length is twice its width. The
diagonals of the tile are 15.0 cm long. Determine the dimensions of the tile.

Solution

Since the diagonals are equal, the tile is a rectangle.
A diagonal divides the rectangle into two right
triangles.

Let the width of the rectangle be w centimetres.
Then the length of the rectangle is $2w$ centimetres.

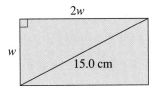

Use the Pythagorean Theorem in one right triangle.
$$w^2 + (2w)^2 = 15^2$$
$$w^2 + 4w^2 = 225$$
$$5w^2 = 225$$
$$w^2 = 45$$
$$w = \sqrt{45}$$
$$\doteq 6.708$$

The width is approximately 6.7 cm and the length is 2×6.708 cm, or approximately 13.4 cm.

DISCUSSING *the* IDEAS

1. a) Is a square a rectangle? Explain.   b) Is a rectangle a square? Explain.

2. a) Is a square a parallelogram? Explain.   b) Is a parallelogram a square? Explain.

3. a) Is a square a rhombus? Explain.   b) Is a rhombus a square? Explain.

4. a) Is a parallelogram a rhombus? Explain.   b) Is a rhombus a parallelogram? Explain.

11.14   EXERCISES

  1. Name each quadrilateral. Explain how you identified it.

a)   b)   c)

2. Sketch and label rectangle ABCD. Draw the diagonals to intersect at E. Give reasons to explain which segments and angles in ABCD are equal.

3. Sketch and label kite PQRS. Draw the diagonals to intersect at T. Give reasons to explain which angles and segments are equal in PQRS.

4. Determine the length of AC in each rectangle.

a) 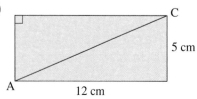   b)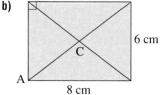

5. What is the special name for each quadrilateral?

   a) It has two diagonals, 6 cm and 14 cm, that bisect each other at right angles.

   b) It has four sides, each 43 cm, and equal diagonals.

   c) It has two adjacent sides 5 cm and two adjacent sides 13 cm.

   d) It has two sides parallel; the other two sides are not parallel.

6. Determine the lengths of the sides of a rhombus with diagonals 6.0 cm and 8.0 cm.

7. A student is walking from her home to school. She walks diagonally across a rectangular field to save time.

   a) The field is 200 m wide and 210 m long. How much shorter will the walk be than if she walked around two sides?

   b) The student walks at 50 m/min. How much time does she save?

8. Recall the question on page 576. Is the pitcher in baseball the same distance from all the bases and from home plate? Explain.

9. Copy and complete this table. Sort the quadrilaterals. A quadrilateral may be listed under more than one heading.

rectangle, square, rhombus, parallelogram, kite, trapezoid

a)	All sides equal	
b)	2 pairs of opposite sides equal	
c)	1 pair of opposite sides parallel	
d)	2 pairs of opposite sides parallel	
e)	Equal diagonals	
f)	Diagonals bisect each other	
g)	Perpendicular sides	
h)	Perpendicular diagonals	

C **10. Academic Focus** A regular polygon has sides of length 5 cm. Each side subtends an angle of 9° at the centre. Determine the perimeter of the polygon.

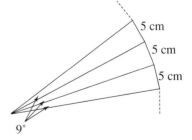

In your journal, explain why a square is a rectangle. Use this idea to explain why an equilateral triangle is also an isosceles triangle.

INVESTIGATION

The Angles in a Pentagon

Use *The Geometer's Sketchpad.*

From the File menu, choose New Sketch.

1. a) Construct pentagon DEFGH.

   b) Predict the sum of the interior angles of DEFGH.

   c) Measure the interior angles. Calculate their sum. Was your prediction correct?

   d) Drag a vertex of the pentagon. Observe what happens to the angle measures and their sum.

   e) From the results of parts a to d, make a statement about the sum of the interior angles of a pentagon.

2. Academic Focus

   a) Predict the sum of the exterior angles of a pentagon.

   b) Check your prediction by constructing a pentagon with rays and measuring the exterior angles.

   c) What do you think is the sum of the exterior angles of a hexagon? of an octagon?

   d) Write a statement about the sum of the exterior angles of a polygon.

3. State whether each statement is true or false. Justify your answers.

   a) A square is a rectangle.   **b)** A parallelogram is a square.

   c) A square is a rhombus.   **d)** A rectangle is a square.

   e) A parallelogram is a rhombus.   **f)** A rhombus is a square.

4. The area of $\triangle ABC$ is $20\,cm^2$ and $CM = 6$ cm.

   a) Determine the area of $\triangle AMC$.

   b) Determine the length of OM.

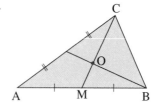

5. Draw △PQR with vertices P(3, 5), Q(5, 1), and R(13, 9). Find the coordinates of the centroid.

6. Determine the measure of each indicated angle. Explain your reasoning.

a)

b)
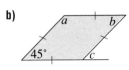

c)

7. ABCD is a rectangle (below left) with BE = 6 cm and CD = 5 cm. Calculate the length of BC to 1 decimal place.

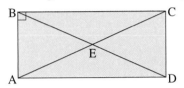
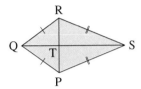

8. PQRS is a kite (above right). Give reasons to explain why PT and TR are equal.

9. A ladder (below left) has to reach a window 10 m above the ground. For safety, the bottom of a ladder should be 1 m away from the wall for every 4 m of height. Determine the length of the ladder to 1 decimal place.

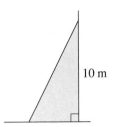
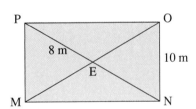

10. Determine the area of rectangle MNOP (above right), to the nearest square metre.

11. A *chevron* is a quadrilateral with adjacent sides equal, and a reflex angle. Use *The Geometer's Sketchpad*. From the File menu, choose New Sketch. To construct a chevron:

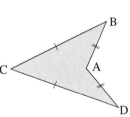

- Construct △ABC, with an obtuse angle at A.
- Double-click on AC to make it a line of reflection.
- Select △ABC. (Click on A, B, C, AB, BC, and CA.)
- From the Transform menu, choose Reflect. Label the fourth vertex D.
- Hide segment AC.

a) Measure the interior angles of the chevron. For the reflex angle at A, you can measure ∠BAD, then use the calculator to subtract ∠BAD from 360°.

b) **Academic Focus** Define the exterior angle at A so the exterior angles add to 360° and the sum of the exterior and interior angles at a vertex is 180°. Explain.

12. Determine the measure of each indicated angle. Explain your reasoning.

a)

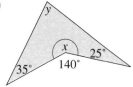

b)

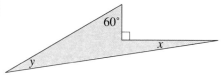

c)

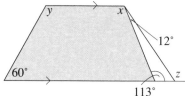

d)

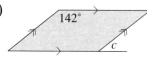

13. Determine the measure of each exterior angle of a regular hexagon.

14. Point Q is on the bisector of each angle. Determine the value of each variable. Explain your reasoning.

a)

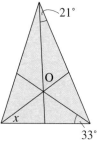

b)

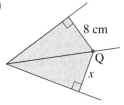

15. Point O is the incentre. Calculate the value of each variable. Explain your reasoning.

a)

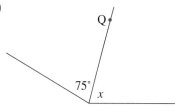

b)

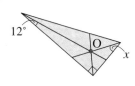

c)

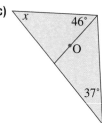

d)

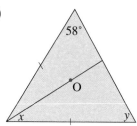

16. Consider the altitudes, medians, and angle bisectors of an equilateral triangle. What special property do these lines have?

17. Triangle ABC is isosceles and AP is the bisector of ∠BAC (below left).
Explain how you know that ∠APB is a right angle.

a)

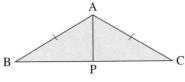

b)

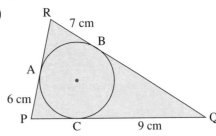

18. Determine the perimeter of △PQR (above right).

19. Point O is the incentre of equilateral △ABC.
Determine the measure of ∠AON.
Explain your reasoning.

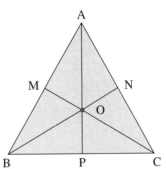

20. Carrie and Peter are making ceramic tiles in the shape of regular pentagons
to put on their kitchen floor. What would you tell them about this project? If
they use the pentagon shaped tiles and fill in the spaces with other tiles,
what shape will they be? Explain.

21. Sketch and label parallelogram EFGH. Draw the diagonals to intersect at J.
Use the properties of a parallelogram on page 586. State which angles and
segments are equal in EFGH.

22. Refer to exercise 21. Suppose EFGH were a rhombus. Which additional
angles and segments would be equal?

23. Mathematical Modelling Most drawings
contain more than one point at a distance. This
diagram shows a box drawn with one-point
perspective and a box with two-point perspective.

Use the diagram as a guide. Modify the
instructions in exercises 1 to 3, pages 576, 577,
to create a box with two-point perspective.

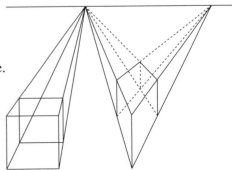

1. A sports store has a clearance sale. All items are sold at 35% off. A tennis racket has an original price of $145.

   a) What is the sale price of the tennis racket?

   b) The taxes are 15%. What is the purchase price of the tennis racket?

2. A printing shop charges $50 per order to set up the printing machines, then $0.14 to print one page.

   a) Create a table to show the prices to print 200, 400, 800, and 1000 pages.

   b) Use the data to draw a graph. Should the points be joined? Explain.

   c) Determine the equation of the relation that describes the data.

   d) Does the relation represent a proportional situation? Explain.

   e) Suppose the owner decides to give a customer a deal by deleting the set-up charges.
   i) How will the graph change?
   ii) How will the equation change?
   iii) Does the relation represent a proportional situation?

3. A group of 5 students, each with a CBR, monitors a 6th student as she walks along a straight line at a constant speed. The students with the CBRs are equally placed around a semicircle (at points A, B, C, D and E). The CBRs are trained on the walker to measure the distances between each CBR and the walker. The walking student starts at the student at point A and walks towards the student at point E. Study the diagram and graphs to determine which graph belongs with which student. Explain your reasoning.

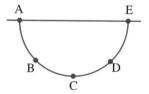

a)
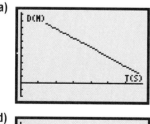

b)
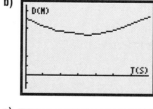

c)
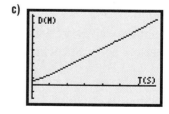

d)
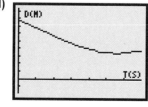

e)
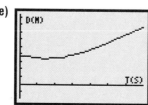

4. For two consecutive integers, the sum of the larger and 3 times the smaller is 117. What are the integers?

5. What are the square roots of each number?

a) 36   b) 100   c) 400   d) 1   e) $\frac{1}{4}$ f) $\frac{25}{9}$

6. Classify each number as natural, integer, rational, or irrational. Some numbers will belong to more than one set.

a) $\frac{4}{5}$ b) $0.21\overline{7}$ c) -6 d) $\sqrt{225}$

e) $\sqrt{7}$ f) $6.121\,121\,121\ldots$ g) 1.8×10^{-4}

7. Solve each equation. Round the solution to the nearest tenth.

a) $1.5x - 3.2 = 4.1$

b) $4.7 + 2.3y = 12.4$

c) $2.6k + 7.6 = 1.2k - 8.3$

d) $8.2 - 1.6x = 2.3x - 9.4$

e) $-2.6(p + 1) = -5.2$

f) $3.1(2a - 2) = 5(a + 3.2)$

8. a) In their first season, the Toronto Blue Jays lost 53 more games than they won. They played 161 games. How many games did they win?

b) The Toronto Blue Jays first won the World Series in 1992. That year, they won 34 more games than they lost. They played 162 regular-season games and 12 championship games. How many games did they win in 1992?

9. Simplify. Determine the value of the polynomial for each indicated value of the variable.

a) $(3x^2 - 2x + 7) - (2x^2 + x - 4)$ for $x = 2$

b) $(3m^2)(-2m)(4m)$ for $m = -1$

c) $-\frac{18a^3}{2a}$ for $a = 2$

d) $3k(k - 5) - 2(k^2 - 2k + 1)$ for $k = 3$

10. Have you ever seen a flash of lightning, then heard thunder a few seconds later? An approximate rule for the distance to a storm is to count the number of seconds between the lightning and thunderclap and divide by 3. This rule is based on the speed of sound in air being about 330 m/s, which is approximately one-third of a kilometre per second.

a) Let d kilometres represent the distance to the storm. Let t seconds represent the time between the lightning and the thunder. Express the rule as an equation.

b) Suppose the time is 3.5 s. Estimate how far away the storm is.

c) Suppose a storm is 8 km away. Estimate the time between the lightning and the thunder.

11. For each table of data, construct a scatter plot and its line of best fit. Determine the equation of the line of best fit.

Amount spent on advertising ($1000s)	100	200	400	700	140	300	400	600	850	700	800	900
Number of new customers	10	16	28	40	15	25	32	29	49	35	52	58

b)

Distance to school (km)	0.8	1.5	1.2	0.9	1.4	0.9	1.2	0.5	1.3	1.5	0.9	1.5
Time to travel (min)	15	25	22	20	25	10	24	12	23	12	21	30

12. The table shows the dimensions used in the construction of birdhouses.

Species	Entrance diameter (cm)	Inside length, width (cm)	Wall height (cm)
House wren	2.5	6	15
Chickadee Downy woodpecker	3.1	8	20
Bluebird Tree swallow English sparrow	3.8	10	26
Hairy woodpecker Crested flycatcher Starling	5.0	12	31
Common flicker	6.3	15	38
Kestrel	7.5	18	43

a) Why do different birds require different sizes of entrances?

b) Plot a graph of *Inside length and width* against *Entrance diameter*.

c) Construct a line of best fit.

d) A red-headed woodpecker needs an entrance hole with a diameter of 4.4 cm. Estimate the inside length and width for a red-headed woodpecker's house.

e) Determine the equation of the line of best fit.

f) Use the equation to estimate the inside length and width for a red-headed woodpecker's house.

g) Compare your answers to parts d and f. Explain any differences.

13. A triangle has vertices A(2, 5), B(−4, 1), and C(6, −3). The midpoints of AC and BC are M and N, respectively.

a) Graph the triangle. Determine the coordinates of M and N.

b) Determine the slopes of MN and AB. What do you notice?

c) Let P be the midpoint of AB. Determine the slopes of PM, BC, PN, and AC. What do you notice?

14. A quadrilateral has vertices A(−4, 0), B(8, 2), C(2, 8), and D(−2, 4).

a) Graph the quadrilateral. Locate the midpoint of each side.

b) Draw the quadrilateral formed by the midpoints. What quadrilateral is it? Explain.

Answers

Chapter 1 Numeracy

Mathematical Modelling: How Many Cereal Boxes?, page 3

1. Yes, it is possible. Explanations may vary.
2. Yes; explanations may vary.

Reviewing Your Skills, page 4

1. 37.6 km/day
2. a) $316.40/km   b) $4597.06/km
   c) About 25 million people contributed $24.7 million, which is almost $1 per person.
3. a) $30 895.22/km   b) About 8.74 million
   c) Answers may vary. The population increased from about 25 million in 1980 to about 30 million in 1998. If we use 27.5 million as the average population for the period, the mean amount raised per Canadian was $6.04.
4. a) 17   b) 20   c) 8
5. a) 4   b) 6   c) 52   d) 44
6. a) 10   b) 9
   c) i) 8   ii) 7   iii) 6   iv) 5
      v) 4   vi) 3   vii) 2   viii) 1
7. a) i) $6 \times 7 = 42$ ii) $42 \div 6 = 7, 42 \div 7 = 6$
   b) Answers may vary.
8. 4
9. a) 2.62   b) 65.18   c) 414.21
10. a) $\frac{1}{3}$ b) $\frac{2}{3}$ c) $\frac{3}{14}$
11. The expressions in b, d, and e have a value less than 50.

1.1 Integers

1.1 Exercises, page 10

1. a) –3, –2, –1, 0, 1, 2, 3   b) –13, –10, –7, –3, 0, 5, 7
2. a) +2   b) –2   c) –4   d) +4   e) –5
   f) –2   g) –15   h) –2   i) –9   j) +10
   k) +15   l) –11   m) –1   n) –1   o) –4
3. a) –6   b) –4   c) +7   d) –4
   e) –8   f) –7   g) +12   h) +4
   i) +6   j) –6   k) –7   l) –4
   m) +7   n) –1   o) –3   p) +12
4. a) +12   b) –6   c) –20   d) +3
   e) –8   f) –10   g) +14   h) 0
   i) 0   j) –30   k) –30   l) –21
   m) +20   n) +24   o) –60   p) +24
5. a) The product is positive.   b) The product is negative.
6. a) $-25 = (-5)(+5)$ b) $-5 = (+5)(-1)$ c) $-10 = (+2)(-5)$
   d) $-6 = (-2)(+3)$ e) $+6 = (-3)(-2)$ f) $+24 = (-3)(-8)$

7. a) +4   b) +4   c) –5   d) –6
   e) –4   f) +5   g) 0   h) –8
   i) –7   j) 0   k) –6   l) –5
8. a) He had $6 more than he has now.
   b) The amount of money the person spent on lottery tickets in the last two weeks
9. a) The car was 6 cm to the right of its present position.
   b) The distance, in centimetres, the car travelled to the left in the last 2 s.
10. The product must equal either +6 or –6. Since $(+3)(-2) = -6$, $(-3)(-2)$ cannot also equal –6. Therefore, it must equal +6.
11. a) 7   b) 4   c) –6
    d) 6   e) 7   f) –16
12.

–9	–6	–3	0	3
–7	–4	–1	2	5
–5	–2	1	4	7
–3	0	3	6	9
–1	2	5	8	11

From left to right, going up, the diagonals are consecutive integers. This is because $(+3) + (-2) = +1$. From left to right, going down, the numbers in each diagonal increase by 5. This is because $(+3) - (-2) = +5$.
13. a) $(+3) + (-2)$ b) $(+3) + (-9)$
    c) $(-8) + (-4)$ d) $(-3) + (+2)$
    e) $(-4) + (+9)$ f) $(-9) + (-5)$
    g) $(+20) + (+15)$ h) $(-7) + (+9)$
    i) $(+3) + (-9)$ j) $(-4) + (+2) + (-3)$
    k) $(+4) + (-9)$, or $(-4) + (+9)$ l) $(+3) + (-4) + (+2)$
14. a) $(+2)(-3)$ b) $(+3)(-4)$ c) $(+5)(+4)$
    d) $\frac{-3000}{+5}$ e) $\frac{-10}{+2}$
15. $(+96) + (+2) + (-4) + (+2) + (-1) + (-3) = +92$; 92 kg
16. $(-3) + (+8) + (-6) = -1$; –1°C
17. $(+5) + (-7) + (-3) = -5$; –5°C
18. $(+14) + (-9) + (+6) = +11$; the 11th floor
19. $(-30) + (-20) + (+40) = -10$; 10 m
20. $(+25\,000) + (-22\,000) + (-4000) + (+5000) = +4000$; $4000
21. $\frac{-12\,000}{5} = -2400$; $2400
22. $(-2)(+4) = -8$; $8
23. a) British Columbia: +7000; Ontario: +122 000; Nova Scotia: +7000; Prince Edward Island: +1000
    b) Yukon Territory: –3000; Alberta: –32 000; Saskatchewan: –3000; Manitoba: –3000; Quebec: –81 000; Newfoundland: –15 000
24. a) Net change is zero.
    b) Answers may vary. For example, Prince Edward Island: from 1976–86, from 1981–91, and from 1986–96, the net change was 0.
    c) Zero

25. Yukon Territory: –2000; Northwest Territories: –6000; British Columbia: +406 000; Alberta: +132 000; Saskatchewan: –93 000; Manitoba: –99 000; Ontario: +64 000; Quebec: –300 000; New Brunswick: –18 000; Nova Scotia: –11 000; Prince Edward Island: 0; Newfoundland: –71 000

26. a) British Columbia
b) Answers may vary. Economic prospects are best in this province, and it has the mildest climate.

27. a) Saskatchewan, Manitoba, Quebec, Newfoundland
b) Answers may vary.

28. Answers may vary. There was an oil boom that didn't last.

29. a) The 21st century begins on Jan 1, 2001. Explanations may vary.
b) Explanations may vary.

30. a) (+1)(+1)(+12); (+1)(+2)(+6); (+1)(+3)(+4); (+2)(+2)(+3)
b) All of part a, plus (+1)(–1)(–12); (–1)(–1)(+12); (+1)(–2)(–6); (–1)(+2)(–6); (–1)(–2)(+6); (+1)(–3)(–4); (–1)(+3)(–4); (–1)(–3)(+4); (+2)(–2)(–3); (–2)(–2)(+3)

1.2 Decimals and Fractions

Investigation, page 15

1. a) 800 h/year **b)** Answers may vary.

2. a) $21 904 000 **b)** Answers may vary.

3. Explanations may vary.
a) Yes **b)** Yes

4. 0.125, 0.1875, 0.25, 0.3125, 0.375, 0.4375, 0.5

5. Exercise 3 can be completed in 6 different ways.

6. Yes; explanations may vary.

1.2 Exercises, page 17

1. a) $\frac{2}{5}$ **b)** $\frac{4}{10}$, or $\frac{2}{5}$ **c)** $\frac{8}{18}$, or $\frac{4}{9}$ **d)** $\frac{15}{24}$, or $\frac{5}{8}$

2. a) $\frac{1}{5}$ **b)** $\frac{2}{5}$ **c)** $\frac{3}{5}$ **d)** $\frac{4}{5}$
e) $\frac{4}{5}$ **f)** $\frac{2}{5}$ **g)** $\frac{4}{15}$ **h)** $\frac{1}{5}$

3. a) 0.3 **b)** 0.24 **c)** 0.24 **d)** 0.4
e) 0.6 **f)** 1.67 **g)** 0.75 **h)** 1.0
i) 0.875 **j)** 2.5 **k)** 0.89 **l)** 2.33

4. a) $\frac{6}{10}$, or $\frac{3}{5}$ **b)** $\frac{3}{100}$ **c)** $\frac{221}{1000}$
d) $\frac{120}{100}$, or $\frac{6}{5}$ **e)** $\frac{125}{100}$, or $\frac{5}{4}$ **f)** $3\frac{125}{1000}$, or $3\frac{1}{8}$
g) $4\frac{85}{100}$, or $4\frac{17}{20}$ **h)** $3\frac{63}{100}$ **i)** $6\frac{94}{100}$, or $6\frac{47}{50}$
j) $10\frac{8}{100}$, or $10\frac{2}{25}$ **k)** $2\frac{71}{100}$ **l)** $1\frac{3}{10}$

5. a) $\frac{1}{2}$ **b)** $\frac{1}{2}$ **c)** $\frac{1}{5}$
d) $\frac{1}{4}$ **e)** $\frac{1}{3}$ **f)** $\frac{1}{10}$
g) $\frac{9}{100}$ **h)** $\frac{9}{10}$ **i)** $\frac{1}{100}$
j) $\frac{8}{100}$, or $\frac{2}{25}$ **k)** $\frac{9}{100}$ **l)** $\frac{36}{100}$, or $\frac{9}{25}$
m) $\frac{19}{100}$

6. a) $\frac{22}{10}$, or $\frac{11}{5}$, 2.2 **b)** $\frac{41}{10}$, 4.1

7. a) $\frac{2210}{1000}$, or $\frac{221}{100}$; 2.21 **b)** $\frac{1222}{1000}$, or $\frac{611}{500}$; 1.222
c) $\frac{1012}{1000}$, or $\frac{253}{250}$; 1.012 **d)** $\frac{372}{1000}$, or $\frac{93}{250}$; 0.372

8. Answers may vary.

9. Answers may vary.

10. a) $\frac{7}{10}$ **b)** $\frac{9}{10}$ **c)** $\frac{11}{10}$, or $1\frac{1}{10}$
d) $\frac{13}{10}$, or $1\frac{3}{10}$ **e)** $\frac{1}{10}$ **f)** $\frac{3}{10}$
g) $\frac{5}{10}$, or $\frac{1}{2}$ **h)** $\frac{7}{10}$

11. a) $\frac{3}{8}$ **b)** $\frac{2}{15}$ **c)** $\frac{5}{9}$ **d)** $\frac{16}{15}$, or $1\frac{1}{15}$
e) $\frac{1}{3}$ **f)** $\frac{2}{5}$ **g)** $\frac{1}{3}$ **h)** $\frac{15}{22}$

12. a) 1.5 **b)** 1.5; same
c) i) 1.15 **ii)** 0.375 **iii)** –0.389
iv) –0.232 **v)** 0.854 **vi)** 0.486

13. a) Maral, 0.311; Ari, 0.286; Kim, 0.288; Ange, 0.267; Nicki, 0.308
b) Maral, Nicki, Kim, Ari, Ange
c) Explanations may vary. Maral is most reliable because she has the highest success rate of the 5 players.
d) Answers may vary.

14. a)

Ownership share	$\frac{9}{16}$	$\frac{5}{8}$	$\frac{11}{16}$	$\frac{3}{4}$	$\frac{13}{16}$	$\frac{7}{8}$
Purchase price ($)	12 321 000	13 690 000	15 059 000	16 428 000	17 797 000	19 166 000

b)

Ownership share	$\frac{1}{12}$	$\frac{1}{6}$	$\frac{1}{4}$	$\frac{1}{3}$	$\frac{5}{12}$	$\frac{1}{2}$
Purchase price ($)	1 825 333	3 650 667	5 476 000	7 301 333	9 126 667	10 952 000

15.

Ownership share	$\frac{1}{8}$	$\frac{3}{16}$	$\frac{1}{4}$	$\frac{5}{16}$	$\frac{3}{8}$	$\frac{7}{16}$	$\frac{1}{2}$
Purchase price ($)	772 500	1 158 750	1 545 000	1 931 250	2 317 500	2 703 750	3 090 000

16. a) $175.22
b) Answers may vary. The fencing material may not be sold in 0.1 m increments, so you might have to buy more than you need.

17. Key sequences may vary. Final calculator displays are shown.
a) 983.62 **b)** 916.37 **c)** 88.32
d) 1068.36 **e)** 19.826 153 85 **f)** 2.900 318 134
g) 0.348 214 285 **h)** 0.248 185 637 **i)** 3.092 105 363
j) 0.361 154 855 **k)** 20 025

18. a) The fraction increases.
b) The fraction decreases.
c) The fraction increases.

19. a) The fraction increases.
b) The fraction decreases.
c) The fraction decreases.

20. It appears that when the numerator is larger than the denominator, and each is increased by 1, the fraction decreases. When the numerator is smaller than the denominator, and each is increased by 1, the fraction increases.

21. a) $4 842 600   **b)** $9685.20/h

22.

Ownership share	$\frac{1}{8}$	$\frac{3}{16}$	$\frac{1}{4}$	$\frac{5}{16}$	$\frac{3}{8}$	$\frac{7}{16}$	$\frac{1}{2}$
Purchase price ($)	2 738 000	4 107 000	5 476 000	6 845 000	8 214 000	9 583 000	10 952 000
Hours per year	100	150	200	250	300	350	400
Monthly cost ($)	15 660	23 490	31 320	39 150	46 980	54 810	62 640
Cost per hour of flying ($)	2330	2330	2330	2330	2330	2330	2330
Total 5-year cost ($)	4 842 600	7 263 900	9 685 200	12 106 500	14 527 800	16 949 100	19 370 400
Mean 5-year cost per hour	9685.20	9685.20	9685.20	9685.20	9685.20	9685.20	9685.20

1.3 Mathematical Modelling: How Many Cereal Boxes?, page 21

1. to **6.** Results of simulations may vary.

7. Explanations may vary. Each model simulates the situation in a slightly different way, but all are equally valid models.

9. to **17.** Results of simulations may vary.

1.4 Percent
Investigation, page 26

1. a) 23%   **b)** 8%   **c)** 3%   **d)** 53%   **e)** 40%

2. a) 1 037 752   **b)** 360 957   **c)** 135 359
d) 2 391 341   **e)** 1 804 786

3. a) 146 335 **b)** 10 452 **c)** 73 167 **d)** 710 769 **e)** 282 217

4. a) Vancouver   **b)** Winnipeg; Calgary
c) Vancouver, Calgary, Ottawa, Quebec City

5. a) Vancouver   **b)** Winnipeg

1.4 Exercises, page 28

1. a) 20%   **b)** 40%   **c)** 60%   **d)** 80%

2. a) 80%   **b)** 25%   **c)** 12.5%   **d)** $33\frac{1}{3}$%
e) $83\frac{1}{3}$%   **f)** $55\frac{5}{9}$%   **g)** 250%   **h)** $266\frac{2}{3}$%
i) 160%   **j)** 240%   **k)** 68%   **l)** 57.5%

3. a) 0.24   **b)** 0.39   **c)** 0.574   **d)** 0.03   **e)** 0.058
f) 0.115   **g)** 0.016   **h)** 0.009   **i)** 1.37   **j)** 2.64
k) 3.75   **l)** 3.758   **m)** 0.001   **n)** 0.0203   **o)** 0.0025

4. a) $\frac{3}{20}$ **b)** $\frac{3}{10}$ **c)** $\frac{9}{20}$ **d)** $\frac{3}{5}$

5. a) $\frac{27}{100}$ **b)** $\frac{9}{25}$ **c)** $\frac{3}{5}$ **d)** $\frac{7}{25}$
e) $\frac{3}{4}$ **f)** $\frac{9}{20}$ **g)** $\frac{12}{25}$ **h)** $\frac{4}{25}$
i) $\frac{17}{20}$ **j)** $\frac{19}{100}$ **k)** $\frac{5}{4}$, or $1\frac{1}{4}$ **l)** $2\frac{3}{20}$

6. a) 4   **b)** 8   **c)** 12   **d)** 16
e) 10   **f)** 20   **g)** 30   **h)** 40

7. a) 10   **b)** 6   **c)** 0.9   **d)** 1.75
e) 81.75   **f)** 6   **g)** 0.665   **h)** 11.7
i) 103.04   **j)** 1.25   **k)** 864.8   **l)** 125

8. a) 100   **b)** 50
c) $\frac{100}{3}$, or 33.33   **d)** 25

9. a) 20   **b)** 15   **c)** 25   **d)** 40   **e)** 70
f) 100   **g)** 27   **h)** 80   **i)** 25   **j)** 70

10. Price decreases by about $34.12. Sale price is $193.38.

11. $99

12. About $9380

13. Estimates may vary; about $13.30.

14. $4 000 000

15. 1280

16. Estimates may vary.
a) About 6 million
b) About 10 million; about 7.5 million
c) About 4 million

17. a) For each 10% decrease in exam mark, the final mark decreases by 2%.

Term mark	Examination mark	Final mark
84%	100%	87%
84%	90%	85%
84%	80%	83%
84%	70%	81%
84%	60%	79%
84%	50%	77%
84%	40%	75%
84%	30%	73%
84%	20%	71%
84%	10%	69%
84%	0%	67%

b) Explanations may vary.

18. Answers may vary.

19. a) i) Compact disc/digital tape equipment
ii) Compact disc/digital tape equipment
b) i) Colour televisions   **ii)** Colour televisions

20. a) $\frac{1}{10}$ **b)** $\frac{1}{100}$ **c)** $\frac{1}{1000}$ **d)** $\frac{1}{10\,000}$
e) $\frac{1}{100\,000}$ **f)** $\frac{1}{1\,000\,000}$ **g)** $\frac{1}{10\,000\,000}$

21. Only 1 out of every 10 000 000 people could afford to live on the island.

22. 3 people

23. 600 people

24. Estimates may vary.
a) i) Men: 210 000; women: 125 000   **ii)** 40%
b) i) Men: 260 000; women: 315 000   **ii)** 55%
c) i) 24%   **ii)** 250%
d) Answers may vary.

25. Estimates may vary.
a) i) 1.8 billion **ii)** 1 billion **iii)** 2.7 billion **iv)** 0.4 billion
b) i) 2.1 billion **ii)** 1.2 billion **iii)** 4.7 billion **iv)** 1.5 billion
c) i) 22.1% **ii)** 12.6% **iii)** 49.5% **iv)** 15.8%

26. a) The percent increase in taxes was 1171%, which is about 1200%.
b) 930%

27. a), b) Answers and explanations may vary.
c) We need to know the total number of players in 1991–92. There are now more teams so the total number of Canadians may be greater but their percent may be less.

1.5 Rational Numbers

Investigation, page 34

1. $\frac{0}{1}, -\frac{5}{1}, -\frac{5}{2}, \frac{5}{100}, -\frac{11}{100}, \frac{11}{20}, -\frac{3}{4}, -\frac{1}{5}$

2. Explanations may vary.

1.5 Exercises, page 37

1. a) 0.27   b) 0.60   c) 0.81   d) 0.21

2. a) Shade all of one 100-square and 42 squares on another 100-square.
   b) Shade all of two 100-squares and 42 squares on another 100-square.
   c) Shade all of forty-two 100-squares and 42 squares on another 100-square.
   d) Shade 70 squares on a 100-square.
   e) Shade 70 squares on a 100-square.
   f) Shade 73 squares on a 100-square.
   g) Shade 73 squares on a 100-square.
   h) Shade 7 squares and $\frac{3}{10}$ of another square on a 100-square.

3. a) A: 1.5; B: −0.5; C: −1.5
   b) A: −1.75; B: −0.25; C: 0.5; D: −1.25
   c) A: 0.9; B: 0.3; C: −0.6; D: −0.1

4. Explanations may vary.
   a) $\frac{1}{4}$ b) $-\frac{1}{4}$ c) $\frac{3}{2}$ d) $\frac{2}{3}$ e) $\frac{1}{2}$ f) $-\frac{1}{2}$

5. Explanations may vary.
   a) $\frac{4}{5}$ b) 0.9   c) $\frac{5}{6}$ d) 0.9
   e) $\frac{1}{3}$ f) 9.8   g) $\frac{3}{4}$ h) 0.3
   i) $\frac{-8}{18}$ j) 6.77   k) $\frac{4}{9}$ l) 5.99

6. a) −4   b) −5   c) −7   d) 0
   e) 0   f) −1   g) −1   h) 0
   i) −8   j) −4   k) −17   l) −7

7. Explanations may vary.
   a) True; −8 can be written as $\frac{-8}{1}$.
   b) False; whole numbers cannot be negative.
   c) True; −9 can be written as $\frac{-9}{1}$; whole numbers cannot be negative.
   d) False; integers cannot contain fractions or decimals.
   e) False; −18 is an integer as well as a rational number.
   f) False; $-5\frac{2}{3}$ is not an integer because it has a fractional part.

8. Explanations may vary.
   a) True   b) False   c) True   d) True

9. a) $-\frac{3}{5}, -\frac{2}{5}, -\frac{1}{5}$ b) $-\frac{1}{2}, \frac{1}{4}, \frac{5}{8}$ c) $-\frac{2}{9}, \frac{3}{7}, 1\frac{2}{5}$
   d) $-\frac{1}{2}, -\frac{1}{4}, \frac{1}{4}$ e) $-\frac{5}{6}, -\frac{1}{2}, \frac{2}{3}$ f) $-\frac{3}{2}, -\frac{5}{4}, \frac{1}{3}$

10. $\frac{-8}{-2}, \frac{+51}{-3}, \frac{630}{-7}, \frac{-480}{16}, \frac{3248}{-4}$

11. a) 0.55   b) 0.25   c) 0.01   d) 0.07

13. Estimates may vary.
   a) −2.5   b) −1.4   c) −0.6   d) 1.4   e) 2.6

15. a) $1.0, 0.6, \frac{1}{9}, 0, -\frac{1}{2}, -\frac{6}{5}$ b) $\frac{7}{5}, 0.5, \frac{1}{3}, \frac{1}{8}, -\frac{5}{6}, -3.25$
   c) $5, 0.9, \frac{1}{2}, \frac{3}{8}, 0, -\frac{1}{10}, -0.7, -1.375$
   d) $2.75, \frac{7}{6}, \frac{9}{8}, -\frac{5}{12}, -1.1, -\frac{10}{5}, -3.6$

16. a) $-1.3, -\frac{2}{3}, -\frac{1}{2}, \frac{1}{4}, 0.5, 1.8$
   b) $-1.3, -0.6, -\frac{2}{5}, \frac{1}{5}, \frac{9}{15}, 1.2$
   c) $-1.4, -0.75, -\frac{5}{12}, -\frac{1}{6}, \frac{1}{4}, 0.8$
   d) $-0.7, -\frac{1}{3}, 0.11, \frac{1}{7}, \frac{2}{3}, 0.67, \frac{3}{4}$

19. a) 0.6   b) −0.667   c) 0.444   d) −0.375
   e) 0.333   f) −0.136   g) 2.143   h) −0.167
   i) 0.3125   j) −0.630   k) 0.917   l) 1.182

20. a) 0.3   b) −0.833   c) −2.4
   d) −0.375   e) −0.444   f) 0.533

21. a) $-\frac{1}{2}$ b) $-\frac{2}{3}$ c) $\frac{2}{5}$ d) $-\frac{2}{5}$
   e) $\frac{6}{11}$ f) $\frac{1}{3}$ g) $\frac{2}{7}$ h) $-\frac{14}{25}$
   i) $-\frac{3}{7}$ j) $-\frac{1}{3}$ k) $-\frac{3}{2}$ l) $\frac{2}{3}$

22. a) >   b) >   c) >   d) <
   e) <   f) <   g) >   h) <

23. Parts b, c, d, g, and i are positive.

24. Key sequences may vary. Final calculator displays are shown.
   i) 613.36   ii) −339.3
   iii) 0.518 248 175   iv) 0.078 307 62

25. b, c, d, g, h, and j

26. Since the remainders repeat, so will the digits in the quotient, because each is related to a remainder.

27. With no remainder eventually, the decimal terminates. When the remainders repeat, there is a limit to what the remainder can be (for example, when dividing by 7, the remainders can only be 0, 1, 2, 3, 4, 5, 6) and hence continuing to divide will produce repeated remainders.

28. Yes; it is called an irrational number.

1.6 Adding and Subtracting Rational Numbers

Investigation, page 41

1. Answers may vary. In each case the number in the units place is the same. The numbers on the left are integers; those on the right are rational numbers.

2. +1, +1.4; −4, −4.3; −7, −8.3

3. Answers may vary. In each case the number in the units place is the same. The numbers on the left are integers; those on the right are rational numbers.

4. +5, +5.6; −9, −9.9; −5, −5.3

1.6 Exercises, page 43

1. a) −0.7   b) −3.0   c) 3.7   d) 0.5   e) −1.75   f) −1.1

2. a) 5.0   b) −1.7   c) −2.5   d) 0.75   e) −0.17   f) 0.75

3. a) +1.0   b) −1.0   c) −1.0   d) +5.0   e) +1.0   f) +3.0

4. a) $\frac{4}{5}$ b) 1   c) $\frac{1}{2}$ d) $\frac{1}{2}$ e) $\frac{1}{10}$ f) $\frac{1}{4}$

5. Estimates may vary.
   a) 0.7   **b)** 2.8   **c)** −3.8   **d)** 3.1   **e)** −8
   f) 1   **g)** 2.3   **h)** 3.9   **i)** 0.9

6. a) −6.0 **b)** −7.2 **c)** −1.6 **d)** −9.6 **e)** 6.8 **f)** −7.2

7. a) $55.40
  b) A cheque was written. The cheque was greater than the balance; DR means overdrawn.
  c) $100 was deposited.

8. 6.7 cm

9. 132.6 cm

10. 10.3 cm

11. −7°C

12. a) $\frac{-5}{5}$, or −1 **b)** $\frac{1}{8}$ **c)** $\frac{9}{10}$ **d)** $\frac{19}{12}$, or $1\frac{7}{12}$
  e) $\frac{14}{15}$ **f)** $\frac{1}{6}$ **g)** $\frac{1}{6}$ **h)** $\frac{5}{14}$
  i) $\frac{7}{10}$ **j)** $\frac{5}{12}$ **k)** $\frac{37}{24}$ **l)** $\frac{5}{18}$

13. a) $\frac{1}{5}$ **b)** $\frac{2}{3}$ **c)** $\frac{7}{12}$
  d) $\frac{18}{17}$, or $1\frac{1}{17}$ **e)** $\frac{10}{6}$, or $1\frac{2}{3}$ **f)** $\frac{9}{20}$

14. a) −0.16 **b)** −0.25 **c)** −0.375
  d) 0.5 **e)** 0.61 **f)** 0.042

15. a) 26.7 m − (−3.6 m) = 30.3 m
  b) 6.5°C − 8.0°C = −1.5°C
  c) $651.24 billion − $2.54 billion = $648.7 billion

16. a)

+5	−6	+2	+1
−4	+12	−8	0
+7	−6	−10	−9
+8	0	−16	−8

b)

−5.2	−8.9	+2.6	−11.5
−6.0	+3.3	+9.4	+6.7
+8.5	−5.7	+15.1	+17.9
−2.7	−11.3	+27.1	+13.1

17. a) Descriptions may vary. In each row, the numbers increase by 3. In each column, the numbers increase by 1.
  b) 11, 14, 17, 20, 23
  c) i) Row 3 **ii)** Row 2 **iii)** Row 1
  iv) Row 3 **v)** Row 1 **vi)** Row 2

18. a) Ann: 5.65 h; Bob: $4\frac{7}{12}$ h **b)** Ann: about 1 h 4 min

19. $1\frac{1}{12}$ h, or 1 h 5 min

20. a) Estimates may vary. About 14.5 m **b)** 5.21 m

21. a) 152.5 cm
  b) i) Explanations may vary. The carpenter cuts the board 3 times. With each cut, some wood will be sawdust and be lost.
  ii) Estimates may vary; about 152 cm

22. a) Estimates may vary. About 49 km **b)** 25.1 km

23. a) Estimates may vary. About $19 **b)** Yes

24. a) Answers may vary. For example, 6:15, 6:15, 6:25
  b) Explanations may vary. There are several answers, which depend on the time you think elapsed between the people arriving.

1.7 Multiplying and Dividing Rational Numbers
Investigation, page 47

1. Answers may vary.
  a) The signs and the units digits are the same.
  b) The tenths digits are different.

2. −6, −7, −7.5; −20, −21, −20.4; 10, 11, 11

3. Answers may vary.
  a) In all cases except one, the denominators are the same. The signs are the same.
  b) The numerators are different.

4. −2, −1.8, −2.1; −4, −3.5, −3.8; 2, 2.1, 1.5

1.7 Exercises, page 49

1. a, c, and e

2. c

3. b, d, e, and f

4. a, b, and d

5. −1.2 m/h

6. Estimates may vary.
  a) 9.6 **b)** −4.8 **c)** 5.5 **d)** 3.84 **e)** −0.273 **f)** −7.65

7. a) −8.6 **b)** 4.8 **c)** −2.1 **d)** $\frac{1}{4}$ **e)** $\frac{2}{9}$ **f)** $\frac{3}{4}$

8. Estimates may vary.
  a) 4 **b)** 4 **c)** 4 **d)** 2 **e)** 0.25 **f)** 3.1

9. a) −1.2 **b)** −24 **c)** 2.75 **d)** 4 **e)** $\frac{3}{8}$ **f)** $\frac{2}{9}$

10. a) −8.4 **b)** −31 **c)** −2.5
  d) −1.86 **e)** −43.2 **f)** 4
  g) −47 **h)** 14.4 **i)** −17.3

11. a) 1.2 **b)** $\frac{5}{6}$ **c)** $\frac{5}{6}$ **d)** −0.462
  e) 0.3 **f)** $\frac{3}{20}$ **g)** $\frac{2}{15}$ **h)** −5.85

12. a) (−12.4 m/min) × (2.5 min) = −31 m
  b) (−10.5°C) ÷ (6 h) = −1.8°C/h
  c) $(-2.5°C) \times \left(\frac{3000 \text{ m}}{500 \text{ m}} \right) = -15°C$

13. 7.82 m^2

14. 2.52 m^2

15. 194.54 cm^2

16. a) Estimates may vary. 20 m^2
  b) 20.28 m^2 **c)** $496.86
  d) Answers may vary. The cost was calculated using an area of 20.28 m^2. You may have to purchase materials and labour in increments of 0.10 m^2, 0.25 m^2, 0.5 m^2, or even 1 m^2.

17. 0.46 L

18. $5.27

19. $\frac{1}{6}$

20. About 0.44 L

21. a) It would be cheaper to pay $2.50 Cdn, since its value in $U.S. is $1.63.
  b) If $1 Cdn is worth 80¢ U.S., the tolls would be equivalent. If the Canadian dollar is worth any more than this, it would be cheaper to pay in U.S. currency.

c) Answers may vary. Stopping to pay a toll slows traffic and could lead to congestion at busy times. With this system, traffic will be affected in only one direction but the money collected can be shared by the two governments. Also more lanes could be devoted to the direction that must pay the toll.

22. a) $2.27 U.S.
b) Less; to buy a Big Mac in Buffalo, more Canadian money is required.
c) 0.88

23. a) $18.20 U.S.
b) More; to buy 60 L of gas in the U.S., less Canadian money is required.
c) 0.80

24. Answers may vary.

25. Estimates may vary. 8.5

26. Estimates may vary. 18

27. 5

28. a) 28.8 m
b) $24.48

29. Cost per item: posts, $96.48; rails, $93.89; palings, $449.86; total cost, $658.58

30. a) $\frac{3}{8}$
b) About 23.8 L
c) About 39.7 L
d) About $23.78
e) Answers may vary. You can usually fill a gas tank until the display shows greater than Full. In fact, people often "top up" the tank once the pump stops so the cost doesn't involve pennies. Therefore, the driver may purchase more than 39.7 L of gasoline.

31. a) Estimates and explanations may vary.
b) 12.9°C
c) Answers may vary.

32. a) $\frac{1}{3}$ b) $\frac{1}{5}$ c) $\frac{3}{8}$

33. a) Cell A3: adds 1 to the number in A2
Cell B3: adds 2 to the number in A3
Cell C3: subtracts 2 from the number in A3
Cell D3: multiplies the number in A3 by 2
Cell E3: multiplies the number in A3 by –2
b) Descriptions and explanations may vary.
c) Descriptions may vary.

34. $37.50

35. Answers may vary.

Consolidating Your Skills, page 55

1. a) Wind-chill equivalent temperature every hour: 4°C, –2°C, –7°C, –12°C, –18°C, –23°C, –28°C, –33°C, –39°C, –44°C
b) It did drop about 5°C every hour, but some hours it dropped 6°C.
c) The wind-chill equivalent temperature changed by –8°C per hour or –7°C per hour.
d) After the first hour, the wind-chill equivalent temperature changed by –18°C every 2 h.

2. a)

Wind speed (km/h)	50	27	18	12	8
Temperature (°C)	–10	–15	–20	–25	–30

3.

26	22	18	14	10
19	15	11	7	3
12	8	4	0	–4
5	1	–3	–7	–11
–2	–6	–10	–14	–18

From left to right, going up, the numbers in each diagonal increase by 3. This is because (–4) + (+7) = + 3. From left to right, going down, the numbers in each diagonal decrease by 11. This is because (–4) – (+7) = –11.

4. –45°C

5. 1.24, 293.3, 2133.3

6. a) 22.6 L   b) 39.55 L   c) $13.09

7. a) 19 days   b) 450 days

8. $\frac{2}{9}$

9. a) $700   b) $707.25   c) $879.75   d) About 29%

10. a) $7649.15   b) $8261.08

11. a) –11 = (–5) + (–6)
b) +18 = (+5) + (+6) + (+7)
c) –14 = (–2) + (–3) + (–4) + (–5)
d) –17 = (–8) + (–9)
e) +21 = (+10) + (+11)
f) +20 = (+2) + (+3) + (+4) + (+5) + (+6)

12. a) 3, 5.5, 8.3
b) 11.4, 14.7, 18.2, 21.7, 25.5, 29.3, 41.3
c)

Number of items in a set	Average number of boxes needed
2	3
3	5.5
4	8.3
5	11.4
6	14.7
7	18.2
8	21.7
9	25.5
10	29.3
13	41.3

f) Descriptions may vary.

Chapter 2 Relationships

Mathematical Modelling: Relating Animal and Human Lifetimes, page 59

1. Answers may vary. 10 to 15 years; 70 to 90 years
2. One year of a cat's or dog's life is equivalent to 7 years of a person's life. Yes; explanations may vary.
3. Yes; explanations may vary.

Reviewing Your Skills, page 60

1. a) 5¢, 17¢
b) In 1982, the price increased to 30¢.
c) 1931, 1943, 1954, 1968, 1971, 1972, 1988, 1989, 1990, 1991, 1993, 1999
d) In 1926, the price decreased to 2¢.
e) Yes; explanations may vary.

2. Explanations may vary.
a) The horizontal line segments show that the price remained the same for a period of time.
b) The price changes in increments of at least 1¢.

3. a) In 1999: 46¢ (not including taxes)

b)

Number of letters	Postage cost in dollars
1	0.46
2	0.92
3	1.38
4	1.84
5	2.30
6	2.76
7	3.22
8	3.68
9	4.14
10	4.60

2.1 Interpreting and Creating Graphs
Investigation, page 62

1. b) Answers and explanations may vary. Graph 2

2. b) Answers and explanations may vary. Graph 3

3. Answers may vary.

2.1 Exercises, page 67

1. a) ii   **b)** i   **c)** iii   **d)** iv

2. Descriptions may vary.
- **a)** The amount earned increases steadily as the number of hours worked increases.
- **b)** The number of bacteria increases rapidly as time increases.
- **c)** The cost of tickets increases steadily as the number of tickets increases.
- **d)** The water drains rapidly at first, then slowly as less water remains.

3. Descriptions may vary. At point A, the tub is empty. A person puts in the plug and turns on the tap. At point B, the person turns off the tap. At point C, the person gets into the tub and sits there for awhile. At point E, the person pulls out the plug and the water starts to drain. At point F, the person gets out and the water continues to drain. At point H, the tub is empty again.

4. Answers and descriptions may vary.
- **a)** Object being thrown in the air: it reaches a maximum height, then falls.
- **b)** The cost of mailing several packages: the postal rate increases in steps, depending on the mass of the package. For example, 0 g to 25 g cost $1.00, 25.1 g to 50.0 g cost $2.00, and so on.
- **c)** The electric charge stored by a battery as time passes: as the battery is used, the amount of charge it contains decreases.
- **d)** Spring oscillating up and down: the spring is initially extended downward, then let go.

5. Answers may vary.

6. a) Descriptions may vary.
- **b)** Answers may vary. Graph 1: speaker invokes strong opinions in audience.

7. Descriptions may vary. Shakira walks from home at a steady rate, then takes a short rest, and continues at the same steady rate to the farthest point from home. Shakira takes a prolonged rest, then returns home at the same steady rate as when she left home.

8. Descriptions may vary. Raoul sets out for school travelling very quickly, then begins slowing down right away as he climbs a hill. Raoul travels at a slow speed for a while. He then begins accelerating steadily until he is travelling even faster than his initial speed.

10. Descriptions may vary.

11. a) 1996
- **b)** 24 million
- **c)** Answers may vary.

12. a) 59 L/person, 60 L/person, 69 L/person, 85 L/person, 98 L/person, 106 L/person
- **b)** 21 million, 23 million, 25 million, 27 million, 29 million, 31 million
- **c)** 1239 million, 1380 million, 1725 million, 2295 million, 2842 million, 3286 million

13. a) 13.5 cm; 1 cm; 13.5 cm
- **b)** 0.3 s, 1.7 s, 2.4 s, 3.7 s, 4.4 s; 0.5 s, 1.4 s, 2.5 s, 3.4 s, 4.5 s
- **c)** 2 s
- **d)** Height increases during the first second. Height decreases during the second second. Height increases during the third second.
- **e)** Moving away from the floor; toward the floor; away from the floor
- **f)** Explanations may vary.

2.2 Investigating Relationships in Data
Investigation, page 72

1. to 4. Answers may vary.

5. Since the pendulum can have any length greater than 0 cm, we can draw a smooth curve through the points.

6. Descriptions may vary. As the length of the pendulum increases, the time required to make 5 swings increases.

7., 8. Descriptions may vary.

2.2 Exercises, page 76

1. Descriptions and explanations may vary.
- **a)** The heavier the mass, the greater the extension of the spring
- **b)** The closer you are to the basket, the higher is the percent of baskets sunk.
- **c)** The closer to noon, the higher the temperature

2. Descriptions and explanations may vary.
- **b)** For every 4 coins that are added, the mass increases by 100 g. The graph shows a linear relationship.
- **c)** Join the points with a straight line; although it is not possible to have parts of coins, the straight line helps us see possible values between points.
- **d)** 25 g   **e)** 450 g

3. Descriptions and explanations may vary.
- **b)** As the length of the side increases, the area of the square increases. The graph is an upward-sloping curve.
- **c)** Join the points with a smooth curve; it is possible to have squares with fractional side lengths.
- **d)** 12.25 cm^2 **e)** About 4.5 cm
- **f)** No, the area is 4 times as great.

4. Descriptions and explanations may vary.

   b) As the number of stairs climbed increases, the heart rate increases. For each successive set of 5 stairs climbed, the change in heart rate becomes greater.

   c) Join the points with line segments to see possible values between points.

   d) About 114 beats/min; about 87 beats/min

   e) About 12 stairs; about 22 stairs

   f) The heart rate would change more rapidly near the beginning of the climb because, toward the end of the climb, you would reach your maximum heart rate.

6. Graph b; explanations may vary. As a number increases, its reciprocal decreases. The rate at which the reciprocal decreases is not constant.

8. Answers may vary.

   c) No, you cannot have a fraction of a textbook

   d) As the number of textbooks increases by 1, the mass increases by a constant amount. The graph is a straight line.

   e) Explanations may vary.

9. a) Predictions may vary.

    i) The height decreases.

    ii) The height increases.

   b) Results may vary.

   d) No; with a longer tube and the same distance from the wall, the height is less.

10. a), b) Answers may vary.

   c) The points for cans with equal diameters lie on a vertical line.

   d) The points for cans with equal heights lie on a horizontal line.

11. a) Answers may vary.

   b) Linear; for the same increase in capacity (mL), there is a constant increase in capacity (oz).

12. Experimental results may vary.

   b) Join the points with a smooth curve.

13. Experimental results may vary.

   c) Linear

   d) As the volume increases by the same amount, the mass increases by a constant amount.

14. b) Answers may vary. The new graph would be an upward curve, since the percent forgotten increases as time increases.

15. a) The distance travelled by the car from the moment the driver realizes the brakes must be applied to the time when the brakes are actually applied.

   b) The distance travelled by the car from the time the brakes are applied to the time the car comes to a stop.

   c) Join the points with a smooth curve.

   d) 35 m; 72 m

   e) Since a wet road is slippery, stopping distances increase.

   f) **i)** Average stopping distance increases; therefore, the graph would lie above that in part c.

    ii) Average stopping distance decreases; therefore, the graph would lie below.

    iii) Average stopping distance increases; therefore, the graph would lie above.

   g) Answers may vary. Tire design and materials, ice or snow on the road

16. Yes, fuel gauge decreases as odometer reading increases.

   a) An odometer measures the distance travelled by the car from when it was manufactured. A trip odometer measures the distance travelled by the car from the beginning of a trip when it was reset to 000.

   b) Explanations may vary. Linear; you would expect the car to travel the same distance for any constant change in fuel gauge reading.

17. a) Fuel gauge readings may vary slightly.

Distance travelled (km)	Fuel gauge reading (amount used)
0	0
112.7	$\frac{1}{8}$
194.6	$\frac{1}{4}$
258.5	$\frac{3}{8}$
312.7	$\frac{1}{2}$
349.1	$\frac{5}{8}$
388.5	$\frac{3}{4}$
418.2	$\frac{7}{8}$

   b) As the distance travelled increases, the fuel gauge reading decreases. However, the relationship is not linear. Either the gauge is not accurate or other factors are affecting the fuel consumption.

   c) About 450 km

18. Answers may vary.

19. Answers may vary.

   d) For dates between April and October, the graph would move down by 1 h.

2.3 Mathematical Modelling: Relating Animal and Human Lifetimes: Part I, page 84

2. a) Table values may vary.

Cat's age	1	2	3	5	7	10	12	14
Human age	7	14	21	35	49	70	84	98

   b) It makes sense to join the points since age need not be a whole number.

   c) Answers may vary.

3. a) Table values may vary.

Cat's age	1	2	3	5	7	10	12	14	20
Human age	21	25	29	37	45	57	65	73	97

4. Answers may vary.

   a) The graph of Model 2 consists of 2 line segments, while that of Model 1 is a single line. The first line segment of Model 2 is much steeper than the line for Model 1.

5. a) Table values may vary.

Dog's age	1	2	3	5	7	10	12	14
Human age	15	25	30	40	50	65	75	95

   c) Like the graph of Model 2, the graph of Model 3 consists of several line segments, each less steep than the preceding segment.

   d) Answers may vary.

6. b) Like the graphs of Models 1 and 3, the graph consists of several line segments.

7. **b)** The graph consists of many short line segments that do not appear to follow a pattern.
   c) Answers may vary.

8. Explanations may vary.

9. **a)** About 20 years
   b) Answers may vary. A cat or dog ages much more quickly than a human. In effect, a cat or dog reaches adulthood in 1 to 2 years.

10., 11. Answers may vary.

2.4 Using a Motion Detector to Investigate Relationships
Investigation 1, page 88

1. **a)** Time in seconds
   b) Distance to the wall in metres

2. **a)** The line segment on the graph slopes downward when you move toward the wall, and upward when you move away from the wall.
   b) The faster you move, the steeper is the line segment. The slower you move, the less steep is the line segment.

3. Answers may vary.

4. **a)** 0.65 m, or 65 cm
   b) 2.499 s
   c) Away from the wall; the line segment on which the point lies slopes upward.
   d) The person stood still for about 1 s. She moved steadily away from the wall for about 12 s, then stopped and stood still.

5. **a)** The person stood still for 3 s, moved steadily toward the wall for about 3.5 s, stood still for 2.5 s, moved steadily away from the wall for 4 s then, once back in the starting position, stood still for several seconds.
   b) The person moved steadily away from the wall for 4 s, stood still 2.357 m away from the wall for about 5 s, moved steadily toward the wall for about 3 s, stood still 1 s, then moved steadily away from the wall for about 5 s.

6. Answers may vary.

Investigation 2, page 91

2. **a)** i) The points lie on a curve that slopes down to the right.
   ii) The points lie on a curve that slopes up to the right.
   b) The curves on the graph become less steep.

3. to 6. Experimental results may vary.

2.5 Using a Graphing Calculator to Investigate Relationships
Investigation 1, page 94

2. Linear; the points appear to lie on a straight line.

3. **b)** No, since we do not know the prices that would be charged for other numbers of flyers.

4. **a)** Predictions may vary.   **d)** Descriptions may vary.

6. **b)** $364.25

8. **c)** Predictions may vary.   **e)** $2239.25

9. **c)** $2396.00

10. **d)** Non-linear; the points appear to lie on a curve.
    e) 16¢

Investigation 2, page 98

2. With the exception of the points for a full page and $\frac{4}{5}$ of a page, the relation appears to be linear as the points lie on a straight line.

3. **b)** Predictions may vary.   **e)** Descriptions may vary.

4. **c)** $1016.50

5. **c)** With the exception of the points for a full page and $\frac{4}{5}$ page, the relation appears to be linear since the points lie on a straight line.
   d) 4¢

6. **d)** $4782.90

7. **b)** Non-linear; the points appear to lie on a curve.

2.6 Relationships in Proportional Situations
Investigation, page 101

Problem 1: 600 words
Problem 2: 5 min
Problem 3: About 27
Problem 4: 30 games
Problem 5: 25
Problem 6: 35

1., 2. Answers may vary.

3. No

4. Problems 1, 2, 3, and 4 represent proportional situations, Problems 5 and 6 do not. The first four problems involve multiplication and division, while the last two involve addition and subtraction.

2.6 Exercises, page 105

1. The problem in part a represents a proportional situation. Explanations may vary.

2. **a)** $3.87   **b)** $6.45   **c)** $9.03
   d) $12.90   **e)** $15.48   **f)** $25.80

3. **a)** $1.44   **b)** $2.88   **c)** $4.32
   d) $9.36   **e)** $12.24   **f)** $72.00

4. $0.29/can

5. **a)** $1.89/bottle   **b)** $18.90

6. **a)** $0.62/L   **b)** $21.70

7. **a)** $4.80   **b)** $0.60   **c)** $0.75   **d)** $2.10

8. **a)** $382 500   **b)** 7 h 51 min

9. **a)** $73.80   **b)** 42.7 h

10. **a)** 250
    b) Explanations may vary. The assumption is that Taborah will hit at a steady rate. This is not a good assumption for small intervals at-bat because she could have a hot or cold streak.

11. a)

Time (min)	Words typed
3	120
6	240
9	360
12	480
15	600

c) Variables may differ. $N = 40t$

d) The number of words typed will be greater if the rate is faster. The graph will rise more steeply upwards to the right; t will be multiplied by a greater number in the formula.

The number of words typed will be smaller if the rate is slower. The graph will rise less steeply upwards to the right; t will be multiplied by a smaller number in the formula.

e) Explanations may vary. The assumption is that Bob types at a constant rate continuously. This is good for short time intervals. However, over very long time intervals, Bob may slow down.

12. 150 kg

13. Bottle

14. a) i) 365 000 L

ii) 1 168 000 000 L

b) i) About 31 s

ii) Answers may vary.

15. The times in parts b to e are rounded to the nearest hour.

a) In 1982, the average hourly wage in Athens was $2.90 and the cost of a basket of food was $212.00.
In 1994, the average hourly wage was $4.90 and the cost of a basket of food was $275.00.

b) 1982: 73 h; 1994: 56 h. People in Athens were better off in 1994 because they could buy more with the money they earned.

c) 1982: 46 h, 1994: 50 h. People in Oslo were better off in 1982.

e) 1982: Cairo (231 h); 1994: Lagos (1472 h)

f) 1982: San Francisco (28 h); 1994: Luxembourg (25 h)

16. a) The formula for cell A3 is =A2+0.5, the formula for cell B2 is =2.95*A2.

b) Explanations may vary.

c) Yes; the graph is a straight line rising upwards to the right and passing through the origin.

d) The cost of 11.5 kg of peanuts is $33.93.

17. 10 mL

18. a) The rates are slightly different.

b) Answers may vary. The label could be changed to "Covers 61.2 m^2," or the inside instructions could be changed to "Seed evenly 500 g per 30 m^2 in two directions."

2.7 Mathematical Modelling: Relating Animal and Human Lifetimes: Part II, page 109

1. b) Answers may vary.

2. a) Cats, dogs, bears, and chimpanzees

b) Dolphin   **c)** Elephant

3. a) Those animals with a longer life span have a slower heart rate than animals with a shorter life span.

b) Graph 3: As the life span increases, the heart rate decreases.

Consolidating Your Skills, page 111

1. to **4.** Results and explanations may vary.

2. b) Descriptions may vary.

3. b) Yes, the graph is a straight line relationship passing through the origin.

4. d) No; the relationship is not proportional.

5. a)

Number of games	Number of hits
3	10
6	20
9	30
12	40
15	50

c) $G = \frac{10}{3} H$, where G is the number of games and H is the number of hits.

6. a) Company B offers the better price per puck.

b) The case of 300 packets

7. a) Above

2 Cumulative Review, page 113

1. a) −11   **b)** 11   **c)** 38

d) 11   **e)** 27   **f)** 11.6

2. a) 1.80   **b)** 154.18

3. a) 5%   **b)** 95%

4. a) $\frac{51}{4}$, or $12\frac{3}{4}$ **b)** $\frac{113}{2}$, or $56\frac{1}{2}$ **c)** $\frac{153}{4}$, or $38\frac{1}{4}$

d) $\frac{537}{20}$, or $26\frac{17}{20}$ **e)** $\frac{389}{100}$, or $3\frac{89}{100}$ **f)** $\frac{29}{2}$, or $14\frac{1}{2}$

g) 164   **h)** $\frac{239}{20}$, or $11\frac{19}{20}$

5. a) 6   **b)** $\frac{1}{12}$ **c)** $\frac{1}{2}$

d) $\frac{21}{8}$ **e)** −0.12   **f)** 0.9

6. a) 4.1 km/h, 2.7 km/h, 2.9 km/h

b) 65.2 km, 20.3 h   **c)** 3.21 km/h

d) 3.23 km/h   **e)** No, explanations may vary.

7. b) Yes, the graph shows accumulated totals over time.

8. 900 mL for $2.39

Chapter 3 Slope
Mathematical Modelling: Who Is the World's Fastest Human?: Part I, page 115

1. to **4.** Answers may vary.

Reviewing Your Skills, page 116

1. a) 136.6, 138.2, 139.8

c) i) 1.6 km   **ii)** 3.2 km   **iii)** 48 km   **iv)** 6.4 km

d) 1.6 km/min   **e)** 96 km/h

f) Answers may vary. Car slowed down briefly

g) 15 km   **h)** 1.5 km/min

2. a) 8°C   **b)** 2°C/h   **c)** 3°C/h

3. a) 2   **b)** −2   **c)** 15   **d)** 3
   e) −8   **f)** −4   **g)** $-\frac{1}{2}$ **h)** −18

3.1 Slope

Investigation, page 117

1. a) Equal

2. c) 3
   d) ii) The board does not change positions.
   e) 3

3. c) $\frac{1}{2}$
   d) ii) The board does not change positions.
   e) $\frac{1}{2}$

4. a) 1, 1   **b)** 3, 3   **c)** $\frac{1}{2}, \frac{1}{2}$
   d) The slope is greater.

5.

		rise	run	slope
a)	1st staircase in exercise 1	2	2	1
b)	staircase in exercise 2	6	2	3
c)	staircase in exercise 3	2	4	$\frac{1}{2}$
d)		8	2	4
e)		6	3	2
f)		1	4	$\frac{1}{4}$
g)		0	2	0

6. Divide the rise by the run.

Investigation 2, page 119

1. a) Roof 1   **b)** Roof 2   **c)** Least to greatest: 2, 3, 1

2. a), b)

House	rise	run	$\frac{rise}{run}$
1	11	5	$\frac{11}{5}$
2	5	8	$\frac{5}{8}$
3	7	6	$\frac{7}{6}$

c) Answers may vary. The steepest slope has the greatest $\frac{rise}{run}$.

3.1 Exercises, page 121

1. c) i) 1.5   **ii)** 0.5   **iii)** 0.25

2. $\frac{1}{3}$

3. $-\frac{5}{3}$

4. Explanations may vary.
   a) The plane must clear any objects such as houses or people.
   b) The wind, the type of plane

5. Answers may vary.

6. a) 4 m; equal
   b) Hill EF; the slope is $\frac{3}{2}$; whereas the slope for hill AB is $\frac{3}{4}$.
   c) Hill GH; the slope is $-\frac{3}{2}$; whereas the slope for hill CD is $-\frac{3}{4}$.
   d) The steepness is independent of the height of a hill.
   e) The speed of a roller coaster is often controlled mechanically; otherwise a steep drop would have an increased speed.

7. a) −0.25   **b)** $\frac{2}{3}$ **c)** $\frac{1}{3}$ **d)** −2.5   **e)** 0

8. Answers may vary. rise = 3, run = 1

9. 24

10. Answers may vary. Make many turns.

11. a) Explanations may vary.
   b) They reduce the ratio $\frac{rise}{run}$.

12. a) 1   **b)** 0   **c)** $\frac{1}{4}$ **d)** 2
   e) $-\frac{1}{4}$ **f)** −2   **g)** −1

13. Answers may vary.
   c) So that the snow may slide from the roof

14. a) There is 1 more riser than tread.
   b) Answers may vary.
   c) C; explanations may vary. To save space, a steep staircase is best.
   d) A; explanations may vary. A long tread gives room for a foot to rest comfortably
   e) Answers may vary. A tread with non-slippery material

15. a) Table values may vary.

Rise (cm)	Run (cm)	Slope
18.5	25	0.74
18	26	0.69
17.5	27	0.65
17	28	0.61
16.5	29	0.57

   b) Yes, explanations may vary.

16. 14 steps, 22 cm run, 20 cm rise, 308 cm horizontal space for the staircase

17. Answers and explanations may vary.

3.2 The Cartesian Plane

Investigation, page 125

2. They lie on a vertical line on the right of the middle.

3. They lie on a horizontal line below the middle.

4. a) In the lower right corner
   b) In the upper left corner
   c) They lie in different parts of the graph.

6. Predictions may vary.
   a) The coordinates change by 0.2.
   b) The coordinates change by 1 unit.
   c) The coordinates are given to 8 decimal places.

3.2 Exercises, page 127

1. Answers may vary. (−3, 0), (−3, 1), (−3, 2), (−3, 3), (−3, 4) They lie on a vertical line.

2. Answers may vary. (0, −5), (1, −5), (2, −5), (3, −5), (4, −5) They lie on a horizontal line.

3. B(2, −4), C(−5, 3), D(2, 5), E(0, 3), F(−4, −2), G(−3, 0), H(5, 0), J(0, −5)

4. a) Square   **b)** Parallelogram   **c)** Quadrilateral

6. Star

8. b) List 1 and List 2 form straight lines. List 3 forms a curve opening upward.

c) Explanations may vary.

d) Answers may vary. List 1: (4, −2), (5, −3); List 2: (4, 9), (5, 11); List 3: (4, 16), (5, 25)

9. Answers may vary. (0, 0), (1, 1), (2, 2), (3, 3), (4, 4) They lie on a straight line.

10. Answers may vary. (1, −1), (2, −2), (−3, 3), (−4, 4), (−5, 5) They lie on a straight line.

11. Answers may vary. (2, −2), (−2, −2); (2, 6), (−2, 6)

12. Answers may vary. (8, 8), (2, 8)

3.3 Slope of a Line Segment

Investigation, page 129

3. b) i) Positive slope   **ii)** Negative slope

     iii) Zero slope   **iv)** Undefined slope

3.3 Exercises, page 134

1. a) AB: $\frac{5}{8}$; AC: $\frac{3}{8}$; AD: $\frac{1}{8}$; AE: 0; AF $= -\frac{1}{4}$; AG: $-\frac{5}{8}$

b) PQ: $-\frac{7}{5}$; PR: $-\frac{7}{2}$; PS: undefined; PT: $\frac{7}{2}$; PU: $\frac{7}{4}$; PV: 1

2. Explanations may vary.

3. a) $-\frac{11}{8}$ **b)** 3   **c)** $-\frac{5}{2}$ **d)** Undefined

e) $\frac{2}{3}$ **f)** 0

4. a) AB: −1; BC: $\frac{9}{2}$; AC: $\frac{4}{7}$ **b)** RS: $\frac{1}{3}$; ST: $\frac{5}{2}$; RT $= -\frac{7}{5}$

c) LM: $-\frac{5}{4}$; MN: 0; LN: undefined

d) EF: −5; FG: 2; EG: 1

5. Answers may vary.

6. a) The interval from 0 to 1600 is not drawn to scale.

b) $\frac{1}{15}, -\frac{1}{50}, -\frac{1}{20}, -\frac{1}{40}$ **c)** 0.022

d) In the first section; that is, in the first 6000 m

7. A(17, 4), B(22, 10), C(25, 8), D(30, 6), E(31, 2), F(37, 1)

8. Answers may vary. (3, 0), (4, 3)

9. Answers may vary.

i) (4, 7), (2, 1)   **ii)** (−3, 3), (−2, −2)

iii) (0, 0), (5, 3)   **iv)** (−3, −3), (−6, 2)

v) (1, 3), (3, −3)   **vi)** (0, 0), (1, 5)

10. a) You are standing still.

b) i) The distance between you and the wall is increasing.

ii) The distance between you and the wall is decreasing.

c) i) Walk very quickly.   **ii)** Do not move.

11. a) Steep incline   **b)** A slight incline   **c)** Flat

d) A slight decline   **e)** Steep decline

12. a) A, B, C

b) A: 10 500 ft, 1312.5 ft/min; B: 20 000 ft, 1538 ft/min; C: 20 000 ft, 1818 ft/min

c) No; A reaches its maximum altitude first. A has the lowest rate of climb.

13. All figures can be drawn.

14. a) 7   **b)** 5   **c)** 4   **d)** 0

15. a) 6   **b)** −2   **c)** −1   **d)** 4

16. Explanations may vary.

17. a) Slope $= \frac{y_2 - y_1}{x_2 - x_1}$ **b)** Slope $= \frac{\Delta y}{\Delta x}$

18. a) (−2, 0) **b)** (1, 0)   **c)** (2, 0)   **d)** (−8, 0) **e)** (7, 0)   **f)** (16, 0)

19. (−2, 0), (8, 0)

3.4 Mathematical Modelling: Who Is the World's Fastest Human?: Part I, page 139

2. b) 10.16 m/s; the average speed for Bailey's 100-m race

3. b) 10.35 m/s; the average speed for Johnson's 200-m race

4. b) 9.88 m/s; the average speed for the first 100 m of Johnson's race

c) Johnson's average speed for the first 100 m is greater.

5. b) 10.16 m/s; the average speed for Bailey's (imagined) 200-m race

c) Bailey's average speed for 200 m is greater.

6. Explanations may vary.

a) No; a runner's speed is not the same throughout a race.

b) Answers may vary.

7. Answers may vary.

3.5 Graphing Linear Relations

Investigation 1, page 141

1. a) i) $5.50   **ii)** $11.00   **iii)** $16.50   **iv)** $22.00

v) $27.50   **vi)** $33.00   **vii)** $38.50

b)

Hours worked	Pay ($)	Difference
0	0	
		5.50
1	5.50	
		5.50
2	11.00	
		5.50
3	16.50	
		5.50
4	22.00	
		5.50
5	27.50	
		5.50
6	33.00	
		5.50
7	38.50	

2. Answers may vary.

3. See exercise 1 part b. All differences are $5.50.

4. a) The points are joined because Monique is paid for parts of an hour worked.

b) Explanations may vary. For every additional hour Monique works, she gets $5.50.

c) $40

5. a), b), c) 5.50

d) They are the same. Explanations may vary.

6. Descriptions may vary. It is a linear relation.

7. a) $p = 5.5\,h$

8. $39.88

9. a) Each entry in the *Earnings* column would increase by $0.50.

b) The graph would be steeper.

c) $p = 6\,h$

10. a) No change

b) The points on the graph would not be joined.

c) No change

Investigation 2, page 143

1.

x	y	Difference
0	−1	
1	2	3
2	5	3
3	8	3
4	11	3
5	14	3
6	17	3

5. See exercise 1. All the differences are 3.

6. b) There is no restriction on x. That is, x can be any number.

7. a) 3   **b)** 3

    c) All the slopes are 3.

    d) Same; explanations may vary.

3.5 Exercises, page 146

1. a) i)

x	y
0	3
−1.5	0
1	5
2	7

ii)

x	y
0	5
$\frac{5}{3}$	0
1	2
2	−1

iii)

x	y
0	12
3	0
1	8
2	4

    b) Answers may vary.

2. a)

n	C
5	220
3	140
0	20
2	100

    b) (1, 60), (2.5, 120), (−2, −60) satisfy the equation of the relation. When we substitute the points in the equation, the statements are true.

    (4, 160) does not satisfy the equation. When we substitute the point into the equation, the statement is $160 = 180$, which is false.

    c) (−2, −60); employees cannot work for −2 h.

3. a) Table values may vary.

x	y	Difference
0	6	
1	8	2
2	10	2
3	12	2
4	14	2

    b) $y = 2(x + 3)$

4. a) Table values may vary.

n	C (¢)
0	70
10	270
20	470
30	670
40	870
50	1070
60	1270
70	1470
80	1670
90	1870
100	2070

    c) $15.70   **d)** 46

5. a) All graphs are straight lines.

    b) Answers may vary.

6. b) Answers may vary.

7. a) Table values may vary.

n	C ($)
0	300
2	340
4	380
6	420
8	460
10	500
12	540
14	580

    c) 12

    d) 300 represents the cost in dollars to play in the tournament excluding the cost per player. 20 represents the additional cost in dollars per player. Explanations may vary.

    e) i) The points only; you cannot include part of a player.

    ii) The points where $n = 5, 6, …, 12$ are reasonable because a starting line-up in basketball has 5 players.

8. a) Table values may vary.

t (h)	d (km)
0	280
0.5	230
1	180
1.5	130
2	80
2.5	30
2.8	0

    b) Explanations may vary; 280 km

    c) Explanations may vary; 2.8 h

    d) 80 km; 200 km

    e) Explanations may vary.

9. a) Table values may vary.

F	C
−40	−40
−22	−30
−4	−20
14	−10
32	0
50	10
68	20
86	30

    b) Estimates may vary.

    i) 194°F   **ii)** 248°F   **iii)** 392°F

    c) Estimates may vary.

    i) 32°F   **ii)** 49°C   **iii)** 93°C

    d) Estimates may vary.

    i) −7°C   **ii)** −18°C   **iii)** −23°C   **iv)** −29°C   **e)** −40°

10. a) Table values may vary.

F	C
−40	−35
−22	−26
−4	−17
14	−8
32	−1
50	10
68	19
86	28

    c) $C = \dfrac{F - 30}{2}$

11., 12. Answers may vary.

13. b) Answers may vary. From 14°F to 86°F, the approximate rule gives a value within 2°C of the true value.

c) Answers may vary. "Add 9, then divide by 2."

14. Answers may vary.

3.6 Graphing Non-Linear Relations
Investigation, page 150

1. a)

x	y	Difference
−2	10	
−1	4	−6
0	0	−4
1	−2	−2
2	−2	0
3	0	2
4	4	4

b) The differences are increasing.

c) Explanations may vary.

5. b) −6   **c)** −4

d) The slopes are the same as the values in the difference column. Explanations may vary.

3.6 Exercises, page 153

1. a) All the differences are −3. $y = -3x - 1$

b) The differences are: 4, 3, 2, 1, 0, −1. No linear equation possible.

c) All the differences are 0. $y = 5$

2. Table values may vary.

a) i)

x	y	Difference
−2	1	
−1	2	1
0	3	1
1	4	1
2	5	1

ii) All numbers can be used.

iii) Linear   **iv)** $y = x + 3$ **vi)** Linear

b) i)

x	y	Difference
−2	−6	
−1	−12	−6
1	12	24
2	6	−6
3	4	−2

ii) 0 cannot be used.

iii) Non-linear   **iv)** $y = \dfrac{12}{x}$ **vi)** Non-linear

c) i)

x	y	Difference
−4	−2	
−2	−1	1
0	0	1
2	1	1
4	2	1

ii) All numbers can be used.

iii) Linear   **iv)** $y = \dfrac{x}{2}$ **vi)** Linear

d) i)

x	y	Difference
−2	8	
−1	3	−5
0	0	−3
1	−1	−1
2	0	1
3	3	3

ii) All numbers can be used.

iii) Non-linear   **iv)** $y = (x - 2)x$ **vi)** Non-linear

3. a) i) Linear   **ii)** Linear   **iii)** Linear
     iv) Non-linear   **v)** Non-linear   **vi)** Linear
     vii) Non-linear   **viii)** Non-linear   **ix)** Non-linear

b) Descriptions may vary.

5. b) Answers may vary.

6. a) iii   **b)** i   **c)** ii

7. −3.25, −1, −0.33, −0.07; all the slopes are different.

8. a) Descriptions may vary.

b) i) 2.02 s   **ii)** 2.47 s   **iii)** 2.86 s

9. a) Explanations may vary; with a smooth curve

b) Estimates may vary.
     i) $1320   **ii)** $1370   **iii)** $1420   **iv)** $1475

c) 46.88, 48.63, 50.45, 52.35, 54.31; since the differences are different, the relation is non-linear.

10. b) 70%   **c)** 52 m

d) −37, −23, −15, −9, −6; since the differences are different, the relation is non-linear.

11. a) BMI $= \dfrac{70}{(\text{height(m)})^2}$

c) Descriptions may vary; as height increases, BMI decreases.

d) Descriptions may vary. The graph would be closer to the y-axis for people with a mass less than 70 kg. The graph would be farther from the y-axis for people with a mass greater than 70 kg.

12. BMI $= \dfrac{\text{mass(kg)}}{1.5^2}$; explanations may vary.

Consolidating Your Skills, page 156

1. $\dfrac{2}{3}$

2. a) $\dfrac{4}{5}$, −2   **b)** Descriptions may vary.

3. Locations of line segments may vary.

4. Answers may vary.

5. b) $-\dfrac{7}{3}$, undefined, 0, $\dfrac{3}{2}$

6. a) All differences are 3. Linear

b) The differences are: −1, −2, −3, −4, −5, −6. Non-linear

c) All differences are −2. Linear

7. Explanations may vary.

a) The hot chocolate will cool.

b) Experimental results may vary.

c) A smooth curve   **e)** Answers may vary.

f) No   **g)** Non-linear   **h)** Yes

9. a) Non-linear   **b)** Linear   **c)** Linear   **d)** Non-linear

10. b) The line segments from 40 m to 50 m and from 60 m to 70 m

c) 14.3 m/s

11. b) The line segment from 50 m to 80 m

c) 14.3 m/s

Chapter 4 The Line

Mathematical Modelling: Setting Up for a Banquet, page 159

1. **a)** Theatre Style, chairs only
   b) Banquet Style, oblong tables
2. Answers may vary. Banquet Style, oblong tables and Theatre Style: 20, $\frac{20}{16}$, 125%
3. Answers may vary.

Reviewing Your Skills, page 160

1. **a)**

Number of toothpicks on one side	Total number of toothpicks in the square
1	4
2	8
3	12
100	400

   b) Number of toothpicks on one side multiplied by 4 equals the total number of toothpicks.
   c) $T = 4n$
   d) No; only whole toothpicks are used.
   e) 4   **f)** 4; the slopes are equal.

2. **a)**

x	y
1	36
2	18
3	12
4	9
6	6
9	4
12	3
18	2
36	1

   b) As x increases, y decreases so that x multiplied by y equals 36.
   c) Explanations may vary.
   d) Answers may vary. (1, 36) and (6, 6); −6
   e) Answers may vary. (2, 18) and (6, 6); −3; the slope depends on the points chosen.

3. **a)** 2, 2, 2, 2,
   b) All the differences are 2.
   c) The slope is equal to the difference; 2.
   d) Descriptions may vary. The graph is a straight line rising to the right, with a slope of 2.

4.1 Finding Relationships in Data

Investigation 1, page 161

1. **b)** $y = 3x - 4$
2. **a)** −0.5, 5.5, −6.55, 13.55
3. **a)** $y = 2x - 5$; Xmin = −0.5, Xmax = 5.5, Ymin = −6.7, Ymax = 6.7
   b) $y = -2x + 9$; Xmin = −0.5, Xmax = 5.5, Ymin = −2.7, Ymax = 10.7
   c) $y = -5x + 20$; Xmin = −0.5, Xmax = 5.5, Ymin = −9.25, Ymax = 24.25
4. Explanations may vary.

Investigation 2, page 163

Answers may vary.

4.1 Exercises, page 165

1. Answers may vary. Multiply the input number by 2. Multiply the input number by 3, then subtract 2. Add 2 to the input number.

2. **a)** $y = 2x$ **b)** $y = 2x + 1$ **c)** $y = 2x + 2$
   d) $y = -x + 8$ **e)** $y = -x - 2$ **f)** $y = x^2$

3. **a)** Square the input number.
   b) i) Square the input number, then add 1. Multiply by 5, then subtract 5.
   ii) Multiply by 4, then subtract 4. Start with output number 4 when the input number is 2. When the input increases by 1, the output increases by 4.

4. **a)** $y = x + 2$ **b)** $y = 2x - 1$
   c) $y = 2x - 3$ **d)** $y = x(x + 1)$

5. **a)**

x	y
1	2
2	4
3	6
4	8
5	10
6	24

   b) For input numbers of 1 to 5, the results are the same. When $x = 6$, the results are different.
   c) No; explanations may vary.

4.2 Slope of a Line

Investigation, page 167

1. **a)**

Hours worked	Earnings ($)	Difference ($)
0	0	
		3
1	3	
		3
2	6	
		3
3	9	
		3
4	12	
		3
5	15	
		3
6	18	

   c) 3; the same   **d)** The pay increases by $3.
   e) For each step she earns $3.   **f)** (0, 0)

2. **a)**

Hours worked	Earnings ($)	Difference ($)
1	3	
		9
4	12	
		3
5	15	
		6
7	21	

   b) The numbers in the first column increase by different amounts from row to row.
   c) 3
   d) The difference equals the slope only when the hours worked increases by 1.

3. **a)**

Hours worked	Earnings ($)	Difference ($)
1	3	
		9
4	12	
		9
7	21	
		9
10	30	

   b) The numbers in the first column increase by the same amount from row to row.

c) The numbers in the first column increase by 3 each time, rather than 1.

d) They are 3 times the slope because the hours worked increase by 3, rather than 1.

4. a) No; explanations may vary.

b) The numbers in the first column change by a constant amount from row to row.

4.2 Exercises, page 171

1. a) 2   **b)** $-\frac{3}{2}$ **c)** $\frac{1}{2}$

2. a) Answers may vary.

i) (1, 7), (2, 10)   **ii)** (1, 5), (−1, 3)   **iii)** (2, 5), (−2, 3)

iv) (2, 4), (5, 4)   **v)** (1, 2), (3, −2)   **vi)** (4, 3), (−4, 5)

vii) (0, 1), (0, 3)

b) Explanations may vary.

3.

Age, *n* years	Allowance, *a* dollars
6	0.75
7	1.50
8	2.25
9	3.00
10	3.75
11	4.50
12	5.25
13	6.00
14	6.75
15	7.50
16	8.25

b) Explanations may vary. There is a constant increase in allowance.

c) No; explanations may vary.

d) 0.75; increase in allowance for one year.

4. Answers may vary.

a) (−1, −3), (0, 0)   **b)** (2, 0), (5, 4)

c) (0, 0), (1, −2)   **d)** (0, 0), (−5, 2)

e) (3, −1), (−1, 2)

5. Answers may vary. There is an infinite number of lines for each slope.

6. Answers may vary.

a) (−3, 0), (1, 4)   **b)** (5, 3), (2, 1)

c) (−1, −2), (−5, 0)   **d)** (3, 4), (0, 4)

7. b) Explanations may vary. There is a constant increase in cost.

c) Explanations may vary. Yes; although it is not possible to have a fraction of an exposure, the straight line helps us to see values between points.

d) 0.35; this represents the additional cost to print each exposure, beyond the flat rate to develop the film.

e) About $9.50, $13.70, $17.90

f) Table values may vary.

Number of exposures	Cost
8	$7.78
10	$8.48
18	$11.28
20	$11.98
30	$15.48
35	$17.23

8. b) The cooking time needed per kilogram

c) The slope would be less steep for large values of *m*.

d) The slope would be steeper.

e) The labels on the horizontal axis are the only parts of the graph that would change.

9. a) (500, 80), (750, 120), (1000, 160), (1250, 200)

b) $\frac{4}{25}$, or 0.16   **c)** 9600 feet

d) 500 s or 8 min 20 s

10. b) $\frac{32}{500}$, or 0.64   **c)** 480 feet

d) Answers may vary.

11. Answers may vary.

a) (3, −1), (4, −5)   **b)** (6, −7), (11, −14)

c) (16, 18), (10.5, 13)   **d)** (−5, −5), (−2, −8)

12. a) All slopes are $\frac{2}{3}$.   **b)** All slopes are $-\frac{1}{2}$.

c) Slopes are $\frac{1}{3}$, $\frac{3}{7}$, and $\frac{1}{5}$.

13. a) 2, $\frac{7}{4}$, $\frac{13}{7}$

b) A, B, and C are not collinear.

c) Answers may vary. Try to draw a straight line through the three points.

14. a) Yes   **b)** No   **c)** No

15. −2

16. a) 4   **b)** Explanations may vary.

17. 1

18. b) i) This adds 1 to the number of exposures.

ii) This adds 35¢ to the cost because this is the charge for each exposure.

iii) This calculates the mean cost for each exposure by dividing the cost by the number of exposures.

c) The mean cost per exposure decreases as the number of exposures increases. When the number of exposures is large, the flat fee of $4.98 for developing the film is divided among a greater number of exposures.

e) The relation is not linear because the mean cost per exposure is not constant.

19. a) 0.24 or −0.24

b) Answers may vary.

i) It may not drop at the same speed through the reentry.

ii) The slope decreases.

4.3 Graphing *y = mx + b*
Investigation 1, page 175

1. a) The one on the right

b) Answers may vary.

2. b) Explanations may vary. Each line passes through the point (0, 1).

c) A horizontal line through the point (0, 1)

3. b) Explanations may vary. The lines are parallel.

c) A line with slope 0.5, passing through the origin

4. *m* is the slope, *b* is the *y*-intercept.

6. *y* = *x* + 4, *y* = −*x* + 4, *y* = *x* − 4, *y* = −*x* − 4

Investigation 2, page 176

1. **b)** All pass through (0, 0); all have different slopes.

2. **a)** $1, 2, \frac{1}{2}, 0, -1, -2, -\frac{1}{2}$
   b) The slope is the number x is multiplied by.

3. m is the slope of the line.

4. **b) i)** All pass through (0, 5); all have different slopes.
   ii) All are parallel; all are in different positions on the grid.

5. **a) i)** $2, 1, \frac{1}{2}, 0, -\frac{1}{2}, -1, -2$ **ii)** 2
   b) The slope is the number that x is multiplied by.

6. m is the slope and b is the y-coordinate of the point where the line crosses the y-axis.

4.3 Exercises, page 179

1. **a)** 3, 5   **b)** −2, 3   **c)** $\frac{2}{5}, -4$ **d)** $-\frac{1}{2}, 6$
   e) −4, −7   **f)** $\frac{3}{8}, -\frac{5}{2}$ **g)** $\frac{4}{3}, -2$ **h)** $\frac{9}{5}, 1$

2. **a)** $y = 2x + 3$ **b)** $y = -x + 4$ **c)** $y = \frac{2}{3}x - 1$
   d) $y = -\frac{4}{5}x + 8$ **e)** $y = -3x + \frac{5}{2}$ **f)** $y = 3$

3. **a)** $\frac{1}{2}, 1, y = \frac{1}{2}x + 1$ **b)** $\frac{3}{2}, -2, y = \frac{3}{2}x - 2$
   c) $-2, 1, y = -2x + 1$

4. **a) i)** $y = -x + 2$ **ii)** $y = -\frac{3}{2}x - 3$ **iii)** $y = \frac{2}{3}x$
   b) Explanations may vary.

5. **b)** Explanations may vary.

6. **b)** (6, 0)   **c)** 9 square units

7. **a)** (1, 6)   **b)** 27 square units

8. (4, 4), (1, −2), (−2, 7)

9. **a) i)** Same shape, but increases in size
   ii) Increases   **iii)** Increases   **iv)** Stays the same
   b) i) Same shape, but decreases in size
   ii) Decreases   **iii)** Decreases   **iv)** Stays the same
   c) Slope of QP $= \frac{y+5}{x}$

10. **a) i)** $b - m = 2$ **ii)** $b \div m = -3$ **iii)** $mb = 1$
    b) i) All lines intersect at (−1, 2).
    ii) All lines intersect at (3, 0).
    c) Explanations may vary.

11. **a) i)** −5   **ii)** 7   **iii)** −11   **iv)** 8
    b) Explanations may vary.

12. **a)** $\frac{1}{4}$ **b)** −5   **c)** −2   **d)** $\frac{1}{5}$

13. **a)** $mb = 1$ **b)** Answers may vary.
    c) Explanations may vary.

14. **a)** The lines have the same y-intercept, 3.
    b) The lines have the same x-intercept, −3.

4.4 Mathematical Modelling: Setting Up for a Banquet, page 182

1. Answers may vary.

2. **a)** 13 277 ft^2 **b)** 6048 ft^2 **c)** 1210 ft^2

3. Canadian Room: 13 277 ft^2, Imperial Room: 6048 ft^2, Manitoba Room: 1210 ft^2; other answers may vary.

4. **a)** $y = \frac{x}{6}$

5. **a)** Canadian Room: 2213, Imperial Room: 1007, Manitoba Room: 202; other answers may vary.
   b) Answers and explanations may vary.

6. **a)** $y = \frac{x}{8}$

7. **a)** Canadian Room: 1660, Imperial Room: 756, Manitoba Room: 151; other answers may vary.
   b) Answers may vary.

8. **a)** $y = \frac{x}{10}$

9. **a)** Canadian Room: 1328, Imperial Room: 605, Manitoba Room: 121; other answers may vary.

4.5 Applications of Linear Relations

4.5 Exercises, page 188

1. **a)** No, the days are whole numbers.
   b) 5800

2. **a)** $t = 20 + 2n$.
   b) Yes; it is possible to have a fraction of a candy.
   c) 5, 20   **d)** Mass of the empty box
   e) Mass of each candy; grams
   f) The rate of change of t is constant. For every additional candy, the mass of the box increases by 5 g.

3. Explanations may vary.
   a) The slope is steeper.
   b) M-intercept is 30.

4. **a)** $T = 180b + 14\ 000$
   b) Yes. In theory it is not correct to join the points, but a straight line is a good representation of the relationship.
   c) 180, 14 000
   d) The mass of the empty truck
   e) The increase in mass for an increase of 1 barrel of crude oil; kg/barrel
   f) The rate of change of T is constant. For every additional barrel of oil, the mass of the truck increases by 180 kg.

5. Answers may vary.

6. **a)** $T = 20 + 10d$
   b) Yes; it is possible to have a fraction of a kilometre.
   c) 10, 20   **d)** Surface temperature
   e) The increase in temperature for each kilometre below the surface; °C/km
   f) The rate of change of T is constant. For every additional kilometre below the surface, the temperature increases by 10°C.
   g) Answers may vary. No; there are more factors involved, such as location on Earth's surface, time of year, and so on.

7. Explanations may vary.
   a) The T-intercept is 5.   **b)** The T-intercept is 40.

8. a) $T = -3.4H + 100$

b) Yes; it is possible to have a fraction of a kilometre.

c) −3.4, 100

d) The temperature at sea level

e) The decrease in the boiling point of water for every kilometre increase in the height above sea level. °C/km

f) The rate of change of T is constant. For every additional kilometre above sea level, the boiling point of water decreases by 3.4°C.

g) 70°C

9. a) Table values may vary.

Cups	People
0	0
4	6
8	12
12	18
16	24
20	30

b) 20   **c)** 18

d) Descriptions may vary. Steeper slope

10. a)

Number of books, n	Total cost ($), C
0	8000
50	8200
100	8400
150	8600
200	8800
250	9000
300	9200

c) $10 000

d) 4, $8000; the cost to print and bind one book; fixed cost to set-up press

e) Descriptions may vary. Slope is less steep.

11. a) 7800 cans   **b)** 31

12. a) $P = 25t - 12\ 000$ **b)** 480; the t-intercept

13. b) (400, 9600); the costs are equal for producing 400 books at both companies.

c) Blue Heron Yearbooks charges less for 0 and 399 books. Miles Ahead Yearbooks charges less for more than 399 books.
Explanations may vary.

Consolidating Your Skills, page 191

3. Answers may vary.

4. a) Answers may vary. Add 6 to the input number. Multiply the input number by 3.

b) Multiply the input number by 3.

c) $3x$

5. a) 82.5%

b) $P = \frac{100}{80}m$ or $P = \frac{5}{4}m$

6. a) i) $195.00

ii) $65.00

iii) $110.50

b) Multiply the number of hours worked by 6.5.

c) $P = 6.5h$

7. a) Table values may vary.

Elapsed time (min)	Odometer reading (km)	Difference
0	237.5	
		1.5
1	239	
		1.5
2	240.5	
		1.5
3	242	
		1.5
4	243.5	
		1.5
5	245	
		1.5
6	246.5	
		1.5
7	248	
		1.5
8	249.5	
		1.5
9	251	
		1.5
10	252.5	
		1.5
11	254	
		1.5
12	255.5	
		1.5
13	257	
		1.5
14	258.5	
		1.5
15	260	

c) 1.5   **d)** 237.5   **e)** $y = 1.5x + 237.5$

f) The distance travelled each minute

g) 327.5 km

8. a) Line 4   **b)** Line 2   **c)** Line 5

d) Line 3   **e)** Line 1   **f)** Line 6

9. a) i) 14   **ii)** 20   **iii)** 26   **iv)** 32   **v)** 38

b)

t	P
1	8
2	14
3	20
4	26
5	32
6	38

c) No; a fraction of a table is not possible.

d) 6; the number of additional people that can be seated when a table is added

e) The rate of change of P is constant.   **f)** $P = 2 + 6t$

10. a) 16

b)

t	P
1	8
2	10
3	12
4	14
5	16
6	18

c) No; a fraction of a table is not possible.

d) 2; the number of additional people that can be seated when a table is added

e) The rate of change of P is constant.   **f)** $P = 6 + 2t$

11. Explanations may vary.

a) The line is less steep.   **b)** $P = 4t + 4$

4 Cumulative Review, page 194

1. a) −13   **b)** −4   **c)** −7.5   **d)** −132

2. Keystrokes may vary.

a) 8.62 ⌈×⌉ ⌈(⌉ 37.11 ⌈−⌉ 51.21 ⌈)⌉ ⌈=⌉ to display −121.542

b) ⌈(⌉ 21.3 ⌈−⌉ 8.8 ⌈)⌉ ⌈×⌉ ⌈(⌉ 65.3 ⌈−⌉ 39.7 ⌈)⌉ ⌈÷⌉ ⌈(⌉ 3.6 ⌈×⌉ ⌈(⌉ 68.5 ⌈−⌉ 31.2 ⌈)⌉ ⌈)⌉ ⌈=⌉ to display 2.383080

c) 181.001 ⌈÷⌉ ⌈(⌉ 21.315 ⌈×⌉ 2.321 ⌈)⌉ ⌈−⌉ 2 ⌈=⌉ to display 1.658 647

3. GST: $2.94; PST: $3.36; $48.30

4. a) $-\frac{43}{24}$ **b)** $\frac{13}{45}$ **c)** $-\frac{27}{2}$ **d)** $-\frac{27}{2}$

5. Explanations may vary.
  a) ii   **b)** i or iii

6. Descriptions may vary.

7. a) 20 pages   **b)** 12.5 min

8. a) $\frac{12}{7}$ **b)** -1

9. b) i and ii; both are straight-line graphs.

10. a) $y = x - 4$ **b)** $y = 3x - 1$ **c)** $y = 3x - 2$

12. -11

13. Explanations may vary.
  a) Yes; the slopes of line segments are equal.
  b) Yes; the slopes of line segments are equal.

14. a) -1; 1   **b)** $\frac{2}{3}$; -8

15. b) Explanations may vary. For part iv, draw a horizontal line through $(0, -3)$.

16. 10; -6

17. b) 2.4 km
  c) 0.2; when the speed increases by 1 km/h, the stopping distance increases by 0.2 km.
  d) 17.5 km/h

Chapter 5 Powers and Roots
Mathematical Modelling: How Thick Is the Pile of Paper?, page 197

1. Answers may vary.

2. The pile of paper is too thick, the paper is too small.

3. Answers may vary.

4. Estimates may vary.

Reviewing Your Skills, page 198

1. a) 16 777 216   **b)** 256 $\boxed{y^x}$ 3

2. a) $2 \times 2 \times 2$ **b)** 3×3
  c) Explanations may vary.

4. Explanations may vary.
  a) 625   **b)** 343
  c) 9   **d)** 100 000

5. a) $2 \times 2 \times 2 \times 2 \times 2 \times 2 \times 2 \times 2 = 256$
  b) $256 \times 256 \times 256$ or 2^{24} or 256^3
  c) Explanations may vary. 256^3 is the number of different colours a computer monitor can display.

6. a) 10^2 **b)** 10^3 **c)** 10^4
  d) 10^6 **e)** 10^9 **f)** 10^{12}

7. a) 14   **b)** 140   **c)** 1400
  d) 254   **e)** 3260   **f)** 175 000

8. a) 2.8×10^2 **b)** 2.8×10^3 **c)** 2.8×10^4
  d) 6.0×10^2 **e)** 6.0×10^3 **f)** 6.0×10^4

9. b) Squares; 4 equal sides with adjacent sides perpendicular

5.1 Multiplying and Dividing Powers
Investigation 1, page 200

1.

	Product of Powers	Product Form	Power Form
a)	$10^3 \times 10^4$	$(10 \times 10 \times 10) \times (10 \times 10 \times 10 \times 10)$	10^7
b)	$10^2 \times 10^6$	$(10 \times 10) \times (10 \times 10 \times 10 \times 10 \times 10 \times 10)$	10^8
c)	$5^4 \times 5^5$	$(5 \times 5 \times 5 \times 5) \times (5 \times 5 \times 5 \times 5 \times 5)$	5^9
d)	$5^3 \times 5^1$	$(5 \times 5 \times 5) \times (5)$	5^4
e)	$2^2 \times 2^9$	$(2 \times 2) \times (2 \times 2 \times 2 \times 2 \times 2 \times 2 \times 2 \times 2 \times 2)$	2^{11}

2. Answers may vary.

$6^3 \times 6^2$	$(6 \times 6 \times 6) \times (6 \times 6)$	6^5
$4^1 \times 4^4$	$(4) \times (4 \times 4 \times 4 \times 4)$	4^5
$3^3 \times 3^3$	$(3 \times 3 \times 3) \times (3 \times 3 \times 3)$	3^6
$7^2 \times 7^4$	$(7 \times 7) \times (7 \times 7 \times 7 \times 7)$	7^6
$8^2 \times 8^6$	$(8 \times 8) \times (8 \times 8 \times 8 \times 8 \times 8 \times 8)$	8^8

3. a) To multiply two powers of 10, keep the base of 10 and add the exponents.
  b) To multiply two powers of 5, keep the base of 5 and add the exponents.
  c) To multiply two powers with the same base, keep the base and add the exponents.

4. No, the bases must be the same.

Investigation 2, page 201

1.

	Quotient of Powers	Product Form	Power Form
a)	$10^8 \div 10^5$	$\dfrac{10 \times 10 \times 10 \times 10 \times 10 \times 10 \times 10 \times 10}{10 \times 10 \times 10 \times 10 \times 10}$	10^3
b)	$10^7 \div 10^3$	$\dfrac{10 \times 10 \times 10 \times 10 \times 10 \times 10 \times 10}{10 \times 10 \times 10}$	10^4
c)	$5^{10} \div 5^4$	$\dfrac{5 \times 5 \times 5 \times 5 \times 5 \times 5 \times 5 \times 5 \times 5 \times 5}{5 \times 5 \times 5 \times 5}$	5^6
d)	$5^5 \div 5^4$	$\dfrac{5 \times 5 \times 5 \times 5 \times 5}{5 \times 5 \times 5 \times 5}$	5
e)	$9^8 \div 9^3$	$\dfrac{9 \times 9 \times 9 \times 9 \times 9 \times 9 \times 9 \times 9}{9 \times 9 \times 9}$	9^5

2. Answers may vary.

$4^4 \div 4^4$	$\dfrac{4 \times 4 \times 4 \times 4}{4 \times 4}$	4^2
$6^7 \div 6^2$	$\dfrac{6 \times 6 \times 6 \times 6 \times 6 \times 6 \times 6}{6 \times 6}$	6^5
$8^7 \div 8^4$	$\dfrac{8 \times 8 \times 8 \times 8 \times 8 \times 8 \times 8}{8 \times 8 \times 8 \times 8}$	8^3
$8^4 \div 8^3$	$\dfrac{8 \times 8 \times 8 \times 8}{8 \times 8 \times 8}$	8
$3^6 \div 3^3$	$\dfrac{3 \times 3 \times 3 \times 3 \times 3 \times 3}{3 \times 3 \times 3}$	3^3

3. a) To divide two powers of 10, keep the base of 10 and subtract the exponent of the divisor from the exponent of the dividend.
  b) To divide two powers of 5, keep the base of 5 and subtract the exponent of the divisor from the exponent of the dividend.
  c) To divide two powers with the same base, keep the base and subtract the exponent of the divisor from the exponent of the dividend.

4. No, the bases must be the same.

5.1 Exercises, page 203

1. a) 10^3 **b)** 10^4 **c)** 10^8
  d) 10^6 **e)** 10^5 **f)** 10^{12}

2. a) 2^3 **b)** 2^5 **c)** 2^8
  d) 2^4 **e)** 2^{10} **f)** 2^6

3. a) $\frac{1}{2^3}$ **b)** $\frac{1}{2^5}$ **c)** $\frac{1}{2^8}$
d) $\frac{1}{2^4}$ **e)** $\frac{1}{2^{10}}$ **f)** $\frac{1}{2^6}$

4. a) 0.125 **b)** 0.031 25 **c)** 0.012 345 679
d) 0.111 **e)** 0.25 **f)** 0.5

5. a) 729 **b)** −1 953 125 **c)** 40.841 01
d) −512 **e)** 8.3521 **f)** 0.0256
g) −0.020 285 **h)** 0.04

6. a) 3^{10} **b)** 7^{11} **c)** $(-5)^{25}$
d) 2.1^{10} **e)** $(-8)^6$ **f)** $(-1.7)^7$

7. a) 3^5 **b)** 2^9 **c)** $(-8)^{15}$
d) 1.5^{12} **e)** $(-6)^6$ **f)** $(-2.3)^4$

8. a) 10^8 m^2 **b)** 10^5 m

9. a) 100 times **b)** 100 000 times

10. a) $3^5 = 243$ **b)** $9^2 = 81$ **c)** $(-8)^3 = -512$
d) $(-2)^7 = -128$ **e)** $5^3 = 125$ **f)** $2^6 = 64$
g) $4^2 = 16$ **h)** $7^2 = 49$

11. Explanations may vary.

12. Explanations and examples may vary.

13. a) $(4.6)^6 = 9474.297$ **b)** $(-1.7)^3 = -4.913$
c) $(8.3)^3 = 571.787$ **d)** $(-3.7)^7 = -9493.188$
e) $(0.2)^3 = 0.008$ **f)** $(0.1)^7 = 0.000$

14. a) 480 **b)** 800 **c)** 0.1875 **d)** 16

15. a) $2^0 = 1$; $2^1 = 2$; $2^2 = 4$; $2^3 = 8$; $2^4 = 16$; $2^5 = 32$;
$2^6 = 64$; $2^7 = 128$; $2^8 = 256$
b) i) $2^8 = 256$ **ii)** $2^7 = 128$
iii) $2^5 = 32$ **iv)** $2^2 = 4$

16. a) To ensure that the final exponent is positive.
b) You cannot divide by zero.

17. a) $(-2)^0 = 1$; $(-2)^1 = -2$; $(-2)^2 = 4$; $(-2)^3 = -8$;
$(-2)^4 = 16$; $(-2)^5 = -32$; $(-2)^6 = 64$; $(-2)^7 = -128$;
$(-2)^8 = 256$
b) When the exponent is an even number
c) When the exponent is an odd number
d) Explanations may vary.

18. a) 9 **b)** −9 **c)** −9 **d)** 9

19. Explanations may vary.

20. Answers may vary.

21. a) 10^4 **b)** 2^6 **c)** 3^5
d) $(-5)^6$ **e)** 6^8 **f)** $(-1)^4$

22. 10^{22}

23. Day 3: 4; Day 4: 8

24. a)

Day	Number who hear about shampoo that day	Total number who have used the shampoo
1	1	1
2	2	$1 + 2 = 3$
3	$2^2 = 4$	$3 + 4 = 7$
4	$2^3 = 8$	$7 + 8 = 15$
5	$2^4 = 16$	$15 + 16 = 31$
6	$2^5 = 32$	$31 + 32 = 63$
7	$2^6 = 64$	$63 + 64 = 127$
8	$2^7 = 128$	$127 + 128 = 255$
9	$2^8 = 256$	$255 + 256 = 511$
10	$2^9 = 512$	$511 + 512 = 1023$

b) Descriptions may vary. The numbers in the second column are all powers of 2. The exponent in each power of 2 is one less than the day number.
c) $2^1 - 1 = 1$, $2^2 - 1 = 3$, $2^3 - 1 = 7$, $2^4 - 1 = 15$, $2^5 - 1 = 31$, $2^6 - 1 = 63$, $2^7 - 1 = 127$, $2^8 - 1 = 255$, $2^9 - 1 = 511$, $2^{10} - 1 = 1023$; the exponent in each power of 2 is equal to the day number.
d) 2^{20} **e)** Day 20

25. Descriptions may vary.

26. Answers may vary.

27. a) 15
b) Answers may vary. The magic number is 2^{15}.

2^8	2^1	2^6
2^3	2^5	2^7
2^4	2^9	2^2

5.2 Zero and Negative Exponents
Investigation, page 207

1., 2. Explanations may vary.

Power	Number
2^4	16
2^3	8
2^2	4
2^1	2
2^{-1}	1
2^{-2}	$\frac{1}{2}$
2^{-3}	$\frac{1}{8}$
2^{-4}	$\frac{1}{16}$

3. Fractions

4. $\frac{1}{2^1}, \frac{1}{2^2}, \frac{1}{2^3}, \frac{1}{2^4}$; answers may vary.

5. a) $\frac{1}{2^5}$ **b)** $\frac{1}{2^6}$

6.

Power	Number
3^4	81
3^3	27
3^2	9
3^1	3
3^0	1
3^{-1}	$\frac{1}{3}$
3^{-2}	$\frac{1}{3^2}$ or $\frac{1}{9}$
3^{-3}	$\frac{1}{3^3}$ or $\frac{1}{27}$
3^{-4}	$\frac{1}{3^4}$ or $\frac{1}{81}$

Power	Number
10^4	10 000
10^3	1 000
10^2	100
10^1	10
10^0	1
10^{-1}	$\frac{1}{10}$
10^{-2}	$\frac{1}{10^2}$ or $\frac{1}{100}$
10^{-3}	$\frac{1}{10^3}$ or $\frac{1}{1000}$
10^{-4}	$\frac{1}{10^4}$ or $\frac{1}{10\ 000}$

7. a) $\frac{1}{3^5}$ **b)** $\frac{1}{3^6}$ **c)** $\frac{1}{10^5}$ **d)** $\frac{1}{10^6}$

8. a) $\frac{1}{2^a}$ **b)** $\frac{1}{3^a}$ **c)** $\frac{1}{10^a}$ **d)** $\frac{1}{n^a}$

9. a) 1, 1, 1 **b)** 1

5.2 Exercises, page 211

1. a) $\frac{1}{3}$ **b)** $\frac{1}{2^2} = \frac{1}{4}$ **c)** $\frac{1}{7}$
d) $\frac{1}{5}$ **e)** $\frac{1}{3^3} = \frac{1}{27}$ **f)** $\frac{1}{6^2} = \frac{1}{36}$

2. a) $-\frac{1}{3}$ **b)** $-\frac{1}{4}$ **c)** $-\frac{1}{7}$ **d)** $-\frac{1}{5}$

e) $-\frac{1}{27}$ **f)** $-\frac{1}{36}$ **g)** $-\frac{1}{3}$ **h)** $\frac{1}{4}$

i) $-\frac{1}{7}$ **j)** $-\frac{1}{5}$ **k)** $-\frac{1}{27}$ **l)** $\frac{1}{36}$

3. Explanations may vary.

4. a) 16 **b)** $\frac{1}{16}$ **c)** -16 **d)** $-\frac{1}{16}$

e) 16 **f)** $\frac{1}{16}$ **g)** -16 **h)** $-\frac{1}{16}$

5. Explanations may vary.

6. a) $2^1 = 2$ **b)** $3^2 = 9$ **c)** $5^2 = 25$
d) $2^3 = 8$ **e)** $-4^2 = -16$ **f)** $-10^4 = -10\,000$

7. Explanations may vary.
a) 5 **b)** 16 **c)** 8
d) 1 **e)** 0.67 **f)** 0.69

8. a) $10^1 = 10$ **b)** $2^{-4} = 0.0625$ **c)** $(-7)^3 = -343$

d) $5^{-3} = 0.008$ **e)** $3^1 = 3$ **f)** $3^4 = 81$

g) $2^{-4} = 0.0625$ **h)** $(-3)^{-2} \doteq 0.111$ **i)** $10^{-4} = 0.0001$

j) $3^{-2} \doteq 0.111$ **k)** $2^1 = 2$ **l)** $2^2 = 4$

9. Explanations may vary.
a) 1 **b)** 1 **c)** -1 **d)** -1
e) -1 **f)** -1 **g)** 1 **h)** 1

10. Explanations may vary.
a) 2^{-3} **b)** Equal **c)** 5^{-2}

11. a) -27 **b)** 9 **c)** -3 **d)** 1
e) $-\frac{1}{3}$ **f)** $\frac{1}{9}$ **g)** $-\frac{1}{27}$ **h)** $\frac{1}{81}$

12. Explanations may vary. After the first answer, each answer is obtained by dividing the preceding answer by -3.

13. a) -64 **b)** -16 **c)** -4 **d)** -1
e) $-\frac{1}{4}$ **f)** $-\frac{1}{16}$ **g)** $-\frac{1}{64}$ **h)** $-\frac{1}{256}$

14. Explanations may vary. After the first answer, each answer is obtained by dividing the preceding answer by -4.

15. a) 1000 **b)** 100 **c)** 10 **d)** 1
e) 0.1 **f)** 0.01 **g)** 0.001 **h)** 0.0001

16. a) 0.000 977 **b)** 0.0016 **c)** 0.000 064
d) $-0.004\,630$ **e)** 0.161 506

17. Explanations may vary.
a) $2^6 = 64$ **b)** $2^5 = 32$ **c)** $2^4 = 16$ **d)** $2^3 = 8$
e) $2^2 = 4$ **f)** $2^1 = 2$ **g)** $2^0 = 1$ **h)** $2^{-1} = \frac{1}{2}$

18. Explanations may vary.
a) $2^0 = 1$ **b)** $2^1 = 2$ **c)** $2^2 = 4$ **d)** $2^3 = 8$
e) $2^4 = 16$ **f)** $2^5 = 32$ **g)** $2^6 = 64$ **h)** $2^7 = 128$

19. a) $\frac{1}{64}$ **b)** 14 641 **c)** 6561
d) $\frac{1}{36}$ **e)** 27 **f)** 125

20. a) 3 **b)** 5 **c)** $\frac{1}{100\,000}$ **d)** 64
e) $\frac{1}{8}$ **f)** 1 **g)** $\frac{1}{2401}$ **h)** 6
i) -3

21. a) 16 000 **b)** 32 000 **c)** 64 000

22. $B = 1000 \times 2^n$

23. a) 500 **b)** 250 **c)** 125
24. a) 2800 **b)** 5700 **c)** 11 200
d) 700 **e)** 350 **f)** 175

25. b) Estimates may vary.
i) 1200 **ii)** 2400 **iii)** 4800
iv) 850 **v)** 420 **vi)** 210

26. a) Answers may vary. Some bacteria could die, insufficient food, temperature not ideal, unable to count the bacteria accurately
b) No; explanations may vary; limited food supply, limited space

27. a) 3 **b)** 5 **c)** 2
d) -3 **e)** -2 **f)** -3

28. a) $\frac{1}{512} \doteq 0.001\,95$ **b)** $\frac{1}{729} \doteq 0.001\,37$ **c)** $\frac{1}{16} = 0.0625$

29. a) 5 **b)** 2 **c)** 3
d) -2 **e)** -6 **f)** -4

30. Explanations may vary.

31. -2

32. 2, 4

5.3 Powers of Powers

5.3 Exercises, page 216

1. a) 2^{-6} **b)** 3^{-8} **c)** 4^{-6}
d) 5^{-8} **e)** 8^0 **f)** 7^2

2. a) 4^6 **b)** 7^8 **c)** 3^{12} **d)** 10^{12}
e) 3^{12} **f)** $(-10)^6$ **g)** 2^{-6} **h)** 5^{-2}
i) 3^{10} **j)** 4^0 **k)** $(-2)^{-6}$ **l)** $(-4)^{-6}$

3. a) 6561 **b)** 4096

4. a) $2^{20} = 1\,048\,576$ **b)** $2^{21} = 2\,097\,152$ **c)** $2^5 = 32$
d) $2^{20} = 1\,048\,576$ **e)** $2^{18} = 262\,144$ **f)** $2^{20} = 1\,048\,576$

5. Explanations may vary.

6. a), b) Patterns and explanations may vary.

7. a) 0.007 812 5 **b)** 1024
c) 1 **d)** 0.25
e) 524 288 **f)** 0.000 000 953 674
g) 0.000 976 562 5 **h)** 0.000 244 140 625

8. a)

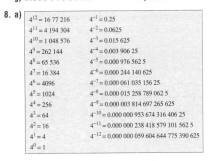

$4^{12} = 16\,77\,216$	$4^{-1} = 0.25$
$4^{11} = 4\,194\,304$	$4^{-2} = 0.0625$
$4^{10} = 1\,048\,576$	$4^{-3} = 0.015\,625$
$4^9 = 262\,144$	$4^{-4} = 0.003\,906\,25$
$4^8 = 65\,536$	$4^{-5} = 0.000\,976\,562\,5$
$4^7 = 16\,384$	$4^{-6} = 0.000\,244\,140\,625$
$4^6 = 4096$	$4^{-7} = 0.000\,061\,035\,156\,25$
$4^5 = 1024$	$4^{-8} = 0.000\,015\,258\,789\,062\,5$
$4^4 = 256$	$4^{-9} = 0.000\,003\,814\,697\,265\,625$
$4^3 = 64$	$4^{-10} = 0.000\,000\,953\,674\,316\,406\,25$
$4^2 = 16$	$4^{-11} = 0.000\,000\,238\,418\,579\,101\,562\,5$
$4^1 = 4$	$4^{-12} = 0.000\,000\,059\,604\,644\,775\,390\,625$
$4^0 = 1$	

b)

$8^8 = 16\,77\,216$	$8^{-1} = 0.125$
$8^7 = 2\,097\,152$	$8^{-2} = 0.015\,625$
$8^6 = 262\,144$	$8^{-3} = 0.001\,953\,125$
$8^5 = 32\,768$	$8^{-4} = 0.000\,244\,140\,625$
$8^4 = 4096$	$8^{-5} = 0.000\,030\,517\,578\,125$
$8^3 = 512$	$8^{-6} = 0.000\,003\,814\,697\,265\,625$
$8^2 = 64$	$8^{-7} = 0.000\,000\,476\,837\,158\,203\,125$
$8^1 = 8$	$8^{-8} = 0.000\,000\,059\,604\,644\,775\,390\,625$
$8^0 = 1$	

9. a) $2^{10} \doteq 10^3$

b) i) 10^9 **ii)** 10^{12} **iii)** 10^{15}

10. a) 3^{14} **b)** 6^4 **c)** 7^{22}

d) 15^0 **e)** 8^{-57} **f)** 4^{-6}

g) 51^{39} **h)** 29^{-32} **i)** 101^{-3}

11. a) 3   **b)** 2   **c)** 5   **d)** 3

12. 5^{2222}, 2^{5555}, 4^{3333}, 3^{4444}

Mathematical Modelling: How Thick is the Pile of Paper?, page 218

Answers in this section may vary. The answers in this section are based on a standard sheet of paper 215 mm by 280 mm.

2.

Number of folds	Number of layers	Area of top layer
0	1	60 200 mm²
1	2	30 100 mm²
2	4	15 050 mm²
3	8	7525 mm²
4	16	3762.5 mm²
5	32	1881.25 mm²
6	64	940.625 mm²

3. a) Answers may vary.   **b)** $\frac{1}{8}$ mm

4. a) 1024   **b)** 128 mm

5. a) $2^{50} \doteq 1.126 \times 10^{15}$

b) About 1.407×10^8 km

c) Distance to the sun

6. a) 215 mm by 280 mm   **b)** 60 200 mm²

c) See chart in exercise 2.

7. a) 1024   **b)** 58.8 mm²

8. a) $2^{50} \doteq 1.126 \times 10^{15}$ **b)** 5.35×10^{-11} mm²

c) Area of a pit in a CD track

9. Answers may vary.

a) The folds are made accurately so that the area of each layer is identical, no area is "lost" in the fold itself

b) i) 6   **ii)** 6

c) Answers and explanations may vary.

10. a)

Number of cuts	Number of layers	Thickness of the pile (mm)	Area of top layer (mm)
0	1	$\frac{1}{16}$	65 536
1	2	$\frac{1}{8}$	32 768
2	3	$\frac{1}{4}$	16 384
3	4	$\frac{1}{2}$	8192
4	16	1	4096
5	32	2	2048
6	64	4	1024
7	128	8	512
8	256	16	256
9	512	32	128
10	1024	64	64
11	2048	128	32
12	4096	256	16
13	8192	512	8
14	16 384	1024	4
15	32 768	2048	2
16	65 536	4096	1

b) 65 536   **c)** 4.096 m

11. a) Descriptions may vary. It takes a long time to make all the cuts, piling very small pieces of paper is not possible.

b) Estimates may vary.

13. a) No; cuts must be whole numbers.

b) The data are too wide spread to be able to plot all points.

14. a) Answers may vary. The sheet of paper has constant thickness, no loss of paper when cutting, piling 1 mm² pieces of paper is possible, cutting is accurate, and so on

b) i) 16   **ii)** 16

5.5 Scientific Notation

5.5 Exercises, page 225

1. a) 1.3×10^6 °C   **b)** 1.0×10^{-5} m

c) 0.000 000 000 000 000 000 000 000 92 g

d) 120 000 000 000   **e)** 4.5×10^9 years

f) 5.0×10^{-9} cm   **g)** 150 000 000 km²

2. a) i) 2.5×10^{12} **ii)** 6.25×10^{-10}

b) i) 3.125×10^{-16} **ii)** 4×10^{24}

c) i) $4.333\,33 \times 10^{22}$ **ii)** 5×10^{-40}

3. a) 1.2×10^3 **b)** 2.7×10^5 **c)** 4.3×10^2

d) 2.4×10^{-1} **e)** 3.7×10^{-3} **f)** 1.48×10^{-5}

g) -1.36×10^4 **h)** -1.88×10^{-5} **i)** 1.8×10^3

j) 1.42×10^7 **k)** 1.6×10^{-1} **l)** 2.36×10^{-4}

4. a) 180 000   **b)** 29 000

c) 33 000 000   **d)** 4 400 000 000

e) 0.16   **f)** 0.084

g) 0.000 224   **h)** 0.000 018 8

i) −0.000 000 000 241   **j)** −1 870 000

k) −0.003 02   **l)** −0.216

5. Explanations may vary.

a) 2.0×10^3 **b)** 2.0×10^9 **c)** 4.83×10^{14}

6. 1.0×10^{-9} g, 2.0×10^{-3} mm

7. Explanations may vary; 15 is not between 1 and 10.

8. a) 1.6×10^{13} **b)** 1.6×10^{17} **c)** 1.6×10^{11}

9. Keystrokes may vary.

a) 5.9 [Exp] 5 [×] 4.7 [Exp] 8 [+/-] [=]

b) 3.5 [Exp] 9 [÷] 8.7 [Exp] 5 [+/-] [=]

c) 2.4 [Exp] 6 [×] 6.5 [Exp] 6 [=]

d) 1 [÷] 5 [Exp] 9 [=]

10. a) 1.2×10^{16} **b)** 5.18×10^{25} **c)** 1.274×10^{16}

d) 2.124×10^{30} **e)** 5.64×10^{22} **f)** 1.312×10^{36}

11. a) 2.53×10^{2} **b)** 2.82×10^{5}

c) 1.06×10^{-3} **d)** 8.5×10^{5}

12. 10^{8}

13. a) $2.0 \times 10^{4}, 8.0 \times 10^{9}$ **b)** 4.0×10^{5} cm^2

c) 4.0×10 m^2; the result is not reasonable. An incorrect number of hairs may have been estimated or stated.

14. a)

Mass (g)	Number of atoms
0	0
2	3.011×10^{23}
4	6.022×10^{23}
6	9.033×10^{23}
8	1.2044×10^{24}
10	1.5055×10^{24}

b) Linear; the points lie on a straight line.

15. a) 1 mole   **b)** 6.022×10^{23}

16. a)

Mass (g)	Number of atoms
0	0
2	1.004×10^{23}
4	2.007×10^{23}
6	3.011×10^{23}
8	4.015×10^{23}
10	5.018×10^{23}
12	6.022×10^{23}

b) Linear; the points lie on a straight line.

17. a) 3 moles   **b)** 1.8066×10^{24} atoms

18. Answers may vary.

19. a) 4.04×10^{13} km   **b)** 4.0×10^{32} kg   **c)** 7.02×10^{8} km

20. 1.5×10^{14} km

21. a) Gold: 8.67×10^{22} atoms; silver: 1.58×10^{23} atoms

b) i) Answers may vary.

   ii) Gold: 6.94×10^{23} atoms; silver: 1.27×10^{24} atoms

5.6 Squares and Square Roots

Investigation, page 229

1.

Side length (cm)	Area (cm²)	Side length (cm)	Area (cm²)
0	0	11	121
1	1	12	144
2	4	13	169
3	9	14	196
4	16	15	225
5	25	16	256
6	36	17	289
7	49	18	324
8	64	19	361
9	81	20	400
10	100		

3. Yes, explanations may vary. Squares with side lengths that are not whole numbers can be drawn.

4. Estimates may vary.

a) 5.5 cm   **b)** 7.5 cm   **c)** 13.5 cm   **d)** 18.7 cm

5. Estimates may vary.

a) 56 cm^2 **b)** 156 cm^2 **c)** 233 cm^2 **d)** 352 cm^2

6. The graphs are identical. The equation $y = x^2$ determines the area, y, of a square with side length x.

7. a) Each number in the second column is a square of the corresponding number in the first column.

b) Each number in the first column is a square root of the corresponding number in the second column.

5.6 Exercises, page 233

1. a) Estimate 13   **b)** Exact 15

c) Estimate 19   **d)** Estimate 9

2. a) -13 **b)** -15 **c)** -19 **d)** -9

3. Since $8^2 = 64$ and $9^2 = 81$, the square roots of numbers between 64 and 81 are between 8 and 9. Thus $\sqrt{67}$, $\sqrt{78}$, and $\sqrt{80}$ are between 8 and 9.

4. Estimates may vary.

a) 4.5   **b)** 7.7   **c)** 11.0   **d)** 16.7

5. Estimates may vary.

a) 90   **b)** 156   **c)** 306   **d)** 380

6. Explanations may vary. Consider a number n. The square root of n is a number which, when multiplied by itself, has product n.

7. a) 2, −2   **b)** 3, −3   **c)** 7, −7

d) 9, −9   **e)** 11, −11   **f)** 8, −8

8. a) $\frac{1}{4}, -\frac{1}{4}$ **b)** $\frac{1}{5}, -\frac{1}{5}$ **c)** $\frac{4}{5}, -\frac{4}{5}$

d) $\frac{2}{3}, -\frac{2}{3}$ **e)** $\frac{5}{7}, -\frac{5}{7}$ **f)** $\frac{8}{9}, -\frac{8}{9}$

9. a) $\sqrt{11}, \sqrt{14}$ **b)** $\sqrt{52}, \sqrt{61}$ **c)** $\sqrt{140}, \sqrt{130}$

d) $\sqrt{118}, \sqrt{110}$ **e)** $\sqrt{190}, \sqrt{171}$ **f)** $\sqrt{330}, \sqrt{360}$

10. Estimates may vary.

a) 8.7   **b)** 9.3   **c)** 10.8

d) 11.8   **e)** 6.7   **f)** 10.2

11. a) 12   **b)** 120   **c)** 1200

d) 1.2   **e)** 0.12   **f)** 0.012

12. a) 20 cm   **b)** 0.5 m   **c)** 9.5 cm

d) 12.2 cm   **e)** 17.3 cm   **f)** 158.1 m

13. Lengths cannot be negative.

14. a) 14   **b)** 44   **c)** 70

d) 48   **e)** 8.37   **f)** 3.74

15. a) 15.17 m   **b)** 60.7 m

16. Estimates and explanations may vary. 21.2 cm

17. Estimates may vary. 26 cm

18. a) Explanations may vary.

b) Answers may vary. The most efficient method is to fold and cut each square along one of its diagonals, creating four right triangles. Then arrange the pieces with the four right angles together to form a large square.

c) About 7.1 cm

d) Answers may vary.

19. Estimates for parts e, g, h, and i may vary.
a) 12   b) 32   c) 54
d) 35   e) 8.6   f) 35
g) 5.7   h) 7.3   i) 3.5

20. a) $y = \sqrt{x}$ **b)** Yes
c) i) 6.7   ii) 7.1   iii) 8.7   iv) 5.8
d) i) 4.2   ii) 6.2   iii) 9.2   iv) 2.8
e) Explanations may vary. The relationship between x and y is non-linear.

21. a) 3.87 m by 3.87 m   **b)** 10 m²

22. a) i) 1.732 05   **ii)** 17.320 5   **iii)** 173.205
iv) 1732.05   **v)** 0.173 205   **vi)** 0.017 320 5
b) Explanations may vary. As each number is multiplied (or divided) by 100, its square root is multiplied (or divided) by 10, since $\sqrt{100} = 10$.

23. Answers may vary.
a) (0, 7), (7, 7), (7, 0)
b) (0, 8), (–8, 8), (–8, 0)
c) (2, 7), (6, 7), (6, 3)

24. The calculator displays an error message because there is no square root of a negative number.

25. a) 9, –9   **b)** 0.5, –0.5
c) 9.80, –9.80   **d)** $\frac{2}{7}, -\frac{2}{7}$ **e)** 6.16, –6.16

26. a) 10, –10   **b)** 2.85, –2.85
c) 5, –5   **d)** 10, –10

27. a) Divide the diameter by 2 to get the radius, then substitute into the formula $A = \pi r^2$.
b) $A = \pi \left(\dfrac{d}{2}\right)^2$
d) Divide the area by π, then take the square root of the result to determine the radius. Multiply by 2 to determine the diameter.
e) $d = 2\sqrt{\dfrac{A}{\pi}}$
f) i) 5.3 cm   ii) 6.5 cm   iii) 7.1 cm   iv) 2.5 m

5.7 The Pythagorean Theorem
5.7 Exercises, page 240

1. a) 5 cm   **b)** 17.9 cm   **c)** 5.7 cm

2. a) 5   **b)** 13

3. a) 8.7 cm   **b)** 7.2 cm   **c)** 2.5 cm   **d)** 2.9 cm

4. a) 7.1 cm   **b)** 11.2 cm   **c)** 15.8 cm

5. 35 cm

6. AB: 3.0 units; CD: 5.7 units; EF: 6.7 units; GH: 7.1 units; IJ: 5.8 units

7. a) 7.1 cm; it is the length of the side of the larger square.
b) Answers may vary.

8. a) 4.5 units   **b)** 2.8 units   **c)** 6.4 units
d) 3.2 units   **e)** 4.2 units   **f)** 3.6 units

9. JK: 5.1 units; KL: 4.5 units; JL: 7.6 units

10. a) PQ and SR have length 5.7 units; PS and QR have length 2.8 units.
b) 16 square units   c) 6.3 units

11. Answers may vary.

12. Sketches and values may vary.
a) $a = 3, b = 4, c = 5$
b) $a = 3, b = 4, c = 4.5$
c) $a = 3, b = 4, c = 6$
d) A right triangle, an acute triangle, and an obtuse triangle

13. Answers may vary. 12 in. by 7 in.; 13 in. by 5 in.; 11 in. by 9 in.; 10 in. by 10 in.

14. Answers may vary. Determine the square roots that provide exact answers.

15. Explanations may vary.
a) $d = \sqrt{x^2 + 5^2}$
c) The length decreases.
d) The length increases.
e) The relationship between x and the length of the diagonal is not linear.

16. a) 12; A(0, 5), B(3, 4), C(4, 3), D(5, 0), E(4, –3), F(3, –4), G(0, –5), H(–3, –4), I(–4, –3), J(–5, 0), K(–4, 3), L(–3, 4)
b) 7; the vertices are as follows: KCEI, LBFH, ADGJ, KBEH, LCFI, BCHI, KLEF
c) KCEI and LBFH have area 48 square units. ADGJ, KBEH, and LCFI have area 50 square units. BCHI and KLEF have area 14 square units.

17. 11.6 m

5.8 Rational and Irrational Numbers
Investigation, page 244

1. a) 0.375   **b)** 0.583 333...   **c)** –1.4375
d) –0.875   **e)** 3.363 636...   **f)** 0.535 333...
g) 0.076 576 576...   **h)** 3.142 857 142...

2. Explanations may vary. In each division, the remainders must always be less than the divisor. At some point in the division process, either the remainder will by 0 (the division terminates) or it will be equal to a remainder that occurred previously (the division repeats).

3. a) ii, iv, vi; the digits either terminate or repeat.
b) The digits neither terminate nor repeat. Yes; they are numbers; explanations may vary.

4. a) i) 4.999 999 9…   **ii)** 17.020 202 020 2…
iii) –8.512 732 732 732 73…
b) $88\ 175.\overline{475}$, $-0.079\ 218\ 836\ 758\ 492\ 000\ \overline{7839}$
c) Answers may vary.

5.8 Exercises, page 246

1. The phrase "appear to be" is used because a number that repeats may eventually break from the pattern, or a number that does not repeat may eventually begin to repeat.
a) Rational   b) Irrational   c) Irrational   d) Irrational

2. Explanations may vary.
a) Rational   b) Rational, integer
c) Rational   d) Rational
e) Rational, natural, integer   f) Rational

3. b, and e

4. Answers may vary.
  a) 3.1, 3.2
  b) −6.4, −6.25
  c) −4.175, −4.173
  d) 7.453, 7.452

5. a, b, and d

6. a, c, and e

7. a) Rational
  b) Rational
  c) Rational, integer
  d) Rational, natural, integer
  e) Rational, natural, integer
  f) Rational
  g) Rational, natural, integer
  h) Rational
  i) Rational
  j) Irrational
  k) Rational
  l) Rational

8. a, b, c, and d

Consolidating Your Skills, page 248

2. a) 3^7 **b)** $(-2)^7$ **c)** -2^8 **d)** 15^5
  e) 4^2 **f)** 3^2 **g)** 12^0 **h)** 16^1

3. a) No, the bases are not the same.
  b) Yes, provided you write 9 as 3^2 and 27 as 3^3.

4. a) 5^4 **b)** 8^{-3} **c)** 4^4 **d)** 6^{-3} **e)** 9^2

5. 5^5, or 3125

6. a) 5^4 **b)** 8^{12} **c)** 12^{10} **d)** 9^{-3} **e)** $(-5)^6$

7. 2.0×10^8

8. a) $\frac{1}{16}$ mm; the thickness of the sheet of paper
  b) 65 536 mm^2; the area of the original sheet of paper

9. a)

Number of cuts	Number of layers	Thickness of the pile (mm)	Area of top layer (mm²)
0	2^0	2^{-4}	2^{16}
1	2^1	2^{-3}	2^{15}
2	2^2	2^{-2}	2^{14}
3	2^3	2^{-1}	2^{13}
4	2^4	2^0	2^{12}
5	2^5	2^1	2^{11}
6	2^6	2^2	2^{10}
7	2^7	2^3	2^9
8	2^8	2^4	2^8
9	2^9	2^5	2^7
10	2^{10}	2^6	2^6
11	2^{11}	2^7	2^5
12	2^{12}	2^8	2^4
13	2^{13}	2^9	2^3
14	2^{14}	2^{10}	2^2
15	2^{15}	2^{11}	2^1
16	2^{16}	2^{12}	2^0

  b) i) 2^n **ii)** 2^{n-4} **iii)** 2^{16-n}
  c) Proofs may vary.

10. a) 9.46×10^{15} m **b)** 9.46×10^{12} km

11. a) $1.670\ 911 \times 10^{-24}$ g **b)** About 1833 times

12. a) 28 cm **b)** 49 cm

13. a) 9 cm^2, 18 cm^2, 36 cm^2
  b) 3 cm, 4.243 cm, 8.6 cm
  c) Answers may vary.

14. 5 cm

Chapter 6 Algebraic Operations and Equations

Mathematical Modelling: Designing Mixtures, page 251

1. Answers may vary.

2. 20 kg peanuts, 10 kg pecans

3. Answers may vary.

Reviewing Your Skills, page 252

1. a) g and b **b)** Yes; explanations may vary.
  c) Yes; explanations may vary.

2. a) Yes, examples may vary. **b)** Yes, examples may vary.

3. Variables may differ.
  a) $x + 5 = 21$ **b)** $x - 11 = 15$
  c) $4x + 6 = 14$ **d)** $\frac{x}{3} = 18$

4. a) 16 **b)** 26 **c)** 2 **d)** 54

5. a) i) $n + 3$ **ii)** $n + 3 = 11$; $n = 8$
  b) i) $2n$ **ii)** $2n = 24$; $n = 12$
  c) i) $\frac{n}{3}$ **ii)** $\frac{n}{3} = 4$; $n = 12$

6. a) 5 **b)** −3 **c)** 4

7. Explanations may vary.

8. a) 1 **b)** −27 **c)** 91 **d)** 0 **e)** −18 **f)** −42

6.1 Representing Variables and Expressions

Investigation 1, page 254

1. 50 m^2; yes

2. Examples may vary.

Investigation 2, page 255

1. a) Yes **b)** Rational numbers

2. Examples may vary.

Investigation 3, page 256

1. Variables may differ.
  a) $3x - 4$ **b)** $-2x + 5$

3. a) $2x + 8$ **b)** $6x - 3$
  c) $12 - 6a$ **d)** $-4m + 6$

4. Answers may vary.

6.1 Exercises, page 259

1. $25(5 + 10)$; $(25 \times 5) + (25 \times 10)$

2. a) $15 + 21$ **b)** $114 - 54$ **c)** $-20 + 30$
  d) $12 + 42 + 6$ **e)** $6 - 3 + 27$ **f)** $-20 - 25 + 10$

3. $6y - 15$; expand using the distributive law.

4. Variables may differ.
  a) $4x + 6$ **b)** $4 - 3x$ **c)** $3x - 7$ **d)** $-2x - 3$

5. a) $-4x - 6$ **b)** $-4 + 3x$ **c)** $-3x + 7$ **d)** $2x + 3$

6. a) 22, −6 **b)** −8, 13 **c)** 5, −16 **d)** −11, 3

7. a) −22, 6; 8, −13; −5, 16; 11, −3
  b) The answers to exercise 7 are the opposites to those in exericse 6.

8. a) 15 + 24   **b)** 30 − 20   **c)** 55 − 77
  d) −48 + 24   **e)** 60 − 72   **f)** −28 + 36
  g) 13 + 13h   **h)** 88 − 8d   **i)** 4k + 20
  j) −72 + 9x   **k)** 18 + 3m   **l)** −5f − 45

9. a) 20 + 50 + 10   **b)** 44 − 20 − 8
  c) 36 + 45 − 72   **d)** −72 + 16 − 64

10. a) 14, 2   **b)** −18, −2   **c)** −2, 6   **d)** −19, 5
  e) 19, 3   **f)** −15, −3   **g)** 1, 9   **h)** 12, −8
  i) 6, −10   **j)** 3, −5   **k)** −4, 8   **l)** −10, −6
  m) 26, 2   **n)** −7, −3   **o)** 19, −5   **p)** −19, −3

11. a) 5k + 5   **b)** 6 − 4w   **c)** 8m + 4   **d)** −4 − 5y
  e) −6 + 3p   **f)** 3 − 9b   **g)** −8t + 10   **h)** −8s − 8

12. a) −35   **b)** 38   **c)** −60   **d)** 36
  e) −30   **f)** 75   **g)** 74   **h)** 56

13. a) 3x + 2, 2 + 3x   **b)** −5g + 4, 4 − 5g
  c) 7 − 2j, −2j + 7   **d)** −3 − 5b, −5b − 3

14. a) 15y − 55.8   **b)** 2.8x + 10.5   **c)** 3 + 4z
  d) 61.2x − 27.9   **e)** −7 − 10.5m   **f)** $\frac{4}{3} - 2z$

15. Part b; expand using the distributive law and simplify.

16. Part b; expand using the distributive law.

17. Part c; expand using the distributive law.

18. a) 3x + 6y − 21   **b)** −2a + 10b − 4   **c)** −6m + 7n
  d) 36p + 4q − 36r   **e)** 5x + 30y − 20   **f)** 21c − 27 + 3d

19. a) 2.5n + 5   **b)** 6.4 − 4.8r   **c)** 2x − 4
  d) 2πR − 2πr   **e)** −2.2c + 9.9   **f)** 9 + 3b
  g) 13π − 26y   **h)** 10d − 2.5

20. Answers may vary. No, different coloured algebra tiles are needed to represent additional variables.

6.2 Combining Like Terms
6.2 Exercises, page 265

1. a, d, f, and g

2. 2x, 5x; 2x, −x; 2x, 4x; 5x, −x; 5x, 4x; −x, 4x; −3y, −y; 3, 5; 3, −1; 5, −1

3. Variables may vary.
  a) 2x + 5   **b)** −x + 4   **c)** 3x − 3

4. a) 9s   **b)** 2v   **c)** b   **d)** 9p
  e) −9c   **f)** 8t + 5   **g)** 5 − 5a   **h)** −n + 6
  i) 9 − d   **j)** 5u − 3   **k)** 2k   **l)** −7q − 7

5. a) 3x − 2; −8, −2   **b)** 5x − 3; −13, −3   **c)** 1 + x; −1, 1
  d) 5x + 3; −7, 3   **e)** 3x + 1; −5, 1   **f)** −x − 9; −7, −9

6. a) 4x   **b)** −2a   **c)** −8 + 2c
  d) 2k + 4   **e)** 13b + 5   **f)** −7u + 6

7. a) −9x + 12; 3, 21   **b)** −3x − 4; −7, −1
  c) 17x − 52; −35, −69   **d)** −5x + 21; 16, 26
  e) 17x − 18; −1, −35   **f)** 10x + 12; 22, 2

8. a) 6x − 2; 22, −20   **b)** −x − 2; −6, 1   **c)** 4x − 9; 7, −21
  d) −5x + 21; 1, 36   **e)** 14x − 6; 50, −48   **f)** 10x − 31; 9, −61

9. a) 11a − 3; 30   **b)** 4m + 21; −7
  c) 14s + 30; 30   **d)** 14x − 3; 32

10. a) x −1; 6, −6, −1   **b)** 2x − 8; 6, −18, −8
  c) −5x + 6; −29, 31, 6   **d)** 2x + 12; 26, 2, 12
  e) −5x + 14; −21, 39, 14   **f)** 11 − 13x; −80, 76, 11

11. a) 10a − 3b   **b)** m − 5n
  c) 40s + 10t − 7   **d)** 3x − 2y
  e) 30p − 16p − 6r   **f)** −47g + 4h + 7
  g) −22 − 3c + 2d   **h)** 4 − x

12. a) 6m − 3n   **b)** −a + 2b + 4c
  c) 2x + 5y   **d)** 9s − 13r + 4
  e) −21d − 27e + 20   **f)** 28q − 36m − 11n
  g) −a − 6b + 6c   **h)** 13x − 47y

13. a) P = 6x, A = 2x²   **b)** P = 12z, A = 6z²

14. a) No; examples may vary; 3x + 2y − 7
  b) Answers and explanations may vary.
  c) Explanations may vary. Write the expression in the neatest and shortest way.

6.3 Solving Equations Algebraically
6.3 Exercises, page 269

1. a) 3   **b)** −5   **c)** 4   **d)** 3
  e) 3   **f)** 2   **g)** 4   **h)** 7
  i) 9   **j)** 7   **k)** −2   **l)** −3

2. a) 3   **b)** 3   **c)** 4   **d)** 7
  e) 4   **f)** −9   **g)** $-\frac{3}{5}$ or −0.6 **h)** 42

3. a) $3353.66   **b)** $2916.16   **c)** 37

4. a) $101   **b)** 7 weeks

5. a) Nasmin, S = 15 + 4.25n; Mayumi, S = 20 + 3.5n
  b) Nasmin, $36.25; Mayumi, $37.50
  c) Nasmin

6. Answers may vary.

7. a) $58.50   **b)** 310 km
  c) Answers may vary. Wear and tear on the car depends on the distance the car is driven.

8. a) 21   **b)** 7   **c)** −5   **d)** −4
  e) 7   **f)** $-2\frac{1}{3}$ **g)** −8   **h)** 4
  i) $\frac{1}{6}$ **j)** 3   **k)** $\frac{4}{3}$ **l)** 3

9. Answers may vary.

10. a) 4   **b)** $\frac{20}{3}$ **c)** 0.6   **d)** −4.5
  e) −0.5   **f)** 3   **g)** 7.2   **h)** $\frac{4}{3}$
  i) $\frac{1}{3}$ **j)** −1.2   **k)** $\frac{5}{9}$ **l)** 0

11. a) 8000 is the fixed cost in dollars. 9n represents the variable cost in dollars, the cost that depends on the number of books printed.
  b) 222   **c)** 1333

12. a) 10d represents the temperature that varies with depth. 20 is the temperature at Earth's surface.
  b) 3 km   **c)** 8 km

13. a) 90 m   **b)** 145 m

14. b) Multiply the number of wins by 2 and add the number of ties.

c) $P = 2W + T$

15. a) 62   **b)** 9   **c)** 34

16. a) The same number   **b)** 3 cm
c) 18 cm, 18 cm^2

17. a) No; explanations may vary.
b) Length of side > 2 cm

6.4 Simplifying Equations before Solving

Investigation, page 273

1. a) 5   **b)** 7   **c)** $-\frac{7}{3}$

2. Answers may vary.

3. Expand using the distributive law.
     a) 4   **b)** $\frac{19}{6}$ **c)** 2

4. Answers may vary.

5. a) 2   **b)** –6   **c)** 10

6. Answers may vary.

6.4 Exercises, page 275

1. a) –6   **b)** 10   **c)** $-\frac{1}{5}$ or –0.2
d) –2   **e)** –3   **f)** 9
g) $-\frac{4}{5}$ or –0.8   **h)** 1   **i)** 2

2. Answers may vary.

3. a) 2.0   **b)** 1.5   **c)** 1   **d)** –16

4. a) 0.5   **b)** –1   **c)** 5
d) –2.2   **e)** 7   **f)** –3
g) 9   **h)** $\frac{7}{6}$ or $1.1\overline{6}$ **i)** –15

5. Explanations may vary.
     a) $15x + 18 = 120$ **b)** $60 = 27 - 4r$

6. a) –2   **b)** 4   **c)** –6   **d)** 7
e) –4   **f)** 4   **g)** $-\frac{4}{3}$ **h)** 1.5

7. a) 9   **b)** 3   **c)** $-\frac{5}{6}$ **d)** –6   **e)** 0.5   **f)** –3

8. Explanations may vary.

9. a) $-\frac{5}{3}$ or $-1.\overline{6}$ **b)** $\frac{1}{5}$ or 0.2   **c)** 0
d) $\frac{7}{2}$ or 3.5   **e)** $-\frac{1}{2}$ or –0.5   **f)** 5

10. a) –56   **b)** $-\frac{4}{13}$ **c)** –10   **d)** $\frac{12}{7}$
e) 10   **f)** 24   **g)** $\frac{32}{3}$ **h)** 11.5

11. a) 39 words/min   **b)** 5   **c)** 180

12. a) $F = 2C + 30$
b) Subtract 30 and divide by 2. $C = \frac{F - 30}{2}$
c) Answers may vary.   **d)** $C = \frac{F - 32}{1.8}$

13. 50°F, 10°C

6.5 Solving Problems with a Spreadsheet

Investigation, page 278

1. a) 82   **b)** 105

2. It is less than the required number of passengers.

3. Greater, explanations may vary.

4. Answers may vary.

6. 170

6.5 Exercises, page 280

1. a) Explanations may vary. Cell B4: the number of quarters is 23 minus the number of dimes. Cell B5: the number of coins is the number of dimes plus the number of quarters. Cell C3: the value of the dimes is $0.10 times the number of dimes. Cell C4: the value of quarters is $0.25 times the number of quarters. Cell C5: the total value of the coins is the value of the dimes plus the value of the quarters.
c) 15 dimes, 8 quarters

2. 21.5 m by 50.0 m

3. 43, 44, 45, 46

4. 20 cm, 12 cm, 12 cm

5. $2.30

6. 10

7. 24 cm, 48 cm

8. Explanations may vary.

9. Explanations may vary. Cell A5: the length of the radius bone is increased by 0.5 cm. Cell B4 (B5): the height of the female is 3.34 times the length of the radius bone plus 81.2 cm. Cell C4 (C5): the height of the male is 3.27 times the length of the radius bone plus 85.9 cm. Cell D4 (D5): the height of the female is subtracted from the height of the male to obtain the difference in heights.

10. a) 163 cm, 166 cm

11. Table values may vary.

r (cm)	h (cm)
21	151.34
22	154.68
24	161.36
25	164.7
26	168.04
28	174.72
29	178.06

12. Table values may vary.

r (cm)	h (cm)
23	161.11
25	167.65
27	174.19
29	180.73
31	187.27
33	193.81
34	197.08

13. Answers may vary. When the length of the radius bone is the same, the man is taller.

6.6 Mathematical Modelling: Designing Mixtures, page 282

1. a) , **b)** Estimates may vary.
c) 20 kg peanuts, 10 kg pecans

2. **a)** Explanations may vary. Cell C4: the mass of pecans is the total mass, 30, minus the mass of peanuts. Cell D3: the value of peanuts is the unit price of peanuts, $5, times the mass of peanuts. Cell D4: the value of pecans is the unit price of pecans, $20, times the mass of pecans. Cell D5: the total value of the mixture is the value of the peanuts plus the value of the pecans.
   b) 20 kg peanuts, 10 kg pecans

3. Yes; explanations may vary. Provided the answers are whole numbers, systematic trial is a useful way.

4. Mass of pecans: $30 - x$; value of peanuts: $5x$; value of pecans $20(30 - x)$, or $600 - 20x$; total value of peanuts and pecans: $600 - 20x + 5x$, or $600 - 15x$; equation: $600 - 15x = 300; x = 20$; 20 kg peanuts, 10 kg pecans

5. **a) i)** 40 kg peanuts, 20 kg pecans
   ii) 24 kg peanuts, 6 kg pecans
   iii) 10.67 kg peanuts, 9.33 kg pecans
   b) 71.89 kg peanuts, 28.11 kg pecans

6. Yes; explanations may vary.

7. **a)** $150
   b) $150; replacing some of the peanuts with pecans
   c) $15; 10 kg
   d) 20 kg; 20 kg peanuts, 10 kg pecans

8. Explanations may vary.

9. Yes; explanations may vary.

10. Explanations may vary. The mixture is a combination of two foods. Therefore, the price is a "combination" of the two prices.

11. Answers may vary.

12. Candy Problem: 4 kg of $7.50/kg candy and 6 kg of $5/kg candy; Hamburger Problem: 18.75 kg of beef with 20% fat and 1.25 kg of fat trim

13. **a)** Vending Machine Problem: 15 dimes and 8 quarters; Exercise Routine Problem: 15 h jogging and 8 h cycling
    b) Answers may vary.
    i) The numbers and equations in each situation are identical. The objects or activities represented by the variables and equations are different.
    ii) They all involve mixtures of objects or activities that contribute to a total at different rates.

14. Descriptions may vary.
    a) When the price of peanuts is higher, use more kilograms of peanuts and fewer kilograms of pecans. When the price of peanuts is lower, use fewer kilograms of peanuts and more kilograms of pecans.
    b) When the price of pecans is higher, use fewer kilograms of pecans and more kilograms of peanuts. When the price of pecans is lower, use more kilograms of pecans and fewer kilograms of peanuts.

6.7 Solving Problems Using Algebraic Modelling
Investigation, page 286

1. Lisa walked 4 km.

2. Answers may vary.

3. Answers may vary.

4. Ashok walked $(x + 6)$ km; $x + (x + 6) = 14$; $x = 4$

6.7 Exercises, page 288

1. **a)** $a + 8$ **b)** $2a + 8$
   c) $2a + 8 = 42$; they are 17 and 25.

2. **a)** $27 - y$ **b)** $2y$
   c) $27 - y + 2y = 43$; they are 16 and 11.

3. **a)** $28 - m$ **b)** $3m$
   c) $28 - m = 3m$; they are 7 kg and 21 kg.

4. **a)** $s - 7.5$ **b)** $2s - 7.5$
   c) $2s - 7.5 = 116.5$; they are 62 kg and 54.5 kg.

5. **a)** Answers may vary. 5¢   **b)** $2x + 1 = 1.1$; 5¢

6. Shaun: 16 bars, Livio: 32 bars

7. Marisa: 3.5 km, Sandy: 6 km

8. Michel: 11.8 kg, Jaquie: 47.2 kg

9. Explanations may vary.

10. **a)** 135 922 330 L   **b)** 136 585 366 L

11. **a)** 153 005 465 L   **b)** 157 977 883 L

12. 136 and 137

13. 3.5 and 3.75

14. $142.50

15. 228 cm

16. 20 cm, 38 cm, and 60 cm

17. Car: 60 km/h, airplane: 480 km/h

18. Answers may vary.

19. Answers may vary.

20. **a)** Between 215 cm and 230 cm
    b) The length decreases by 1 cm.

21. Two pairs of numbers; 12, 108 and −12, −108.

6.8 Mathematical Modelling: Mixtures and Linear Relations, page 291

1. **a)** 20 kg; $100; determine the coordinates of the point of intersection of the two line segments (point A)
   b) 10 kg; $200; subtract the coordinates of the point of intersection (point A) from (30, 300) (point B)

2. **b)** 10 kg; $200; determine the coordinates of the point of intersection of the two line segments
   c) 20 kg; $100; subtract the coordinates of the point of intersection from (30, 300)

3. **a)** Graph 1: Marika adds 10 kg of peanuts, 10 kg of pecans, then 10 more kg of peanuts; Graph 2: Marika adds 4 kg of peanuts, then 2 kg of pecans, and continues adding in this manner until she has 30 kg in total
   b) Answers may vary.

4. **a)** Descriptions may vary.
   b) The maximum price is $10/kg, otherwise the mixture costs more that $10/kg.

5. a) Descriptions may vary.
   b) The minimum price is $10/kg, otherwise the mixture costs less than $10/kg.

6. a) 40 kg peanuts, 20 kg pecans
   b) 24 kg peanuts, 6 kg pecans; 10.67 kg peanuts, 9.33 kg pecans

7. a) Yes; explanations may vary.
   b) Yes; explanations may vary.

8. a) 71.89 kg peanuts, 28.11 kg pecans
   b) 4 kg of $7.50/kg candy and 6 kg of $5/kg candy
   c) 17.5 kg of beef with 20% fat and 2.5 kg of fat trim
   d) 15 dimes and 8 quarters
   e) 15 h jogging and 8 h cycling

9. a) $y = 5x$ b) $y = 20x - 300$
   c) Explanations may vary.

10. Answers may vary.
    a) For part a, $y = 4.29x$, $y = 22.79x - 1330$
    b) $4.29x = 22.79x - 1330$

11. Explanations may vary.

12. Answers and explanations may vary.

Consolidating Your Skills, page 297

1. The sum is 4 times the number in the middle.

2. Multiply by 4.

3. $4n$; from 9 to 23

4. a) 50 m   b) Table values may vary.

Length (m)	Perimeter (m)
15	50
20	60
25	70
30	80
35	90
40	100

c) Add the length to 10 m, and double the answer.
d) $2(10 + l)$; l is any rational number greater than 10.
e) 27 m

5. a) $6x + 21$ b) $-20 - 15n$ c) $48s - 60$
   d) $-8b + 6$ e) $-6p - 10$ f) $2 - t$
   g) $18c + 30$ h) $-22 + 4.4k$ i) $-2a + 4$

6. a) $5x + 2$ b) $-4m - 10$ c) $13a - 7b$
   d) $-5y + 5$ e) $-13t$ f) $-5m - 25n$
   g) $2q + 6$ h) $-9k - 1$ i) $6v - 0.3$

7. a) $7x$; 28, −21, −7   b) $12x + 6$; 54, −30, −6
   c) $-4x - 4$; −20, 8, 0   d) $7x - 22$; 6, −43, −29
   e) $-5x + 2$; −18, 17, 7   f) $-10x - 17$; −57, 13, −7
   g) $7x - 5$; 23, −26, −12   h) $13x - 14$; 38, −53, −27
   i) $20x - 36$; 44, −96, −56

8. a) 2   b) 2   c) 3   d) −7   e) −3
   f) 4   g) 4   h) 3   i) −3

9. a) 5   b) −6   c) −9   d) −5   e) $\frac{1}{6}$
   f) 2   g) 3   h) 3   i) −1

10. a) i) 19.6 m/s   ii) 49 m/s   iii) 78.4 m/s
    b) i) 3 s   ii) 9 s   iii) 14 s
    c) 3.3 m/s, 8.2 m/s, 13.0 m/s; 18.0 s, 54.1 s, 84.2 s

11. a) 2.5   b) −2   c) 4   d) 9   e) 60
    f) 20   g) −27   h) −15   i) 12

12. 14 quarters, 17 dollars

13. 12, 13

14. Mercedes: 120 km/h; Jaguar: 144 km/h

15. 11 cm by 16 cm

16. 17 Delicious, 136 Macintosh

17. 10 kg of $18/kg coffee and 30 kg of $24/kg coffee

18. 750 barrels of $22.50/barrel oil and 500 barrels of $35/barrel oil

19. 200 km, 10 L

6 Cumulative Review, page 300

1. a) 21   b) 50   c) $-\frac{3}{5}$ d) 49

2. a) 25.7 L   b) 38.55 L   c) $14.11

3. GST: $5.88, PST: $7.56, total price: $97.43

4. a) 96¢   b) 276 g

5. a) $y = 10 - x$ b) $y = x + 3$

6. b) 20; dollars per player; the additional cost per additional player to play in the tournament
   c) 300; the entry fee in dollars for the school in addition to the cost per player

7. a) $5 \times 5 \times 5$; 125   b) $\frac{1}{3 \times 3 \times 3 \times 3 \times 3}$; $\frac{1}{243}$
   c) $(-5)(-5)(-5)$; −125   d) $\frac{1}{(-3)(-3)(-3)(-3)(-3)}$; $-\frac{1}{243}$
   e) 1

8. a) 3   b) 2   c) 0.5
   d) 5   e) 4   f) 3

9. a) 6^{26} b) 15^{-2} c) 8^{-18}
   d) 3^{-28} e) 11^{19} f) −7

10. a) About 1.98×10^{30} kg   b) About 7.4×10^{22} kg

11. a) Estimates may vary. 9%, 11%, 14%, 17.5%, 20%, 22%
    b) Estimates may vary. 28 million, 30 million, 32 million, 34 million, 36 million, 37.5 million
    c) Answers may vary. 2.5 million, 3.3 million, 4.5 million, 6.0 million, 7.2 million, 8.25 million

12. About 7.75 m

13. a) $3a + 6b - 9c$ b) $0.39x + 0.2y$
    c) $-3m - 15n + 3p$ d) $5d - 6e$

14. a) $11a - 9$; 46   b) $2 - 4x$; 14   c) $-7b - 5c$; −19

15. a) $-\frac{1}{4}$ b) $\frac{55}{4}$ c) −14   d) −3

Chapter 7 Polynomials

Mathematical Modelling: Could a Giant Survive?, page 303

1. to 3. Answers may vary.

Reviewing Your Skills, page 304

1. a) $1 \times 1 \times 24$; $1 \times 2 \times 12$; $1 \times 3 \times 8$; $1 \times 4 \times 6$; $2 \times 2 \times 6$; $2 \times 3 \times 4$

b) Answers may vary. For $2 \times 3 \times 4$, the bottom of the carton can have 3×4, or 12 cans of tuna with 2 levels. Alternatively, the bottom can have 2×3, or 6 cans of tuna with 4 levels. Finally, the bottom can have 2×4, or 8 cans of tuna with 3 levels.

2. a) $1 \times 1 \times 48$; $1 \times 2 \times 24$; $1 \times 3 \times 16$; $1 \times 4 \times 12$; $1 \times 6 \times 8$; $2 \times 2 \times 12$; $2 \times 3 \times 8$; $2 \times 4 \times 6$; $3 \times 4 \times 4$

b) Answers may vary. For $1 \times 1 \times 48$, the bottom of the carton can have 1×1, or 1 can of tuna with 48 cans piled on top. Alternatively, the bottom can have 1×48, or all 48 cans of tuna.

3. a) 1, 2, 3, 4, 6, 9, 12, 18, 36
b) 1, 13   **c)** 1, 5, 25
d) 1, 3, 5, 15   **e)** 1, 2, 4, 8, 16

4. a) $2 \times 2 \times 3 \times 3$ **b)** 13   **c)** 5×5
d) 3×5 **e)** $2 \times 2 \times 2 \times 2$

5. $(60 \times 170) + (60 \times 80)$; $60(170 + 80)$

6. a) 3 m   **b)** $(2 \times 24) + (2 \times 8)$; $2(24 + 8)$

7. a) $24x + 54$ **b)** $-15c - 9$ **c)** $33 - 88z$
d) $20 - 70y$ **e)** $30z + 10$ **f)** $-3y + 6$

8. Parts a and e contain like terms; explanations may vary.

9. a) $6x + 2$ **b)** $3x + 2$ **c)** $-4x - 2$ **d)** $3a + 8$
e) $-x$ **f)** $8a - 8$ **g)** $-20a - 6$ **h)** $15a - 9$

10. a) 2^6 **b)** -3^4 **c)** -2^6

11. a) 2^2 **b)** -1 **c)** -2^2

12. a) 2^8 **b)** -1 **c)** 4^{10} **d)** 2^5

7.1 The Concept of a Polynomial
Investigation, page 307

Answers to exercise 1 and 2 may be interchanged.

1. a) 4   **b)** 1   **c)** 4   **d)** 10

2. a) 2   **b)** 2   **c)** 4   **d)** 8

3. The rectangles formed have equal areas but different perimeters.

4. a) 3
b) One rectangle: $4x$, 1, $4x$, $8x + 2$; another rectangle: $2x$, 2, $4x$, $4x + 4$; the third rectangle: x, 4, $4x$, $2x + 8$

5. a) 3
b) One rectangle: $x + 1$, 4, $4x + 4$, $2x + 10$; another rectangle: $4x + 4$, 1, $4x + 4$, $8x + 10$; the third rectangle: $2x + 2$, 2, $4x + 4$, $4x + 8$

6. a) They are equal.   **b)** They are different.

7.1 Exercises, page 310

1. $37 Can, $37 U.S.

2. a, b, c, and e; reasons may vary. All are 1 term or a sum of two or more terms. d and f contain variables with negative exponents; therefore, they are not polynomials.

3. a) Binomial; two terms   **b)** Monomial; one term
c) Binomial; two terms   **d)** Monomial; one term
e) Trinomial; three terms   **f)** Monomial; one term
g) Trinomial; three terms   **h)** Binomial; two terms

4. a) $3x^2 + 4x + 3$ **b)** $4x^2 + 6x - 3$
c) $x^2 - 5x + 4$ **d)** $-2x^2 - 5x - 6$

6. a) 14   **b)** 7   **c)** 1   **d)** -1 **e)** π **f)** $\sqrt{3}$

7. a) 6   **b)** -5 **c)** 7   **d)** $-\frac{2}{5}$ **e)** 0   **f)** 0

8. a) Coefficients: 6, 2; constant term: 3
b) Coefficients: 1, -2, 9
c) Coefficient: 1.8; constant term: 32
d) Coefficient: 2π
e) Coefficients: 7, -3; constant term: -9
f) Coefficients: 4.9, -1.2, -0.5; constant term: 2

9. a) $5a$ and $-a$ **b)** $3y^2$ and y^2
c) $9g$ and $\frac{1}{9}g$, $9g^2$ and g^2 **d)** 16 and -8; d and $0.5d$

10. a) 7   **b)** 13   **c)** 16   **d)** 1

11. a) -5 **b)** -2 **c)** -8 **d)** 16

12. a) $2x + 4$ **b)** $8x$ **c)** $2x + 8$

13. a) $2x$ **b)** $4x^2$ **c)** $4x$

15. a) $6x + 2$, $3x$ **b)** $6x$, $2x^2$ **c)** $2x + 12$, $6x$

16. Answers may vary. For example:
a) $\frac{1}{x}$, or $3\sqrt{x}$ **b)** $y^2 + 3$

17. a) $4x + 6$ **b)** $6x + 10$ **c)** $8x + 10$

18. a) 22 cm, 12 m   **b)** 34 cm, 19 m   **c)** 42 cm, 22 m

19. a) $4s^2$
b) i) $4s^2$ **ii)** s^2 **iii)** $3s^2$
c) i) 25 cm²   **ii)** 6.25 cm²   **iii)** 18.75 cm²

20. a) 181°C   **b)** 220°C

21. 47.5 m, 170 m

22. Yes

24. b) 1681   **c)** No

26. Answers may vary.

27. a) $1681 = 41^2$
b) Answers may vary. N = 81 generates $1763 = 41 \times 43$

28. Answers may vary. For example:
a) 7   **b)** 17   **c)** 42

7.2 Adding and Subtracting Polynomials
Investigation, page 314

1. $x^2 + 5x - 4$; explanations may vary.

2. $5x^2 - x + 6$; explanations may vary.

7.2 Exercises, page 316

1. a) $3x^2 + 5x + 2$ **b)** $4x^2 - 3x + 1$
c) $-4x^2 - 8x - 5$ **d)** 0

2. Answers may vary.
a) If we ignore the signs, the terms are the same.
b) The like terms have opposite signs.

3. Explanations may vary. $x^2 + 2x + 1$

4. a) $(-2x^2 + 5x - 3) + (x^2 + x + 7)$
  b) Explanations may vary. $-x^2 + 6x + 4$

5. a) $9x + 6$ **b)** $7a + 4$
  c) $5 - 6m$ **d)** $6x + 2$
  e) $6n^2 - 8n - 4$ **f)** $-2x^2 + 5x - 4$
  g) $7 - 7c - 3c^2$ **h)** $5 - 3n + 3n^2$
  i) $3ab - b - 11$ **j)** $mn - 6n - 2m + 5$

6. a) $-3x^2 - 7$ **b)** $-2x^2 + 5x - 3$ **c)** $4n^2 - 3n + 5$

7. a) $-3x^2 + 2x + 1$ **b)** $2x^2 + 2$

8. Explanations may vary.
  a) The first terms have the same sign.
  b) The first terms have different exponents.
  c) The last terms have the same sign.
  d) The last terms are not like terms.

9. a) $-5x - 2$ **b)** $-2 + 3a$ **c)** $-7x^2 + 5x - 4$
  d) $-5 + 2m + 4m^2$ **e)** $-6n^2 + 3n - 1$ **f)** $\frac{1}{2}x + 5$

10. a) $(3x^2 + 5) + (-2x^2 - 1)$ **b)** $(x^2 + 2x) + (x + 1)$
  c) $(x^2 + 3x - 2) + (x^2 + x - 1)$

11. a) $-5x + 1$ **b)** $2 + n$ **c)** $14a^2 - 2a - 10$
  d) $-10x^2 + 7x - 4$ **e)** $-4 + 4m - 2n^2$ **f)** $-5 + 9x^2$
  g) $2 - 5t^2$ **h)** 0

12. a) $2x - 1$ **b)** $8a + 2$ **c)** $4x^2 - 5x$
  d) $8t - 5$ **e)** $3 - 6x + 2x^2$ **f)** $-4n + 6$

13. b) Explanations may vary. $2x^2 + x + 6$

14. a) $4x^2 - 2x + 7$ **b)** $2x^2 - 2x + 1$
  c) $-m^2 + 5m - 6$ **d)** $-3m^2 + 5m + 6$

15. $2x^5 + 3x^4 + 2x^3 + 8x^2 - 7$; because we have no tiles to represent powers of x greater than x^2

16. a) $-5x^2 + x - 6$; $-10, -28$ **b)** $x^2 - 3x + 10$; $8, 20$

17. a) $x^2, 2x, x^2 + 2x$
  b) $x^2, x^2, 4x, 4x, 4x, 16, 2x^2 + 12x + 16$
  c) $x^2, x^2, x^2, x^2, 3x, 3x, 4x^2 + 6x$

18. a) $-4x^2 - 2x + 10$ **b)** $x^2 - 4x + 15$
  c) $x^3 - 10x^2 + 2x + 8$ **d)** $8x - 7$

19. a) $2x^2 + 3x + 7$ **b)** $4m^2 - 6m + 11$
  c) $3a^2 - a^3 + 6$ **d)** $-9x^2 + 5x - 12$

20. a) $5x^2 - 15x + 3$; $53, 3$ **b)** $2x^3 + x^2 - 7x - 5$; $-3, 37$

21. a) i) $1 - 9m + 4m^2$ **ii)** $2m^2 - 2m - 1$
  b) i) $1, 35$ **ii)** $-1, 11$

22. a) i) $y^2 - 5$ **ii)** $10y$
  b) i) $11, -4$ **ii)** $40, 10$

23. Answers may vary.

24. a) i) $x - 7$ **ii)** $x + 7$
  iii) $3x - 3, 3x, 3x + 3$ **iv)** $9x$
  b) Divide the sum by 9.

25. a) $-7x^2 - 10x + 25$ **b)** 28.25

7.3 Multiplying and Dividing Monomials

7.3 Exercises, page 322

1. a) $3 \cdot x \cdot x$ **b)** $2 \cdot 2 \cdot x \cdot x \cdot x$
  c) $-1 \cdot x \cdot x$ **d)** $2 \cdot x \cdot x \cdot x \cdot x \cdot x \cdot x$
  e) $-\frac{1}{2} \cdot a \cdot a \cdot a \cdot a$ **f)** $3 \cdot 3 \cdot x \cdot x \cdot y$
  g) $-2 \cdot 3 \cdot a \cdot a \cdot b \cdot b$ **h)** $5 \cdot m \cdot m \cdot n \cdot n \cdot n$

2. a) $12x^5$ **b)** $-2x^8$ **c)** $\frac{1}{4}a^6$ **d)** $-30a^3$

3. a) $\frac{5}{2}m^2$ **b)** $-\frac{5}{2}x^3$ **c)** $-5x^4$

4. There are many possible answers. Explanations may vary.
  a) $x, 3x^5$ **b)** $(-5b), b^2$ **c)** $(-3), 2x$
  d) $4x^3, 2x$ **e)** $3x^4, 2x$ **f)** $x, 4x$

5. a) $12b$ **b)** $-14k$ **c)** $20t$ **d)** $-16p$
  e) $5ab$ **f)** $-3pq$ **g)** $4mn$ **h)** $-2xy$

6. a) $6a^2$ **b)** $-10c^2$ **c)** $10a^2$ **d)** $21x^2$ **e)** $10x^2$
  f) $-56y^2$ **g)** $5x^2$ **h)** $-6a^2$ **i)** $6a^2$

7. a) $144x^2$ **b)** $-27x^3y^3$ **c)** $-25a^2b^2$ **d)** $4a^2$
  e) $81m^{10}n^2$ **f)** $9x^2$ **g)** $-125a^3b^6$ **h)** $9m^2n^8$

8. a) $4x^3$ **b)** $2y^4$ **c)** $9y^3$ **d)** $-3m^2$
  e) $9y^2$ **f)** $\frac{3}{5}n^2$ **g)** -5 **h)** $\frac{3}{2}c^3$

9. a) $-x^5$ **b)** $6p^5$ **c)** $-12y^4$
  d) $6a^3b^3$ **e)** $36x^4y^2$ **f)** $-4x^2y^6$

10. a) πr^3 **b)** x^3 **c)** $3x^3$ **d)** $8y^3$

11. a) $5x^2$ **b)** $-3y$ **c)** $-5a$
  d) $3bn$ **e)** $5m^3a^2$ **f)** $3y^3$

12. a) $3r$ **b)** $1.5x$ **c)** $3m$ **d)** $2.5a$

13. a) $21m^9$ **b)** $8x^5$ **c)** $56a^{14}$ **d)** $-10b^7$
  e) $-18x^8$ **f)** $48p^6$ **g)** $\frac{2}{5}y^{11}$ **h)** $\frac{3}{16}s^8$

14. a) $-7a^5$ **b)** $-4s^2$ **c)** $4c^6$ **d)** $5x^6$ **e)** $6y^2$
  f) $7m^8$ **g)** $4k$ **h)** $7z^3$ **i)** $7ab^2$ **j)** $4y^2$

15. a) $10m^5$ **b)** $-3x^5$ **c)** $\frac{2}{3}x^2$
  d) $-\frac{3}{4}m^3$ **e)** $3x^5$ **f)** $6a^3b^7$
  g) $-3x^2y$ **h)** $-72x^{11}$ **i)** $\frac{25}{3}a$ **j)** $\frac{4}{3}a^3b^7$

16. a) $(3x)(3x)(3x)$ **b)** $27x^3$ **c)** $42x^9$

17. a) $10d^7$ **b)** $5mn^2$ **c)** $-5x^3$
  d) $6x^2$ **e)** $-\frac{5}{3}a^5$ **f)** $\frac{2}{3}a^4b^2$

18. a) -4 **b)** 4 **c)** -96 **d)** -640 **e)** -32 **f)** -72

19. a) 324 **b)** -405 **c)** -18 **d)** -567

7.4 Mathematical Modelling: Could a Giant Survive?, page 325

1.

Edge length (cm)	Volume (cm³)	Surface area (cm²)	Volume / Surface area
1	1	6	$\frac{1}{6}$
2	8	24	$\frac{1}{3}$
3	27	54	$\frac{1}{2}$
4	64	96	$\frac{2}{3}$
5	126	150	$\frac{5}{6}$
6	216	216	1
7	343	294	$\frac{7}{6}$
8	512	384	$\frac{4}{3}$
9	729	486	$\frac{3}{2}$
10	1000	600	$\frac{5}{3}$

2. a) Volume   b) It increases.

3. a) i) x^3 ii) $6x^2$ iii) $\frac{x}{6}$
   c) Explanations may vary.

4. a) Surface area would be 144 times as great; volume would be 1728 times as great.
   b) Giant's ratio would be 12 times as great.

5. a) 1024; 32 768   b) 32 times as great

6. Answers may vary.

7. Answers may vary.

8. a), b) Answers to exercises 4b and 5 do not change. Explanations may vary.

7.5 Multiplying a Polynomial by a Monomial
Investigation, page 329

3. Descriptions may vary. The corresponding diagrams for exercises 1 and 2 are similar. To see this, imagine replacing each x-tile in the diagram in exercise 1 with an x^2-tile and each 1-tile with an x-tile.

7.5 Exercises, page 331

1. a) $x(x + 2)$ b) $2x(x + 2)$ c) $x(2x + 1)$
   d) $x(2x)$ e) $x(3x + 1)$ f) $3x(2x)$

2. a) $x^2 + x$ b) $3x^2 + 2x$
   c) $2x^2 + 2x + 6$ d) $2x^2 + 4x$

3. a) $5x - 15$ b) $7a + 7$ c) $-6 - 3n$
   d) $4x + 8$ e) $-2x + 5$ f) $18x - 12$
   g) $5x^2 - 30x + 15$ h) $6 - 10n + 6n^2$

4. a) B   b) F   c) E   d) C   e) A   f) D

5. a) $3x^2 + 2x$ b) $5a^2 - a$ c) $3n - 7n^2$
   d) $-x^2 + 2x$ e) $5y - y^2$ f) $4x^2 - x$
   g) $-7x + 2x^2 - x^3$ h) $5n^3 - n^2 + 4n$

6. a) $x^2 + 3x$ b) $-5a + 15$ c) $2b^3 - 3b^2 + b$
   d) $4p - 3p^2 - p^3$ e) $-42a^2 - 49$ f) $36t^2 - 24t$
   g) $-k^3 + 5k^2 - k$ h) $-21 + 6m - 9m^2$

7. a) $5x^3 - 6x$ b) $2x + 6x^2$ c) $-3b^4 + 3b^3$
   d) $6a^2 + 2a$ e) $-4m^3 + 4m^2$ f) $x^2 - x^5$

8. a) $10x^2 + 15x$ b) $6a^2 - 8a$
   c) $15c - 6c^2$ d) $-8n^2 + 4n$
   e) $-14y^3 + 35y^2 - 14y$ f) $18k - 6k^2 + 12k^3$
   g) $15s^3 - 10s^2 - 35s$ h) $-6p^2 + 9p^3 + 3p^4$

9. a) 1652   b) $14x^2 + 21x + 42, 1652$
   c) Answers for parts a and b are equal.

10. a) $\frac{3}{4}x$ b) $\frac{3}{4}(x + 4)$ c) $\frac{3}{4}x^2 + 6x + 12$
    d) $6x + 12$ e) 243 square units, 363 square units

11. a) i) $15x^3 - 3x^2$ ii) $46x^2 - 8x$
    b) i) 4998 cm³   ii) 2198 cm²

13. b) $6xy$

14. a) $x(2y + 2) = 2xy + 2x$ b) $2x(2y + 4) = 4xy + 8x$
    c) $y(2x + y) = 2xy + y^2$ d) $2y(x + y) = 2xy + 2y^2$
    e) $y(2x + 1) = 2xy + y$ f) $2x(3y + 2) = 6xy + 4x$

15. a) $6xy + 3x$ b) $10x + 5y + 10$
    c) $2y^2 + 6xy + 2y$ d) $6x^2 + 3xy + 12x$

7.6 Academic Focus: Factoring Polynomials
Investigation, page 334

1. $3x + 6$

2. There are 2 possible rectangles.
   First rectangle: a) $x + 2$ b) 3   c) $3(x + 2)$, or $3x + 6$
   Second rectangle: a) $3x + 6$ b) 1   c) $3x + 6$

3. Answers may vary.

4. There are 3 possible rectangles: one has length $4x + 8$ and width 1; a second has length $x + 2$ and width 4; a third has length $2x + 4$ and width 2. All three have area $4x + 8$.

5. Explanations may vary.

7.6 Exercises, page 338

1. a) x b) $3b$ c) $5y$ d) $3x$ e) $2x$ f) $2y$

2. a) 3   b) 6   c) 25   d) 4   e) 12
   f) 18   g) 70   h) 165   i) 90

3. a) xy b) $3xy$ c) ab d) 4   e) $-5xy^2$
   f) $6pq$ g) 2   h) $3xy^2$ i) $6ab$

4. a) $2(x + 1)$ b) $3(x + 3)$ c) $2(2x + 5)$ d) $3(x + 5)$
   e) $3(k + 4)$ f) $4(m + 2)$ g) $2(2n + 3)$ h) $5(w + 3)$

5. a) $x(x + 2)$ b) $2x(x + 2)$ c) $3(x^2 + 3)$ d) $4x(x + 2)$
   e) $2(2m^2 + 3)$ f) $3k(k + 6)$ g) $k(k + 1)$ h) $2z(z + 2)$
   i) $2x(2x + 1)$ j) $2(y^2 + 4)$

6. a) $5(y - 2)$ b) $6(2a + 3)$ c) $3x(x + 2)$
   d) $2a(a - 5)$ e) $w(4 + 3w)$ f) $4y^2(2y - 1)$
   g) $2s(3 + s)$ h) $7k^3(1 + 5k)$ i) $6m^2(1 - 6m)$
   j) $2y^3(4y - 1)$

7. a) $7x(2x + 5)$ b) $5a(5 + 6a)$ c) $20(n^2 + 4)$
   d) $5x(-1 + 2x)$ e) $3c(3c^2 + 5)$ f) $-x(x^2 + 1)$
   g) $-3y^2(2 + y)$ h) $4x(1 + 3x^2)$ i) $4m^2(4 - m)$
   j) $-8d(1 + d^2)$

8. a) $xy(1 + x)$ b) $3xy(-xy + 2)$ c) $ab(1 - ab)$
   d) $-4(xy + 4)$ e) $5xy^2(1 + 2x)$ f) $6pq(p - 2q)$
   g) $2mn(m - 2)$ h) $3x^2y^2(1 + 3y)$

9. a) $4x^2 + 8x + 12, 4(x^2 + 2x + 3)$
b) $7x^2 - 21x + 7, 7(x^2 - 3x + 1)$
c) $16a^2 - 24a - 16, 8(2a^2 - 3a - 2)$
d) $6t^2 + 4t, 2t(3t + 2)$
e) $4m - 4, 4(m - 1)$
f) $-6k^3 - 6k^2 - 10, -2k(3k^2 + 3k + 5)$
g) $10x^2 - 5x + 5, 5(2x^2 - x + 1)$
h) $7x^2 + 7x + 14, 7(x^2 + x + 2)$

10. a) $8(2x + 5)$　　**b)** $3(5n - 8)$　　**c)** $-2a(a + 3)$
d) $6n(3n - 2)$　　**e)** $a(a^2 + 9a + 3)$　　**f)** $3x(x + 3)$

11. a) $5(2x + 3)$　　**b)** $3(2x - 3)$　　**c)** $5(3x + 5)$
d) $2x(x - 2)$　　**e)** $4x(x - 4)$　　**f)** $3y^2(y + 3)$
g) $2(x^2 + 2x + 4)$　　**h)** $3x(4x^2 - 3x + 2)$

12. a) $a(a^2 - 9a + 3)$　　**b)** $-3(9x^2 + 3x - 1)$
c) $x(5x^2 + 3x - 1)$　　**d)** $a(9a^2 + 7a + 18)$
e) $-8d(1 + 3d + d^2)$　　**f)** $17k(1 - 5k - 3k^2)$

13. a) $3xy(y + 2x - 3)$　　**b)** $-2ab(a - 3b + 2)$
c) $5m^2n(n - 2mn + 5)$　　**d)** $-7x^2y^2(4 - 2xy + y)$

14. a) $(a + 6)(a + 7)$　　**b)** $(x - 9)(x - 2)$
c) $2(1 + y)(4 + y)$　　**d)** $(2 - x)(5 + x)$
e) $2(x + 3)(x + 2)$　　**f)** $-3(2a - 1)(a - 2)$

15. a) $2(x - 3)$　　**b)** $2(x - 2)(x - 1)$
c) $2(x^2 + 3)$　　**d)** $2(x^2 - 3)$

Consolidating Your Skills, page 340

2. a) $4x + 8, x^2 + 4x$　　**b)** $6x + 8, 2x^2 + 5x + 3$
c) $6x + 12, 2x^2 + 11x + 5$

3. a, b, and d

4. a) Binomial　　**b)** Monomial　　**d)** Trinomial

5. a) 5　　**b)** −2　　**c)** 1　　**d)** $\frac{1}{3}$

6. a) 4　　**b)** 3　　**c)** −1　　**d)** 0

7. a) $6x^2 + y^2$　　**b)** $12x - 1$　　**c)** $14a^2 - 2a - 10$
d) $6x - 4$　　**e)** $6x^2 - 6x$　　**f)** $x^2 + 9x - 2$

8. a) $6x$; 12, −18
b) $3x^2 - 2x + 12$; 20, 45

9. a) $-200n^4$　　**b)** $140c^5$　　**c)** $85x^5$　　**d)** $-140n^4$

10. a) $9y^2$　　**b)** $\frac{3}{5}n^2$　　**c)** −5　　**d)** $\frac{3}{2}c^3$　　**e)** $6x^3$　　**f)** $-4y$

11. a) $2x(2y + 5) = 4xy + 10x$　　**b)** $3y(x + y) = 3xy + 3y^2$

12. a) $4y - 8$　　**b)** $8a - 24$
c) $-4x - 8$　　**d)** $15x - 3x^2$
e) $2y^2 - 12y$　　**f)** $-15x + 5x^2$
g) $35y - 10y^2 + 15y^3$　　**h)** $-18x^3 - 30x^2 + 72x$

13. a) $15c - 6c^2$　　**b)** $-8n^2 + 4n$
c) $-14y^3 + 35y$　　**d)** $18k - 6k^2 + 6k^3$
e) $15s^3 - 10s^2 - 35s$　　**f)** $6p^2 - 9p^3 - 3p^4$

14. a) $5(y - 2)$　　**b)** $6(2a + 3)$　　**c)** $-3(x^2 - 2x + 4)$
d) $2(a^2 - 5a + 1)$　　**e)** $w(4 + 3w - 7w^2)$　　**f)** $2y(4y^2 - 2y + 1)$

15. a) $6y(1 + 3y)$　　**b)** $-3a(1 - 4a^3)$
c) $5a^2(1 - 5a)$　　**d)** $a(3a^2 + 4a + 7)$
e) $3m(1 - 3m + 5m^2)$　　**f)** $6k^2(2 - 8k^2 - 3k^4)$

16. a) $7(2x^2 + 5x - 1)$　　**b)** $5(6x^2 - 5x + 2)$

17. a) If an object is reduced to $\frac{1}{12}$ of its original size, the volume will decrease more rapidly than the surface area. So, the ratio $\frac{V}{A}$ will decrease.
b) Answers may vary.

Chapter 8 Revisiting the line

Mathematical Modelling: Pushing Your Physical Limits, page 343

1. Answers may vary.

2. Answers may vary. Weight, muscle tone, cardiovascular system

3. Descriptions may vary.

Reviewing Your Skills, page 344

1. a) $L = 72 + 4x$
b) Yes; framing material may have any width.
c) 4, 72
d) The perimeter of the picture
e) The increase in framing material needed for every centimetre of the framing material

2. Explanations may vary.
a) The L-intercept is less.
b) The L-intercept is greater.

3. a) $\frac{3}{4}$　　**b)** $\frac{9}{4}$　　**c)** $-\frac{9}{4}$　　**d)** $-\frac{9}{4}$

4. a), c), d) Explanations may vary.

6. a) 2, 1　　**b)** −2, 1　　**c)** $-\frac{1}{2}$, 1　　**d)** $\frac{1}{2}$, 1

7. a) $-\frac{4}{3}, 4, y = -\frac{4}{3}x + 4$
b) $\frac{2}{3}, -4, y = \frac{2}{3}x - 4$　　**c)** $0, 6, y = 6$

8.1 The Equation of a Line: Part I
8.1 Exercises, page 350

1. a) i) (3, −1)　　**ii)** (2, 2)　　**iii)** (−2, 3)
b) i) −1　　**ii)** 2　　**iii)** $-\frac{3}{2}$
c) i) 2　　**ii)** −2　　**iii)** 0
d) i) $y = -x + 2$　　**ii)** $y = 2x - 2$　　**iii)** $y = -\frac{3}{2}x$

2. a) $y = \frac{5}{2}x + 3$　　**b)** $y = -\frac{4}{3}x - 4$　　**c)** $y = 4x + 2$

3. a) i) (−1, 3), (1, −1)　**ii)** (0, −3), (1, 0)　**iii)** (−2, 2), (2, −4)
b) i) −2　　**ii)** 3　　**iii)** $-\frac{3}{2}$
c) i) 1　　**ii)** −3　　**iii)** −1
d) i) $y = -2x + 1$　　**ii)** $y = 3x - 3$　　**iii)** $y = -\frac{3}{2}x - 1$

4. a) $y = -x + 3$　　**b)** $y = 2x + 5$　　**c)** $y = \frac{2}{3}x - 2$

5. B, D, E, F, and G

6. a) ii, iii, iv, and vi
b) Explanations may vary. For part i, substitute the point (−4, 2) into the equation to get $2 = -(-4)$. Since, this equation is not true, the line does not pass through (−4, 2).

7. a) i) $-\frac{13}{2}$ ii) $\frac{6}{5}$ iii) $-\frac{1}{3}$

   b) i) $y = \frac{5}{2}x - \frac{13}{2}$ ii) $y = -\frac{3}{5}x + \frac{6}{5}$ iii) $y = \frac{4}{3}x - \frac{1}{3}$

8. a) i) $y = 3x - 1$ ii) $y = 7x + 30$ iii) $y = -4x + 16$

   iv) $y = -\frac{3}{5}x - 3$ v) $y = \frac{2}{3}x - \frac{16}{3}$ vi) $y = -\frac{7}{2}x - \frac{7}{2}$

   b) Explanations may vary. For part i, substitute the coordinates (2, 5) and the slope 3 into the equation $y = mx + b$ to get $5 = 3(2) + b$. Solve for b to get $b = -1$. Therefore, the equation is $y = 3x - 1$.

9. b) i) -15 ii) -10 iii) -5 iv) 0

   v) 5 vi) 10 vii) 15

   c) i) $y = 3x - 15$ ii) $y = 2x - 10$ iii) $y = x - 5$

   iv) $y = 0$ v) $y = -x + 5$

   vi) $y = -2x + 10$ vii) $y = -3x + 15$

   d) $y = mx - 6m$

   e) $y = mx - am$

10. a) i) $-\frac{3}{4}$ ii) $\frac{3}{4}$ iii) $-\frac{2}{5}$

    b) i) $-\frac{3}{2}$ ii) $-\frac{5}{4}$ iii) $\frac{1}{5}$

    c) i) $y = -\frac{3}{4}x - \frac{3}{2}$ ii) $y = \frac{3}{4}x - \frac{5}{4}$ iii) $y = -\frac{2}{5}x + \frac{1}{5}$

11. a) i) $y = \frac{1}{2}x + 1$ ii) $y = \frac{2}{3}x + 2$ iii) $y = -2x + 3$

    vi) $y = -\frac{1}{3}x - 2$ v) $y = -\frac{1}{4}x + 2$ vi) $y = -\frac{2}{7}x + \frac{41}{7}$

    b) Explanations may vary.

12. a) For point A, 2 is the number of years it takes a cat or a dog to become an adult. 20 is the number of years it takes a human to become an adult. For point B, 20 is the number of years a cat or dog has in a lifetime. 100 is the number of years a human has in a lifetime.

    b) $y = \frac{40}{9}x + \frac{100}{9}$

    c) The number of years in a human's life for every year of a cat's or dog's life

    d) Explanations and examples may vary.

13. b) i) $-\frac{3}{6}$ ii) $-\frac{2}{6}$ iii) $-\frac{1}{6}$ iv) 0

    v) $\frac{1}{6}$ vi) $\frac{2}{6}$ vii) $\frac{3}{6}$

    c) i) $y = -\frac{3}{6}x + 3$ ii) $y = -\frac{2}{6}x + 2$ iii) $y = -\frac{1}{6}x + 1$

    iv) $y = 0$ v) $y = \frac{1}{6}x - 1$ vi) $y = \frac{2}{6}x - 2$

    vii) $y = \frac{3}{6}x - 3$

    d) $y = -\frac{b}{6}x + b$ e) $y = -\frac{b}{a}x + b$

14. a) AB: $y = \frac{2}{3}x + 4$; BC: $y = -\frac{3}{2}x - 9$; CD: $y = \frac{2}{3}x - \frac{14}{3}$; DA: $y = -\frac{3}{2}x + 4$

    b) AC: $y = 5x + 4$; BD: $y = -\frac{1}{5}x - \frac{6}{5}$

15. b) AB: $y = 2x$; CD: $y = \frac{1}{2}x$; EF: $y = -3x$; GH: $y = -\frac{1}{3}x$; they pass through the origin.

    c) AI: $y = \frac{1}{2}x + 6$; CJ: $y = 2x - 12$; KL: $y = -\frac{1}{3}x + 16$; MN: $y = -3x + 48$; (12, 12)

8.2 Academic Focus: The Equation of a Line: Part II

8.2 Exercises, page 357

1. a) 3, 4, $-\frac{4}{3}$ b) No x-intercept, 3, 0

   c) -2, no y-intercept, undefined

2. a) 3, $\frac{3}{2}$ b) $\frac{3}{2}$, 3 c) -2, -2

   d) -2, 2 e) 4, 6 f) -4, 6

3. a) $2x + y - 3 = 0$ b) $3x - y - 2 = 0$ c) $x - 2y + 2 = 0$

   d) $2x - 3y - 6 = 0$ e) $3x + 2y - 8 = 0$ f) $8x - 2y - 5 = 0$

4. a) $y = -x + 4$ b) $y = -2x - 6$ c) $y = 2x - 10$

   d) $y = -\frac{1}{2}x + 4$ e) $y = \frac{1}{3}x + 3$ f) $y = -\frac{2}{3}x + 2$

   g) $y = \frac{3}{2}x + \frac{9}{2}$ h) $y = -\frac{4}{3}x + 4$ i) $y = \frac{5}{2}x + 5$

5. a) 6, 6 b) 3, 6 c) 6, 3

   d) -2, -3 e) -2, 3 f) 3, -2

6. a) 1, 4 b) 2, 4 c) $\frac{1}{2}$, 2

   d) $\frac{3}{2}$, 6 e) $-\frac{3}{2}$, 6 f) $-\frac{2}{3}$, 4

7. a) i) $A = B = 1$, C starts at -9 and increases by 3 on each line.

   ii) $B = 2$, $C = -6$, A starts at 9 and decreases by 3 on each line.

   iii) A starts at 4 and decreases by 1 on each line. B starts at 5 and decreases by 1 on each line. C starts at 6 and decreases by 1 on each line.

   b) i) All have the same slope, -1.

   ii) All have the same y-intercept, 3.

   iii) All have different slopes and different y-intercepts.

   c) i) Since $A = B = 1$, all have slope $-\frac{A}{B}$, or -1.

   ii) Since $B = 2$ and $C = -6$, all have the same y-intercept $-\frac{C}{B}$, or 3.

   iii) Since A, B, and C are different, all slopes and all y-intercepts are different.

8. a) i) The pattern on the left.

   ii) $x - y = 4$, $x + y = -4$, $x - y = -4$, $x - y = 8$, $x + y = -8$, $x - y = -8$, $x + y = 8$, $x + y = 0$, $x - y = 0$

   b) $x + y = 3$, $x + y = 9$, $x + y = -3$, $x + y = -9$, $x - y = 3$, $x - y = -3$, $x - y = -9$, $x - y = 9$

9. a) L_2 and L_4 b) L_3 c) L_1 and L_5

10. a) i) $3x - y - 5 = 0$ ii) $2x + 5y - 18 = 0$

    iii) $2x - y - 6 = 0$ iv) $4x + 3y - 12 = 0$

    v) $3x - 4y - 12 = 0$ vi) $2x + y - 5 = 0$

    vii) $15x - 18y + 10 = 0$ viii) $2x - 5y + 10 = 0$

    b) Answers may vary.

11. a) $2x - 3y - 12 = 0$, $2x + 3y + 12 = 0$, $2x - 3y + 12 = 0$

    b) 48 square units, $8\sqrt{13}$ units

8.3 Academic Focus: Intersection of Lines

Investigation 1, page 360

1. a)

Time (min)	0	1	2	3	4	5	6	7	8
Distance from Thunder Bay (km)	0	70	140	210	280	350	420	490	510

2. a)

Time (min)	0	1	2	3	4	5	6	7	8
Distance from Thunder Bay (km)	510	430	350	270	190	110	30	0	0

3. a) About (3.4, 238); the cars pass each other after 3.4 h, 238 km from Thunder Bay.

4. Answers may vary.

Investigation 2, page 361

4. (6250, 343.75)

5. The point represents where the salesperson receives the same monthly pay from either plan. The horizontal coordinate represents the monthly sales. The vertical coordinate represents the monthly pay.

6. Plan B is better for monthly sales less than $6250 because monthly pay is greater. Plan A is better for monthly sales greater than $6250 because monthly pay is greater.

8.3 Exercises, page 365

1. a) Part i: (1, 3); part v: (2, 0)
  b) Estimates may vary.
  ii) $\left(\frac{5}{3}, \frac{5}{3}\right)$ iii) (1, −3)   iv) $\left(-2, \frac{3}{2}\right)$ vi) $\left(\frac{7}{2}, \frac{7}{2}\right)$

2. About 275 km from Thunder Bay

3. About 184 km from Thunder Bay

4. Plan B is always better.

5. a) (1.71, 3.14)   **b)** (6.67, 5.33)   **c)** (−1, −3.5)
  d) (2.86, 1.29)   **e)** (4, 1)   **f)** (2, 2)

6. a) i) (-1, 6)   ii) (2, 4)   iii) (4, 3)
  iv) (−3, −5)   v) (0, −4)   vi) (4, 5)
  b) Explanations may vary.

7. Answers may vary.

8. Answers may vary.

9. a) $P = 6 + 2x$ **b)** $A = 3x$
  d) i) 6 cm   ii) Less than 6 cm
  iii) Greater than 6 cm

10. Explanations may vary.
  a) No   **b)** Greater than 2 cm

8.4 Mathematical Modelling: Pushing Your Physical Limits, page 367

1. b) Answers may vary.

2. a) 42.4 mL/kg/min   **b)** Greater

3. a) 60.3 beats/min   **b)** Greater

4. Explanations may vary.

5., 6. Answers may vary.

8.5 Slopes of Parallel and Perpendicular Line Segments

Investigation 1, page 369

1. Answers may vary.

2. Answers may vary.

3. a) Parallel; definition of a rectangle
  b) Equal   **c)** Equal
  d) Equal; both the rises and both the runs are equal.

4. Parallel line segments have equal slopes.

Investigation 2, page 371

1. Answers may vary.

2. Answers may vary.

3. a) Perpendicular; definition of a rectangle
  b) Opposites   **c)** Equal
  d) Negative reciprocals; by observation

4. Perpendicular line segments have slopes that are negative reciprocals.

8.5 Exercises, page 374

1. AB ∥ CD; SR ∥ QP; the slopes are equal.

2. a) CD ⊥ AB; GF ⊥ EF; the slopes are negative reciprocals.

3. a) $-\frac{3}{2}$ **b)** $-\frac{8}{5}$ **c)** $\frac{4}{3}$ **d)** 2   **e)** 3

4. a and d

5. a) AB: 2; CD: 2; AB ∥ CD   **b)** EF: $\frac{3}{8}$; GH: $\frac{2}{5}$
  c) RS: $-\frac{3}{4}$, TU: $-\frac{2}{3}$

6. a) OB: $\frac{2}{3}$; CD: $-\frac{3}{2}$; OB ⊥ CD
  b) HI: $\frac{1}{3}$; JK: −3; HI ⊥ JK   **c)** LM: $-\frac{7}{4}$; NP: $\frac{3}{5}$

7. Explanations may vary.

8. a) Parallelogram   **b)** Not a parallelogram
  c) Parallelogram

9. Explanations may vary.

10. a) Right triangle   **b)** Right triangle
  c) Right triangle   **d)** Not a right triangle

11. a) AB: $\frac{3}{2}$; BC: $-\frac{2}{3}$; AC: $\frac{1}{5}$
  b) Right triangle; slopes AB and BC are negative reciprocals; therefore, AB and BC are perpendicular.
  c) (4, −4)

12. b) AB: $\frac{3}{2}$; BD: $\frac{1}{3}$; AC: $\frac{1}{3}$; CD: $\frac{3}{2}$
  c) Parallelogram; two pairs of opposite sides have equal slopes and are therefore parallel.

13. b) Answers may vary.
  c) Two pairs of opposite sides have equal slopes and are therefore parallel.

14. a) Rectangle   **b)** Not a rectangle   **c)** Rectangle

15. Answers may vary.
  a) C(−3, 5)   **b)** C(2, 10)   **c)** C(2, 3)

16. Explanations may vary.

17. a) (4, 2)   **b)** (2, −4)   **c)** (5, 1)   **d)** (5, −2)

18. Explanations may vary.

19. a) Answers may vary.   **b)** Explanations may vary.

20. a) Answers may vary.   **b)** Explanations may vary.

21. D(0, 5.5)

22. D(0, 6)

23. a) $P(9, 0)$ **b)** $P(0, 6)$

24. $T(0, 0)$ or $T(5, 0)$

8.6 Academic Focus: The Equation of a Line: Part III

Investigation 1, page 377

2. a) 3

   b) Answers may vary. $y = 3x + 1$, $y = 3x + 3$, $y = 3x$

   c) Yes; explanations may vary. The lines appear to be parallel.

   d) In the equation $y = mx + b$, all the values of m are 3.

3. a) $y = 3x - 1$

4. a) $-\frac{1}{3}$

   b) Answers may vary. $y = -\frac{1}{3}x + 2$, $y = -\frac{1}{3}x + 1$, $y = -\frac{1}{3}x$

   c) Yes; explanations may vary. The lines appear to be parallel to each other and perpendicular to $y = 3x + 2$.

   d) In the equation $y = mx + b$, all the values of m are $-\frac{1}{3}$.

5. a) $y = -\frac{1}{3}x - 1$

6. a) When the equations are in the form $y = mx + b$, they have the same value of m. In other words, the slopes of the lines are equal.

   b) When two equations are in the form $y = mx + b$, the values of m are negative reciprocals. In other words, the slopes of the two lines are negative reciprocals.

Investigation 2, page 378

1. a) 3; 2

2. b) Answers may vary.

   c) Answers may vary. All the slopes are 3.

3. $y = 3x - 1$

4. a) $-\frac{1}{3}$

   c) Answers may vary.

   d) Answers may vary. All the slopes are $-\frac{1}{3}$.

5. a) $y = -\frac{1}{3}x - 1$

6. a) When the equations are in the form $y = mx + b$, they have the same value of m. In other words, the slopes of the lines are equal.

   b) When two equations are in the form $y = mx + b$, the values of m are negative reciprocals. In other words, the slopes of the two lines are negative reciprocals.

8.6 Exercises, page 381

1. None; no two lines have equal slopes.

2. c; the only pair that has slopes that are negative reciprocals.

3. a) $y = 0.5x + 5$, $y = 0.5x$; $y = -\frac{3}{2}x + 3$, $y = -\frac{3}{2}x - 4$; the slopes are equal.

   b) $y = 0.5x + 5$, $y = -2x$; $y = 0.5x$, $y = -2x$; $y = \frac{2}{3}x + 5$, $y = -\frac{3}{2}x + 3$; $y = \frac{2}{3}x + 5$, $y = -\frac{3}{2}x + 4$; $y = -\frac{2}{3}x$, $y = \frac{3}{2}x - \frac{1}{2}$; the slopes are negative reciprocals.

4. c) 2

5. b) i) 1   **ii)** 1

   d) $y = x - 2$

6. b) i) 2   **ii)** $-\frac{1}{2}$

   d) $y = -\frac{1}{2}x + 5$

7. a) ii) $y = \frac{2}{5}x + \frac{17}{5}$ **b) ii)** $y = -\frac{5}{2}x + 15$

8. b) ii) $y = \frac{3}{2}x + 1$ **c) ii)** $y = -\frac{2}{3}x + \frac{1}{3}$

9. $3x - 2y = 0$

10. $x - 2y - 5 = 0$

11. a) $y = 2x + 4$, $y = 2x + 2$, $y = 2x$, $y = 2x - 2$, $y = 2x - 4$, $y = 2x - 6$

   b) $y = 2x + 4$, $y = 2x + 3$, $y = 2x + 2$, $y = 2x + 1$, $y = 2x$, $y = 2x - 1$

   c) $y = 2x + 4$, $y = 2x + 1$, $y = 2x - 2$, $y = 2x - 5$, $y = 2x - 8$, $y = 2x - 11$

12. a) $y = 5$ **b)** $x = 3$ **c)** $x = -1$ **d)** $y = 4$

13. a) $y = -2x + 1$

   b) An infinite number of lines; a line parallel to L_1 has slope -2. For example $y = -2x - 1$, $y = -2x + 2$, and so on

   c) $y = \frac{1}{2}x + 6$

   d) No line; a line with x-intercept 2 and y-intercept 3 has slope $-\frac{3}{2}$ and cannot be perpendicular to L_1, which has slope -2.

Consolidating Your Skills, page 384

1. b) i) -10 **ii)** -6 **iii)** -2

   iv) 2   **v)** 6   **vi)** 10

   c) i) $y = 2x - 10$ **ii)** $y = 2x - 6$ **iii)** $y = 2x - 2$

   iv) $y = 2x + 2$ **v)** $y = 2x + 6$ **vi)** $y = 2x + 10$

   d) $y = mx - 6m$ **e)** $y = mx - am$

2. b) i) $-\frac{6}{3}$ **ii)** $-\frac{6}{2}$ **iii)** $-\frac{6}{1}$

   iv) $\frac{6}{1}$ **v)** $\frac{6}{2}$ **vi)** $\frac{6}{3}$

   c) i) $y = -\frac{6}{3}x + 6$ **ii)** $y = -\frac{6}{2}x + 6$ **iii)** $y = -\frac{6}{1}x + 6$

   iv) $y = \frac{6}{1}x + 6$ **v)** $y = \frac{6}{2}x + 6$ **vi)** $y = \frac{6}{3}x + 6$

   d) $y = -\frac{6}{a}x + 6$ **e)** $y = -\frac{b}{a}x + b$

3. Not a parallelogram

4. Explanations may vary.

5. Neither; determine the slopes of the sides; AB: 1; BC: $-\frac{5}{6}$; CD: -5; DA: $\frac{1}{6}$. Since no sides are parallel, the quadrilateral is neither a parallelogram, nor a rectangle.

6. a) $S(5, 0)$ **b)** $S(0, -15)$

7. a) $S(-5, 0)$ **b)** $S\left(0, -\frac{5}{3}\right)$

9. b) Explanations may vary.

10. $C(3, 2)$, $F(8, 4)$, $G\left(\frac{1}{2}, 1\right)$

11. a) $y = x + 2$ **b)** $y = -\frac{11}{9}x + \frac{19}{9}$

12. a) $y = -\frac{3}{4}x + \frac{35}{4}$ **b)** $y = \frac{2}{5}x + 3$

14. a) $(-3, -5)$ **b)** $(4, 1)$

15. a) 39.7 mL/kg/min   **b)** 138.9 beats/min

16. a) Lower recovery heart rate

   b) Explanations may vary.

1. a) $-\frac{2}{3}, -\frac{1}{2}, 0.33, \frac{1}{3}, 0.45, \frac{4}{3}$ **b)** $-\frac{8}{3}, -1.6, -\frac{8}{7}, 0, \frac{9}{8}, 1.2$
   c) $-\frac{1}{8}, -0.12, -\frac{1}{9}, \frac{1}{9}, \frac{1}{4}, 0.29$

2. a) 100   **b)** 236   •   **c)** 46.25

3. a) 140   **b)** 81   **c)** 111

4. b) Explanations may vary.

5. a) 7^{16} **b)** 3^{16} **c)** 11^6
   d) 7^{20} **e)** 5^{-9} **f)** 10^{-12}

6. a) About 1.43×10^{18} km³   **b)** About 2.24×10^{10} km³

7. Examples may vary.
   a) 3.66, 3.67   **b)** $-1.471, -1.472$
   c) 0.398, 0.399   **d)** $-5.3768, -5.3769$
   e) $\frac{25}{28}, \frac{26}{29}$ **f)** 2.236 068, 2.236 069

8. a) 9   **b)** 7   **c)** 3   **d)** 1

9. a) 6   **b)** -0.90 **c)** 0.11   **d)** 1.39

10. 21 nickels and 11 quarters

11. a) 2; 44 L   **b)** 5.5; 16 L   **c)** 750 km

12. a) $5a^2 - 3a - 7$ **b)** $-9x + 3$ **c)** $-18a^7$
   d) $-7x^3$ **e)** $\frac{25}{2}b^3$ **f)** $-6a^2 + 8a - 6$

13. a) $9x^4 - 12x^2 + 6x^5$ **b)** $-2m^4 + 8m^6$
   c) $14a^3 - 21a^2$ **d)** $-6p^2 + 12p^3 - 15p$

14. a) $3a(3a + 1)$ **b)** $8xy(x + 2y - 3)$

15. a) $-2, \frac{1}{2}$ **b)** $\frac{1}{2}, -2$ **c)** $-1, 1$
   d) $\frac{2}{5}, -\frac{5}{2}$ **e)** 0, undefined   **f)** undefined, 0

16. a) $2x - 3y + 6 = 0$ **b)** $3x + 2y - 19 = 0$

Chapter 9 Line of Best Fit

Mathematical Modelling: Good News for Migraine Sufferers, page 389

1. Answers may vary.

2. No; explanations may vary.

3. Explanations may vary.

Reviewing Your Skills, page 390

1. a) Answers may vary.
   c) $y = -x + 7$
   d) Answers may vary.
   e) There are only six possibilities for (x, y) and they lie on the line $y = -x + 7$.

2. Question every tenth student entering the auditorium for an assembly. Explanations may vary.

3. a) $y = 3x + 6$ **b)** $y = -2x + 7$ **c)** $y = 3x + 4$
   d) $y = 1.5x + 3$ **e)** $y = 1.5x + 0.5$

9.1 Sampling Data

Investigation, page 392

1., 2. Answers may vary.

3. No conclusions can be made based on this single experiment.

4. Answers may vary.

5. a) Answers may vary. No, guessing two correct cards consistently is better than average.
   b) Answers may vary.
   c) Answers may vary. Use more cards.

9.1 Exercises, page 397

1. Answers may vary.
   a) The ages of students from all classes, and not only from one class must be considered.
   b) The choice of music varies with people of different age groups. A survey of the senior citizens does not include students, children, and middle-aged people.
   c) The people working in the Assembly Plant will be encouraged to buy the cars they produce. This sample does not cover students, senior citizens, and many other groups.
   d) Close friends are likely to have similar tastes, and they would not be a random sample.
   e) There are many people of different groups not listening to the talk show, so the sample is not random.

2. Answers may vary.
   a) The sample is not representative. People who read the magazine are probably in favour of health food.
   b) The sample is not representative. People who walk into the City Stock Exchange are probably in favour of tax reductions.
   c) This sample is not representative, but it is more representative than b. Every person in the city has a chance of being selected, but other members of the community (rural, unlisted, other cities) are excluded.
   d) The sample is not representative. The light bulbs would tend to be the same because they are made at the same time and come from the same batch.
   e) The sample is representative. Every carton has an equal chance of being selected, and every chip within that carton has an equal chance of being selected.

3. Answers may vary.
   a) All flash bulbs; when a bulb has been checked, it cannot be sold or used.
   b) All Canadian families; it would be impossible to survey the entire population of Canada.
   c) All processed food; food, when cooked in bulk, has the same ingredients; so for its purity, a small sample is sufficient.
   d) All aluminum extension ladders; testing all ladders until they break will not leave any ladders to be sold.
   e) All ski equipment; it is not possible to ask every shop manager how much he or she charges.
   f) The population; it is not possible to check the blood sample of every person.

4. Answers may vary.
   a) There are so many new drivers, it might be impractical to obtain data for everyone.

b) Each test destroys the light bulb, so only a sample should be tested.

c) It may be too time-consuming and wasteful to measure every bag.

5. a) Answers may vary. Balfour, Hood, Majic, Tabori, Walker, Gianelia: 6, 6, 6

b) 3.7, 4, 4   **c)** 10.5, 10, 10

6. to 9. Answers may vary.

10. Answers may vary.

a) i) The songs on the CD   **ii)** Listening to one song
iii) No; the title song can be quite different from all the others.

b) i) Wheat and canola farmers
ii) Names are selected at random from farm mailing lists.
iii) Yes

c) i) Ontario's residents
ii) Names are selected at random from Toronto directory.
iii) No; the sample would not include rural residents.

d) i) Canadian teenagers
ii) Interviewing teens at a mall
iii) No; the sampling would not include teens from various communities or teens who shop by catalogue or by computer.

e) i) Canadian voters
ii) Names are selected from each political riding.
iii) Yes, provided the names are selected randomly.

11. Answers may vary.

12. a) No; every number from 0 to 9 is used in every row and every column, exactly once.
b) Answers may vary.

9.2 Mathematical Modelling: Good News for Migraine Sufferers: Part I, page 401

1. Answers may vary.
3. Answers may vary.
b) Graph the samples on one graph, but ensure the two samples are distinguishable. This allows for observation of any differences.

4. Answers and explanations may vary.
5. Answers may vary.

9.3 Scatter Plots and Lines of Best Fit

Investigation 1, page 404

1. to 7. Answers may vary.

Investigation 2, page 405

3. Answers may vary.
4. c) Explanations may vary.

9.3 Exercises, page 409

1. a) Yes, all but one of the points lie on a line.
b) No, the line of best fit crosses the y-axis at about 10.
c) No, we need to consider all points. Try to have as many points above the line as below.

2. No, the pattern of points does not suggest a line. A smooth curve through the points would be more appropriate.

3. Graph b would give the most reliable predictions because the line fits the data more closely than the lines in part a and c, where the points are more widely scattered.

4. Results may vary.

5. a) Answers may vary. $y = 0.375x - 676.5$
b) 78 m

6. Results may vary.

7. Results may vary.

8. Answers may vary.
a) 101 s, 109 s   **b)** 2100

9. b) Answers may vary. Since the points are all within about 1 s of the line, it does provide a good representation of the data.
c) Estimates may vary; about 48 s. The actual 1992 winning time was 49.02 s.
d) Answers may vary. $y = -0.2145x + 474.881$
e) 47.6 s
f) The estimates are both less than the actual time.

9.4 Using Technology to Draw Lines of Best Fit

Investigation, page 413

1. Table values may vary.

Number of pennies	Length (mm)
4	76
6	114
8	152
10	190

3. c) $y = 19x$
d) The diameter of one penny

4. Answers may vary.
a) (5, 95), (12, 228)
b) (2, 38), (7, 133)

5. Nickel; the diameter of a nickel is slightly greater than that of a penny.

9.4 Exercises, page 416

1. a) Linear
d) Descriptions may vary. Linear; same
e) $y = 4.6x$
g) The height the seedlings grow in one day. Every day the seedlings grow about 4.6 mm.

2. a) to e) Results may vary.
f) The number of heartbeats in one second. Explanations may vary.

3. a) to h) Answers may vary.
i) The extension in centimetres per gram. Explanations may vary.

4. Results may vary.

5. b) Answers may vary. $y = 7.4x$
c) Answers may vary. Different trees grow at different rates; rates also depend on the weather, amount of rainfall, temperature, soil conditions, and so on.

6. b) Answers may vary. White pine: $y = 0.5x$; black spruce: $y = 0.3x$.

c) The growth of DBH in centimetres per year; the white pine grows 0.5 cm, in DBH every year. The black spruce grows 0.3 cm in DBH every year.

d) White pine; about 1.67 times

e) White pine: 25 cm, black spruce 15 cm

f) White pine: 60 years, black spruce: 100 years

9.5 Equation of the Line of Best Fit

Investigation, page 420

3. d) i) 157.1 cm

ii) The predicted height is less than Kiki's height.

e) Tuffy's height is closest.

9.5 Exercises, page 423

1. Answers and explanations may vary. Two points are needed to determine a line, but three points are needed to determine a line of best fit.

2. a) $y = 3.186x - 0.107$

b) Answers may vary. Yes; the radius and circumference of a circle are linearly related.

3. a) $y = 2.671x - 1.964$

b) Answers may vary. No; the radius and area of a circle are not related linearly. The y-intercept of -1.964 is also not realistic.

4. b) Answers may vary.

c) $y = 1.533x + 1.149$; answers may vary.

5. b) $y = 0.5507x - 1024.37$

6. Results may vary.

7. Results may vary.

8. a) $y = -0.0094x + 0.0943$

b) 0.0835 mL/100 mL

c) Answers may vary.

9. a) Answers may vary. For exercise 4, (152. 9, 235.5), for exercise 8, (0.75, 0.8725)

b) Yes

10. a) i) The ball is falling when the graph displays an upward arc, for example, to the right of A, B, C, and D.

ii) The ball is rising when the graph displays a downward sloping curve, for example to the left of B, C, and D.

c) Answers may vary. For the screen shown: A(0.1, 0.67), B(1.19, 0.98), C(1.95, 1.21), D(2.68, 1.37)
$y = -0.275x + 1.100$

d)

Time, x seconds	0.10	1.19	1.95	2.68
Height of ball, y metres	1.08	0.77	0.54	0.38

f) Yes; the points appear to be in a straight line.

g) i) 4; in 4 s the ball is at rest.

ii) At about 3.27 s before the ball was dropped.

11. Lines of best fit may vary.

b) $y = 11.05x - 21\,800.15$; 2009

c) $y = -236.97x + 472\,516.36$; 1994

d) Answers may vary.

12. Lines of best fit may vary.

a) ii) $y = -1.20x + 2413.22$

iii) 21.62%, 19.22%, 16.82%

b) ii) $y = 1.135x - 2237.365$ iii) 31.5%

c) Answers may vary. Price of cigarettes dropped, more teenagers trying to fit into a 'cool' image

9.6 Mathematical Modelling: Who is the World's Fastest Human?: Part II, page 428

1. Lines of best fit may vary.

c) $y = 10.79x - 9.1$

d) $d = 10.79t - 9.1$

2. Explanations may vary.

a) i) 97.07 m   ii) 51.32 m

b) -9.1 m; explanations may vary. The line of best fit does not go through (0, 0).

c) 10.79 m/s

d) Explanations may vary.

3. Lines of best fit may vary.

c) $y = 11.08x - 13.85$

d) $d = 11.08t - 13.85$

4 a) i) 200.22 m   ii) 98.28 m

Explanations may vary. The line of best fit does not necessarily go through the data points, as is the case for both of these times.

b) -13.85; explanations may vary. The line of best fit does not go through (0, 0).

c) 11.08 m/s

d) Explanations may vary.

5. a) Bailey; he travels 0.29 m/s faster.

b) Answers may vary.

6. a) Johnson

b) 12.29 s, 13.06 s

c) Answers may vary. Yes; these predictions are based on the results of races of different distances and may not be reliable over a distance of 150 m.

7. Answers may vary.

8. a) Explanations may vary. The slowest time was the first 50 m and his fastest time was the last 50 m.

b) Explanations may vary. He completed the first 100 m in a slower time than he completed the first 100 m when he ran 200 m.

9.7 Mathematical Modelling: Good News for Migraine Sufferers: Part II, page 430

1. a) $y = 1.011x - 0.169$

b) Answers may vary. $y = x$; the number of migraines should be the same before and after taking the placebo.

c) Yes; $y = 1.011x - 0.169$ is very close to $y = x$.

2. a) $y = 0.841x + 0.863$

b) Comparing the lines of best fit, there is a 17% reduction in the incidence of headaches. Therefore, the drug is effective.

3. Answers may vary.

Consolidating Your Skills, page 432

1. Results may vary.

2. to **4.** Answers may vary.

5. Results may vary.

6. Answers may vary.
  a) Men: 72 m; women: 76 m
  b) 1977

7. Explanations may vary.
  a) No, it is not realistic to expect the same improvement in performance at every Olympic Games.
  b) No, it is not realistic for humans to continue to improve performance for a long period of time.
  c) The graph of the model will flatten or curve.

8., **9.** Answers may vary.

Chapter 10 Measurement

Mathematical Modelling: Designing a Cooler, page 435

1. to **3.** Answers may vary.

Reviewing Your Skills, page 436

5. $A = 2(lw + lh + hw)$

6. Answers may vary.

8. $n = lwh$

9. Answers may vary.

10. $A = 2(lw + lh + hw)$; $V = lwh$

11. a) A: rectangle; B: circle; C: trapezoid;
  D: rectangular prism; E: square; F: cube; G: triangle
  b) Explanations may vary.
  c) $A = lw$: area of rectangle A; $C = 2\pi r$: circumference of circle B; $A = \pi r^2$: area of circle B; $A = \frac{1}{2}bh$: area of triangle G; $A = s^2$: area of square E; $V = x^3$: volume of cube F; $A = 6x^2$: surface area of cube F; $A = 2(lw + lh + hw)$: surface area of rectangular prism D; $V = lwh$: volume of rectangular prism D; $P = 4s$: perimeter of square E; $C = \pi d$: circumference of circle B; $P = 2(l + w)$: perimeter of rectangle A; $A = \frac{h(a + b)}{2}$: area of trapezoid C
  d) Summaries may vary.

10.1 Applied Focus: Areas of Composite Figures
Investigation, page 438

1. 2 congruent small triangles, 1 medium triangle, 2 congruent large triangles, 1 parallelogram, 1 square

2. 25 cm², 25 cm², 50 cm², 100 cm², 100 cm², 50 cm², 50 cm²

3. Descriptions may vary. The area of each small triangle is one-half the area of the square. The area of the square is equal to the area of the parallelogram and the area of the medium triangle. Each large triangle is double the area of the medium triangle.

4. 400 cm²; yes

10.1 Exercises, page 441

1. a) 12 cm   **b)** 30 cm   **c)** 66 m   **d)** 36 km

2. a) 6 cm²   **b)** 30 cm²   **c)** 208.25 m²   **d)** 60 km²

3. a) 62.8 cm²   **b)** 257.5 cm²   **c)** 28.2 m²   **d)** 10 cm²

4. Rectangles: 14; triangles: 7

5. Descriptions may vary.
  a) The region between concentric circles with radii 5.2 and 4.8
  b) A rectangle with length 4 and width 3 with a semicircle radius 1.5 at one end of the rectangle

6. a) 4.6 cm   **b)** 2.3 cm   **c)** 16.7 cm²

7. a) 4.5 m   **b)** 9.0 m   **c)** 28.3 m

8. 354 cm

9. a) 416 cm²   **b)** 102.4 cm
  c) The answer does not change; explanations may vary.

10. a) 100 m   **b)** 63.66 m   **c)** 9950 m²   **d)** 120
  e) $1516.80

11. 21 m²

12. 3 m²

13. 420 L

14. 17.5 m

15. 20 cans

16. b) 7 m²

17. 16 cm

10.2 Optimal Value of Measurements (Two Dimensions)
Investigation 1, page 445

1., **2.** Answers may vary.

3. a) 100 cm²   **b)** 10 cm by 10 cm

4. a) i) Adds 0.1 to the number in cell A4.
  ii) Subtracts the number in cell A4 from 20.
  iii) Multiplies the numbers in cells A4 and B4.
  b) 100 cm²   **c)** 10 cm by 10 cm

5. The maximum areas are equal.

Investigation 2, page 446

1. a) 10   **b)** 9 m by 30 m   **c)** 270 m²

2. See table below.

3. b)

Number along width	Number along length	Width of enclosure (m)	Length of enclosure (m)	Area enclosed (m²)
3	10	9	30	270
4	9	12	27	324
5	8	15	24	360
6	7	18	21	378

  c) 6 stands for width, 7 stands for length; 18 m by 21 m

10.2 Exercises, page 447

1. a) 7 stands by 8 stands, which is 21 m by 24 m, or 504 m²
  b) No; explanations may vary. An area of 50 m² requires fractions of stands, which is not possible.

2. a) 1 tile by 36 tiles, or 0.6 m by 21.6 m
  b) 6 tiles by 6 tiles, or 3.6 m by 3.6 m

3. a), b)

Number along width	Number along length	Width of garden (m)	Length of garden (m)	Area enclosed (m²)
1	4	1.8	7.2	12.96
2	3	3.6	5.4	19.44

4. Explanations may vary. 5 m by 5 m

5. a) Explanations may vary. Yes

b), c), d)

Length of side parallel to beach (m)	Length of side perpendicular to beach (m)	Total length of rope (m)	Area enclosed (m²)
300	50	400	15 000
250	75	400	18 750
200	100	400	20 000
150	125	400	18 750
100	150	400	15 000

e) 200 m by 100 m; length is twice the width.

6. Explanations may vary.
  a) 1.5 m by 1.5 m   **b)** 1.5 m by 3.0 m   **c)** 3.0 m by 3.0 m

7. b) Descriptions of graphs may vary.
  c) Explanations may vary.

8. a) Either 42 m by 18 m or 36 m by 21 m, for an area of 756 m²
  b) 39 m by 39 m, for an area of 1521 m²

9. a) 216 m²
  b)

Number along each of 3 sides	Number along each of other 2 sides	Overall width (m)	Overall length (m)	Combined area (m²)
2	10	6	30	180
4	7	12	21	252
6	4	18	12	216

  c) 4 stands along 3 sides, and 7 stands along the other 3 sides for a total area of 252 m².

10. a) For a rectangle, the greatest area is a square with side length $\frac{1}{4}$ of the length of the loop. The largest region is a circle.
  b) Answers may vary.
  c) For a rectangle, the greatest area is a square with side length approximately 10.6 cm. The largest region is a circle with diameter approximately 13.5 cm.

11. 30

10.3 Surface Area and Volume of a Prism
10.3 Exercises, page 454

1. a) 96 cm², 64 cm³   **b)** 161.5 cm², 105 cm³
  c) Approximately 92 cm², 30 cm³
  d) 184 cm², 120 cm³

2. a) 3 cm   **b)** 10 cm   **c)** 8 cm

3. A rectangular prism with dimensions 10 by 6 by 4

4. A rectangular prism with no lid, base 3 by 5 and height 4

5. a) Approximately 2870 cm²; 10 625 cm³
  b) 2300 cm²; 7000 cm³
  c) 2450 cm²; 7625 cm³
  d) 2338 cm²; 7380 cm³

6. The soil was piled higher than the sides of the truck.

7. Answers may vary. 1 ft by 1 ft by 24 ft; 1 ft by 2 ft by 12 ft; 1 ft by 3 ft by 8 ft; 1 ft by 4 ft by 6 ft; 2 ft by 2 ft by 6 ft; 2 ft by 3 ft by 4 ft; the last set of dimensions is most likely.

8. a) $V = \frac{1}{2}lwh$ **b)** $A = lw + hw + lh + h\sqrt{l^2 + w^2}$

9. 228 cm²

10. Answers may vary. 10 cm by 10 cm by 20 cm, 8 cm by 8 cm by 31.25 cm; 12 cm by 12 cm by approximately 14 cm; the first set of dimensions is most likely.

11. Explanations may vary. The dimensions are probably given to the nearest centimetre, and the calculated volume is 50 000 cm³ to the nearest 1000 cm³.

12. 25 cm; 7400 cm²

13. a) Explanations may vary. One million   **b)** 25%

14. a) Answers may vary. 2 m by 2 m by 2 m
  b) 8 m³   **c)** 18 m²   **d)** 1 m³

15. 6 m by 2 m by 4 m

10.4 Mathematical Modelling: Designing a Cooler: Part I, page 457

1. to 4. Answers may vary.

5. a) Explanations may vary.
  b) 150 cm²; 5 cm

6. a) Height equals side length of base.   **b)** Cube
  c) Edge length cubed is equal to volume.

7. a) Cube   **c)** Explanations may vary.

8. a) x^2 **b)** $\frac{125}{x^2}$ **c)** $y = 2x^2 + \frac{500}{x}$

10. a) 5 cm   **b)** Equal   **c)** Cube
  d) The edge length raised to the exponent 3 is the volume.

11. a) Cube

12. Answers may vary.

13. a) The prism is a cube.
  b) The edge length raised to the exponent 3 is the volume.

15. Approximately 8143 cm²

10.5 Optimal Value of Measurements (Three Dimensions)
Investigation, page 463

1. a) 100 cm²   **b)** 10 cm   **c)** 700 cm²

2., 3. a)

Length (cm)	Width (cm)	Height (cm)	Volume (cm³)	Surface area (cm²)
20	5	10	1000	700
25	4	10	1000	780
25	8	5	1000	730
10	10	10	1000	600

  b) 20 cm by 5 cm by 10 cm
  c) Answers may vary. 10 cm by 10 cm by 10 cm; surface area 600 cm²
  d) A cube

10.5 Exercises, page 464

1. a)

Length (cm)	Width (cm)	Height (cm)	Volume (cm³)	Surface area (cm²)
1	1	24	24	98
2	1	12	24	76
2	2	6	24	56
2	3	4	24	52
3	1	8	24	70
4	1	6	24	68

b) 2 cm by 3 cm by 4 cm, with a surface area of 52 cm²

2. a)

Length (cm)	Width (cm)	Height (cm)	Volume (cm³)	Surface area (cm²)
1	1	32	32	130
2	1	16	32	100
2	2	8	32	72
4	1	8	32	88
4	2	4	32	64

b) 4 cm by 2 cm by 4 cm, with a surface area of 64 cm²

3. a)

Length (cm)	Width (cm)	Height (cm)	Volume (cm³)	Surface area (cm²)
1	1	100	100	402
1	10	10	100	240
2	1	50	100	304
2	2	25	100	208
2	5	10	100	160
4	1	25	100	258
5	1	20	100	250
5	5	4	100	130

b) 5 cm by 5 cm by 4 cm, with a surface area of 130 cm²

4. a), b), c)

Length (cm)	Width (cm)	Height (cm)	Volume (cm³)	Surface area (cm²)
10	10	40.00	4000	1700
12	12	27.78	4000	1477
14	14	20.41	4000	1339
16	16	15.63	4000	1256
18	18	12.35	4000	1213
20	20	10.00	4000	1200
22	22	8.26	4000	1211
24	24	6.94	4000	1242
26	26	5.92	4000	1292
28	28	5.10	4000	1355
30	30	4.44	4000	1433

d) 20 cm by 20 cm by 10 cm, for a surface area of 1200 cm²; the base is a square and the height is half the side length of the base.

Answers may vary. This would probably not be a good idea for movie theatres because the box is too shallow. The popcorn would get cold faster, and it would spill easily.

5., 6.

Length (cm)	Width (cm)	Height (cm)	Surface area (cm²)	Volume (cm³)
1	1	36	146	36
2	2	9	80	36
3	3	4	66	36
6	6	1	96	36

7. a) 66 cm²   **b)** 3 cm by 3 cm by 4 cm

8. a) i) Divides 36 by the square of the number in cell A4.
  ii) Squares the number in cell A4.
  iii) Adds twice the number in cell C4 to the product of 4 and the numbers in cells A4 and B4.
  iv) Adds 0.1 to the number in cell A4.
b) Approximately 65.42 cm²
c) Approximately 3.3 cm by 3.3 cm by 3.3 cm

9. Answers may vary. Surface area is a minimum when the dimensions are as close to being equal as possible.

10. a) 384 cm²; 768 cm²; 1536 cm²   **b)** 3072 cm²
  c) Multiply the area by 2.   **d)** 196 608 cm²

11. a) 216 square units
  b) Answers may vary; 2 cubes by 8 cubes by 9 cubes, or 212 square units; 2 cubes by 3 cubes by 24 cubes, or 252 square units; 3 cubes by 3 cubes by 16 cubes, or 210 square units
  c) 4 cubes by 6 cubes by 6 cubes, to use 168 square units
  d) Answers may vary.

12. a) Answers may vary.   **b)** 320

13. a) Standard juice box size is approximately 4.1 cm by 6.3 cm by 10.5 cm. Surface area is approximately 270 cm². The box contains 250 mL of juice.
  b) Answers may vary. To one decimal place, the best dimensions are 6.4 cm by 6.4 cm by 6.4 cm, with an area of 246 cm².
  c) Answers may vary. It would probably not be a good idea to change because people are used to the current shape of the box. Also, a cubical box might be harder to hold without spilling the juice.

14. a), b), c)

Length of cut-out square (cm)	Length of box (cm)	Width of box (cm)	Height of box (cm)	Volume (cm³)
1.0	26.0	19.6	1.0	509.6
2.0	24.0	17.6	2.0	844.8
3.0	22.0	15.6	3.0	1029.6
4.0	20.0	13.6	4.0	1088.0
5.0	18.0	11.6	5.0	1044.0
6.0	16.0	9.6	6.0	921.6
7.0	14.0	7.6	7.0	744.8
8.0	12.0	5.6	8.0	537.6
9.0	10.0	3.6	9.0	324.0

d) i) About 1088 cm³, when the height is 4.0 cm
  ii) About 6.1 cm

15. b), d) Explanations may vary.

Length (m)	Width (m)	Height (m)	Volume (m³)	Outside surface area (m²)	Ratio of surface area to volume
30	30	3	2700	1260	0.467
30	15	6	2700	990	0.367
25	18	6	2700	966	0.358
30	10	9	2700	1020	0.378
25	9	12	2700	1041	0.386

  e) A low ratio of surface area to volume would be better. Answers may vary. When a lower surface area is exposed to the cold, less heat is lost through the walls and windows. Therefore, heating costs would be lower.

16. Descriptions and explanations may vary.

17. a) 486 cm²   **b)** 378 cm²

18. a) 16   **b)** 150

10.6 Surface Area of a Cylinder
Investigation, page 470

1. a) It is a rectangle.
  b) Answers may vary. The area is the product of length and width. The curved surface area can be considered as a rectangle.

2. The product of π and the radius squared

3., 4. Answers may vary.

5. $A = 2\pi rh + 2\pi r^2$

10.6 Exercises, page 473

1. Estimates may vary.
   a) 314.2 cm^2 **b)** 50.3 cm^2 **c)** 141.0 cm^2

2. a) 6.28 cm   **b)** 1.0
   c) They are equal.   **d)** 25.1 cm^2

3. Estimates may vary.
   a) 18.8 cm^2 **b)** 1885.0 cm^2
   c) 176.0 cm^2 **d)** 201.8 cm^2

4. a) 1000π cm^2 **b)** 3141.59 cm^2

5. The second cylinder; explanations may vary.

6. a) Approximately 132 cm^2 and 176 cm^2 **b)** 3 to 4

7. Estimates may vary. Calculations are to nearest square centimetre.
   a) 595 cm^2 **b)** 1098 cm^2 **c)** 560 cm^2

8. Approximately 7.9 m

9. a) 3.18 cm   **b)** Approximately 464 cm^2

10. a) 240.5 cm^2 **b)** 34.2 cm^2 **c)** 308.9 cm^2

11. a) $A = 2\pi r(h + r)$
   c) Answers and explanations may vary.

12. Approximately 60 243 cm^2

13. c) The vertical intercept is the surface area for zero height; that is, the areas of the bases of the cans.

16. Answers may vary.

17. a) 40.8 cm^2 **b)** 37.8 cm^2

18. a), b) Surface area increases in each case.
   c) Surface area is multiplied by 4, multiplied by 9, and multiplied by n^2.

10.7 Volume of a Cylinder

Investigation, page 477

2. a) Descriptions may vary. Fill the can with cubes, then count the cubes.

3. a) The volume is the product of the base area and height.
   c) The answers will vary because the cubes do not completely fill the can.

4. a) $V = \pi r^2 h$

10.7 Exercises, page 479

1. Estimates may vary.
   a) 452.4 cm^2 **b)** 0.5 cm^2
   c) 63.6 cm^2 **d)** 132.7 cm^2

2. Estimates may vary.
   a) 6.3 cm^3 **b)** 6283 cm^3
   c) 150.8 cm^3 **d)** 188.5 cm^3

3. a) Approximately 785 cm^3 **b)** Approximately 78.5%

4. 1062 cm^3; answers may vary.

5. a) 157.1 cm^3 **b)** 62.8 cm^3

6. a) Volume is doubled; tripled.
   b) Volume is quadrupled; multiplied by 9.
   c) Volume is multiplied by 8; multiplied by 27.

7. a) 50 kg   **b)** 255 kg   **c)** 112.5 kg

8. a) Approximately 1.12 m^3 **b)** Answers may vary.

9. a) Approximately 35 000 mm^3
   b) Approximately 0.2 mm

10. c) Answers and explanations may vary.

11. c) Volumes are different.

12. Square

13. Answers may vary.

14. Length has to be twice the width.

15. The volumes are approximately equal.
   a) 250 cm^3 **b)** 251 cm^3 **c)** 250 cm^3 **d)** 250 cm^3

16. a) 99.4 cm^3 **b)** 166.4 cm^3

17. a) 0.9 m   **b)** 3.1 m^3

19. a) 325 117 cm^3; about 325 L   **b)** 28 149 cm^2

20. a) 14.1 cm^3 **b)** 9.4 cm^3

21. a) Approximately 14 260 m^3 **b)** Approximately 510

22. Answers may vary.

23. Same amount of milk in water as water in milk

10.8 Mathematical Modelling: Designing a Cooler: Part II, page 484

1. to 3. Answers may vary.

4. d) The height and diameter are closest in value.

5. a) Explanations may vary.
   b) Approximately 138.6 cm^2; 2.6 cm

6. a) Approximately 5.2 cm
   b) Height and diameter are close in value.

7. a) Equal   **b)** Explanations may vary.

8. a) πr^2 **b)** $\dfrac{125}{\pi r^2}$ **c)** $A = 2\pi r^2 + \dfrac{250}{r}$

10. a) Approximately 5.42 cm   **b)** Approximately 5.42 cm
   c) Height and diameter are equal.

11. a) Equal

12. Answers may vary.

13. a) The cylinder has base diameter equal to height.
   b) The volume is 2π times the cube of the radius. The volume is $\frac{1}{4}\pi$ times the cube of the height.

15. a) 19.96 cm   **b)** 39.93 cm   **c)** 7513.25 cm^2

10.9 Academic Focus: Surface Areas of a Pyramid and a Cone

Investigation 1, page 489

3. Rectangular pyramid

4. a) 5

b) Yes; two pairs of congruent triangular faces

c) Base: 24 cm^2; triangular faces: 7.5 cm^2 and 6.5 cm^2

d) 52 cm^2

5. Answers may vary. Calculate the area of the base. Calculate the area of one face, then multiply by 4. Add these areas.

6. Answers may vary. Calculate the area of each face. Add the four areas.

Investigation 2, page 491

1. The surface area of the cone is $\frac{3}{4}$ the area of the circle.

2. Answers may vary.

10.9 Exercises, page 494

1. Answers may vary. Usually, only exposed faces need to be considered for objects that cannot be moved.

2. Answers may vary.

3. Answers may vary.

a) The faces are congruent when the base is an equilateral triangle. There may be no congruent faces when the base is a scalene triangle.

b) Six faces are congruent when the base is a regular hexagon. There may be no congruent faces when the base is not regular.

4. The cone with radius greater than height has the greater total surface area; explanations may vary.

5. a) Approximately 113 cm^2 and 75 cm^2

b) 3 to 2

6. The net in part a; the faces are triangles that will have a common vertex.

7. a) 40.0 cm^2 **b)** 85.0 cm^2 **c)** 260.0 cm^2

8. a) 204.2 cm^2 **b)** 102.4 m^2 **c)** 3383.6 cm^2

9. a) 15.6 cm^2 **b)** 35.1 cm^2

10. a) 53.4 m^2 **b)** 3393.3 cm^2 **c)** 24 429 cm^2

11. a) 756 cm^2 **b)** 1887 cm^2 **c)** 18.7 m^2

12. a) 122.7 cm^2 **b)** 373.5 cm^2 **c)** 29.1 cm^2

13. Spreadsheets may vary.

14. Approximately 1975 m^2

15. a) 47.1 m^2; 19.3 m^2

b) The one with the square pyramid roof

c) Approximately \$724; \$297

16. a) 156 cm^2 **b)** 624 cm^2 **c)** 1404 cm^2

d) Answers may vary. Doubling the length of base and height quadruples surface area; tripling the length of base and height multiplies surface area by 9.

17. a) 7.5 cm   **b)** 29.0 cm

c) Approximately 707 cm^2

18. a) $C = \pi r\sqrt{r^2 + h^2}$ **b)** $A = \pi r^2 + \pi r\sqrt{r^2 + h^2}$

19. a) $A = \frac{\pi x^2}{4}\left(\sqrt{5} + 1\right)$

b) Predictions may vary. An upward-sloping curve

10.10 Volumes of a Pyramid and a Cone

Investigation, page 498

1. to **5.** Answers may vary.

6. The volume of the pyramid is $\frac{1}{3}$ the volume of the cube.

7. Descriptions may vary.

8. The volume of the cone is $\frac{1}{3}$ the volume of the cylinder.

10.10 Exercises, page 503

1. The formulas are the same: volume equals one-third base area times height.

2. All volumes are the same; explanations may vary.

3. a) 24 cm^3 **b)** 126 m^3 **c)** 367 m^3

4. 32 cm^3

5. 162 cm^3

6. a) Approximately 785 cm^3; 262 cm^3

b) 78.5%; 26.2%

7. The height of the cone is 3 times the height of the cylinder; explanations may vary.

8. a) 235.6 m^3 **b)** 187.8 cm^3 **c)** 1.8 cm^3 **d)** 1.8 cm^3

9. a) 192 m^3 **b)** 384 m^3 **c)** 384 m^3 **d)** 768 m^3

10. 4500 cm^3

11. a) Doubled; tripled   **b)** Doubled; tripled

c) Quadrupled; multiplied by 9

d) Multiplied by 8; multiplied by 27

12. Approximately 9023 m^3

13. a) Approximately 2.2 times   **b)** Answers may vary.

14. a) 9.38 cm^3 **b)** 0.23 m^3

c) 1809.56 cm^3 **d)** 105 293.62 cm^3

15. 146.3 cm^3

16. Approximately 1466 m^3

17. 21.2 m

18. Cone A: 6541.7 cm^3; cone B: 2616.7 cm^3; cone A has the greater volume.

19. 3.0 cm

20. 10.0 m

21. a) 52.4 cm^3 **b)** 20.9 cm^3

22. a) **i)** 6.0 cm, 5.3 cm, 199.8 cm^3

ii) 4.0 cm, 6.9 cm, 115.6 cm^3

iii) 2.0 cm, 7.7 cm, 32.3 cm^3

10.11 Surface Area and Volume of a Sphere

Investigation 1, page 506

1. Answers may vary. 3.1

2. Areas are equal.

3. The ratio is π to 1.

4. $A = \pi d^2$

Investigation 2, page 507

1. The volume of the water is equal to the volume of the ball.

2. $\frac{2}{3}$

3. The volume of the sphere is $\frac{2}{3}$ the volume of the cylinder.

4. $V_c = 2\pi r^3$; $V_s = \frac{4}{3}\pi r^3$

10.11 Exercises, page 510

1. a) 1257 cm^2, 4189 cm^3 **b)** 314 cm^2, 524 cm^3
   c) 2903 cm^2, 14 710 cm^3

2. a) 172.0 cm^2, 212.2 cm^3 **b)** 58.1 cm^2, 41.6 cm^3
   c) 43.0 cm^2, 26.5 cm^3 **d)** 1372.2 cm^2, 4780.1 cm^3

3. a) Estimates may vary. 20 cm
   b) For diameter of 20 cm: 1257 cm^2; 4189 cm^3

4. a) 8.1×10^9 km^2; 6.9×10^{13} km^3
   b) 3.2×10^7 km^2; 1.7×10^{10} km^3

5. Sphere; explanations may vary.

6. 3.804×10^7 km^2, 2.207×10^{10} km^3

7. a) 9   **b)** 27

8. Surface area: multiplied by 4, multiplied by 9; volume: multiplied by 8, multiplied by 27

9. The surface area of the part we see is double the area of the circle that it appears to be.

10. a) 2.2 m   **b)** 1.8 cm   **c)** 6.9 mm

11. 314.2 cm^2, 523.6 cm^3

12. πx^2 cm^2, $\frac{\pi d^3}{6}$ cm^3

13. a) 12 cm   **b)** 1790 cm^2 **c)** 7124 cm^3

14. Answers may vary.

15. a) $A = \pi d^2$, $V = \frac{\pi d^3}{6}$ **b)** $A = \frac{C^2}{\pi}$, $V = \frac{C^3}{6\pi^2}$

16. Answers may vary.

17. Answers may vary.

18. Answers may vary.

19. b) Approximately 314.16 cm^2
   c) Approximately 2.82 cm

20. b) Approximately 523.60 cm^3
   c) Approximately 2.88 cm

21. a) Approximately 50.3 cm^2, 96.0 cm^2; assumptions may vary; the edge of the box is equal to the diameter of the ball.
   b) π to 6   **c)** Approximately 33.5 cm^3; 64 cm^3
   d) π to 6; the ratios are equal.

22. a) Cell B4: the formula doubles the radius, which gives the side length of the cube; cell C4: the formula cubes the side length of the cube, which gives the volume of the cube; cell D4: the formula multiplies the cube of the radius by $\frac{4}{3}\pi$, which gives the volume of the ball.
   b) =C4–D4
   c) Explanations may vary. The statement is reasonable. The length of the radius does not affect the answer.

10.12 Mathematical Modelling: Designing a Cooler: Part III, page 514

2. a) 8125.44 cm^2, 7502.17 cm^2
   b) The cylinder because it has the smaller surface area
   c) 623.27 cm^2

3. a) Approximately 22.85 cm
   b) Approximately 6563.43 cm^2

4. The sphere because it has the smallest surface area

5. Answers may vary; it would roll.

6. For the cylinder and 2 hemispheres:
   a) $\frac{10}{3}\pi r^3$ **b)** $\frac{10}{3}\pi r^3 = 50\ 000$ **c)** $r \doteq 16.84$ cm
   For the cylinder and 1 hemisphere:
   a) $\frac{8}{3}\pi r^3$ **b)** $\frac{8}{3}\pi r^3 = 50\ 000$ **c)** $r \doteq 18.14$ cm

7. For the cylinder and 2 hemispheres:
   a) $8\pi r^2$ **b)** Approximately 7126 cm^2
   For the cylinder and 1 hemisphere:
   a) $7\pi r^2$ **b)** Approximately 7236 cm^2
   c) For each model in exercise 6, its surface area is greater than that of the sphere, but less than that of the cylinder.

Consolidating Your Skills, page 516

1. a) Parallelogram   **c)** Answers may vary.

2. c) 3.8 cm, 12.0 cm; 5.4 cm, 8.5 cm

3. The parallelogram is a rhombus.

4. a) 6   **b)** 1350 cm^2, 3375 cm^3
   c) 7200 cm^2, 40 500 cm^3

5. a) 2494 m^3 **b)** 2788 cm^3 **c)** 3666 cm^3
   d) 2219 cm^3

6. a) 1063 m^2 **c)** 1339 cm^2

7. b) 1230 cm^2 **d)** 1101 cm^2

8. a) 4.77 cm, 7.96 cm
   b) Approximately 1643 cm^2, 1898 cm^2
   c) Approximately 3581 cm^3, 5968 cm^3

9. Approximately 7.5 m^3

10. 1810 cm^2, 7238 cm^3; 50.3 cm^2, 33.5 cm^3; 133 cm^2, 144 cm^3

11. 6.05×10^{12} km^2, 1.40×10^{18} km^3

12. 2714 cm^2, 10 857 cm^3; 1810 cm^2, 7238 cm^3

13. 471 m^3

14. 16 753 cm^3

15. a) 5 m^3 **b)** 3800 cm^3 **c)** 53 cm^3

16. 5772 cm^3

17. 209 m^3

18. 4 cm

19. a) A cube with edge length approximately 79.4 cm
   b) Approximately 37 826 cm^2

20. a) Radius approximately 43 cm, height approximately 86 cm
   b) Approximately 34 853 cm^2

21. Approximately 49.2 cm, 30 465 cm^2

22. Sphere, cylinder, cube

23. Answers may vary.

24. a) Answers may vary.
  b) i) 8962.8 square units
    ii) 47.3 units, 67.0 units
    iv) Cell C3 multiplies the volume by 3 to get 150 000 cubic units and divides this by the base area. Cell D3 calculates the square root of the height squared plus $\frac{1}{4}$ of the base area. Cell E3 adds the base area to 2 times the base length and height of the face.
  c)iii) 47.336 cm and 66.943 cm

Chapter 11 Geometry

Mathematical Modelling: Representing 3-Dimensional Objects in 2 Dimensions, page 521

1. The Annunciation

2. Examples may vary.

Reviewing Your Skills, page 522

1. Explanations may vary.

2. Angles and explanations may vary.

3. Examples may vary.

4. a) Parallelogram   **b)** Hexagon
  c) Isosceles triangle   **d)** Trapezoid

5. a) When two lines intersect, opposite angles are equal.
  b) 36°

6. 54°; the sum of the angles in a triangle is 180°.

7. Explanations may vary.
  a) 78°   **b)** 39°   **c)** 65°, 115°
  d) 50°, 100°   **e)** 34°   **f)** 60°

8. Answers may vary.
  a) 63° and 27°   **b)** 102 and 78°

11.1 Introduction to *The Geometer's Sketchpad*
11.1 Exercises, page 531

Answers may vary.

11.2 Using *The Geometer's Sketchpad*: Medians of Triangles

Investigation 1, page 534

6. The area measurements change but remain equal.

7. A median of a triangle divides the area into two equal parts.

Investigation 2, page 534

4. The medians intersect.

7. In a triangle, the medians intersect at one point.

Investigation 3, page 535

5. The ratio AO to OP is 2 to 1.

9. In a triangle, the centroid divides the median in the ratio 2 to 1, measured from the vertex to the midpoint of the opposite side.

11.3 Medians of Triangles
11.3 Exercises, page 537

1. 36 cm^2

2. 6 cm

3. 20 cm

4. Explanations may vary.
  a) No   **b)** Yes   **d)** No

5. a) The areas on each side of the median are equal.

6. a) The triangles are congruent with angles 30°, 60°, 90°.
  b) The medians in an equilateral triangle intersect to form six congruent right triangles.

7. 1.0 m

8. a) (2, 4), (7, 4), (6, 7)   **b)** (5, 5)

9. Explanations may vary. 72 cm^2

10. c) The areas are equal.
  e) The medians in a triangle divide the area into 6 equal parts.
  f) Explanations may vary.

11. a) (4, 3)   **b)** $x = 4$; $y = 3$; $y = \frac{1}{2}x + 1$

12. Explanations may vary. 2 to 1

13. 17.32 cm

11.4 Using *The Geometer's Sketchpad*: Altitudes of Triangles

Investigation 1, page 541

7. Explanations may vary.

Investigation 2, page 542

7. The height

Investigation 3, page 543

6. The altitudes intersect at one point.

8. Explanations may vary.

11.5 Altitudes of Triangles
11.5 Exercises, page 545

1. a) 25 cm^2 **b)** 32 cm^2 **c)** 96 cm^2

2. 6 cm

3. Explanations may vary. The altitude from A intersects BC extended.

4. a) No
  b) The centroid and orthocentre lie on the median (which is also the altitude) from the vertex, formed by the equal sides to the opposite side.

c) The centroid and orthocentre are the same point.

d) Explanations may vary.

5. 768 cm^2

6. a) 30 m^2 **b)** 13 cm   **c)** 2.3 m

7. 14 m^2, 22.95 m^2

8. 73.9 m^2

9. a) 7.4 m^2 **b)** 81.3 m^2

10. 28

11. a) 352 m^2 **b)** 118 bundles   **c)** $1829

12. 37 bundles

13. a) D(5, 1)   **b)** $x = 5$

14. $-\frac{1}{3}$

17. The three triangles contain the same three angles.

19. a) The sides are parallel.

b) Answers may vary.

c) Corresponding sides are in the same ratio.

11.6 Using *The Geometer's Sketchpad*: Angle Bisectors of Triangles

Investigation 2, page 550

5. The lengths are equal.

8. Any point on an angle bisector is equidistant from the arms of the angle.

Investigation 3, page 551

6. In a triangle, the three angle bisectors intersect at one point.

Investigation 4, page 551

3. The circle appears to touch the sides of the triangle.

5. In a triangle, the intersection point of the angle bisectors is equidistant from the sides of the triangle.

11.7 Angle Bisectors of Triangles

11.7 Exercises, page 554

1. Explanations may vary.

a) 3 cm   **b)** 62°

2. Explanations may vary.

a) 30°   **b)** 20.5°   **c)** 32°   **d)** 23°

3. Explanations may vary; 115°

4. The centroid of an equilateral triangle is the same point as the incentre.

5. c) RA = RB; QB = QC; PC = PA

d) Explanations may vary.

6. Explanations may vary; 90°, 30°

7. Explanations may vary; 90°

8. e) AP = BP

g) A point on the perpendicular bisector of a line segment is equidistant from the endpoints of the segment.

9. e) The perpendicular bisectors intersect at a single point.

i) The circle passes through the vertices of the triangle.

10. Explanations may vary.

11. Explanations may vary.

12. (2, 2)

13. a) 12.57 cm^2 **b)** 30 cm^2

d) 4.83 cm, 4.83 cm, 9.66 cm.

11.8 Using *The Geometer's Sketchpad*: Interior and Exterior Angles

Investigation 1, page 558

6. 180°

Investigation 2, page 559

1. The sum of the angles in a triangle is 180°.

3. 360°

6. The sum of the angles changes from 360°.

7. Explanations may vary.

8. The sum of the angles in a quadrilateral is 360°.

9. Each triangle has an angle sum of 180°. The two triangles together have an angle sum of 360°, which is the sum of the angles in a quadrilateral.

Investigation 3, page 560

3. Explanations may vary.

5. An exterior angle of a triangle is the supplement of the interior angle at that vertex.

10. An exterior angle of a triangle is equal to the sum of the two interior opposite angles.

Investigation 4, page 561

4. Conjectures may vary.

5. Explanations may vary.

6. Predictions may vary.

8. The exterior angles of a triangle and of a quadrilateral have a sum of 360°.

11.9 Interior and Exterior Angles

11.9 Exercises, page 564

1. Explanations may vary.

a) 99°   **b)** 40°   **c)** 45°   **d)** 105°

2. Explanations may vary.

a) 135°   **b)** 35°   **c)** 125°   **d)** 127°

3. Explanations may vary.

e) Yes   **f)** Yes   **g)** The sum is 360°.

h) All triangles and all quadrilaterals tessellate.

5. Explanations may vary.

a) 36°, 108°   **b)** 40°, 50°

c) 46°, 64°, 110°   **d)** 120°

e) 29°, 145°, 145°   **f)** 60°, 60° 120°, 120°

6. a) i) 155°, 155° **ii)** 108°, 108°
b) The exterior angles of an isosceles triangle formed by extending the base are equal.

7. a) i) 157°, 113°, 270° **ii)** 140°, 130°, 270°
b) These exterior angles have a sum of 270°; explanations may vary.

8. Explanations may vary.
a) 280° **b)** 10°, 20° **c)** 52°, 30°

9. 72°

10. 540°

11. 720°, 900°

12.

Polygon	Number of sides	Sum of the interior angles
Triangle	3	180°
Quadrilateral	4	360°
Pentagon	5	540°
Hexagon	6	720°
Heptagon	7	900°

13. The sum of the interior angles of a polygon is the product of 180° and 2 less than the number of sides.

14. 1440°

15. a) Equilateral **b)** Square
c) Answers may vary; stop sign

16. 1620°

17. 147.3°

18. $s = 180°(n - 2)$

19. 36°, 72°, 108°, 144°

20. Explanations may vary.

21. Explanations may vary.
a) i) No **ii)** Yes **iii)** Yes **iv)** Yes **v)** No
b) Square

11.10 Using *The Geometer's Sketchpad*: Angles and Parallel Lines

Investigation, page 571

5. Opposite angles are equal; the sum of the angle measures is 360°.

7. CD appears to be parallel to AB and MN.

8. When a transversal intersects two non-parallel lines, there is no apparent relationship among the angles formed, except for those mentioned in exercise 5 above.

9. When a transversal intersects two parallel lines, pairs of equal angles and pairs of supplementary angles are formed.

11.11 Angles and Parallel Lines
11.11 Exercises, page 574

1. At P: 45°, 135°, 135°; at Q: 45°, 45°, 135°, 135°; at R: 130°, 50°, 50°

2. a) ∠ABE, ∠BEF **b)** ∠GBA, ∠GED; or ∠FEH, ∠CBE
c) ∠ABE, ∠BED; or ∠CBE, ∠BEF

3. Explanations may vary. l_1 and l_3 are parallel; interior angles are supplementary.

4. Explanations may vary.
a) 50° **b)** 70° **c)** 98°, 118° **d)** 78°, 78°

5. Explanations may vary.
a) 48.5°, 48.5° **b)** 49°, 90°

6. 55°, 50°, 55°

7. 35°, 40°, 40°, 105°

8. No, diagrams may vary.

9. Explanations may vary.

10. Answers may vary: yes, if the straws are in the same plane; no, if the straws are in 2 different planes.

11.12 Mathematical Modelling: Representing 3-Dimensional Objects in 2 Dimensions, page 576

4. Explanations may vary.

5. a) The angles are equal; explanations may vary.
b) ∠OAB **c)** ∠OFE

6. a) ∠MEO **b)** ∠FEO

11.13 Using *The Geometer's Sketchpad*: Sides and Diagonals of Quadrilaterals
Investigation 1, page 580

1. d) There is no apparent relationship.
e) There is no apparent relationship.
f) The quadrilateral is a square.
g) The diagonals in a quadrilateral intersect. There is no apparent relationship among the lengths of the parts of the diagonals.

2. d) PT = TR; ST = TQ
e) True for other parallelograms
g) PT = TR; ST = TQ
h) The diagonals in a parallelogram bisect each other.

3. d) KO = OM **f)** LO = ON = KO = OM
h) The diagonals in a rectangle are equal, and they bisect each other.

Investigation 2, page 581

1. b) ∠AEB = ∠CED; ∠CEB = ∠AED
c) The angles in part b are always equal; they are opposite angles.
d) 90°
e) There is no apparent relationship.
g) The diagonals of a quadrilateral intersect to form equal pairs of opposite angles. The diagonals of a kite are perpendicular.

2. b) ∠PTQ = ∠RTS; ∠RTQ = ∠PTS
c) The angles in part b are always equal; they are opposite angles.
d) PQRS is a rhombus.
f) The diagonals of a parallelogram intersect to form equal pairs of opposite angles. The diagonals of a rhombus are perpendicular.

3. b) ∠KOL = ∠MOL = ∠KON = ∠MON

d) KLMN is a square.

e) The diagonals of a rectangle intersect to form equal pairs of opposite angles. The diagonals of a square are perpendicular.

Investigation 3, page 582

4. The diagonals of a trapezoid intersect to form equal pairs of opposite angles.

Investigation 4, page 583

1. e) MNOP is a parallelogram.

g) When the midpoints of adjacent sides of a quadrilateral are joined, they form a parallelogram.

2. Explanations may vary.

3. The diagonals must intersect at right angles. Explanations may vary.

Investigation 5, page 583

1. g) Explanations may vary.

2. a) Answers may vary. The diagonals are equal.

f) The diagonals of a regular pentagon intersect to form a smaller regular pentagon.

3. h) The sum of the angles at the points in a 5-pointed star is 180°.

4. a) 2; 5   **b)** 3; 9

c)

Polygon	Number of sides	Number of diagonals at each vertex	Total number of diagonals
Triangle	3	0	0
Quadrilateral	4	1	2
Pentagon	5	2	5
Hexagon	6	3	9
Heptagon	7	4	14
Octagon	8	5	20

d) $d = n - 3$ **e)** $D = \frac{1}{2}n(n - 3)$

f) i) 17   **ii)** 170

5. Explanations may vary.

11.14 Sides and Diagonals of Quadrilaterals
11.14 Exercises, page 588

1. Explanations may vary.

a) Rhombus   **b)** Trapezoid   **c)** Square

2. Sketches may vary. AB = DC; AD = BC,
AE = EB = EC = ED, ∠A = ∠B = ∠C = ∠D = 90°;
∠AEB = ∠DEC; ∠AED = ∠BEC;
∠EAD = ∠EDA = ∠EBC = ∠ECB;
∠BAE = ∠ECD = ∠ABD = ∠BDC

3. Sketches may vary. PQ = PS, QR = RS , QT = TS,
∠PQS = ∠PSQ; ∠SQR = ∠QSR; ∠QPT = ∠SPT;
∠QRT = ∠SRT; ∠PQR = ∠PSR;
∠PTQ = ∠PTS = ∠QTR = ∠RTS = 90°

4. a) 13 cm   **b)** 5 cm

5. a) Rhombus   **b)** Square   **c)** Kite   **d)** Trapezoid

6. 5.0 cm

7. a) 120 m   **b)** 2.4 min

8. No; explanations may vary.

9. a) Square, rhombus

b) Rectangle, parallelogram, rhombus, square

c) Trapezoid

d) Rectangle; square, rhombus, parallelogram

e) Rectangle, square

f) Rectangle, square, rhombus, parallelogram

g) Rectangle, square

h) Square, rhombus, kite

10. 200 cm.

Consolidating Your Skills, page 590

1. e) The sum of the interior angles of a pentagon is 540°.

2. c) 360°, 360°

d) The sum of the exterior angles of a polygon is 360°.

3. Explanations may vary.

| **a)** True | **b)** False | **c)** True |
| **d)** False | **e)** False | **f)** False |

4. a) 10 cm²   **b)** 2 cm

5. (7, 5)

6. Explanations may vary.

a) 90°   **b)** 135°, 45°, 45°   **c)** 72°

7. 10.9 cm

8. Explanations may vary.

9. 10.3 m

10. 125 m²

11. a) Answers may vary.

b) The exterior angle at A is equal to the measured angle less 90°. The interior angle at A is equal to the measured angle less 90°. Explanations may vary.

12. Explanations may vary.

a) 220°, 80°   **b)** 15°

c) 113°, 120°, 125°   **d)** 38°

13. 60°

14. Explanations may vary.

a) 75°   **b)** 8 cm

15. Explanations may vary.

a) 36°   **b)** 33°   **c)** 51°   **d)** 32°, 58°

16. These lines coincide in an equilateral triangle.

17. Explanations may vary.

18. 44 cm

19. Explanations may vary; 60°

20. Regular pentagons do not tessellate; isosceles triangle shaped tiles are also needed.

21. Sketches may vary. EF = HG; EH = FG, EJ = JG, HJ = JF;
∠FEH = ∠FGH; ∠EFG = ∠EHG, ∠FEG = ∠EGH,
∠HEG = ∠EGF, ∠EHF = ∠HFG, ∠EFH = ∠FHG,
∠EJH = ∠FJG, ∠EJF = ∠GJH

22. EF = FG = GH = HE,
∠EJF = ∠FJG = ∠GJH = ∠HJE = 90°

23. Explanations may vary.

11 Cumulative Review, page 594

1. a) $94.25   **b)** $108.39

2. a)

Number of pages	Price ($)
200	78
400	106
800	162
1000	190

b) Yes; even though it is not possible to print a fraction of a page, joining the points provides for a better representation of the relation.

c) $C = 50 + 0.14n$

d) No; the graph of the relation does not go through $(0, 0)$.

e) i) The graph shifts down to go through $(0, 0)$.
   ii) $C = 0.14n$ **iii)** Yes

3. Explanations may vary.
  a) To the student at E   **b)** To the student at C
  c) To the student at A   **d)** To the student at D
  e) To the student at B

4. 29 and 30

5. a) 6, –6   **b)** 10, –10   **c)** 20, –20
  d) 1, –1   **e)** $\frac{1}{2}, -\frac{1}{2}$ **f)** $\frac{5}{3}, -\frac{5}{3}$

6. a) Rational   **b)** Rational   **c)** Integer, rational
  d) Natural, integer, rational   **e)** Irrational
  f) Rational   **g)** Rational

7. a) 4.9   **b)** 3.3   **c)** –11.4
  d) 4.5   **e)** 1   **f)** 18.5

8. a) 54   **b)** 104

9. a) $x^2 - 3x + 11; 9$ **b)** $-24m^4; -24$
  c) $-9a^2; -36$ **d)** $k^2 - 11k - 2; -26$

10. a) $d = \frac{t}{3}$ **b)** About 1.17 km   **c)** 24 s

11. Lines of best fit may vary.
  a) $y = 0.05x + 6.67$ **b)** $y = 11.49x + 6.90$

12. a) Answers may vary. Some birds are much larger than others, so they need larger entrances to their houses. Small entrances help to keep out predators.
  d) Estimates may vary. 10.8 cm
  e) $y = 2.3x + 0.69$ **f)** 10.81 cm
  g) Explanations may vary.

13. a) $(4, 1), (1, -1)$
  b) $\frac{2}{3}, \frac{2}{3}$; the slopes are equal.
  c) $-\frac{2}{5}, -\frac{2}{5}, -2, -2$; the slope of PM equals the slope of BC; the slope of PN equals the slope of AC.

14. a) Midpoint of AB: $(2, 1)$, midpoint of BC: $(5, 5)$, midpoint of CD: $(0, 6)$, midpoint of DA: $(-3, 2)$
  b) Parallelogram

Glossary

acute angle: an angle measuring less than 90°

acute triangle: a triangle with three acute angles

additive inverses: a number and its opposite; the sum of additive inverses is 0; for example, +3 + (−3) = 0

algebraic expression: a mathematical expression containing a variable: for example, $6x − 4$ is an algebraic expression

alternate angles: angles that are between two lines and are on opposite sides of a transversal that cuts the two lines

Angles 1 and 3 are alternate angles.
Angles 2 and 4 are alternate angles.

altitude: the perpendicular distance from the base of a figure to the opposite side or vertex

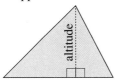

angle: the figure formed by two rays from the same endpoint

angle bisector: the line that divides an angle into two equal angles

approximation: a number close to the exact value of an expression; the symbol $\doteq$ means "is approximately equal to"

area: the number of square units needed to cover a region

array: an arrangement in rows and columns

average: a single number that represents a set of numbers; see *mean*, *median*, and *mode*

balance: the result when money is added to or subtracted from an original amount

bar notation: the use of a horizontal bar over a decimal digit to indicate that it repeats; for example, $1.\overline{3}$ means 1.333 333 …

base: the side of a polygon or the face of a solid from which the height is measured; the factor repeated in a power

bias: an emphasis on characteristics that are not typical of the entire population

binomial: a polynomial with two terms; for example, $3x − 8$

bisector: a line that divides a line segment into two equal parts

The broken line is a bisector of AB.

broken-line graph: a graph that displays data by using points joined by line segments

Calculator-Based-Ranger™ unit: a sonic motion detector that collects data and displays them on the calculator screen

capacity: the amount a container can hold

Cartesian plane: the x- and y-axes used to plot a point identified by a pair of numbers

CBR™: See *Calculator-Based-Ranger™*

centroid: the point where the three medians of a triangle intersect; see page 536

circle: the set of points in a plane that are a given distance from a fixed point (the centre)

circumcentre: the point where the perpendicular bisectors of the sides of a triangle intersect; see page 556

circumcircle: a circle drawn through each of the vertices of a triangle, and with its centre at the circumcentre of the triangle

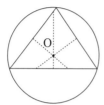

circumference: the distance around a circle, and sometimes the circle itself

coefficient: the numerical factor of a term; for example, in the terms $3x$ and $3x^2$, the coefficient is 3

commission: a fee or payment given to a sales-person, usually a specified percent of the person's sales

common denominator: a number that is a multiple of each of the given denominators; for example, 12 is a common denominator for the fractions $\frac{1}{3}, \frac{5}{4}, \frac{7}{12}$

common factor: a number that is a factor of each of the given numbers; for example, 3 is a common factor of 15, 9, and 21

commutative property: the property stating that two numbers can be added or multiplied in any order; for example, $6 + 8 = 8 + 6$ and $4 \times 7 = 7 \times 4$

complementary angles: two angles whose sum is 90°

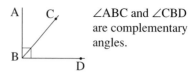

$\angle ABC$ and $\angle CBD$ are complementary angles.

composite number: a number with three or more factors; for example, 8 is a composite number because its factors are 1, 2, 4, and 8

compound event: a combination of two or more events

compound interest: see *interest*; if the interest due is added to the principal and thereafter earns interest, the interest earned is compound interest

cone: a solid formed by a region and all line segments joining points on the boundary of the region to a point not in the region

congruent: figures that have the same size and shape, but not necessarily the same orientation

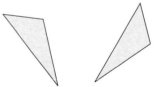

consecutive numbers: integers that come one after the other without any integers missing; for example, 34, 35, 36 are consecutive numbers, so are -2, -1, 0, and 1

constant term: a number

Consumer Price Index (CPI): the change in the costs of goods and services, based on their costs on a set date

coordinate axes: the x- and y-axes on a grid that represents a plane

coordinate plane: a two-dimensional surface on which a coordinate system has been set up

coordinates: the numbers in an ordered pair that locate a point in the plane

corresponding angles: angles that are on the same side of a transversal that cuts two lines and on the same side of each line

Angles 1 and 3 are corresponding angles.
Angles 2 and 4 are corresponding angles.
Angles 5 and 7 are corresponding angles.
Angles 6 and 8 are corresponding angles.

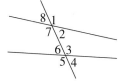

cube: a solid with six congruent, square faces

cubic units: units that measure volume

cylinder: a solid with two parallel, congruent, circular bases

data: facts or information

database: an organized collection of facts or information, often stored on a computer

denominator: the term below the line in a fraction

density: the mass of a unit volume of a substance

diagonal: a line segment that joins two vertices of a figure, but is not a side

diameter: the distance across a circle, measured through the centre; a line segment through the centre of the circle with its endpoints on the circle

digit: any of the symbols used to write numerals; for example, in the base-ten system the digits are 0, 1, 2, 3, 4, 5, 6, 7, 8, and 9

dilatation: a transformation in which the image is the same shape as the object, but is enlarged or reduced in size

direct variation: a relation that has the form $y = mx$

Distributive Law: the property stating that a product can be written as a sum or difference of two products; for example, for all real numbers a, b, and c: $a(b + c) = ab + ac$ and $a(b - c) = ab - ac$

double-bar graph: a bar graph that shows two sets of data

equation: a mathematical statement that two expressions are equal

equidistant: the same distance apart

equilateral triangle: a triangle with three equal sides

evaluate: to substitute a value for each variable in an expression

even number: an integer that has 2 as a factor; for example, 2, 4, –6

event: any set of outcomes of an experiment

expanding: multiplying a polynomial by a polynomial

exponent: a number, shown in a smaller size and raised, that tells how many times the number before it is used as a factor; for example, 2 is the exponent in 6^2

expression: a mathematical phrase made up of numbers and/or variables connected by operations

extremes: the highest and lowest values in a set of numbers

factor: to factor means to write as a product to factor a given integer means to write it as a product of integers, the integers in the product are the factors of the given integer to factor a polynomial with integer coefficients means to write it as a product of polynomials with integer coefficients

formula: a rule that is expressed as an equation

fraction: an indicated quotient of two quantities

frequency: the number of times a particular number occurs in a set of data

grouping property of addition (and multiplication): when three or more terms are added (or multiplied), the operations can be performed in any order

hectare: a unit of area that is equal to 10 000 m²

hendecagon: a polygon with 11 sides

hexagon: a six-sided polygon

horizontal intercept: the horizontal coordinate of the point where the graph of a line or a relation intersects the horizontal axis

hypotenuse: the side that is opposite the right angle in a right triangle

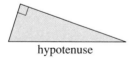
hypotenuse

identity for addition: a number that can be added to any number without changing the number; 0 is the identity for addition of real numbers

identity for multiplication: a number that can be multiplied by any number without changing the number; 1 is the identity for multiplication of real numbers

image: the figure that results from a transformation

incentre: the point at which the three angle bisectors of a triangle intersect; see page 552

incircle: a circle drawn inside a triangle, with its centre at the incentre and with the radius the shortest distance from the incentre to one of the sides of the triangle

inequality: a statement that one quantity is greater than (or less than) another quantity

integers: the set of numbers… −3, −2, −1, 0, +1, +2, +3,…

interest: money that is paid for the use of money, usually according to a predetermined percent

interpolate: to estimate a value between two known values

intersecting lines: lines that meet or cross; lines that have one point in common

interval: a regular distance or space between values

inverse: see *additive inverses* and *multiplicative inverses*

irrational number: a number that cannot be written in the form $\frac{m}{n}$ where m and n are integers ($n \neq 0$)

isometric view: a representation of an object as it would appear in three dimensions

isometry: a transformation that preserves length; for example, a translation

isosceles acute triangle: a triangle with two equal sides and all angles less than 90°

isosceles obtuse triangle: a triangle with two equal sides and one angle greater than 90°

isosceles right triangle: a triangle with two equal sides and a 90° angle

isosceles triangle: a triangle with two equal sides

kilojoule: a measure of energy

kite: a quadrilateral with two pairs of equal adjacent sides

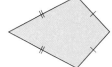

lattice point: on a coordinate grid, a point at the intersection of two grid lines

legs: the sides of a right triangle that form the right angle

light-year: a unit for measuring astronomical distances; one light-year is the distance light travels in one year

like terms: terms that have the same variables; for example, $4x$ and $-3x$ are like terms

line of best fit: a line that passes as close as possible to a set of plotted points

line segment: the part of a line between two points on the line

line symmetry: a figure that maps onto itself when it is reflected in a line is said to have line symmetry; for example, line l is the line of symmetry for figure ABCD

linear relation: a relation that can be represented by a straight-line graph

magic square: an array of numbers in which the sum of the numbers in any row, column, or diagonal is always the same; see page 206

magic sum: the sum of the numbers in a row, column, or diagonal of a magic square

mapping: a correspondence of points or figures under a transformation or rule

mass: the amount of matter in an object

mean: the sum of a set of numbers divided by the number of numbers in the set

median: the middle number when data are arranged in numerical order

median of a triangle: a line from one vertex to the midpoint of the opposite side

midpoint: the point that divides a line segment into two equal parts

mode: the number that occurs most often in a set of numbers

monomial: a polynomial with one term; for example, 14 and $5x^2$ are each a monomial

multiple: the product of a given number and a natural number; for example, some multiples of 8 are 8, 16, 24,…

multiplicative inverses: a number and its reciprocal; the product of multiplicative inverses is 1; for example, $3 \times \frac{1}{3} = 1$

natural numbers: the set of numbers 1, 2, 3, 4, 5,…

negative number: a number less than 0

non-linear relation: a relation that cannot be represented by a straight-line graph

numeracy: the ability to read, understand, and use numbers

numerator: the term above the line in a fraction

obtuse angle: an angle greater than 90° and less than 180°

obtuse triangle: a triangle with one angle greater than 90°

octagon: an eight-sided polygon

odd number: an integer that does not have 2 as a factor; for example, 1, 3, −7

operation: a mathematical process or action such as addition, subtraction, multiplication, or division

opposite angles: the equal angles that are formed by two intersecting lines

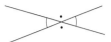

opposite number: a number whose sum with a given number is 0; for example, 3 and −3 are opposites

opposites: two numbers whose sum is zero; each number is the opposite of the other

Opposites Principle: when two equal expressions are multiplied by −1, the results will be equal

optimization: making a system or object as efficient as possible

order of operations: the rules that are followed when simplifying or evaluating an expression

order property of addition (and multiplication): two terms that are added (or multiplied) can be added (or multiplied) in any order

orthocentre: the point at which the altitudes of a triangle intersect

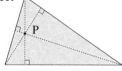

outcome: a possible result of an experiment or a possible answer to a survey question

parallel lines: lines in the same plane that do not intersect

parallelogram: a quadrilateral with both pairs of opposite sides parallel

partial variation: a relation that has the form $y = mx + b$

pentagon: a five-sided polygon

per capita: for each person

percent: the number of parts per 100; the numerator of a fraction with denominator 100

perfect square: a number that is the square of a whole number; a polynomial that is the square of another polynomial

perimeter: the distance around a closed figure

perpendicular: intersecting at right angles

perpendicular bisector: the line that is perpendicular to a line segment and divides it in two equal parts

The broken line is the perpendicular bisector of AB.

pi (π): the ratio of the circumference of a circle to its diameter; $\pi \doteq 3.1416$

plane geometry: the study of two-dimensional figures; that is, figures drawn or visualized on a plane

point of balance: see *centroid*

point of intersection: a point that lies on two or more figures

polygon: a closed figure that consists of line segments; for example, triangles and quadrilaterals are polygons

polynomial: a mathematical expression with one or more terms, in which the exponents are whole numbers and the coefficients are real numbers

population: the set of all things or people being considered

population density: the average number of people for each square unit of land

positive number: a number greater than 0

power: an expression of the form a^n, where a is called the base and n is called the exponent; it represents a product of equal factors; for example, $4 \times 4 \times 4$ can be expressed as 4^3

prime number: a whole number with exactly two factors, itself and 1; for example, 3, 5, 7, 11, 29, 31, and 43

prism: a solid that has two congruent and parallel faces (the *bases*), and other faces that are parallelograms

proportion: a statement that two ratios are equal

pyramid: a solid that has one face that is a polygon (the *base*), and other faces that are triangles with a common vertex

Pythagorean Theorem: for any right triangle, the area of the square on the hypotenuse is equal to the sum of the areas of the squares on the other two sides

quadrant: one of the four regions into which coordinate axes divide a plane

quadrilateral: a four-sided polygon

radius (plural, **radii**): the distance from the centre of a circle to any point on the circumference, or a line segment joining the centre of a circle to any point on the circumference

radius bone: that one of the two bones of the forearm that is shorter and thicker and that is on the thumb side

random numbers: a list of numbers in a given range such that each number has an equal chance of occurring

random sample: a sampling in which all members of the population have an equal chance of being selected

range: the difference between the highest and lowest values (the *extremes*) in a set of data

rate: a certain quantity or amount of one thing considered in relation to a unit of another thing

ratio: a comparison of two or more quantities with the same unit

rational number: a number that can be written in the form $\frac{m}{n}$ where m and n are integers ($n \neq 0$)

real numbers: the set of rational numbers and the set of irrational numbers; that is, all numbers that can be expressed as decimals

reciprocals: two numbers whose product is 1; for example, $\frac{3}{4}$ and $\frac{4}{3}$ are reciprocals, 2 and $\frac{1}{2}$ are reciprocals

rectangle: a quadrilateral that has four right angles

rectangular prism: a prism that has rectangular faces

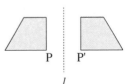

rectangular pyramid: a pyramid with a rectangular base

reflection: a transformation that maps every point P onto an image point P′ such that P and P′ are equidistant from line *l*, and line PP′ is perpendicular to line *l*

P   P′

l

reflex angle: an angle between 180° and 360°

regular hexagon: a polygon that has six equal sides and six equal angles

regular octagon: a polygon that has eight equal sides and eight equal angles

regular polygon: a polygon that has all sides equal and all angles equal

relation: a connection between a pair of quantities, often expressed in words, as a table of values, a graph or an equation

relationship: see *relation*

rhombus: a parallelogram with four equal sides

right angle: a 90° angle

right circular cone: a cone in which a line segment from the centre of the circular base to the vertex is perpendicular to the base

right triangle: a triangle that has one right angle

rise: the vertical distance between 2 points

rotation: a transformation in which the points of a figure are turned about a fixed point

rotational symmetry: a figure that maps onto itself in less than one full turn is said to have rotational symmetry; for example, a square has rotational symmetry about its centre O

run: the horizontal distance between 2 points

sample/sampling: a representative portion of a population

scale: the ratio of the distance between two points on a map, model, or diagram to the distance between the actual locations; the numbers on the axes of a graph

scale factor: the ratio of corresponding lengths on two similar figures

scalene triangle: a triangle with no two sides equal

scatter plot: a graph of data that is a series of points

scientific notation: a number expressed as the product of a number greater than −10 and less than −1 or greater than 1 and less than 10, and a power of 10; for example, 4700 is written as 4.7×10^3

semicircle: half a circle

Sharing Principle: when two equal expressions are divided by the same number, the results will be equal

similar figures: figures with the same shape, but not necessarily the same size

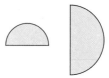

slope: describes the steepness of a line or line segment; the ratio of the rise of a line or line segment to its run

spreadsheet: a computer-generated arrangement of data in rows and columns, where a change in one value results in appropriate calculated changes in the other values

square: a rectangle with four equal sides square of a number: the product of a number multiplied by itself; for example, 25 is the square of 5

square root: a number which, when multiplied by itself, results in a given number; for example, 5 and −5 are the square roots of 25

standard form of the equation of a line: the equation of a line in the form Ax + By + C = 0

statistics: the branch of mathematics that deals with the collection, organization, and interpretation of data

straight angle: an angle measuring 180°

straightedge: a strip of wood, metal, or plastic with a straight edge, but no markings

supplementary angles: two angles whose sum is 180°

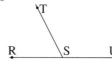

∠RST and ∠TSU are supplementary angles.

symmetrical: possessing symmetry; see *line symmetry* and *rotational symmetry*

term: of a fraction is the numerator or the denominator of the fraction; when an expression is written as the sum of several quantities, each quantity is called a term of the expression

tessellation: a tiling pattern

tetrahedron: a solid with four triangular faces

three-dimensional: having length, width, and depth or height

transformation: a mapping of the points of a figure that results in a change in position, shape, size, or appearance of the figure; for example, translations, rotations, reflections, and dilatations are transformations

translation: a transformation that moves a point or a figure in a straight line to another position in the same plane

transversal: a line crossing two or more lines

trapezoid: a quadrilateral that has only one pair of parallel sides

ria ... a three-sided polygon

trinomial: a polynomial with three terms; for example, $3x^2 + 6x + 9$ two-dimensional: having length and width, but no thickness, height, or depth

unit fraction: a fraction that has a numerator of 1

unit price: the price of one item, or the price for a particular mass or volume of an item

unit rate: the quantity associated with a single unit of another quantity; for example, 6 m in 1 s is a unit rate

unlike terms: terms that have different variables, or the same variable but different exponents; for example, $3x$, $-4y$ and $3x^2$, $-3x$

variable: a letter or symbol representing a quantity that can vary

vertex (plural, vertices): the corner of a figure or a solid

vertical intercept: the vertical coordinate of the point where the graph of a line or a relation intersects the vertical axis

volume: the amount of space occupied by an object

whole numbers: the set of numbers 0, 1, 2, 3,...

x-axis: the horizontal number line on a coordinate grid

x-intercept: the x-coordinate where the graph of a line or a relation intersects the x-axis

y-axis: the vertical number line on a coordinate grid

y-intercept: the y-coordinate where the graph of a line or a relation intersects the y-axis

Zero Principle: the sum of opposites is zero

Index

PHOTO CREDITS AND ACKNOWLEDGMENTS

The publisher wishes to thank the following sources for photographs, illustrations, articles, and other materials used in this book. Care has been taken to determine and locate ownership of copyright material used in the test. We will gladly receive information enabling us to rectify any errors or omissions in credits.

PHOTOS

Cover (chameleon) First Light, (bkgd sky, keyboard) Artbase, Inc., (ruler) Pronk&Associates **p. 2–3** Ron Tanaka; **p. 4, 5** Canapress Picture Archives (Canadian Press CP); **p. 6** (top left) Daryl Benson/Masterfile, (top right) Mike McCabe/Tony Stone Images, (bottom right) Cosmo Condina/Tony Stone Images, (bottom left) Canapress Picture Archives/Robert Galbraith; **p. 7** (top) Joe Devenney/Image Bank, (middle, bottom) Artbase, Inc.; **p. 8** (top) D. Reede/First Light, (middle) Douglas E. Walker, (bottom) Daryl Benson/Masterfile; **p. 11** (top) Gary Cralle/Image Bank, (bottom) The Granger Collection, New York; **p. 13** Dave Starrett; **p. 15** Richard Neville/Check Six; **p. 18** The Granger Collection, New York; **p. 21** Ron Tanaka; **p. 22** Dave Starrett; **p. 26** (left) Bill Brookes/Masterfile, (top right) J. A. Kraulis/Masterfile, (bottom right) Dave Starrett; **p. 27** (top) Artbase, Inc., (bottom) Dave Starrett; **p. 28** (top) Artbase, Inc., (bottom) Dave Starrett; **p. 33** (top) Canapress Picture Archives (Canadian Press CP); **p. 34** (top) Bob Anderson/Masterfile; **p. 36** (bottom) Canapress Picture Archives (CP Laserphoto 1989); **p. 44** Dave Starrett; **p. 46** Ron Sherman/Tony Stone Images; **p. 49** Brent P. Kent/Earth Scenes; **p. 50** Artbase, Inc.; **p. 51** Mike Robinson; **p. 53** Doug Wilson/First Light; p. 55 Canapress Picture Archives; **p. 56** (top, bottom) Artbase, Inc.; **p. 64–65** David Michael Allen (photo manipulation Jun Park); **p. 68** Jim Pickerell/Tony Stone Images; **p. 71** Michael Rosenfeld/Tony Stone Images; **p. 75** Dave Starrett; **p. 83** (top) Dave Starrett, (bottom) Ian Crysler; **p. 84** David Michael Allen; **p. 85, 86** L. J. Lozano; **p. 89, 90** Artbase, Inc.; **p. 92** Detlef Schnepel; **p. 95** Dave Starrett; **p. 97, 99** Detlef Schnepel; **p. 104** Artbase, Inc.; **p. 106** (bottom) David Michael Allen; **p. 107** Vic Cox/Peter Arnold, Inc.; **p. 108** Dave Starrett; **p. 110** Artbase, Inc.; **p. 111** Greg ProbstTony Stone Images; **p. 113** Artbase, Inc.; **p. 114** (middle) Canapress Picture Archives **p. 115** (bottom left) Canapress Picture Archives (Associated Press AP); **p. 116** Steve Allen/Image Bank; **p. 118** Larry Williams/Masterfile; **p. 119** L. J. Lozano; **p. 120** Alex Williams - TCL/Masterfile; **p. 122** Lloyd Sutton/Masterfile; **p. 124** (bottom) Artbase, Inc.; **p. 125** Hulton Getty/Liaison Agency; **p. 127, 128, 129, 131** Dave Starrett; **p. 133** Ken Straiton/First Light; **p. 135** Manfred Mehlig/Tony Stone; **p. 136** Dave Starrett; **p. 139, 140** Canapress Picture Archives (Associated Press AP); **p. 150** Dave Starrett; **p. 151** Courtesy of NASA/Finley Holiday; **p. 155** Canapress Picture Archives (Canadian Press CP); **p. 156** Ray Lum Photography; **p. 158–159** Buenos Dias Bildagentur/Liaison International; **p. 160, 162, 163, 167, 169** Dave Starrett; **p. 170** Pete Saloutos/The Stock Market/First Light; **p. 172** Artbase, Inc.; **p. 174** Canapress Picture Archives (Associated Press AP); **p. 182** Buenos Dias Bildagentur/Liaison International; **p. 184** Ken Straiton/First Light; **p. 186** Dave Starrett; **p. 196–197** Ron Tanaka; **p. 205** Nancy Brown/Image Bank; **p. 213** S. Lowry/University of Ulster; **p. 218** Ron Tanaka; **p. 220** (bottom) Dave Starrett; **p. 223** M. Kage/Peter Arnold; **p. 224** (top) Andy Caulfield/Image Bank, (bottom) David Woodfall/Tony Stone Images; **p. 228** Artbase, Inc.; **p. 230** Sherman Hines/Masterfile; **p. 234, p. 237** (top) David Michael Allen; **p. 237** (middle) Yale Babylonian Collection; **p. 242** Dave Starrett; **p. 250–251, 253** Dave Starrett; **p. 254** (bottom) Hans Reinhard/Bruce Coleman Inc.; **p. 256** Dave Starrett; **p. 268** (top) Ken Straiton/First Light, (bottom) Martin W. Grosnick/Bruce Coleman Inc.; **p. 270** Gloria H. Chomica/Masterfile **p. 271** Artbase, Inc.; **p. 279** (bkgd) Artbase, Inc., (frgd) Air Canada; **p. 281** Artbase, Inc.; **p. 282** Dave Starrett; **p. 285** (top) Artbase, Inc., (bottom) Peter Griffith/Masterfile; **p. 287** Bill Ivy; **p. 289, 290** Artbase, Inc.; **p. 294, 295** Dave Starrett; **p. 296** Dennis O'Clair/Tony Stone Images; **p. 299** Daryl Benson/Masterfile; **p. 303** Canapress Picture Archives (Associated Press AP), Hulton Getty/Liaison International, CORBIS/Bettmann; **p. 304** (bottom) Per Eriksson/Image Bank; **p. 305** (right) Peter Griffith/Masterfile; **p. 307** Dave Starrett; **p. 313** The Granger Collection, New York; **p. 319** David E. Myers/Tony Stone Images; **p. 326** The Everett Collection, Inc.; **p. 335** Paul Eckoff; **p. 342** (top left, bottom left) Canapress Picture Archives; **p. 342–343** (top) Canapress Picture Archives, (bottom) Superstock; **p. 343** (right) Artbase, Inc.; **p. 344** Artbase, Inc.; **p. 349** Courtesy of Moniika Vega; **p. 360** (top) Map Art, (bottom) Larry J. MacDougal/First Light; **p. 361** Ian Crysler; **p. 363** Artbase, Inc.; **p. 364** David Michael Allen; **p. 365** Artbase, Inc.; **p. 366** Dave Starrett; **p. 367** (from top to bottom) Canapress Picture Archives, Superstock, Canapress Picture Archives, Canapress Picture Archives; **p. 369** Artbase, Inc.; **p. 371** Dave Starrett; **p. 373** Mike Dobel/Masterfile; **p. 377** Detlef Schnepel; **p. 383,**

385. 386 Artbase, Inc.; **p. 390** Dave Starrett; **p. 394** (top to bottom) L. MacDougal/First Light, Canapress Picture Archives (Canadian Press CP), Karen Percy/Masterfile, Canapress Picture Archives (Canadian Press CP); **p. 398** Artbase, Inc.; **p. 399** Artbase, Inc.; **p. 401** Marc Romanelli/Image Bank; **p. 403** Artbase, Inc.; **p. 404** Detlef Schnepel; **p. 405** Canapress Picture Archives (Associated Press AP); **p. 406** Canapress Picture Archives (Associated Press AP); **p. 410** Dave Starrett; **p. 411** Artbase, Inc.; **p. 412** Canapress Picture Archives (Associated Press AP); **p. 413, 416, 417** Dave Starrett; **p. 418** Grant V. Faint/Image Bank; **p. 419** Roy Ooms/Masterfile; **p. 420** Artbase, Inc.; **p. 424, 426,** Dave Starrett; **p. 428, 429** Canapress Picture Archives (Associated Press AP); **p. 430** Alan Marsh/First Light; **p. 434** Canapress Picture Archives (CP Laserphoto), Dave Starrett; **p. 452** Brian Milne/First Light; **p. 453, 457** Dave Starrett; **p. 462** David Michael Allen; **p. 466** Dave Starrett; **p. 470, 471, 474** (bottom) Pronk&Associates; **p. 475** (top) Abitibi Price, (bottom) David Michael Allen; **p. 477** (left) Ian Crysler, (right) David Michael Allen; **p. 480** D. Baswick/First Light; **p. 482** Charlie Waite/Tony Stone Images; **p. 484** Dave Starrett; **p. 489** (left) David Sutherland, (right) Jean Marc Truchet/Tony Stone Images; **p. 490** Stephen Studd/Tony Stone Images; **p. 491** Pronk&Associates; **p. 493** (bkgd) Werner H. Muller/Peter Arnold, Inc., (frgd and bottom) David Michael Allen; **p. 496** Jean Marc Truchett/Tony Stone Images; **p. 498** Dave Starrett; **p. 506** (bottom), **507, 508** Pronk&Associates; **p. 510** Hand with reflecting sphere by M. C. Escher. ©1999 Cordon - Art - Baarn - Holland. All rights reserved.; **p. 512** (left) Gerard Vandystadt/Photo Researchers, (right) Animals, Animals; **p. 516** David Michael Allen; **p. 520** *The Annunciation.* Reproduced courtesy of the Trustees, The National Gallery, London. *Satire on False Perspective.* Copyright British Museum. *Paradise Garden* From the collection of Stadelsches Kunstinstitut, Frankfurt Am Main/Artothek. **p. 522** Dale Knuepfer/Bruce Coleman Inc.; **p. 532** Peter Griffith/Masterfile; **p. 535** David Michael Allen; **p. 538** (top) Dave Starrett, (bottom) David Michael Allen; **p. 540** (left) Frank Hudec/First Light, (right, inset) CORBIS/Jim Sugar Photography; **p. 546, 549** Dave Starrett; **p. 555** (top) Abrams/Lacagnina/Image Bank, (bottom) Map Art; **p. 563, 567, 569** Dave Starrett; **p. 576** Brian Sytnyk/Masterfile; **p. 578** John de Visser/Masterfile

ILLUSTRATIONS
Steve Attoe: 48, 105, 106, 166, 181, 183, 220 (top), 266, 308, 310, 330, 337, 341, 392, 393, 395, 492, 553
David Bathurst: 73
Michael Herman: 12, 24, 36 (top), 41, 124 (top), 141, 143, 152, 201, 247, 254 (top), 321, 327, 437, 443, 463
Ted Nasmith: 96,
Martha Newbigging: 177, 431
Jun Park: 87, 154, 481
Pronk&Associates: 34, 252, 353
Theresa Sakno: 32, 227
Ron Sherman: 478
Greg Stevenson: 62–62, 389–388–389
Bill Suddick: 66, 67
Rose Zgodzinski: 98, 102

Special thanks to the staff and students at ASE 2 in Scarborough for their patience and support during the development of this textbook.